ULTIMATE FAMILY
VISUAL
dictionary

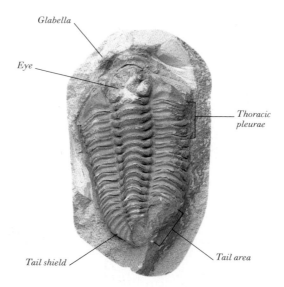

Glabella

Eye

Thoracic
pleurae

Tail shield

Tail area

PREHISTORIC TRILOBITE

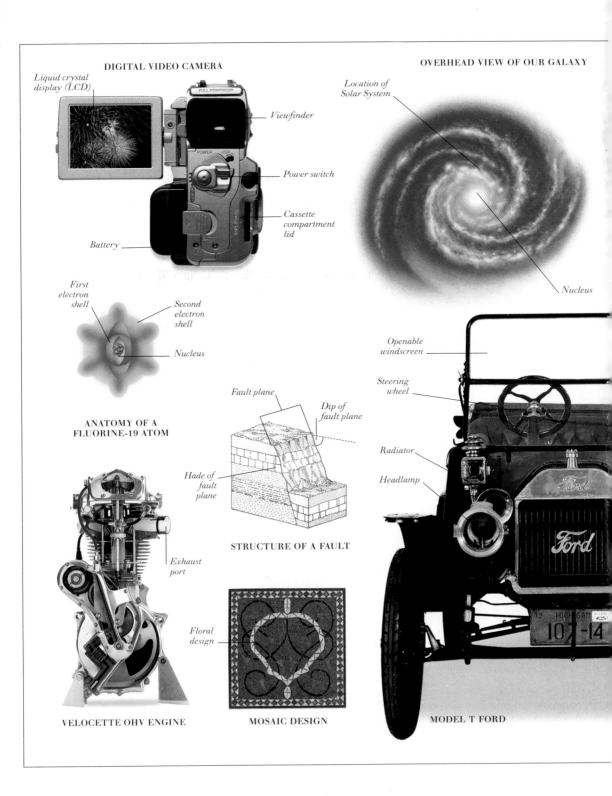

DIGITAL VIDEO CAMERA

Liquid crystal display (LCD)

Viewfinder

Power switch

Cassette compartment lid

Battery

First electron shell

Second electron shell

Nucleus

ANATOMY OF A FLUORINE-19 ATOM

OVERHEAD VIEW OF OUR GALAXY

Location of Solar System

Nucleus

Fault plane

Dip of fault plane

Hade of fault plane

STRUCTURE OF A FAULT

Exhaust port

Floral design

VELOCETTE OHV ENGINE

MOSAIC DESIGN

Openable windscreen

Steering wheel

Radiator

Headlamp

MICHIGAN

107-14

MODEL T FORD

ULTIMATE FAMILY
VISUAL
dictionary

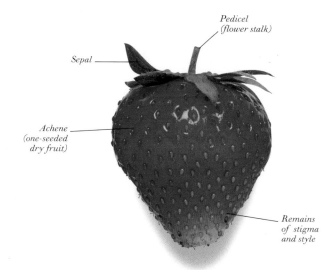

Pedicel
(flower stalk)

Sepal

Achene
(one-seeded
dry fruit)

Remains
of stigma
and style

STRAWBERRY

A DORLING KINDERSLEY BOOK

LONDON, NEW YORK, MUNICH, MELBOURNE, AND DELHI

THIS EDITION

DK LONDON

Editorial Consultants Ian Graham, Darren Naish, Carole Stott
Picture Researcher Karen VanRoss
Jacket Designer Silke Spingies
Digital Conversion Coordinator Linda Zacharia
Production Editor Joanna Byrne
Production Controller Linda Dare
Managing Editor Julie Ferris
Managing Art Editor Owen Peyton Jones
Art Director Philip Ormerod
Associate Publishing Director Liz Wheeler
Publishing Director Jonathan Metcalf

DK DELHI

Managing Art Editor Arunesh Talapatra
Managing Editor Saloni Talwar
Deputy Managing Art Editor Priyabrata Roy Chowdhury
Senior Art Editor Rajnish Kashyap
Senior Editor Neha Gupta
Art Editors Arijit Ganguly, Pooja Pipil
Assistant Art Editor Pooja Pawwar
DTP Manager Balwant Singh
DTP Designer Jaypal Singh Chauhan
Managing Director Aparna Sharma

Anatomical And Botanical Models Supplied By Somso Modelle, Coburg, Germany

ORIGINAL EDITION (*Ultimate Visual Dictionary*)
Project Art Editors Heather McCarry, Johnny Pau, Chris Walker, Kevin Williams
Designer Simon Murrell
Project Editors Luisa Caruso, Peter Jones, Jane Mason, Geoffrey Stalker
Editor Jo Evans
DTP Designer Zirrinia Austin
Picture Researcher Charlotte Bush
Managing Art Editor Toni Kay
Senior Editor Roger Tritton
Managing Editor Sean Moore
Production Manager Hilary Stephens

First published in Great Britain in 1994
under the title Ultimate Visual Dictionary by
Dorling Kindersley Limited
80 Strand, London WC2R 0RL
A Penguin Random house Company

PENGUIN GROUP (UK)
16 18 20 19 17 15
001–178144–NOV/2011
Revised editions in 1996, 1997, 1998, 1999, 2000, 2002, 2006, 2011, 2012

THIS EDITION *ULTIMATE FAMILY VISUAL DICTIONARY* PUBLISHED IN **2012**

Reprinted in 2015

A CIP catalogue record for this book is available from the British Library

ISBN 978-0-1434-1954-9

Colour Reproduction by Colourscan, Singapore
Printed at Replika Press Pvt. Ltd.

See our complete catalogue at www.dk.com

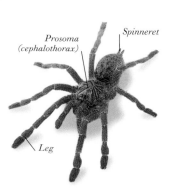

Prosoma (cephalothorax) — *Spinneret*

Leg

**EXTERNAL FEATURES
OF A SPIDER**

Canopy — *Fin*

G-BNHB

Main landing gear

SIDE VIEW OF ARV SUPER 2 AEROPLANE

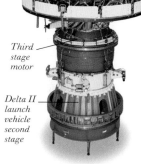

Heat shield

Third stage motor

Delta II launch vehicle second stage

MARS PATHFINDER

CONTENTS

Barrel

Permanent black ink

FOUNTAIN PEN AND INK

Face light emitting diodes (LEDs)

Movable tail

**SONY AIBO
ROBOT DOG**

Parallel bands

ONYX

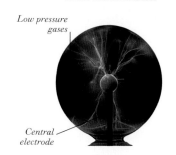

Low pressure gases

Central electrode

**BALL CONTAINING HIGH
TEMPERATURE GAS (PLASMA)**

Non-breakable plastic

Shock absorber

**AMERICAN FOOTBALL
HELMET**

Introduction

THE VISUAL DICTIONARY is a completely new kind of reference book. It provides a link between pictures and words in a way that no ordinary dictionary ever has. Most dictionaries simply tell you what a word means, but the *Visual Dictionary* shows you – through a combination of detailed annotations, explicit photographs, and illustrations. In the *Visual Dictionary*, pictures define the annotations around them. You do not read definitions of the annotated words, you see them. The highly accessible format of the *Visual Dictionary*, the thoroughness of its annotations, and the range of its subject matter make it a unique and helpful reference tool.

How to use the VISUAL DICTIONARY

You will find the *Visual Dictionary* simple to use. Instead of being organized alphabetically, it is divided by subject into 14 sections – The Universe, Prehistoric Earth, Plants, Animals, The Human Body, etc. Each section begins with a table of contents listing the major entries within that section. For example, The Visual Arts section has entries on *Drawing, Tempera, Fresco, Oils, Watercolour, Pastels, Acrylics, Calligraphy, Printmaking, Mosaic*, and *Sculpture*. Every entry has a short introduction explaining the purpose of the photographs and illustrations, and the significance of the annotations.

If you know what something looks like, but don't know its name, find the term you need by turning to the annotations surrounding the pictures; if you know a word, but don't know what it refers to, use the comprehensive index to direct you to the appropriate page.

Suppose that you want to know what the bone at the end of your little finger is called. With a standard dictionary, you wouldn't know where to begin. But with the *Visual Dictionary* you simply turn to the entry called *Hands* – within The Human Body section – where you will find four fully annotated, colour photographs showing the skin, muscles, and bones of the human hand. In this entry you will quickly find that the bone you are searching for is called the distal phalanx, and for good measure you will discover that it is attached to the middle phalanx by the distal interphalangeal joint.

Perhaps you want to know what a catalytic converter looks like. If you look up "catalytic converter" in an ordinary dictionary, you will be told what it is and possibly what it does – but you will not be able to tell what shape it is or what it is made of. However, if you look up "catalytic converter" in the index of the *Visual Dictionary*, you will be directed to the *Modern engines* entry on page 344 – where the introduction gives you basic information about what a catalytic converter is – and to page 350 – where there is a spectacular exploded-view photograph of the mechanics of a Renault Clio. From these pages you will find out not only what a catalytic converter looks like, but also that it is attached at one end to an exhaust downpipe and at the other to a silencer.

Whatever it is that you want to find a name for, or whatever name you want to find a picture for, you will find it quickly and easily in the *Visual Dictionary*. Perhaps you need to know where the vamp on a shoe is; or how to tell obovate and lanceolate leaves apart; or what a spiral galaxy looks like; or whether birds have nostrils. With the *Visual Dictionary* at hand, the answers to each of these questions, and thousands more, are readily available.

The *Visual Dictionary* does not just tell you what the names of the different parts of an object are. The photographs, illustrations, and annotations are all specially arranged to help you understand which parts relate to one another and how objects function.

With the *Visual Dictionary* you can find in seconds the words or pictures that you are looking for; or you can simply browse through the pages of the book for your own pleasure. The *Visual Dictionary* is not intended to replace a standard dictionary or conventional encyclopedia, but is instead a stimulating and valuable companion to ordinary reference volumes. Giving you instant access to the language that is used by astronomers and architects, musicians and mechanics, scientists and sportspeople, it is the ideal reference book for specialists and generalists of all ages.

Sections of the VISUAL DICTIONARY

The 14 sections of the *Visual Dictionary* contain a total of more than 30,000 terms, encompassing a wide range of topics:

•In the first section, THE UNIVERSE, spectacular photographs and illustrations are used to show the names of the stars and planets and to explain the structure of solar systems, galaxies, nebulae, comets, and black holes.

•PREHISTORIC EARTH tells the story in annotations of how our own planet has evolved since its formation. It includes examples of prehistoric flora and fauna, and fascinating dinosaur models – some with parts of the body stripped away to show anatomical sections.

•PLANTS covers a huge range of species – from the familiar to the exotic. In addition to the colour photographs of plants included in this section, there is a series of micrographic photographs illustrating plant details – such as pollen grains, spores, and cross-sections of stems and roots – in close-up.

•In the ANIMALS section, skeletons, anatomical diagrams, and different parts of animals' bodies have been meticulously annotated. This section provides a comprehensive guide to the vocabulary of zoological classification and animal physiology.

•The structure of the human body, its parts, and its systems are presented in THE HUMAN BODY. The section includes lifelike, three-dimensional models and the latest false-colour images. Clear and authoritative annotations indicate the correct anatomical terms.

•GEOLOGY, GEOGRAPHY, AND METEOROLOGY describes the structure of the Earth – from the inner core to the exosphere – and the physical phenomena – such as volcanoes, rivers, glaciers, and climate – that shape its surface.

•PHYSICS AND CHEMISTRY is a visual journey through the fundamental principles underlying the physical universe, and provides the essential vocabulary of these sciences.

•In RAIL AND ROAD, a wide range of trains, trams and buses, cars, bicycles, and motorcycles are described. Exploded-view photographs show mechanical details with striking clarity.

•SEA AND AIR gives the names for hundreds of parts of ships and aeroplanes. The section includes civil and fighting craft, both historical and modern.

•THE VISUAL ARTS shows the equipment and materials used by painters, sculptors, printers, and other artists. Well-known compositions have been chosen to illustrate specific artistic techniques and effects.

•ARCHITECTURE includes photographs of exemplary architectural models and illustrates dozens of additional features such as columns, domes, and arches.

•MUSIC provides a visual introduction to the special language of music and musical instruments. It includes clearly annotated photographs of each of the major groups of traditional instruments – brass, woodwind, strings, and percussion – together with modern electronic instruments.

•The SPORTS section is a guide to the playing areas, formations, equipment, and techniques needed for many of today's most popular sports.

•In THE MODERN WORLD, items that are a familiar part of our daily lives are taken apart to reveal their inner workings and give access to the language used by their manufacturers. It also includes systems and concepts, such as the Internet, that increasingly influence our 21st century world.

THE UNIVERSE

Anatomy of the Universe

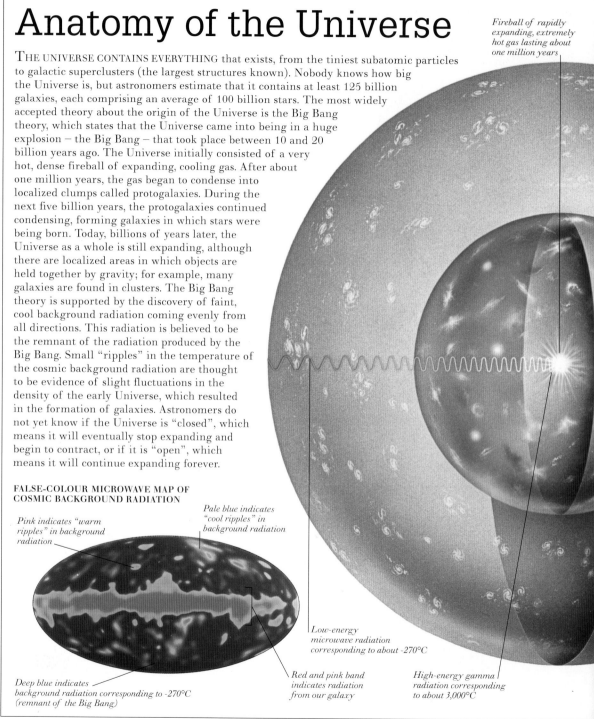

Fireball of rapidly expanding, extremely hot gas lasting about one million years

THE UNIVERSE CONTAINS EVERYTHING that exists, from the tiniest subatomic particles to galactic superclusters (the largest structures known). Nobody knows how big the Universe is, but astronomers estimate that it contains at least 125 billion galaxies, each comprising an average of 100 billion stars. The most widely accepted theory about the origin of the Universe is the Big Bang theory, which states that the Universe came into being in a huge explosion – the Big Bang – that took place between 10 and 20 billion years ago. The Universe initially consisted of a very hot, dense fireball of expanding, cooling gas. After about one million years, the gas began to condense into localized clumps called protogalaxies. During the next five billion years, the protogalaxies continued condensing, forming galaxies in which stars were being born. Today, billions of years later, the Universe as a whole is still expanding, although there are localized areas in which objects are held together by gravity; for example, many galaxies are found in clusters. The Big Bang theory is supported by the discovery of faint, cool background radiation coming evenly from all directions. This radiation is believed to be the remnant of the radiation produced by the Big Bang. Small "ripples" in the temperature of the cosmic background radiation are thought to be evidence of slight fluctuations in the density of the early Universe, which resulted in the formation of galaxies. Astronomers do not yet know if the Universe is "closed", which means it will eventually stop expanding and begin to contract, or if it is "open", which means it will continue expanding forever.

FALSE-COLOUR MICROWAVE MAP OF COSMIC BACKGROUND RADIATION

Pink indicates "warm ripples" in background radiation

Pale blue indicates "cool ripples" in background radiation

Deep blue indicates background radiation corresponding to -270°C (remnant of the Big Bang)

Low-energy microwave radiation corresponding to about -270°C

Red and pink band indicates radiation from our galaxy

High-energy gamma radiation corresponding to about 3,000°C

ORIGIN AND EXPANSION OF THE UNIVERSE

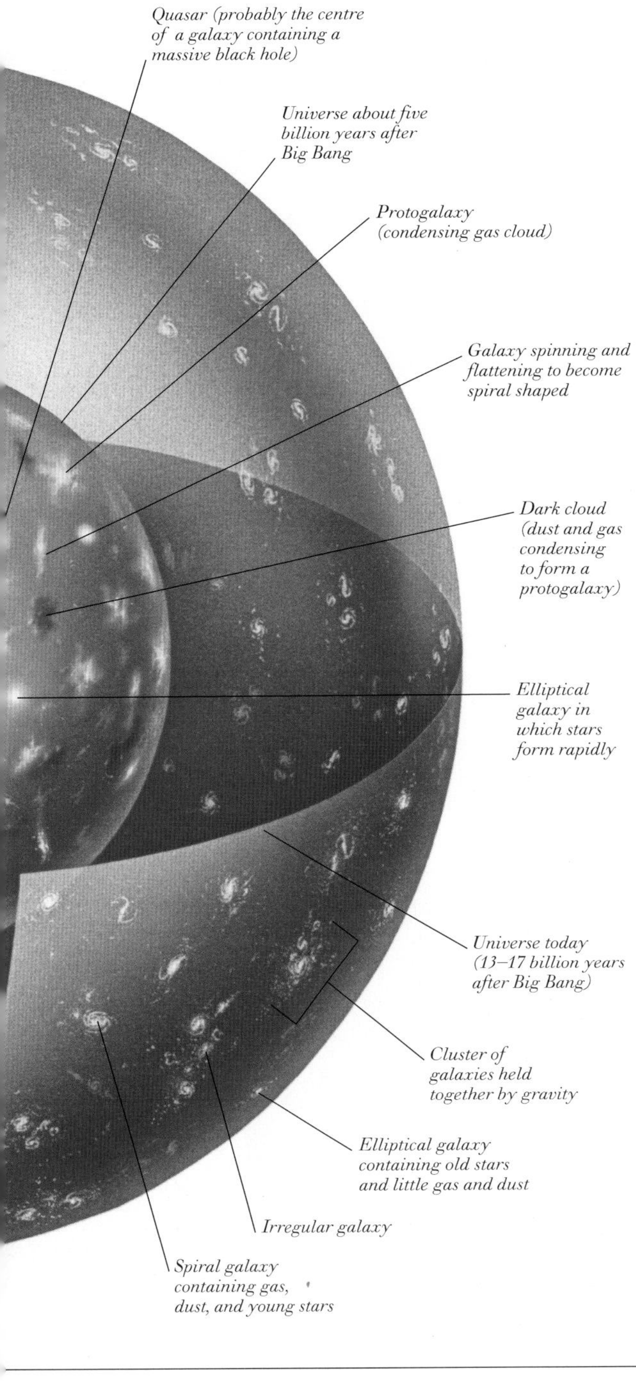

Quasar (probably the centre
of a galaxy containing a
massive black hole)

Universe about five
billion years after
Big Bang

Protogalaxy
(condensing gas cloud)

Galaxy spinning and
flattening to become
spiral shaped

Dark cloud
(dust and gas
condensing
to form a
protogalaxy)

Elliptical
galaxy in
which stars
form rapidly

Universe today
(13–17 billion years
after Big Bang)

Cluster of
galaxies held
together by gravity

Elliptical galaxy
containing old stars
and little gas and dust

Irregular galaxy

Spiral galaxy
containing gas,
dust, and young stars

OBJECTS IN THE UNIVERSE

CLUSTER OF
GALAXIES IN VIRGO

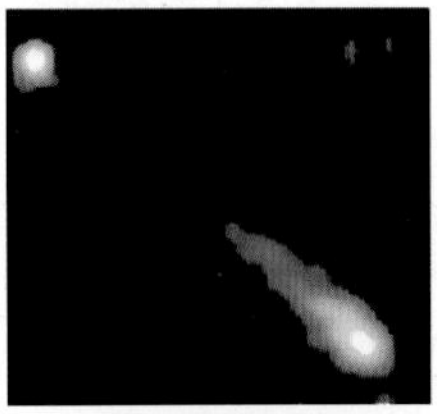

FALSE-COLOUR IMAGE
OF 3C273 (QUASAR)

NGC 4406
(ELLIPTICAL GALAXY)

NGC 5236
(BARRED SPIRAL GALAXY)

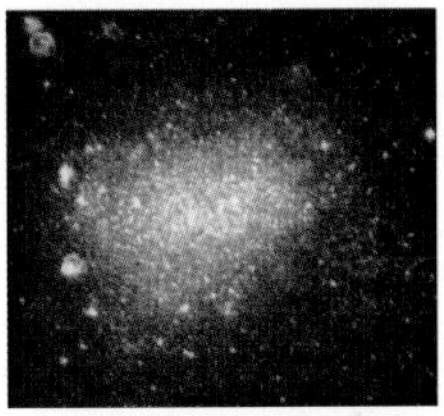

NGC 6822
(IRREGULAR GALAXY)

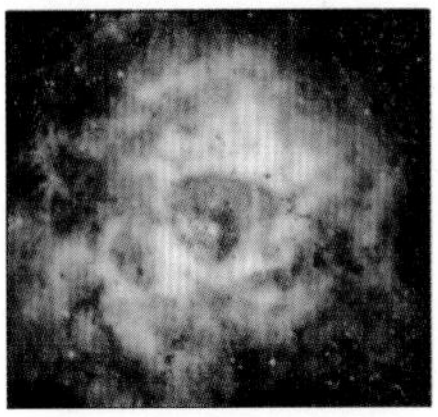

THE ROSETTE NEBULA
(EMISSION NEBULA)

THE JEWEL BOX
(STAR CLUSTER)

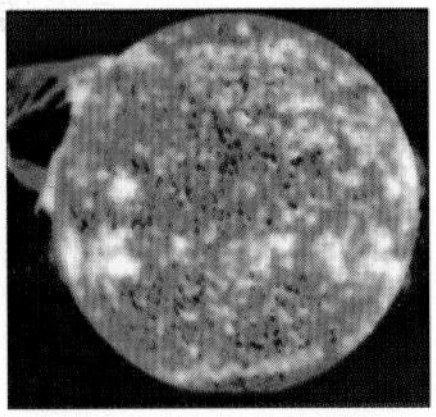

THE SUN
(MAIN SEQUENCE STAR)

EARTH

THE MOON

Galaxies

SOMBRERO,
A SPIRAL GALAXY

A GALAXY IS A HUGE MASS OF STARS, nebulae, and interstellar material. The smallest galaxies contain about 100,000 stars, while the largest contain up to 3,000 billion stars. There are three main types of galaxy, classified according to their shape: elliptical, which are oval shaped; spiral, which have arms spiralling outwards from a central bulge (those whose arms spiral from a bar-shaped bulge are called spirals); and irregular, which have no obvious shape. Sometimes, the shape of a galaxy is distorted by a collision with another galaxy. Quasars (quasi-stellar objects) are thought to be galactic nuclei but are so far away that their exact nature is still uncertain. They are compact, highly luminous objects in the outer reaches of the known Universe: while the furthest known "ordinary" galaxies are about 12 billion light years away, the furthest known quasar is about 13 billion light years away. Active galaxies, such as Seyfert galaxies and radio galaxies, emit intense radiation. In a Seyfert galaxy, this radiation comes from the galactic nucleus; in a radio galaxy, it also comes from huge lobes on either side of the galaxy. The radiation from active galaxies and quasars is thought to be caused by material falling into central black holes (see pp. 28-29).

OPTICAL IMAGE OF NGC 4486 (ELLIPTICAL GALAXY)

Globular cluster containing very old red giants

Central region containing old red giants

Less densely populated region

Neighbouring galaxy

OPTICAL IMAGE OF LARGE MAGELLANIC CLOUD (IRREGULAR GALAXY)

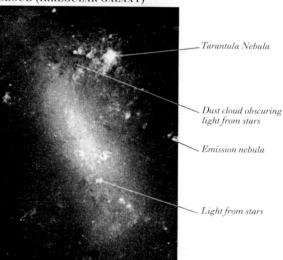

Tarantula Nebula

Dust cloud obscuring light from stars

Emission nebula

Light from stars

OPTICAL IMAGE OF NGC 2997 (SPIRAL GALAXY)

Glowing nebula in spiral arm

Spiral arm containing young stars

Galactic nucleus containing old stars

Dust in spiral arm reflecting blue light from hot young stars

Hot, ionized hydrogen gas emitting red light

Dust lane

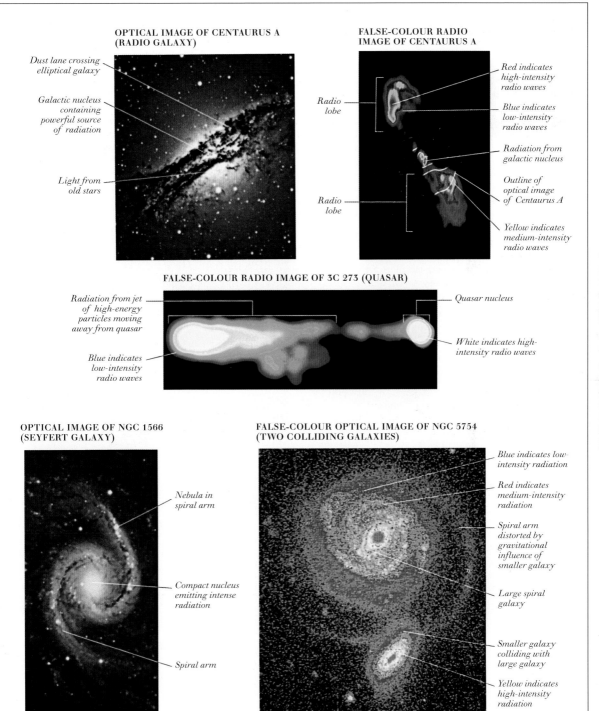

**OPTICAL IMAGE OF CENTAURUS A
(RADIO GALAXY)**

Dust lane crossing
elliptical galaxy

Galactic nucleus
containing
powerful source
of radiation

Light from
old stars

**FALSE-COLOUR RADIO
IMAGE OF CENTAURUS A**

Radio
lobe

Radio
lobe

Red indicates
high-intensity
radio waves

Blue indicates
low-intensity
radio waves

Radiation from
galactic nucleus

Outline of
optical image
of Centaurus A

Yellow indicates
medium-intensity
radio waves

FALSE-COLOUR RADIO IMAGE OF 3C 273 (QUASAR)

Radiation from jet
of high-energy
particles moving
away from quasar

Blue indicates
low-intensity
radio waves

Quasar nucleus

White indicates high-
intensity radio waves

**OPTICAL IMAGE OF NGC 1566
(SEYFERT GALAXY)**

Nebula in
spiral arm

Compact nucleus
emitting intense
radiation

Spiral arm

**FALSE-COLOUR OPTICAL IMAGE OF NGC 5754
(TWO COLLIDING GALAXIES)**

Blue indicates low-
intensity radiation

Red indicates
medium-intensity
radiation

Spiral arm
distorted by
gravitational
influence of
smaller galaxy

Large spiral
galaxy

Smaller galaxy
colliding with
large galaxy

Yellow indicates
high-intensity
radiation

13

The Milky Way

VIEW TOWARDS GALACTIC CENTRE

THE MILKY WAY IS THE NAME GIVEN TO THE FAINT BAND OF LIGHT that stretches across the night sky. This light comes from stars and nebulae in our galaxy, known as the Milky Way Galaxy or simply as "the Galaxy". The Galaxy is believed to be a barred spiral, with a dense central bar of stars encircled by four arms spiralling outwards and surrounded by a less dense halo. We cannot see the spiral shape because the Solar System is in one of the spiral arms, the Orion Arm (also called the Local Arm). From our position, the centre of the Galaxy is completely obscured by dust clouds; as a result, optical maps give only a limited view of the Galaxy. However, a more complete picture can be obtained by studying radio, infra-red, and other radiation. The central part of the Galaxy is relatively small and dense and contains mainly older red and yellow stars. The halo is a less dense region in which the oldest stars are situated; some of these stars are as old as the Galaxy itself (possibly 13 billion years). The spiral arms contain main sequence stars and hot, young, blue stars, as well as nebulae (clouds of dust and gas inside which stars are born). The Galaxy is vast, about 100,000 light years across (a light year is about 9,460 billion kilometres); in comparison, the Solar System seems small, at about 12 light hours across (about 13 billion kilometres). The entire Galaxy is rotating in space, although the inner stars travel faster than those further out. The Sun, which is about two-thirds out from the centre, completes one lap of the Galaxy about every 220 million years.

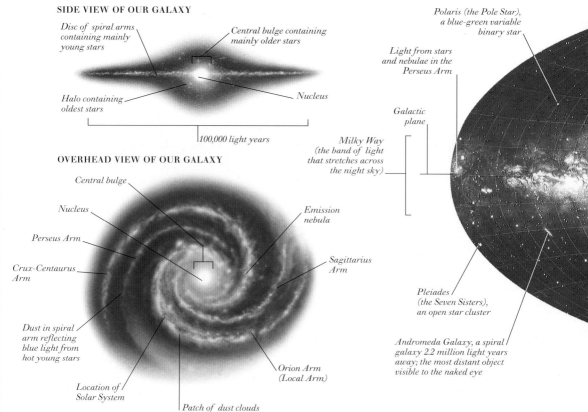

PANORAMIC OPTICAL MAP OF OUR GALAXY AND NEARBY GALAXIES

SIDE VIEW OF OUR GALAXY

Disc of spiral arms containing mainly young stars

Central bulge containing mainly older stars

Halo containing oldest stars

Nucleus

100,000 light years

OVERHEAD VIEW OF OUR GALAXY

Central bulge

Nucleus

Perseus Arm

Crux-Centaurus Arm

Dust in spiral arm reflecting blue light from hot young stars

Location of Solar System

Patch of dust clouds

Emission nebula

Sagittarius Arm

Orion Arm (Local Arm)

Polaris (the Pole Star), a blue-green variable binary star

Light from stars and nebulae in the Perseus Arm

Galactic plane

Milky Way (the band of light that stretches across the night sky)

Pleiades (the Seven Sisters), an open star cluster

Andromeda Galaxy, a spiral galaxy 2.2 million light years away; the most distant object visible to the naked eye

PANORAMIC RADIO MAP OF OUR GALAXY

North Galactic spur
(possibly radio emission
from a supernova remnant)

North Galactic
Pole

Red indicates
high-intensity
radio-wave emission

Galactic
plane

Galactic
plane

Galactic
plane

Blue indicates
low-intensity
radio-wave emission

South
Galactic Pole

Yellow and green
indicate medium-intensity
radio-wave emission

PANORAMIC INFRA-RED MAP OF OUR GALAXY

North Galactic
Pole

Low-intensity infra-red
radiation from interstellar
gas and dust

Galactic
plane

South Galactic Pole

High-intensity infra-red
radiation from interstellar
gas and dust

High-intensity
infra-red
radiation
from region
of starbirth

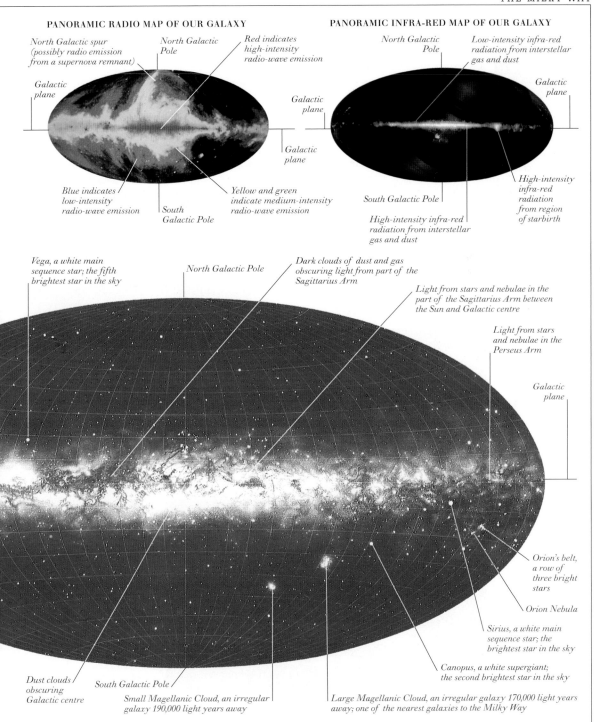

Vega, a white main
sequence star; the fifth
brightest star in the sky

North Galactic Pole

Dark clouds of dust and gas
obscuring light from part of the
Sagittarius Arm

Light from stars and nebulae in the
part of the Sagittarius Arm between
the Sun and Galactic centre

Light from stars
and nebulae in the
Perseus Arm

Galactic
plane

Orion's belt,
a row of
three bright
stars

Orion Nebula

Sirius, a white main
sequence star; the
brightest star in the sky

Canopus, a white supergiant;
the second brightest star in the sky

Dust clouds
obscuring
Galactic centre

South Galactic Pole

Small Magellanic Cloud, an irregular
galaxy 190,000 light years away

Large Magellanic Cloud, an irregular galaxy 170,000 light years
away; one of the nearest galaxies to the Milky Way

Nebulae and star clusters

A NEBULA IS A CLOUD OF DUST AND GAS inside a galaxy. Nebulae become visible if the gas glows, or if the cloud reflects starlight or obscures light from more distant objects. Emission nebulae shine because their gas emits light when it is stimulated by radiation from hot young stars. Reflection nebulae shine because their dust reflects light from stars in or around the nebula. Dark nebulae appear as silhouettes because they block out light from shining nebulae or stars behind them. Two types of nebula are associated with dying stars: planetary nebulae and supernova remnants. Both consist of expanding shells of gas that were once the outer layers of a star. A planetary nebula is a gas shell drifting away from a dying stellar core. A supernova remnant is a gas shell moving away from a stellar core at great speed following a violent explosion called a supernova (see pp. 26-27). Stars are often found in groups known as clusters. Open clusters are loose groups of a few thousand young stars that were born from the same cloud and are drifting apart. Globular clusters are densely packed, roughly spherical groups of hundreds of thousands of older stars.

TRIFID NEBULA (EMISSION NEBULA)

Reflection nebula

Emission nebula

Dust lane

Starbirth region (area in which dust and gas clump together to form stars)

PLEIADES (OPEN STAR CLUSTER) WITH A REFLECTION NEBULA

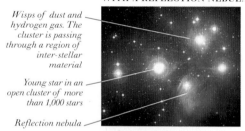

Wisps of dust and hydrogen gas. The cluster is passing through a region of inter-stellar material

Young star in an open cluster of more than 1,000 stars

Reflection nebula

HORSEHEAD NEBULA (DARK NEBULA)

Glowing filament of hot, ionized hydrogen gas

Alnitak (star in Orion's belt)

Dust lane

Emission nebula

Star near southern end of Orion's belt

Emission nebula

Horsehead Nebula

Reflection nebula

Dark nebula obscuring light from distant stars

ORION NEBULA (DIFFUSE EMISSION NEBULA)

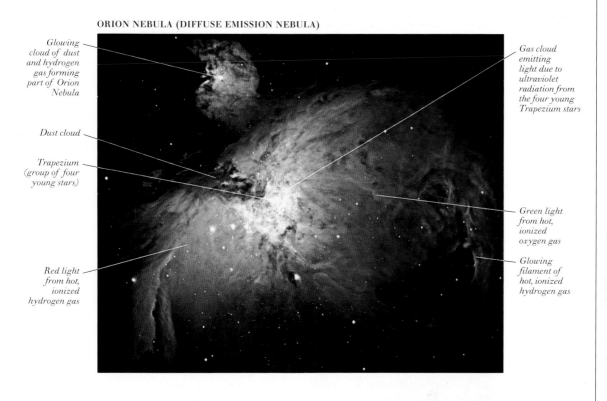

Glowing cloud of dust and hydrogen gas forming part of Orion Nebula

Gas cloud emitting light due to ultraviolet radiation from the four young Trapezium stars

Dust cloud

Trapezium (group of four young stars)

Green light from hot, ionized oxygen gas

Glowing filament of hot, ionized hydrogen gas

Red light from hot, ionized hydrogen gas

VELA SUPERNOVA REMNANT

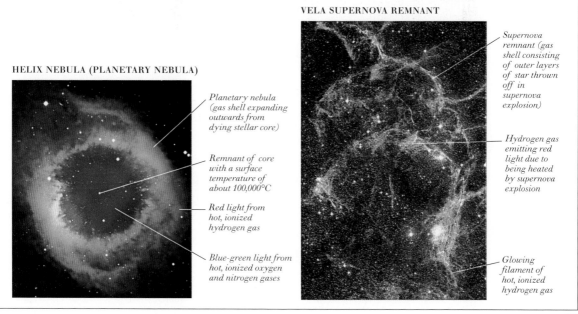

HELIX NEBULA (PLANETARY NEBULA)

Planetary nebula (gas shell expanding outwards from dying stellar core)

Remnant of core with a surface temperature of about 100,000°C

Red light from hot, ionized hydrogen gas

Blue-green light from hot, ionized oxygen and nitrogen gases

Supernova remnant (gas shell consisting of outer layers of star thrown off in supernova explosion)

Hydrogen gas emitting red light due to being heated by supernova explosion

Glowing filament of hot, ionized hydrogen gas

Stars of northern skies

When you look at the northern sky, you look away from the densely populated Galactic centre, so the northern sky generally appears less bright than the southern sky (see pp. 20-21). Among the best-known sights in the northern sky are the constellations Ursa Major (the Great Bear) and Orion. Some ancient civilizations believed that the stars were fixed to a celestial sphere surrounding the Earth, and modern maps of the sky are based on a similar idea. The North and South Poles of this imaginary celestial sphere are directly above the North and South Poles of the Earth, at the points where the Earth's axis of rotation intersects the sphere. The celestial North Pole is at the centre of the map shown here, and Polaris (the Pole Star) lies very close to it. The celestial equator marks a projection of the Earth's equator on the sphere. The ecliptic marks the path of the Sun across the sky as the Earth orbits the Sun. The Moon and planets move against the background of the stars because the stars are much more distant; the nearest star outside the Solar System (Proxima Centauri) is more than 50,000 times further away than the planet Jupiter.

ORION

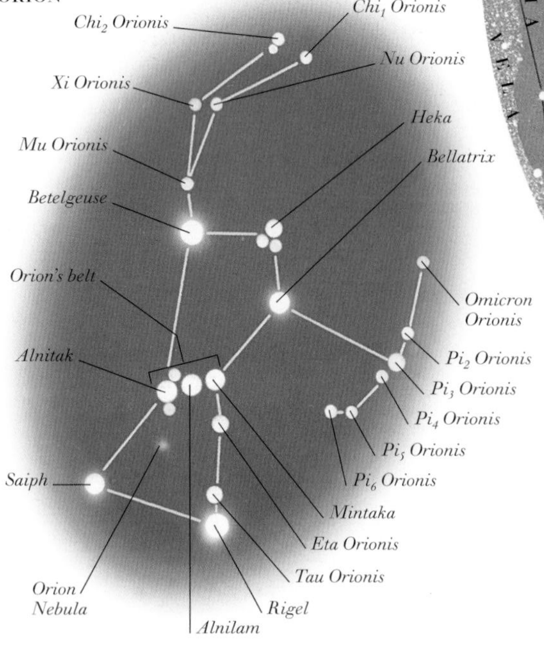

Chi₂ Orionis
Chi₁ Orionis
Nu Orionis
Xi Orionis
Heka
Mu Orionis
Bellatrix
Betelgeuse
Orion's belt
Omicron Orionis
Alnitak
Pi₂ Orionis
Pi₃ Orionis
Pi₄ Orionis
Pi₅ Orionis
Saiph
Pi₆ Orionis
Mintaka
Eta Orionis
Tau Orionis
Orion Nebula
Rigel
Alnilam

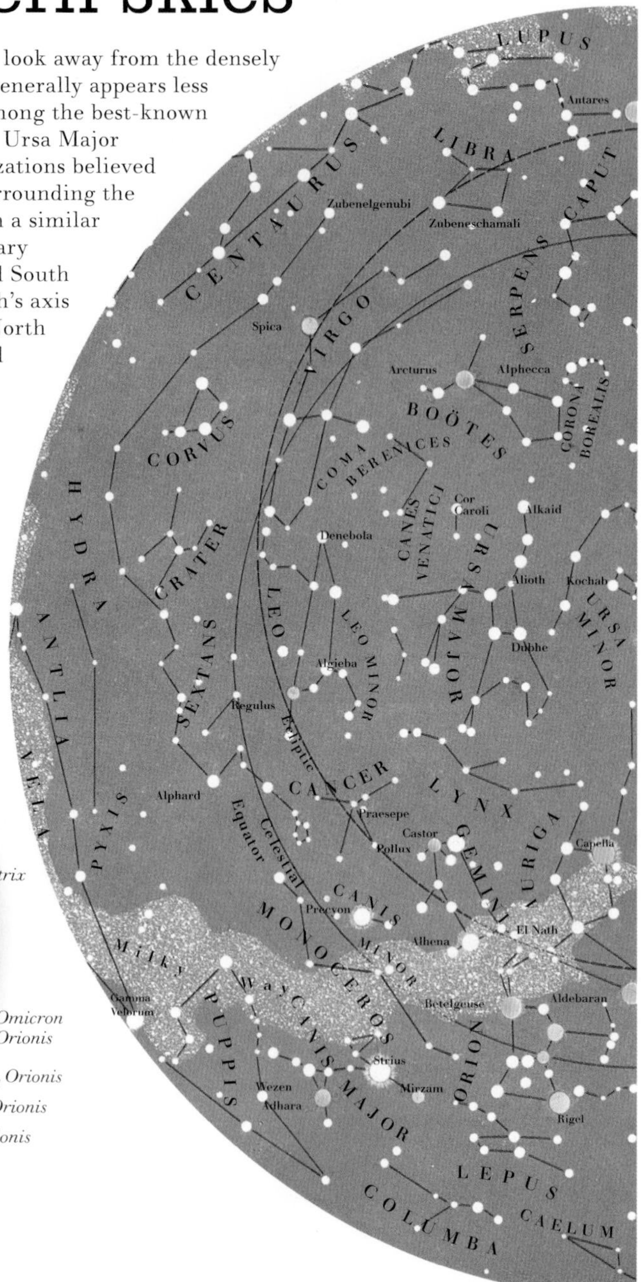

VISIBLE STARS IN THE NORTHERN SKY

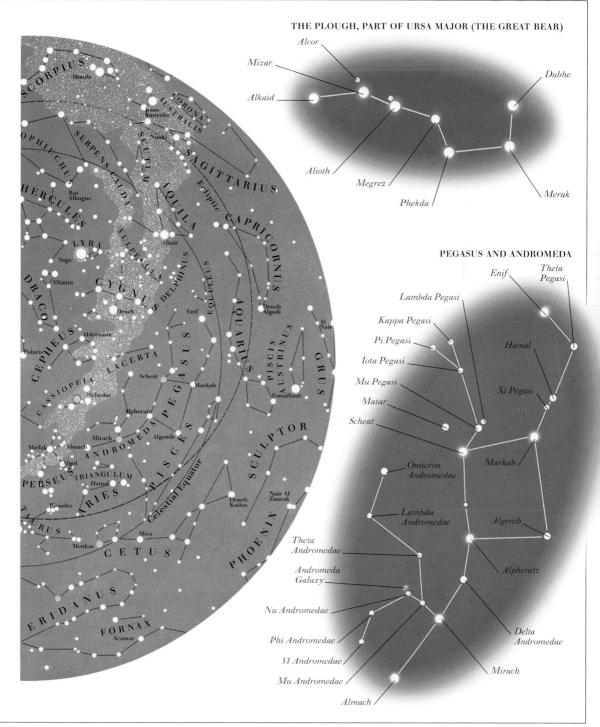

THE PLOUGH, PART OF URSA MAJOR (THE GREAT BEAR)

Alcor
Mizar
Alkaid
Dubhe
Alioth
Megrez
Phekda
Merak

PEGASUS AND ANDROMEDA

Enif
Theta Pegasi
Lambda Pegasi
Kappa Pegasi
Pi Pegasi
Iota Pegasi
Mu Pegasi
Matar
Scheat
Omicron Andromedae
Lambda Andromedae
Theta Andromedae
Andromeda Galaxy
Nu Andromedae
Phi Andromedae
51 Andromedae
Mu Andromedae
Almach
Hamal
Xi Pegasi
Markab
Algenib
Alpheratz
Delta Andromedae
Mirach

SCORPIUS
Shaula
CORONA AUSTRALIS
Kaus Australis
Nunki
OPHIUCHUS
SERPENS CAUDA
SCUTUM
SAGITTARIUS
Ras Alhague
AQUILA
CAPRICORNUS
HERCULES
Ecliptic
VULPECULA
Altair
LYRA
Vega
CYGNUS
DELPHINUS
EQUULEUS
Deneb Algedi
Eltanin
DRACO
Deneb
Enif
AQUARIUS
PISCIS AUSTRINUS
Al Nair
CEPHEUS
Alderamin
LACERTA
PEGASUS
Fomalhaut
GRUS
Polaris
CASSIOPEIA
Scheat
Markab
Schedar
Alpheratz
Algenib
ANDROMEDA
PISCES
Mirach
SCULPTOR
Mirfak
Almach
Algol
PERSEUS
TRIANGULUM
Hamal
Celestial Equator
Deneb Kaitos
Nair Al Zaurak
Pleiades
ARIES
TAURUS
Menkar
Mira
CETUS
PHOENIX
ERIDANUS
FORNAX
Acamar

19

Stars of southern skies

WHEN YOU LOOK AT THE SOUTHERN SKY, you look towards the Galactic centre, which has a huge population of stars. As a result, the Milky Way appears brighter in the southern sky than in the northern sky (see pp. 18-19). The southern sky is rich in nebulae and star clusters. It contains the Large and Small Magellanic Clouds, which are two of the nearest galaxies to our own. Stars make fixed patterns in the sky called constellations. However, the constellations are only apparent groupings of stars, since the distances to the stars in a constellation may vary enormously. The shapes of constellations may change over many thousands of years due to the relative motions of stars. The movement of the constellations across the sky is due to the Earth's motion in space. The daily rotation of the Earth causes the constellations to move across the sky from east to west, and the orbit of the Earth around the Sun causes different areas of sky to be visible in different seasons. The visibility of areas of sky also depends on the location of the observer. For instance, stars near the celestial equator may be seen from either hemisphere at some time during the year, whereas stars close to the celestial poles (the celestial South Pole is at the centre of the map shown here) can never be seen from the opposite hemisphere.

HYDRUS (THE WATER SNAKE) AND MENSA (THE TABLE)

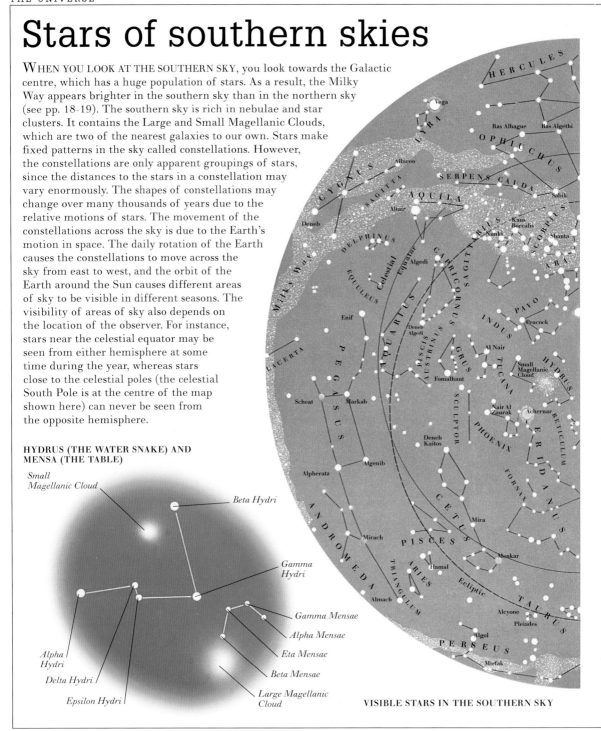

Small Magellanic Cloud

Beta Hydri

Gamma Hydri

Gamma Mensae

Alpha Mensae

Eta Mensae

Beta Mensae

Large Magellanic Cloud

Alpha Hydri

Delta Hydri

Epsilon Hydri

VISIBLE STARS IN THE SOUTHERN SKY

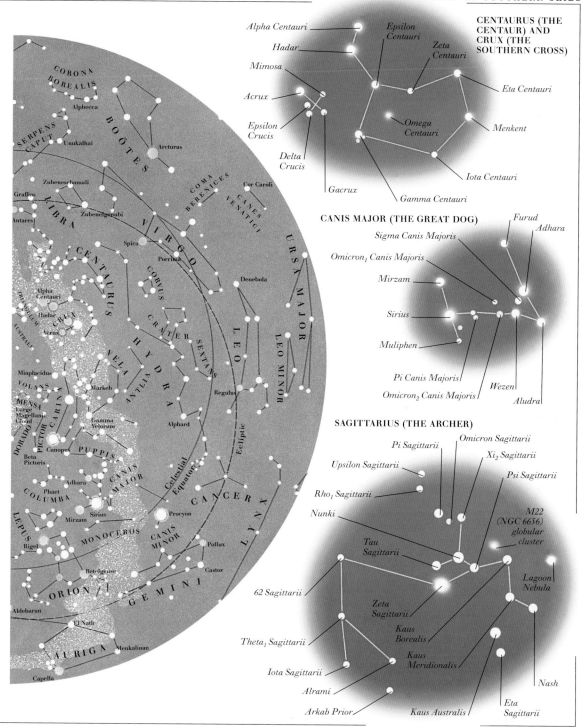

CENTAURUS (THE CENTAUR) AND CRUX (THE SOUTHERN CROSS)

Alpha Centauri

Hadar

Mimosa

Acrux

Epsilon Crucis

Delta Crucis

Gacrux

Epsilon Centauri

Zeta Centauri

Eta Centauri

Omega Centauri

Menkent

Iota Centauri

Gamma Centauri

CANIS MAJOR (THE GREAT DOG)

Sigma Canis Majoris

Omicron₁ Canis Majoris

Mirzam

Sirius

Muliphen

Pi Canis Majoris

Omicron₂ Canis Majoris

Furud

Adhara

Wezen

Aludra

SAGITTARIUS (THE ARCHER)

Pi Sagittarii

Upsilon Sagittarii

Rho₁ Sagittarii

Nunki

Tau Sagittarii

62 Sagittarii

Theta₁ Sagittarii

Iota Sagittarii

Alrami

Arkab Prior

Omicron Sagittarii

Xi₂ Sagittarii

Psi Sagittarii

M22 (NGC 6656) globular cluster

Lagoon Nebula

Zeta Sagittarii

Kaus Borealis

Kaus Meridionalis

Nash

Kaus Australis

Eta Sagittarii

CORONA BOREALIS

Alphecca

SERPENS CAPUT

Unukalhai

BOÖTES

Arcturus

COMA BERENICES

CANES VENATICI

Cor Caroli

Zubeneschamali

Graffias

LIBRA

Zubenelgenubi

Antares

VIRGO

Spica

Porrima

CORVUS

URSA MAJOR

Denebola

LEO

LEO MINOR

Regulus

CENTAURUS

Alpha Centauri

Hadar

CRUX

Acrux

TRIANGULUM AUSTRALE

HYDRA

CRATER

SEXTANS

Miaplacidus

VOLANS

MENSA

Large Magellanic Cloud

DORADO

PICTOR

CARINA

Beta Pictoris

Canopus

VELA

ANTLIA

Markeb

Gamma Velorum

Alphard

PUPPIS

COLUMBA

Phact

Adhara

Mirzam

Sirius

CANIS MAJOR

MONOCEROS

CANIS MINOR

Procyon

CANCER

Pollux

Castor

LYNX

GEMINI

ORION

Betelgeuse

Rigel

LEPUS

Aldebaran

El Nath

AURIGA

Menkalinan

Capella

Celestial Equator

Ecliptic

Stars

OPEN STAR CLUSTER AND DUST CLOUD

STARS ARE BODIES of hot, glowing gas that are born in nebulae (see pp. 24-27). They vary enormously in size, mass, and temperature: diameters range from about 450 times smaller to over 1,000 times bigger than that of the Sun; masses range from about a twentieth to over 50 solar masses; and surface temperatures range from about 3,000°C to over 50,000°C. The colour of a star is determined by its temperature: the hottest stars are blue and the coolest are red. The Sun, with a surface temperature of 5,500°C, is between these extremes and appears yellow. The energy emitted by a shining star is usually produced by nuclear fusion in the star's core. The brightness of a star is measured in magnitudes – the brighter the star, the lower its magnitude. There are two types of magnitude: apparent magnitude, which is the brightness seen from Earth, and absolute magnitude, which is the brightness that would be seen from a standard distance of 10 parsecs (32.6 light years). The light emitted by a star may be split to form a spectrum containing a series of dark lines (absorption lines). The patterns of lines indicate the presence of particular chemical elements, enabling astronomers to deduce the composition of the star's atmosphere. The magnitude and spectral type (colour) of stars may be plotted on a graph called a Hertzsprung-Russell diagram, which shows that stars tend to fall into several well-defined groups. The principal groups are main sequence stars (those which are fusing hydrogen to form helium), giants, supergiants, and white dwarfs.

STAR SIZES

Red giant (diameters between about 15 million and 150 million km)

The Sun (main sequence star with diameter about 1.4 million km)

White dwarf (diameters between about 3,000 and 50,000 km)

ENERGY EMISSION FROM THE SUN

Nuclear fusion in core produces gamma rays and neutrinos

Neutrinos travel to Earth directly from Sun's core in about 8 minutes

Lower-energy radiation travels to Earth in about 8 minutes

Earth

Lower-energy radiation (mainly ultraviolet, infra-red, and light rays) leaves surface

Sun

High-energy radiation (gamma rays) loses energy while travelling to surface over 2 million years

STAR MAGNITUDES

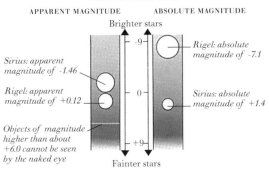

APPARENT MAGNITUDE   ABSOLUTE MAGNITUDE

Brighter stars

Sirius: apparent magnitude of -1.46

Rigel: apparent magnitude of +0.12

Objects of magnitude higher than about +6.0 cannot be seen by the naked eye

Rigel: absolute magnitude of -7.1

Sirius: absolute magnitude of +1.4

Fainter stars

NUCLEAR FUSION IN MAIN SEQUENCE STARS LIKE THE SUN

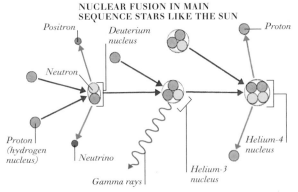

Positron

Deuterium nucleus

Proton

Neutron

Proton (hydrogen nucleus)

Neutrino

Gamma rays

Helium-3 nucleus

Helium-4 nucleus

HERTZSPRUNG-RUSSELL DIAGRAM

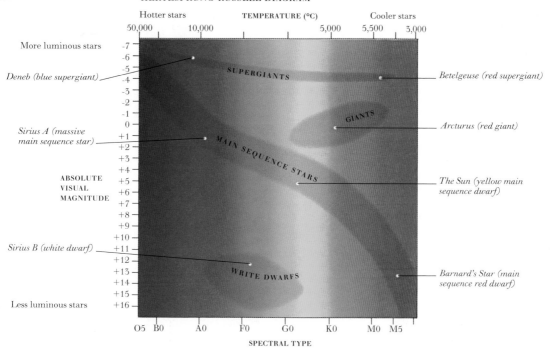

Hotter stars
TEMPERATURE (°C)
Cooler stars

50,000   10,000   5,000   5,500   3,000

More luminous stars

SUPERGIANTS

Deneb (blue supergiant)

Betelgeuse (red supergiant)

GIANTS

Arcturus (red giant)

Sirius A (massive
main sequence star)

MAIN SEQUENCE STARS

The Sun (yellow main
sequence dwarf)

ABSOLUTE
VISUAL
MAGNITUDE

-7
-6
-5
-4
-3
-2
-1
0
+1
+2
+3
+4
+5
+6
+7
+8
+9
+10
+11
+12
+13
+14
+15
+16

Sirius B (white dwarf)

WRITE DWARFS

Barnard's Star (main
sequence red dwarf)

Less luminous stars

O5 B0   A0   F0   G0   K0   M0 M5

SPECTRAL TYPE

STELLAR SPECTRAL ABSORPTION LINES

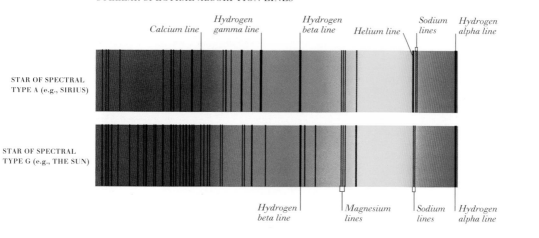

Calcium line   Hydrogen
gamma line   Hydrogen
beta line   Helium line   Sodium
lines   Hydrogen
alpha line

STAR OF SPECTRAL
TYPE A (e.g., SIRIUS)

STAR OF SPECTRAL
TYPE G (e.g., THE SUN)

Hydrogen
beta line   Magnesium
lines   Sodium
lines   Hydrogen
alpha line

Small stars

**REGION OF
STAR FORMATION
IN ORION**

SMALL STARS HAVE A MASS of up to about one and a half
times that of the Sun. They begin to form when a region of
higher density in a nebula condenses into a huge globule
of gas and dust that contracts under its own gravity.
Within a globule, regions of condensing matter heat
up and begin to glow, forming protostars. If a
protostar contains enough matter, the central
temperature reaches about 8 million °C. At this
temperature, nuclear reactions in which hydrogen
fuses to form helium can start. This process releases
energy, which prevents the star from contracting
further and also causes it to shine; it is now a main
sequence star. A star of about one solar mass remains
on the main sequence for about 10 billion years, until much of the hydrogen in
the star's core has been converted into helium. The helium core then contracts,
and nuclear reactions continue in a shell around the core. The core becomes hot
enough for helium to fuse to form carbon, while the outer
layers of the star expand and cool. The expanding
star is known as a red giant. When the
helium in the core runs out, the outer
layers of the star may be blown
away as an expanding gas shell
called a planetary nebula. The
remaining core (about 80
per cent of the original
star) is now in its final
stages. It becomes
a white dwarf star
that gradually cools
and dims. When it
finally stops shining
altogether, the dead
star will become
a black dwarf.

STRUCTURE OF A MAIN SEQUENCE STAR

*Core containing hydrogen
fusing to form helium*

*Radiative
zone*

*Convective
zone*

*Surface temperature
about 5,500°C*

*Core temperature
about 15 million °C*

STRUCTURE OF A NEBULA

*Young main
sequence star*

*Dense region of dust and
gas (mainly hydrogen)
condensing under gravity
to form globules*

*Hot, ionized hydrogen
gas emitting red light
due to being stimulated
by radiation from hot
young stars*

*Dark globule of dust and
gas (mainly hydrogen)
contracting to form protostars*

LIFE OF A SMALL STAR OF ABOUT ONE SOLAR MASS

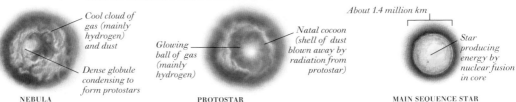

*Cool cloud of
gas (mainly
hydrogen)
and dust*

*Dense globule
condensing to
form protostars*

*Glowing
ball of gas
(mainly
hydrogen)*

*Natal cocoon
(shell of dust
blown away by
radiation from
protostar)*

About 1.4 million km

*Star
producing
energy by
nuclear fusion
in core*

NEBULA

PROTOSTAR
Duration: 50 million years

MAIN SEQUENCE STAR
Duration: 10 billion years

STRUCTURE OF A RED GIANT

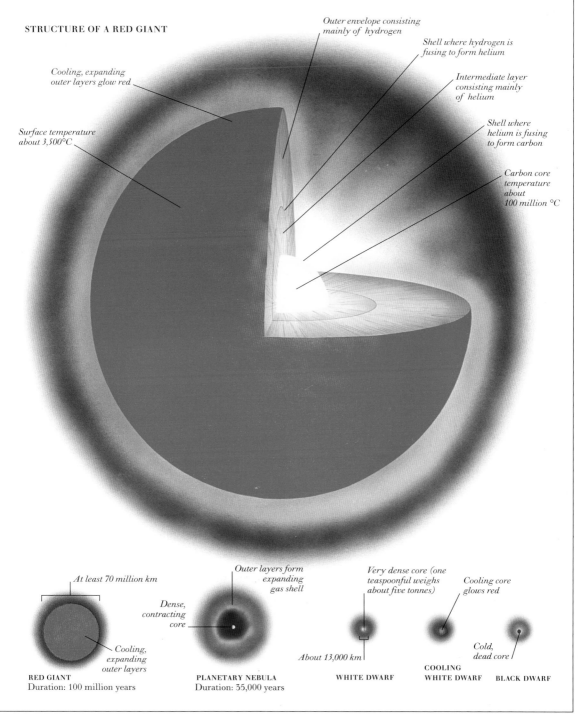

*Outer envelope consisting
mainly of hydrogen*

*Shell where hydrogen is
fusing to form helium*

*Intermediate layer
consisting mainly
of helium*

*Shell where
helium is fusing
to form carbon*

*Carbon core
temperature
about
100 million °C*

*Cooling, expanding
outer layers glow red*

*Surface temperature
about 3,500°C*

At least 70 million km

*Dense,
contracting
core*

*Cooling,
expanding
outer layers*

RED GIANT
Duration: 100 million years

*Outer layers form
expanding
gas shell*

PLANETARY NEBULA
Duration: 35,000 years

*Very dense core (one
teaspoonful weighs
about five tonnes)*

About 13,000 km

WHITE DWARF

*Cooling core
glows red*

**COOLING
WHITE DWARF**

*Cold,
dead core*

BLACK DWARF

Massive stars

MASSIVE STARS HAVE A MASS AT LEAST THREE TIMES that of the Sun, and some stars are as massive as about 50 Suns. A massive star evolves in a similar way to a small star until it reaches the main sequence stage (see pp. 24-25). During its life as a main sequence star, it shines steadily until the hydrogen in its core has fused to form helium. This process takes billions of years in a small star, but only millions of years in a massive star. A massive star then becomes a red supergiant, which initially consists of a helium core surrounded by outer layers of cooling, expanding gas. Over the next few million years, a series of nuclear reactions form different elements in shells around an iron core. The core eventually collapses in less than a second, causing a massive explosion called a supernova, in which a shock wave blows away the outer layers of the star. Supernovae shine brighter than an entire galaxy for a short time. Sometimes, the core survives the supernova explosion. If the surviving core is between about one and a half and three solar masses, it contracts to become a tiny, dense neutron star. If the core is greater than three solar masses, it contracts to become a black hole (see pp. 28-29).

SUPERNOVA

TARANTULA NEBULA BEFORE SUPERNOVA

STRUCTURE OF A RED SUPERGIANT

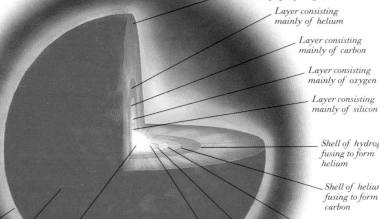

Outer envelope consisting mainly of hydrogen

Layer consisting mainly of helium

Layer consisting mainly of carbon

Layer consisting mainly of oxygen

Layer consisting mainly of silicon

Shell of hydrogen fusing to form helium

Shell of helium fusing to form carbon

Shell of carbon fusing to form oxygen

Shell of oxygen fusing to form silicon

Shell of silicon fusing to form iron core

Surface temperature about 3,000°C

Cooling, expanding outer layers glow red

Core of mainly iron at a temperature of 3-5 billion °C

LIFE OF A MASSIVE STAR OF ABOUT 10 SOLAR MASSES

Dense globule condensing to form protostars

Cool cloud of gas (mainly hydrogen) and dust

NEBULA

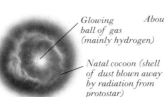

Glowing ball of gas (mainly hydrogen)

About 3 million km

Star producing energy by nuclear fusion in core

Natal cocoon (shell of dust blown away by radiation from protostar)

PROTOSTAR
Duration: a few hundred thousand years

MAIN SEQUENCE STAR
Duration: 10 million years

FEATURES OF A SUPERNOVA

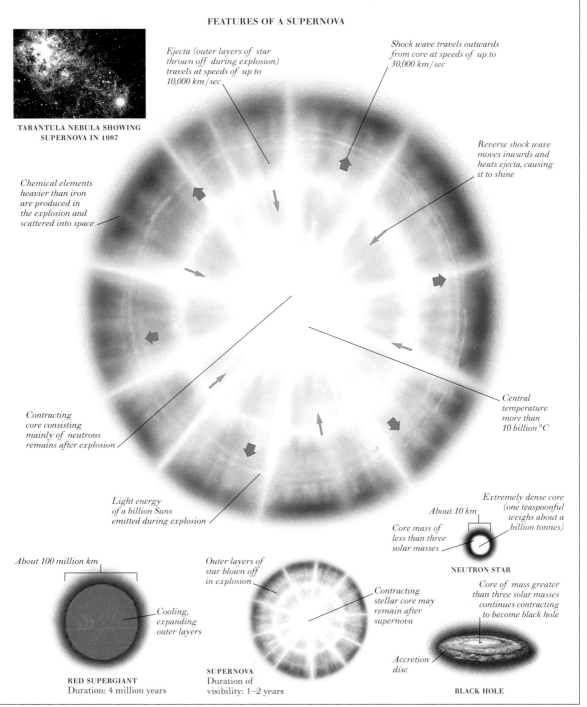

TARANTULA NEBULA SHOWING
SUPERNOVA IN 1987

*Ejecta (outer layers of star
thrown off during explosion)
travels at speeds of up to
10,000 km/sec*

*Shock wave travels outwards
from core at speeds of up to
30,000 km/sec*

*Reverse shock wave
moves inwards and
heats ejecta, causing
it to shine*

*Chemical elements
heavier than iron
are produced in
the explosion and
scattered into space*

*Central
temperature
more than
10 billion °C*

*Contracting
core consisting
mainly of neutrons
remains after explosion*

*Light energy
of a billion Suns
emitted during explosion*

About 100 million km

*Cooling,
expanding
outer layers*

RED SUPERGIANT
Duration: 4 million years

*Outer layers of
star blown off
in explosion*

*Contracting
stellar core may
remain after
supernova*

SUPERNOVA
Duration of
visibility: 1–2 years

*Extremely dense core
(one teaspoonful
weighs about a
billion tonnes)*

About 10 km

*Core mass of
less than three
solar masses*

NEUTRON STAR

*Core of mass greater
than three solar masses
continues contracting
to become black hole*

*Accretion
disc*

BLACK HOLE

Neutron stars and black holes

NEUTRON STARS AND BLACK HOLES form from the stellar cores that remain after stars have exploded as supernovae (see pp. 26-27). If the remaining core is between about one and a half and three solar masses, it contracts to form a neutron star. If the remaining core is greater than about three solar masses, it contracts to form a black hole. Neutron stars are typically only about 10 kilometres in diameter and consist almost entirely of subatomic particles called neutrons. Such stars are so dense that a teaspoonful would weigh about a billion tonnes. Neutron stars are observed as pulsars, so-called because they rotate rapidly and emit two beams of radio waves, which sweep across the sky and are detected as short pulses. Black holes are characterized by their extremely strong gravity, which is so powerful that not even light can escape; as a result, black holes are invisible. However, they can be detected if they have a close companion star. The gravity of the black hole pulls gas from the other star, forming an accretion disc that spirals around the black hole at high speed, heating up and emitting radiation. Eventually, the matter spirals in to cross the event horizon (the boundary of the black hole), thereby disappearing from the visible Universe.

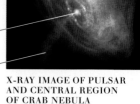

Nebula of gas and dust surrounds pulsar

Rapidly rotating pulsar

Beam of radiation from pulsar

X-RAY IMAGE OF PULSAR AND CENTRAL REGION OF CRAB NEBULA (SUPERNOVA REMNANT)

PULSAR (ROTATING NEUTRON STAR)

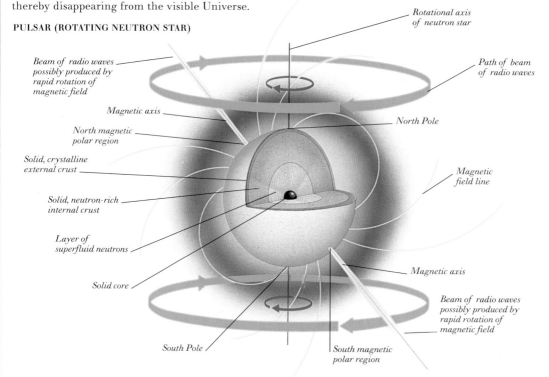

Beam of radio waves possibly produced by rapid rotation of magnetic field

Magnetic axis

North magnetic polar region

Solid, crystalline external crust

Solid, neutron-rich internal crust

Layer of superfluid neutrons

Solid core

South Pole

Rotational axis of neutron star

Path of beam of radio waves

North Pole

Magnetic field line

Magnetic axis

Beam of radio waves possibly produced by rapid rotation of magnetic field

South magnetic polar region

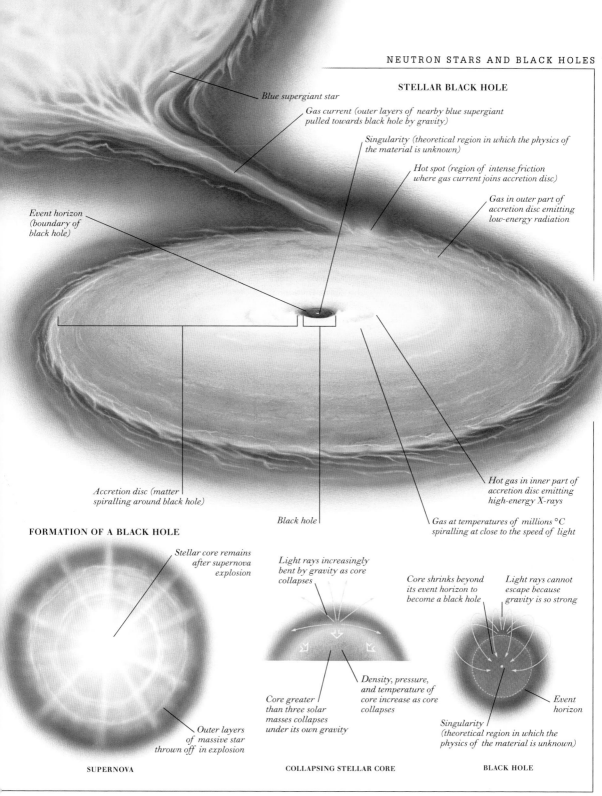

STELLAR BLACK HOLE

Blue supergiant star

Gas current (outer layers of nearby blue supergiant pulled towards black hole by gravity)

Singularity (theoretical region in which the physics of the material is unknown)

Hot spot (region of intense friction where gas current joins accretion disc)

Gas in outer part of accretion disc emitting low-energy radiation

Event horizon (boundary of black hole)

Accretion disc (matter spiralling around black hole)

Black hole

Hot gas in inner part of accretion disc emitting high-energy X-rays

Gas at temperatures of millions °C spiralling at close to the speed of light

FORMATION OF A BLACK HOLE

Stellar core remains after supernova explosion

Light rays increasingly bent by gravity as core collapses

Core shrinks beyond its event horizon to become a black hole

Light rays cannot escape because gravity is so strong

Outer layers of massive star thrown off in explosion

Core greater than three solar masses collapses under its own gravity

Density, pressure, and temperature of core increase as core collapses

Event horizon

Singularity (theoretical region in which the physics of the material is unknown)

SUPERNOVA

COLLAPSING STELLAR CORE

BLACK HOLE

The Solar System

THE SUN

THE SOLAR SYSTEM consists of a central star (the Sun) and the bodies that orbit it. These bodies include eight planets and their more than 160 known moons; dwarf planets; Kuiper Belt objects; asteroids; comets; and meteoroids. The Solar System also contains interplanetary gas and dust. The planets fall into two groups: four small rocky planets near the Sun (Mercury, Venus, Earth, and Mars); and four planets further out, the giants (Jupiter, Saturn, Uranus, and Neptune). Between the rocky planets and giants is the asteroid belt, which contains thousands of chunks of rock orbiting the Sun. Beyond Neptune is the Kuiper Belt and, more distant, the Oort Cloud. Most of the bodies in the planetary part of the Solar System move around the Sun in elliptical orbits located in a thin disc around the Sun's equator. All the planets orbit the Sun in the same direction (anticlockwise when viewed from above) and all but Venus and Uranus also spin about their axes in this direction. Moons also spin as they, in turn, orbit their planets. The entire Solar System orbits the centre of our galaxy, the Milky Way (see pp. 14-15).

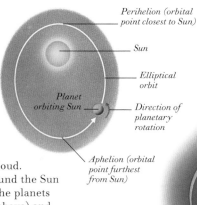

Perihelion (orbital point closest to Sun)

Sun

Elliptical orbit

Planet orbiting Sun

Direction of planetary rotation

Aphelion (orbital point furthest from Sun)

Aphelion of Neptune: 4,545 million km

ORBITS OF INNER PLANETS

Mercury

Perihelion of Mercury: 46 million km

Perihelion of Venus: 107.5 million km

Perihelion of Earth: 147.1 million km

Average orbital speed of Venus: 35.02 km/sec

Average orbital speed of Mercury: 47.87 km/sec

Average orbital speed of Earth: 29.78 km/sec

Average orbital speed of Mars: 24.13 km/sec

Mars

Perihelion of Mars: 206.6 million km

Earth

Venus

Sun

Aphelion of Mercury: 69.8 million km

Asteroid belt

Aphelion of Venus: 108 million km

Aphelion of Earth: 152 million km

Aphelion of Pluto: 7,375.9 million km

Aphelion of Mars: 249.2 million km

MERCURY
Year: 87.97 Earth days
Mass: 0.06 Earth masses
Diameter: 4,878 km

VENUS
Year: 224.7 Earth days
Mass: 0.81 Earth masses
Diameter: 12,103 km

EARTH
Year: 365.26 days
Mass: 1 Earth mass
Diameter: 12,756 km

MARS
Year: 1.88 Earth years
Mass: 0.11 Earth masses
Diameter: 6,786 km

JUPITER
Year: 11.87 Earth years
Mass: 317.83 Earth masses
Diameter: 142,984 km

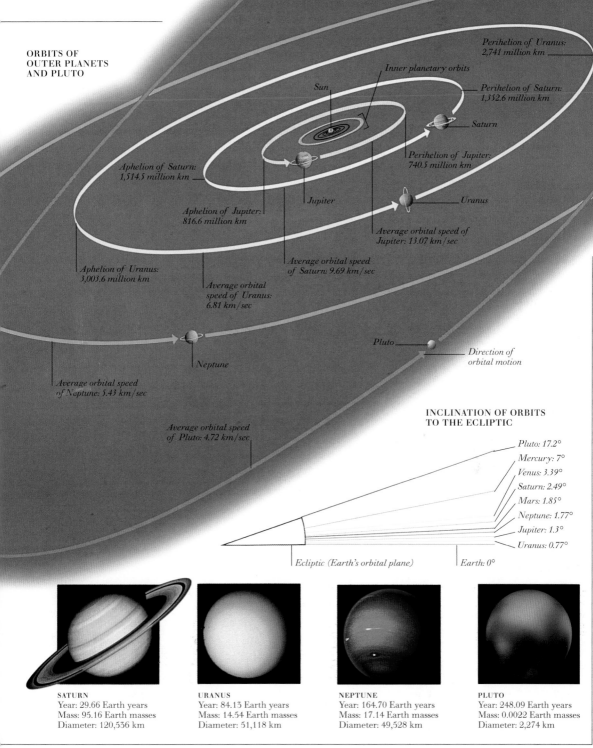

ORBITS OF
OUTER PLANETS
AND PLUTO

Perihelion of Uranus:
2,741 million km

Inner planetary orbits

Sun

Perihelion of Saturn:
1,352.6 million km

Saturn

Perihelion of Jupiter:
740.5 million km

Aphelion of Saturn:
1,514.5 million km

Jupiter

Uranus

Average orbital speed of
Jupiter: 13.07 km/sec

Aphelion of Jupiter:
816.6 million km

Average orbital speed
of Saturn: 9.69 km/sec

Aphelion of Uranus:
3,003.6 million km

Average orbital
speed of Uranus:
6.81 km/sec

Pluto

Direction of
orbital motion

Neptune

Average orbital speed
of Neptune: 5.43 km/sec

Average orbital speed
of Pluto: 4.72 km/sec

INCLINATION OF ORBITS
TO THE ECLIPTIC

Pluto: 17.2°

Mercury: 7°

Venus: 3.39°

Saturn: 2.49°

Mars: 1.85°

Neptune: 1.77°

Jupiter: 1.3°

Uranus: 0.77°

Ecliptic (Earth's orbital plane)

Earth: 0°

SATURN
Year: 29.66 Earth years
Mass: 95.16 Earth masses
Diameter: 120,536 km

URANUS
Year: 84.13 Earth years
Mass: 14.54 Earth masses
Diameter: 51,118 km

NEPTUNE
Year: 164.70 Earth years
Mass: 17.14 Earth masses
Diameter: 49,528 km

PLUTO
Year: 248.09 Earth years
Mass: 0.0022 Earth masses
Diameter: 2,274 km

The Sun

SOLAR PHOTOSPHERE

THE SUN IS THE STAR AT THE CENTRE of the Solar System. It is about five billion years old and will continue to shine as it does now for about another five billion years. The Sun is a yellow main sequence star (see pp. 22-23) about 1.4 million kilometres in diameter. It consists almost entirely of hydrogen and helium. In the Sun's core, hydrogen is converted to helium by nuclear fusion, releasing energy in the process. The energy travels from the core, through the radiative and convective zones, to the photosphere (visible surface), where it leaves the Sun in the form of heat and light. On the photosphere there are often dark, relatively cool areas called sunspots, which usually appear in pairs or groups and are caused by the cooling effect of the magnetic field. Other types of solar activity are flares, which are usually associated with sunspots, and prominences. Flares are sudden discharges of high-energy radiation and atomic particles. Prominences are huge loops or filaments of gas extending into the solar atmosphere; some last for hours, others for months. Beyond the photosphere is the chromosphere (inner atmosphere) and the extremely rarified corona (outer atmosphere), which extends millions of kilometres into space. Tiny particles that escape from the corona give rise to the solar wind, which streams through space at hundreds of kilometres per second. The chromosphere and corona can be seen from Earth when the Sun is totally eclipsed by the Moon.

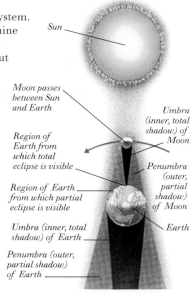

Sun

Moon passes between Sun and Earth

Region of Earth from which total eclipse is visible

Region of Earth from which partial eclipse is visible

Umbra (inner, total shadow) of Earth

Penumbra (outer, partial shadow) of Earth

Umbra (inner, total shadow) of Moon

Penumbra (outer, partial shadow) of Moon

Earth

SURFACE FEATURES

Gas loop (looped prominence)

Prominence (jet of gas at edge of Sun's disc up to hundreds of thousands of kilometres high)

Spicule (vertical jet of gas)

Photosphere (visible surface)

Chromosphere (inner atmosphere)

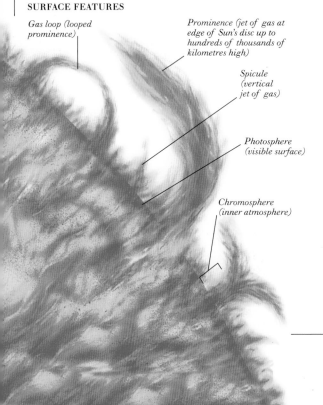

TOTAL SOLAR ECLIPSE

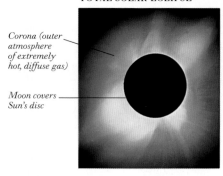

Corona (outer atmosphere of extremely hot, diffuse gas)

Moon covers Sun's disc

SUNSPOTS

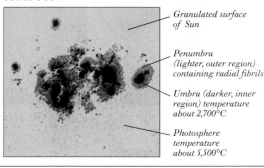

Granulated surface of Sun

Penumbra (lighter, outer region) containing radial fibrils

Umbra (darker, inner region) temperature about 2,700°C

Photosphere temperature about 5,500°C

EXTERNAL FEATURES AND
INTERNAL STRUCTURE OF THE SUN

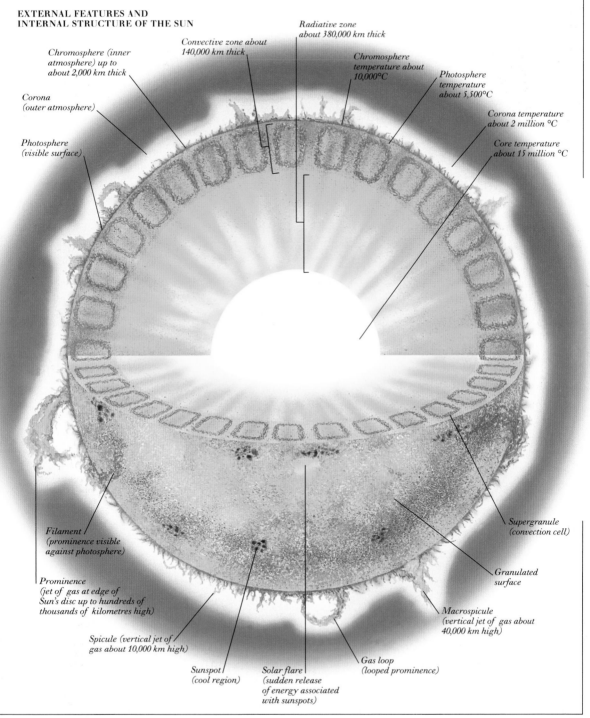

Chromosphere (inner
atmosphere) up to
about 2,000 km thick

Convective zone about
140,000 km thick

Radiative zone
about 380,000 km thick

Chromosphere
temperature about
10,000°C

Photosphere
temperature
about 5,500°C

Corona
(outer atmosphere)

Corona temperature
about 2 million °C

Core temperature
about 15 million °C

Photosphere
(visible surface)

Filament
(prominence visible
against photosphere)

Supergranule
(convection cell)

Prominence
(jet of gas at edge of
Sun's disc up to hundreds of
thousands of kilometres high)

Granulated
surface

Macrospicule
(vertical jet of gas about
40,000 km high)

Spicule (vertical jet of
gas about 10,000 km high)

Sunspot
(cool region)

Solar flare
(sudden release
of energy associated
with sunspots)

Gas loop
(looped prominence)

Mercury

MERCURY

MERCURY IS THE NEAREST PLANET to the Sun, orbiting at an average distance of about 58 million kilometres. Because Mercury is the closest planet to the Sun, it moves faster than any other planet, travelling at an average speed of nearly 48 kilometres per second and completing an orbit in just under 88 days. Mercury is very small (only 40 per cent bigger than the Moon) and rocky. Most of the surface has been heavily cratered by the impact of meteorites, although there are also smooth, sparsely cratered lava-covered plains. The Caloris Basin is the largest crater, measuring about 1,300 kilometres across. It is thought to have been formed when a 60-kilometre-diameter asteroid hit the planet, and is surrounded by concentric rings of mountains thrown up by the impact. The surface also has many cliff-like ridges (called rupes) that are thought to have been formed when the hot core of the young planet cooled and shrank about four billion years ago, buckling the planet's surface in the process. The planet rotates about its axis very slowly, taking nearly 59 Earth days to complete one rotation. As a result, a solar day (sunrise to sunrise) on Mercury is about 176 Earth days – twice as long as the 88-day Mercurian year. Mercury has extreme surface temperatures, ranging from a maximum of 430°C on the sunlit side to -170°C on the dark side. At nightfall, the temperature drops very quickly because the planet's atmosphere is almost non-existent. It consists only of minute amounts of helium and hydrogen captured from the solar wind, plus traces of other gases.

TILT AND ROTATION OF MERCURY

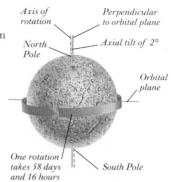

Axis of rotation

Perpendicular to orbital plane

North Pole

Axial tilt of 2°

Orbital plane

One rotation takes 58 days and 16 hours

South Pole

DEGAS AND BRONTË (RAY CRATERS)

Bright ray of ejecta (ejected material)

Brontë

Unmapped region

Degas with central peak

FORMATION OF A RAY CRATER

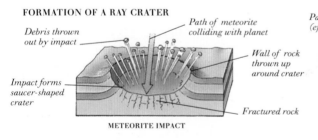

Debris thrown out by impact

Path of meteorite colliding with planet

Impact forms saucer-shaped crater

Wall of rock thrown up around crater

Fractured rock

METEORITE IMPACT

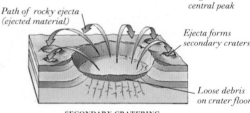

Path of rocky ejecta (ejected material)

Ejecta forms secondary craters

Loose debris on crater floor

SECONDARY CRATERING

Wall of rock forms ring of mountains

Small secondary crater

Central mountain rings form if floor of large crater recoils from meteorite impact

Ray of ejecta (ejected material)

Loose ejected rock

Falling debris forms ridges on side of wall

RAY CRATER

COMPOSITION OF ATMOSPHERE

Principal constituents
helium and hydrogen

Minor constituents
sodium and oxygen

Traces of neon, argon,
and potassium

EXTERNAL FEATURES AND INTERNAL
STRUCTURE OF MERCURY

CRATERS AND PLAINS NEAR
MERCURY'S NORTH POLE

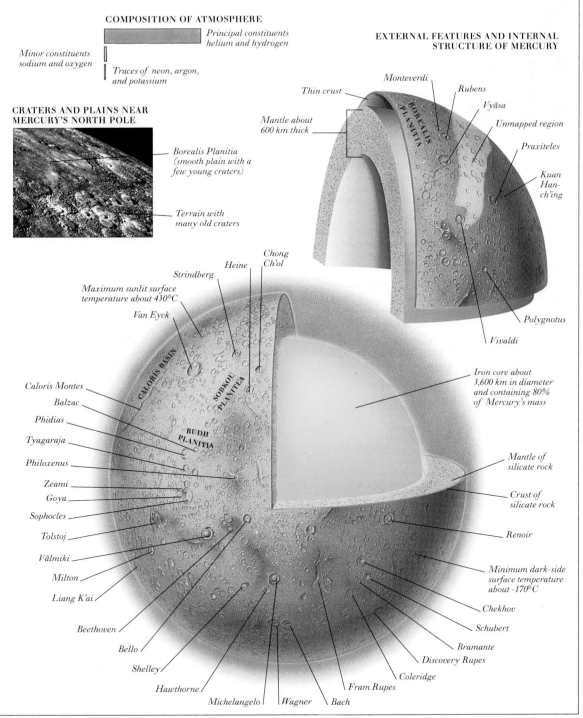

Borealis Planitia
(smooth plain with a
few young craters)

Terrain with
many old craters

Monteverdi

Thin crust

Rubens

Vyāsa

BOREALIS
PLANITIA

Unmapped region

Mantle about
600 km thick

Praxiteles

Kuan
Han-
ch'ing

Chong
Ch'ol

Heine

Strindberg

Maximum sunlit surface
temperature about 430°C

Van Eyck

Polygnotus

Vivaldi

CALORIS BASIN

SOBKOU
PLANITIA

Iron core about
3,600 km in diameter
and containing 80%
of Mercury's mass

Caloris Montes

Balzac

Phidias

BUDH
PLANITIA

Tyagaraja

Philoxenus

Mantle of
silicate rock

Zeami

Goya

Crust of
silicate rock

Sophocles

Tolstoj

Renoir

Vālmiki

Milton

Minimum dark-side
surface temperature
about -170°C

Liang K'ai

Chekhov

Beethoven

Schubert

Bello

Bramante

Shelley

Discovery Rupes

Hawthorne

Coleridge

Michelangelo

Wagner

Bach

Fram Rupes

35

Venus

VENUS IS A ROCKY PLANET and the second planet from the Sun. Venus spins slowly backwards as it orbits the Sun, causing its rotational period to be the longest in the Solar System, at about 243 Earth days. It is slightly smaller than Earth and probably has a similar internal structure, consisting of a semi-solid metal core, surrounded by a rocky mantle and crust. Venus is the brightest object in the sky after the Sun and Moon because its clouds reflect sunlight strongly. The main component of the atmosphere is carbon dioxide, which traps heat in a greenhouse effect far stronger than that on Earth. As a result, Venus is the hottest planet, with a maximum surface temperature of about 480°C. The thick cloud layers contain droplets of sulphuric acid and are driven around the planet by winds at speeds of up to 360 kilometres per hour. Although the planet takes 243 Earth days to rotate once, the high-speed winds cause the clouds to circle the planet in only four Earth days. The high temperature, acidic clouds, and enormous atmospheric pressure (about 90 times greater at the surface than that on Earth) make the environment extremely hostile. However, space probes have managed to land on Venus and photograph its dry, dusty surface. The Venusian surface has also been mapped by probes with radar equipment that can "see" through the cloud layers. Such radar maps reveal a terrain with craters, mountains, volcanoes, and areas where craters have been covered by plains of solidified volcanic lava. There are two large highland regions called Aphrodite Terra and Ishtar Terra.

TILT AND ROTATION OF VENUS

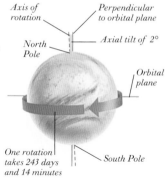

Axis of rotation
Perpendicular to orbital plane
North Pole
Axial tilt of 2°
Orbital plane
One rotation takes 243 days and 14 minutes
South Pole

CLOUD FEATURES

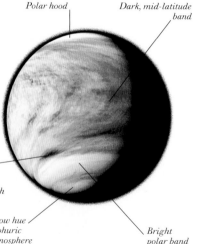

Polar hood
Dark, mid-latitude band
Cloud features swept around planet by winds of up to 360 km/h
Dirty yellow hue due to sulphuric acid in atmosphere
Bright polar band

VENUSIAN CRATERS

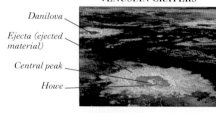

Danilova
Ejecta (ejected material)
Central peak
Howe

FALSE-COLOUR RADAR MAP OF THE SURFACE OF VENUS

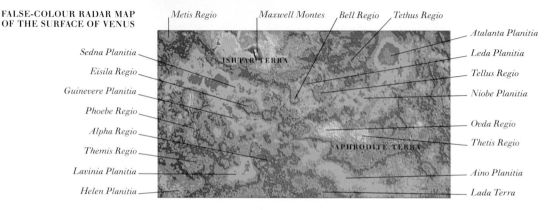

Metis Regio
Maxwell Montes
Bell Regio
Tethus Regio
Atalanta Planitia
Sedna Planitia
ISHTAR TERRA
Leda Planitia
Eisila Regio
Tellus Regio
Guinevere Planitia
Niobe Planitia
Phoebe Regio
Alpha Regio
Ovda Regio
Themis Regio
Thetis Regio
APHRODITE TERRA
Lavinia Planitia
Aino Planitia
Helen Planitia
Lada Terra

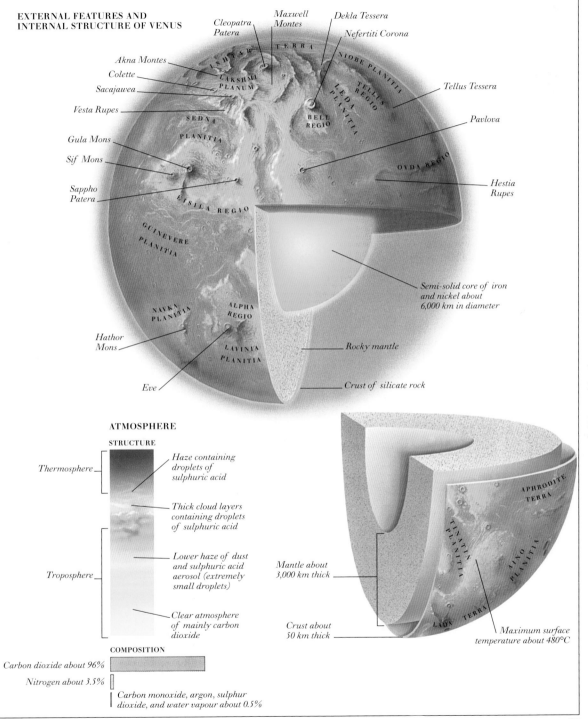

EXTERNAL FEATURES AND INTERNAL STRUCTURE OF VENUS

Cleopatra Patera
Maxwell Montes
Dekla Tessera
Nefertiti Corona

Akna Montes
Colette
Sacajawea
Vesta Rupes
Gula Mons
Sif Mons
Sappho Patera
Hathor Mons
Eve

ISHTAR TERRA
LAKSHMI PLANUM
SEDNA PLANITIA
EISILA REGIO
GUINEVERE PLANITIA
NAVKA PLANITIA
ALPHA REGIO
LAVINIA PLANITIA

NIOBE PLANITIA
LEDA PLANITIA
TELLUS REGIO
BELL REGIO
OVDA REGIO

Tellus Tessera
Pavlova
Hestia Rupes

Semi-solid core of iron and nickel about 6,000 km in diameter

Rocky mantle

Crust of silicate rock

ATMOSPHERE

STRUCTURE

Thermosphere

Troposphere

Haze containing droplets of sulphuric acid

Thick cloud layers containing droplets of sulphuric acid

Lower haze of dust and sulphuric acid aerosol (extremely small droplets)

Clear atmosphere of mainly carbon dioxide

Mantle about 3,000 km thick

Crust about 50 km thick

APHRODITE TERRA
TINATIN PLANITIA
LADA TERRA
AINO PLANITIA

Maximum surface temperature about 480°C

COMPOSITION

Carbon dioxide about 96%

Nitrogen about 3.5%

Carbon monoxide, argon, sulphur dioxide, and water vapour about 0.5%

The Earth

THE EARTH

THE EARTH IS THE THIRD of the eight planets that orbit the Sun. It is the largest and densest rocky planet, and the only one known to support life. About 70 per cent of the Earth's surface is covered by water, which is not found in liquid form on the surface of any other planet. There are four main layers: the inner core, the outer core, the mantle, and the crust. At the heart of the planet the solid inner core has a temperature of about 6,600°C. The heat from this inner core causes material in the molten outer core and mantle to circulate in convection currents. It is thought that these convection currents generate the Earth's magnetic field, which extends into space as the magnetosphere. The Earth's atmosphere helps screen out some of the harmful radiation from the Sun, stops most meteoroids from reaching the planet's surface, and traps enough heat to prevent extremes of cold. The Earth has one natural satellite, the Moon, which is thought to have formed when a huge asteroid impacted Earth in the distant past.

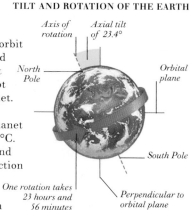

Axis of rotation

Axial tilt of 23.4°

North Pole

Orbital plane

South Pole

One rotation takes 23 hours and 56 minutes

Perpendicular to orbital plane

THE FORMATION OF THE EARTH

The heat of the collisions caused the planet to glow red

The cloud formed a disc of material around the young Sun's equator. The disc material stuck together to form planets

Micro-organisms began to photosynthesize, creating a build up of oxygen

4,600 MILLION YEARS AGO, THE SOLAR SYSTEM FORMED FROM A CLOUD OF ROCK, ICE, AND GAS

THE EARTH WAS FORMED FROM COLLIDING ROCKS

4,500 MILLION YEARS AGO THE SURFACE COOLED TO FORM THE CRUST

THE CONTINENTS BROKE UP AND REFORMED, GRADUALLY MOVING TO THEIR PRESENT POSITIONS

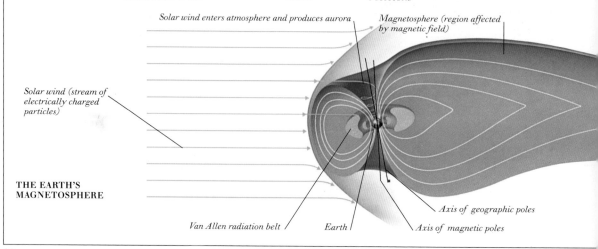

Solar wind enters atmosphere and produces aurora

Magnetosphere (region affected by magnetic field)

Solar wind (stream of electrically charged particles)

THE EARTH'S MAGNETOSPHERE

Van Allen radiation belt

Earth

Axis of geographic poles

Axis of magnetic poles

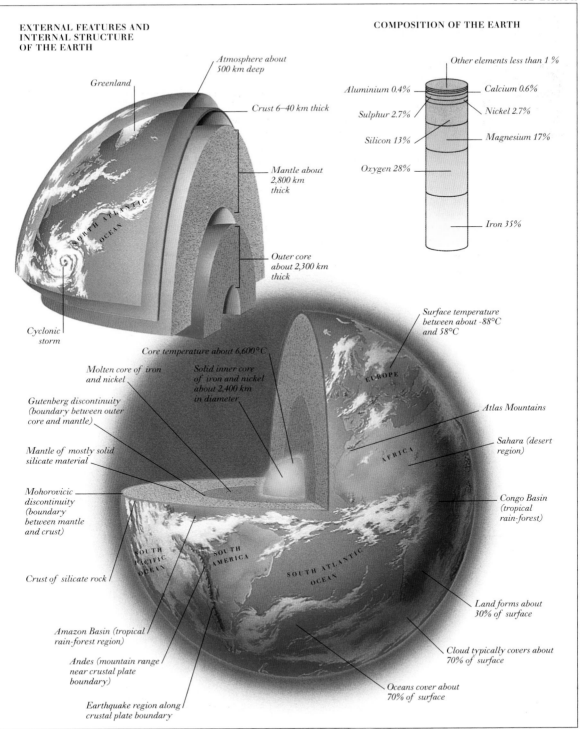

**EXTERNAL FEATURES AND
INTERNAL STRUCTURE
OF THE EARTH**

Greenland

*Atmosphere about
500 km deep*

Crust 6–40 km thick

NORTH ATLANTIC OCEAN

*Mantle about
2,800 km
thick*

*Outer core
about 2,300 km
thick*

*Cyclonic
storm*

COMPOSITION OF THE EARTH

Other elements less than 1 %

Aluminium 0.4%

Calcium 0.6%

Sulphur 2.7%

Nickel 2.7%

Silicon 13%

Magnesium 17%

Oxygen 28%

Iron 35%

Core temperature about 6,600°C

*Surface temperature
between about -88°C
and 58°C*

*Molten core of iron
and nickel*

*Solid inner core
of iron and nickel
about 2,400 km
in diameter*

*Gutenberg discontinuity
(boundary between outer
core and mantle)*

EUROPE

Atlas Mountains

*Mantle of mostly solid
silicate material*

AFRICA

*Sahara (desert
region)*

*Mohorovicic
discontinuity
(boundary
between mantle
and crust)*

*Congo Basin
(tropical
rain-forest)*

SOUTH
PACIFIC
OCEAN

SOUTH
AMERICA

SOUTH ATLANTIC
OCEAN

Crust of silicate rock

*Land forms about
30% of surface*

*Amazon Basin (tropical
rain-forest region)*

*Cloud typically covers about
70% of surface*

*Andes (mountain range
near crustal plate
boundary)*

*Oceans cover about
70% of surface*

*Earthquake region along
crustal plate boundary*

39

The Moon

THE MOON FROM EARTH

THE MOON IS THE EARTH'S only natural satellite. It is relatively large for a moon, with a diameter of about 3,470 kilometres – just over a quarter that of the Earth. The Moon takes the same time to rotate on its axis as it takes to orbit the Earth (27.3 days), and so the same side (the near side) always faces us. However, the amount of the surface we can see – the phase of the Moon – depends on how much of the near side is in sunlight. The Moon is dry and barren, with negligible atmosphere and water. It consists mainly of solid rock, although its core may contain molten rock or iron. The surface is dusty, with highlands covered in craters caused by meteorite impacts, and lowlands in which large craters have been filled by solidified lava to form dark areas called maria or "seas". Maria occur mainly on the near side, which has a thinner crust than the far side. Many of the craters are rimmed by mountain ranges that form the crater walls and can be thousands of metres high.

TILT AND ROTATION OF THE MOON

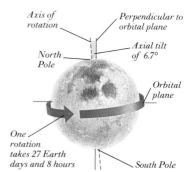

Axis of rotation

Perpendicular to orbital plane

North Pole

Axial tilt of 6.7°

Orbital plane

One rotation takes 27 Earth days and 8 hours

South Pole

CRATERS ON OCEANUS PROCELLARUM

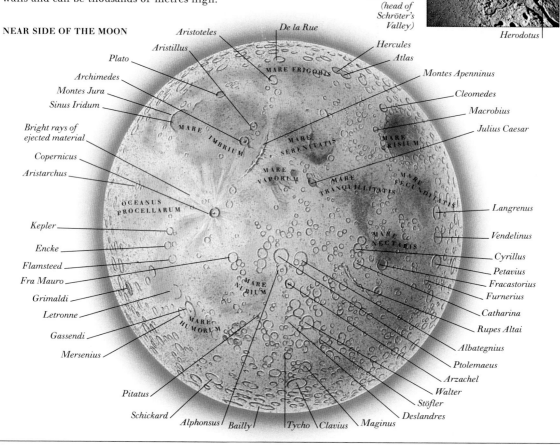

Aristarchus

Cobra Head (head of Schröter's Valley)

Herodotus

NEAR SIDE OF THE MOON

Aristoteles

De la Rue

Aristillus

Hercules

Plato

Atlas

Archimedes

Montes Apenninus

Montes Jura

Cleomedes

Sinus Iridum

Macrobius

Bright rays of ejected material

Julius Caesar

Copernicus

Aristarchus

Kepler

Langrenus

Encke

Vendelinus

Flamsteed

Cyrillus

Fra Mauro

Petavius

Grimaldi

Fracastorius

Letronne

Furnerius

Gassendi

Catharina

Mersenius

Rupes Altai

Albategnius

Ptolemaeus

Arzachel

Pitatus

Walter

Schickard

Stöfler

Alphonsus

Bailly

Tycho

Clavius

Maginus

Deslandres

MARE FRIGORIS

MARE IMBRIUM

MARE SERENITATIS

MARE CRISIUM

MARE VAPORUM

MARE TRANQUILLITATIS

MARE FECUNDITATIS

OCEANUS PROCELLARUM

MARE NECTARIS

MARE NUBIUM

MARE HUMORUM

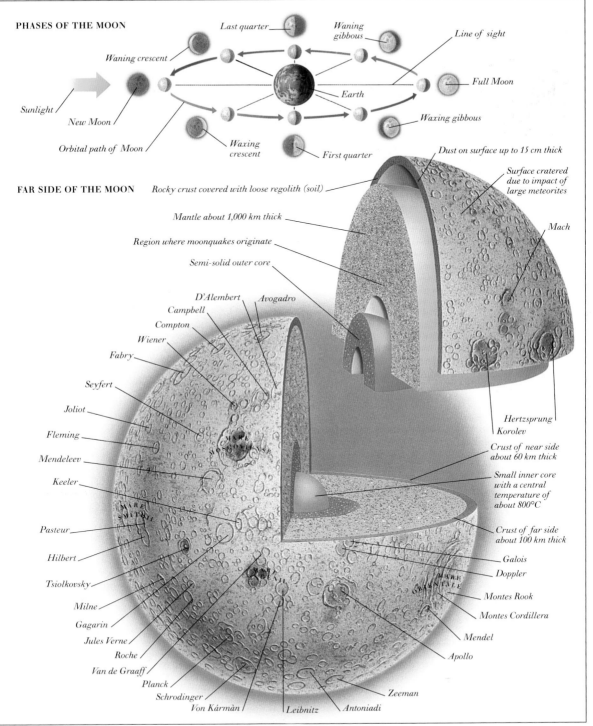

PHASES OF THE MOON

Last quarter

Waning gibbous

Line of sight

Waning crescent

Sunlight

New Moon

Earth

Full Moon

Orbital path of Moon

Waxing crescent

First quarter

Waxing gibbous

FAR SIDE OF THE MOON

Rocky crust covered with loose regolith (soil)

Dust on surface up to 15 cm thick

Surface cratered due to impact of large meteorites

Mantle about 1,000 km thick

Region where moonquakes originate

Semi-solid outer core

Mach

D'Alembert

Avogadro

Campbell

Compton

Wiener

Fabry

Seyfert

Joliot

Fleming

Mendeleev

Keeler

Pasteur

Hilbert

Tsiolkovsky

Milne

Gagarin

Jules Verne

Roche

Van de Graaff

Planck

Schrodinger

Von Kármàn

Leibnitz

Antoniadi

Zeeman

Apollo

Mendel

Montes Cordillera

Montes Rook

Doppler

Galois

Crust of far side about 100 km thick

Small inner core with a central temperature of about 800°C

Crust of near side about 60 km thick

Hertzsprung

Korolev

MARE MOSCOVIENSE

MARE SMYTHII

MARE ORIENTALE

Mars

MARS

MARS, KNOWN AS THE RED PLANET, is the fourth planet from the Sun and the outermost rocky planet. In the 19th century, astronomers first observed what were thought to be signs of life on Mars. These signs included apparent canal-like lines on the surface, and dark patches that were thought to be vegetation. It is now known that the "canals" are an optical illusion, and the dark patches are areas where the red dust that covers most of the planet has been blown away. The fine dust particles are often whipped up by winds into dust storms that occasionally obscure almost all the surface. Residual fine dust in the atmosphere gives the Martian sky a pinkish hue. The northern hemisphere of Mars has many large plains formed of solidified volcanic lava, whereas the southern hemisphere has many craters and large impact basins. There are also several huge, extinct volcanoes, including Olympus Mons, which, at 600 kilometres across and 25 kilometres high, is the largest known volcano in the Solar System. The surface also has many canyons and branching channels. The canyons were formed by movements of the surface crust, but the channels are thought to have been formed by flowing water that has now dried up. The Martian atmosphere is much thinner than Earth's, with only a few clouds and morning mists. Mars has two tiny, irregularly shaped moons called Phobos and Deimos. Their small size indicates that they may be asteroids that have been captured by the gravity of Mars.

TILT AND ROTATION OF MARS

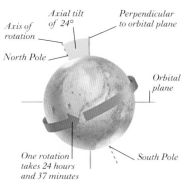

Axis of rotation

Axial tilt of 24°

Perpendicular to orbital plane

North Pole

Orbital plane

One rotation takes 24 hours and 37 minutes

South Pole

SURFACE FEATURES OF MARS

Bright water-ice fog

Fog in canyon about 20 km wide at end of Valles Marineris

Syria Planum

NOCTIS LABYRINTHUS (CANYON SYSTEM)

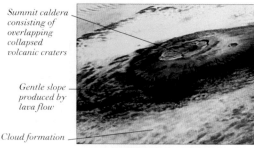

Summit caldera consisting of overlapping collapsed volcanic craters

Gentle slope produced by lava flow

Cloud formation

OLYMPUS MONS (EXTINCT SHIELD VOLCANO)

THE SURFACE OF MARS

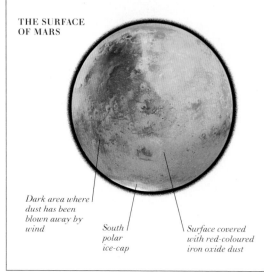

Dark area where dust has been blown away by wind

South polar ice-cap

Surface covered with red-coloured iron oxide dust

MOONS OF MARS

PHOBOS
Average diameter: 22 km
Average distance from planet: 9,400 km

DEIMOS
Average diameter: 13 km
Average distance from planet: 23,500 km

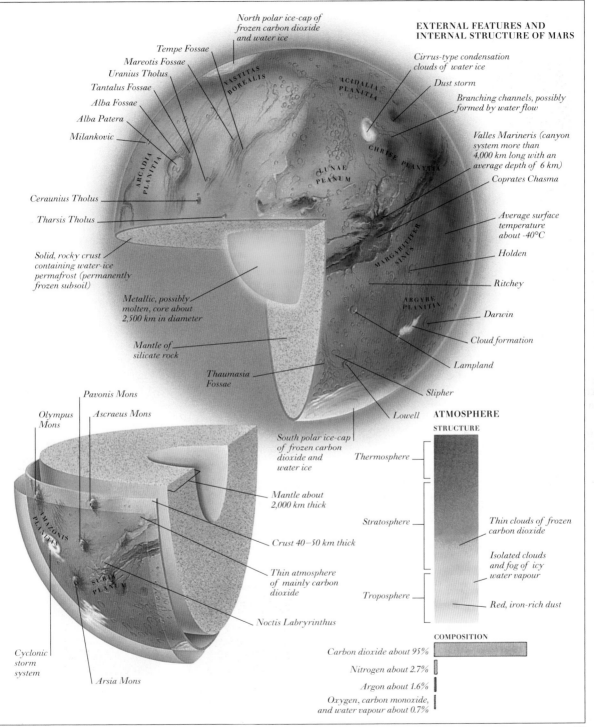

EXTERNAL FEATURES AND INTERNAL STRUCTURE OF MARS

North polar ice-cap of frozen carbon dioxide and water ice

Tempe Fossae

Mareotis Fossae

Uranius Tholus

Tantalus Fossae

Alba Fossae

Alba Patera

Milankovic

Ceraunius Tholus

Tharsis Tholus

Solid, rocky crust containing water-ice permafrost (permanently frozen subsoil)

Metallic, possibly molten, core about 2,500 km in diameter

Mantle of silicate rock

Thaumasia Fossae

VASTITAS BOREALIS

ACIDALIA PLANITIA

ARCADIA PLANITIA

LUNAE PLANUM

CHRISE PLANITIA

MARGARITIFER SINUS

ARGYRE PLANITIA

Cirrus-type condensation clouds of water ice

Dust storm

Branching channels, possibly formed by water flow

Valles Marineris (canyon system more than 4,000 km long with an average depth of 6 km)

Coprates Chasma

Average surface temperature about -40°C

Holden

Ritchey

Darwin

Cloud formation

Lampland

Slipher

Lowell

Pavonis Mons

Olympus Mons

Ascraeus Mons

AMAZONIS PLANITIA

SYRIA PLANUM

South polar ice-cap of frozen carbon dioxide and water ice

Mantle about 2,000 km thick

Crust 40–50 km thick

Thin atmosphere of mainly carbon dioxide

Noctis Labryrinthus

Cyclonic storm system

Arsia Mons

ATMOSPHERE

STRUCTURE

Thermosphere

Stratosphere

Troposphere

Thin clouds of frozen carbon dioxide

Isolated clouds and fog of icy water vapour

Red, iron-rich dust

COMPOSITION

Carbon dioxide about 95%

Nitrogen about 2.7%

Argon about 1.6%

Oxygen, carbon monoxide, and water vapour about 0.7%

Jupiter

JUPITER

JUPITER IS THE FIFTH PLANET from the Sun and the innermost of the four giant planets. It is the largest and the most massive planet, with a diameter about 11 times that of the Earth and a mass about 2.5 times the combined mass of the seven other planets. Jupiter is thought to have a small rocky core surrounded by an inner mantle of metallic hydrogen (liquid hydrogen that acts like a metal). Outside the inner mantle is an outer mantle of liquid hydrogen and helium that merges into the gaseous atmosphere. Jupiter's rapid rate of rotation causes the clouds in its atmosphere to form belts and zones that encircle the planet parallel to the equator. Belts are dark, low-lying, relatively warm cloud layers, and zones are bright, high-altitude, cooler cloud layers. Within the belts and zones, turbulence causes the formation of cloud features such as white ovals and red spots, both of which are huge storm systems. The most prominent cloud feature is a storm called the Great Red Spot, which consists of a spiralling column of clouds three times wider than the Earth that rises about eight kilometres above the upper cloud layer. Jupiter has a thin, faint, main ring, inside which is a tenuous halo ring of tiny particles. Beyond the main ring's outer edge is a broad and faint two-part gossamer ring. There are 63 known Jovian moons. The four largest moons (called the Galileans) are Ganymede, Callisto, Io, and Europa. Ganymede and Callisto are cratered and icy. Europa is smooth and icy and is thought to have a subsurface water ocean. Io is covered in bright red, orange, and yellow splotches. This colouring is caused by sulphurous material from active volcanoes that shoot plumes of lava hundreds of kilometres above the surface.

TILT AND ROTATION OF JUPITER

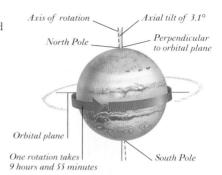

Axis of rotation

Axial tilt of 3.1°

North Pole

Perpendicular to orbital plane

Orbital plane

One rotation takes 9 hours and 55 minutes

South Pole

GREAT RED SPOT AND WHITE OVAL

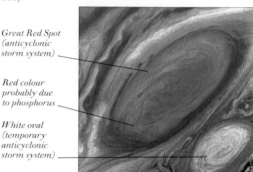

Great Red Spot (anticyclonic storm system)

Red colour probably due to phosphorus

White oval (temporary anticyclonic storm system)

GALILEAN MOONS OF JUPITER

EUROPA
Diameter: 3,130 km
Average distance from planet: 670,900 km

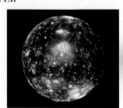

CALLISTO
Diameter: 4,806 km
Average distance from planet: 1,883,000 km

GANYMEDE
Diameter: 5,268 km
Average distance from planet: 1,070,000 km

IO
Diameter: 3,642 km
Average distance from planet: 421,800 km

INNER RINGS OF JUPITER

Main ring

Halo ring

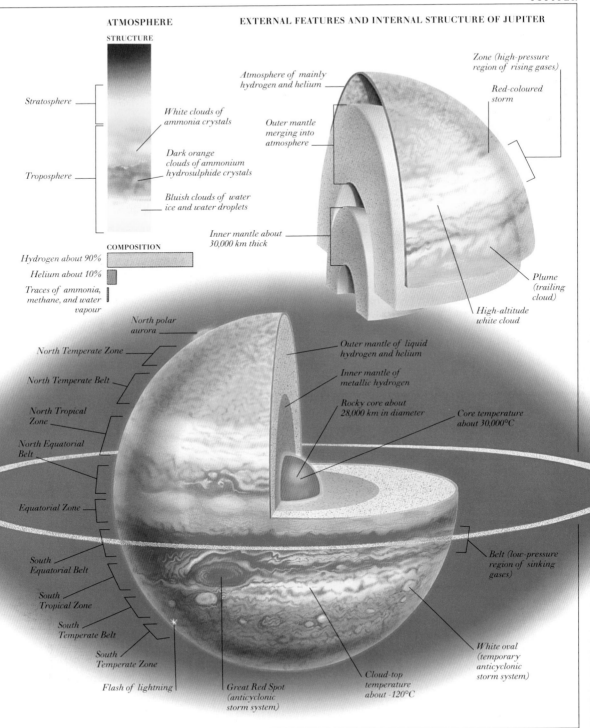

ATMOSPHERE

STRUCTURE

Stratosphere

Troposphere

*White clouds of
ammonia crystals*

*Dark orange
clouds of ammonium
hydrosulphide crystals*

*Bluish clouds of water
ice and water droplets*

COMPOSITION

Hydrogen about 90%

Helium about 10%

*Traces of ammonia,
methane, and water
vapour*

EXTERNAL FEATURES AND INTERNAL STRUCTURE OF JUPITER

*Atmosphere of mainly
hydrogen and helium*

*Outer mantle
merging into
atmosphere*

*Inner mantle about
30,000 km thick*

*Zone (high-pressure
region of rising gases)*

*Red-coloured
storm*

*Plume
(trailing
cloud)*

*High-altitude
white cloud*

*North polar
aurora*

North Temperate Zone

North Temperate Belt

*North Tropical
Zone*

*North Equatorial
Belt*

Equatorial Zone

*South
Equatorial Belt*

*South
Tropical Zone*

*South
Temperate Belt*

*South
Temperate Zone*

Flash of lightning

*Great Red Spot
(anticyclonic
storm system)*

*Cloud-top
temperature
about -120°C*

*Outer mantle of liquid
hydrogen and helium*

*Inner mantle of
metallic hydrogen*

*Rocky core about
28,000 km in diameter*

*Core temperature
about 30,000°C*

*Belt (low-pressure
region of sinking
gases)*

*White oval
(temporary
anticyclonic
storm system)*

45

Saturn

FALSE-COLOUR
IMAGE OF SATURN

SATURN IS THE SIXTH PLANET from the Sun. It is a gas giant almost as big as Jupiter, with an equatorial diameter of about 120,500 kilometres. Saturn is thought to consist of a small core of rock and ice surrounded by an inner mantle of metallic hydrogen (liquid hydrogen that acts like a metal). Outside the inner mantle is an outer mantle of liquid hydrogen that merges into a gaseous atmosphere. Saturn's clouds form belts and zones similar to those on Jupiter, but obscured by overlying haze. Storms and eddies, seen as red or white ovals, occur in the clouds. Saturn has an extremely thin but wide system of rings that is less than one kilometre thick but extends outwards to about 420,000 kilometres from the planet's surface. The main rings comprise thousands of narrow ringlets, each made of icy rock lumps that range in size from tiny particles to chunks several metres across. The D, E, and G rings are very faint, the F ring is brighter, and the A, B, and C rings are bright enough to be seen from Earth with binoculars. In 2009, a huge dust ring was discovered 6 kilometres (4 million miles) beyond the main system. Saturn has more than 60 known moons, some of which orbit inside the rings and are thought to exert a gravitational influence on the shapes of the rings. Unusually, seven of the moons are co-orbital – they share an orbit with another moon. Astronomers believe that such co-orbital moons may have originated from a single satellite that broke up.

TILT AND ROTATION OF SATURN

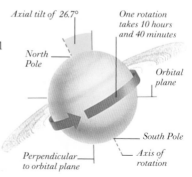

Axial tilt of 26.7°

One rotation takes 10 hours and 40 minutes

North Pole

Orbital plane

South Pole

Perpendicular to orbital plane

Axis of rotation

FALSE-COLOUR IMAGE OF SATURN'S CLOUD FEATURES

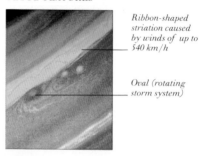

Ribbon-shaped striation caused by winds of up to 540 km/h

Oval (rotating storm system)

INNER RINGS OF SATURN

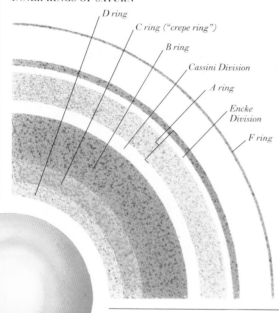

D ring

C ring ("crepe ring")

B ring

Cassini Division

A ring

Encke Division

F ring

MOONS OF SATURN

ENCELADUS
Diameter: 498 km
Average distance from planet: 238,000 km

TETHYS
Diameter: 1,066 km
Average distance from planet: 295,000 km

DIONE
Diameter: 1,123 km
Average distance from planet: 377,000 km

MIMAS
Diameter: 397 km
Average distance from planet: 186,000 km

ATMOSPHERE

EXTERNAL FEATURES AND
INTERNAL STRUCTURE
OF SATURN

COMPOSITION

Hydrogen about 96.3%

Helium about 3.3%

*Traces of ammonia, methane,
and water vapour*

STRUCTURE

Stratosphere

Troposphere

*Haze of
ammonia crystals*

*White clouds of
ammonia crystals*

*Dark orange clouds
of ammonium
hydrosulphide
crystals*

*Blue clouds of water
ice and water vapour*

*Clouds form belts (dark,
low-altitude layers) and
zones (bright, high-
altitude layers)*

*Atmosphere of mainly
hydrogen and helium*

*Outer mantle merging
into atmosphere*

*Inner mantle about
15,000 km thick*

F ring

*A ring (broad ring
comprising many ringlets)*

*B ring (broad ring
comprising many ringlets)*

*C ring ("crepe ring"; broad ring
comprising many ringlets)*

D ring

*Outer mantle of
liquid hydrogen*

*Inner mantle of
liquid metallic hydrogen*

*Core of rock and ice
about 30,000 km
in diameter*

*Core temperature
about 15,000°C*

*Cassini Division
(apparent gap
containing at least
100 ringlets)*

*Encke Division (gap
in which the moon
Pan orbits)*

*Equator swept by
winds of up to
1,800 km/h*

*Cloud-top temperature
about -180°C*

*Radial spoke
(probably dust particles
above plane of rings)*

*Anne's Spot
(anticyclonic storm system)*

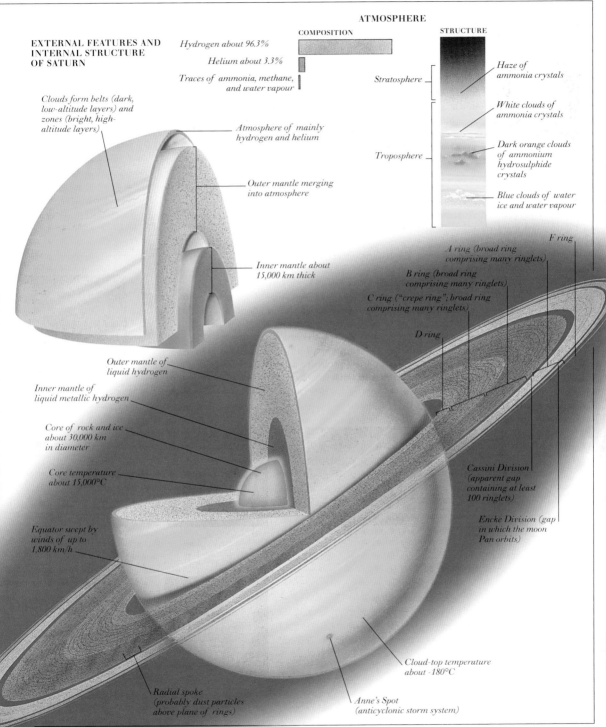

Uranus

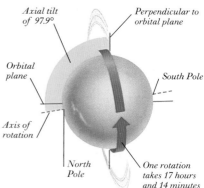

Axial tilt
of 97.9°

Perpendicular to
orbital plane

Orbital
plane

South Pole

Axis of
rotation

North
Pole

One rotation
takes 17 hours
and 14 minutes

FALSE-COLOUR
IMAGE OF URANUS

URANUS IS THE SEVENTH PLANET from the Sun
and the third largest, with a diameter of about
51,000 kilometres. It is thought to consist of
a dense mixture of different types of ice and
gas around a solid core. Its atmosphere contains
traces of methane, giving the planet a blue-green
hue, and the temperature at the cloud tops is
about -210°C. Uranus is the most featureless
planet to have been closely observed: only a
few icy clouds of methane have been seen so far. Uranus is unique
among the planets in that its axis of rotation lies close to its orbital
plane. As a result of its strongly tilted rotational axis, Uranus rolls on
its side along its orbital path around the Sun, whereas other planets spin
more or less upright. Uranus is encircled by main rings that consist of rocks
interspersed with dust lanes and too distant outer rings made of dust. The rings
contain some of the darkest matter in the Solar System and are extremely
narrow, making them difficult to detect: most of them are less than 10
kilometres wide, whereas most of Saturn's rings are thousands of kilometres in
width. There are 27 known Uranian moons, all of which are icy and most of
which are further out than the rings. The 13 inner moons are small and dark,
with diameters of less than 160 kilometres, and the five major moons are
between about 470 and 1,600 kilometres in diameter. The major moons have a
wide variety of surface features. Miranda has the most varied surface, with
cratered areas broken up by huge ridges and cliffs 20 kilometres high. Beyond
these are nine much more distant moons with diameters less than 150 km.

MAJOR MOONS

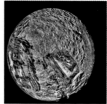

MIRANDA
Diameter: 470 km
Average distance from
planet: 129,800 km

RINGS OF URANUS

Epsilon ring

Lambda ring

Delta ring

Gamma ring

Eta ring

Beta ring

Alpha ring

Rings 4 and 5

Ring 6

Zeta ring

RINGS AND DUST LANES

ARIEL
Diameter: 1,158 km
Average distance from
planet: 191,200 km

TITANIA
Diameter: 1,578 km
Average distance from
planet: 435,800 km

UMBRIEL
Diameter: 1,170 km
Average distance from
planet: 266,000 km

OBERON
Diameter: 1,523 km
Average distance from
planet: 583,600 km

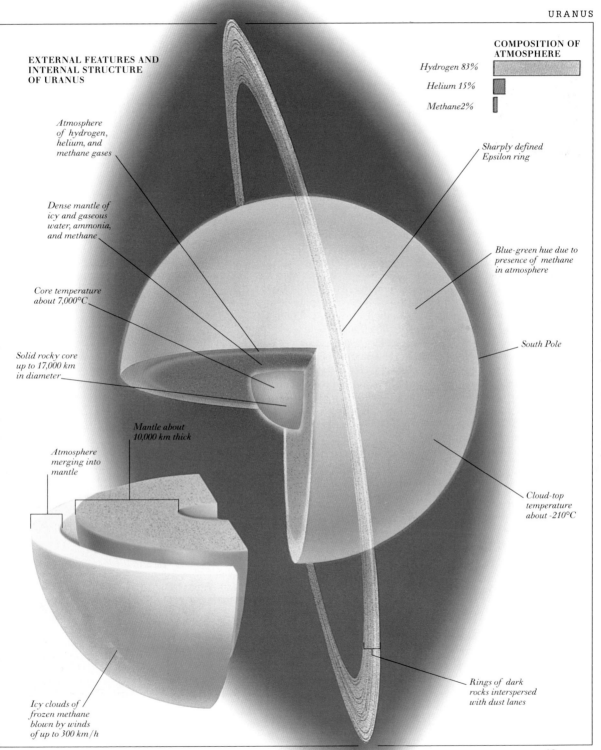

EXTERNAL FEATURES AND
INTERNAL STRUCTURE
OF URANUS

**COMPOSITION OF
ATMOSPHERE**

Hydrogen 83%

Helium 15%

Methane 2%

Atmosphere
of hydrogen,
helium, and
methane gases

Dense mantle of
icy and gaseous
water, ammonia,
and methane

Core temperature
about 7,000°C

Solid rocky core
up to 17,000 km
in diameter

Mantle about
10,000 km thick

Atmosphere
merging into
mantle

Icy clouds of
frozen methane
blown by winds
of up to 300 km/h

Sharply defined
Epsilon ring

Blue-green hue due to
presence of methane
in atmosphere

South Pole

Cloud-top
temperature
about -210°C

Rings of dark
rocks interspersed
with dust lanes

49

Neptune and Pluto

FALSE-COLOUR IMAGE OF NEPTUNE

NEPTUNE IS the furthest planet from the Sun, at an average distance of about 4,500 million kilometres. Neptune is the smallest of the giant planets and is thought to consist of a small rocky core surrounded by a mixture of liquids and gases. Several transient cloud features have been observed in its atmosphere. The largest of these were the Great Dark Spot, which was as wide as the Earth, the Small Dark Spot, and the Scooter. The Great and Small Dark Spots were huge storms that were swept around the planet by winds of about 2,000 kilometres per hour. The Scooter was a large area of cirrus cloud. Neptune has six tenuous rings and 13 known moons. Triton is the largest Neptunian moon and the coldest object in the Solar System, with a temperature of -240°C. Unlike most moons in the Solar System, Triton orbits its mother planet in the opposite direction to the planet's rotation. The region extending out from Neptune's orbit is populated by Kuiper Belt objects and dwarf planets. They make a dough-nut shaped belt called the Kuiper Belt. The Kuiper Belt objects are a mix of rock and ice, irregular in shape, and less than 1,000 kilometres across. The larger dwarf planets, which include Pluto, are almost round bodies. Pluto was the first object discovered beyond Neptune and was considered a planet until the dwarf planet category was introduced in 2006. It is made of rock and ice and is 2,274 kilometres across. It has three known moons. The largest, Charon, is about half Pluto's size and the two probably had a common origin.

TILT AND ROTATION OF NEPTUNE

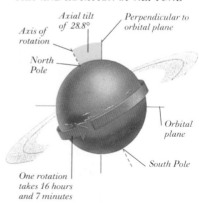

Axis of rotation

North Pole

Axial tilt of 28.8°

Perpendicular to orbital plane

Orbital plane

South Pole

One rotation takes 16 hours and 7 minutes

CLOUD FEATURES OF NEPTUNE

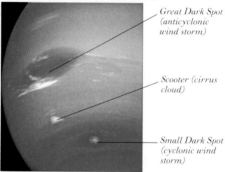

Great Dark Spot (anticyclonic wind storm)

Scooter (cirrus cloud)

Small Dark Spot (cyclonic wind storm)

RINGS OF NEPTUNE

Adams ring and unnamed ring on its inner edge

Arago ring

Lassell ring

Le Verrier ring

Galle ring

HIGH-ALTITUDE CLOUDS

Methane cirrus clouds 40 km above main cloud deck

Cloud shadow

Main cloud deck blown by winds at speeds of about 2,000 km/h

MOONS OF NEPTUNE

TRITON
Diameter: 2,705 km
Average distance from planet: 354,800 km

PROTEUS
Diameter: 416 km
Average distance from planet: 117,600 km

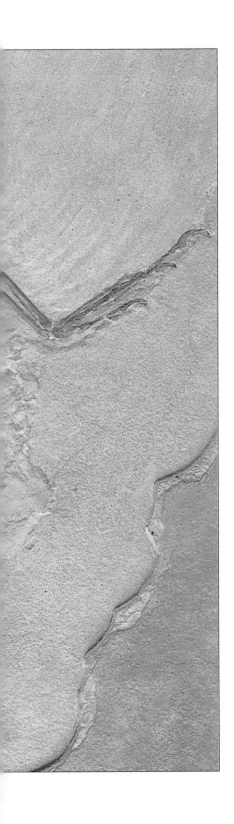

PREHISTORIC EARTH

The changing Earth

THE EARTH FORMED FROM A CLOUD OF DUST and gas drifting through space about 4,600 million years ago. Dense minerals sank to the centre while lighter ones formed a thin rocky crust. However, the first known life-forms – bacteria and blue-green algae – did not appear until about 3,400 million years ago, and it was only about 700 million years ago that more complex plants and animals began to develop. Since then, thousands of animal and plant species have evolved; some, such as the dinosaurs, survived for many millions of years, while others died out quickly. The Earth itself is continually changing. Although continents neared their present locations about 50 million years ago, they are still drifting slowly over the planet's surface, and mountain ranges such as the Himalayas – which began to form 40 million years ago – are continually being built up and worn away. Climate is also subject to change: the Earth has undergone a series of ice ages interspersed with warmer periods (the most recent glacial period was at its height about 20,000 years ago).

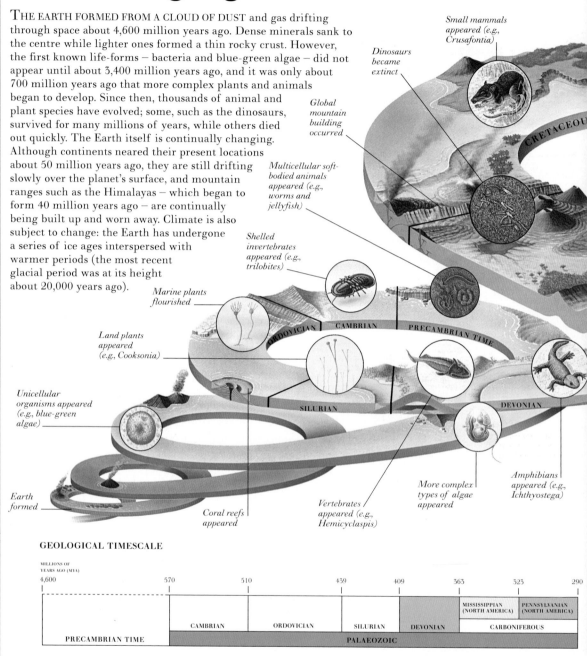

Small mammals appeared (e.g., Crusafontia)

Dinosaurs became extinct

Global mountain building occurred

Multicellular soft-bodied animals appeared (e.g., worms and jellyfish)

Shelled invertebrates appeared (e.g., trilobites)

Marine plants flourished

Land plants appeared (e.g., Cooksonia)

Unicellular organisms appeared (e.g., blue-green algae)

Earth formed

Coral reefs appeared

Vertebrates appeared (e.g., Hemicyclaspis)

More complex types of algae appeared

Amphibians appeared (e.g., Ichthyostega)

CRETACEOUS

ORDOVICIAN   CAMBRIAN   PRECAMBRIAN TIME

SILURIAN

DEVONIAN

GEOLOGICAL TIMESCALE

MILLIONS OF
YEARS AGO (MYA)

4,600	570	510	439	409	363	323	290

PRECAMBRIAN TIME	CAMBRIAN	ORDOVICIAN	SILURIAN	DEVONIAN	MISSISSIPPIAN (NORTH AMERICA)	PENNSYLVANIAN (NORTH AMERICA)
					CARBONIFEROUS	
	PALAEOZOIC					

EVOLUTION OF THE EARTH

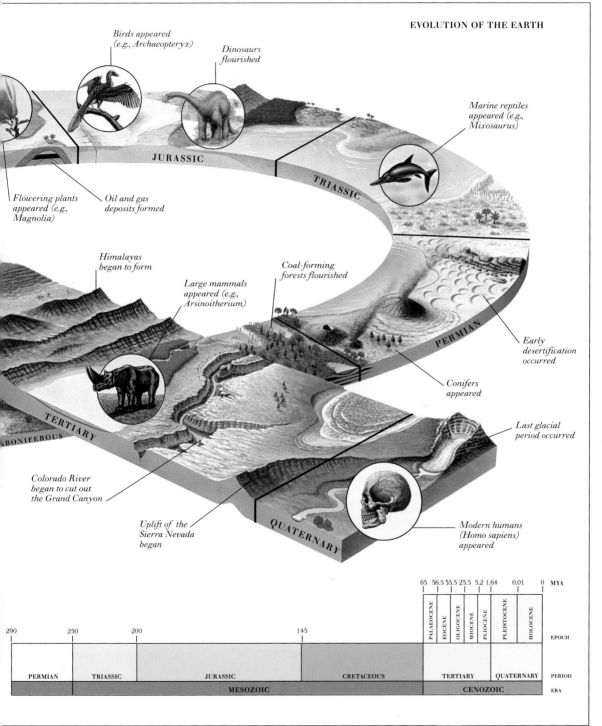

Birds appeared
(e.g., Archaeopteryx)

Dinosaurs
flourished

Marine reptiles
appeared (e.g.,
Mixosaurus)

JURASSIC

TRIASSIC

Flowering plants
appeared (e.g.,
Magnolia)

Oil and gas
deposits formed

Himalayas
began to form

Coal-forming
forests flourished

Large mammals
appeared (e.g.,
Arsinoitherium)

PERMIAN

Early
desertification
occurred

Conifers
appeared

Last glacial
period occurred

TERTIARY

ARBONIFEROUS

Colorado River
began to cut out
the Grand Canyon

Uplift of the
Sierra Nevada
began

QUATERNARY

Modern humans
(Homo sapiens)
appeared

		65	56.5	35.5	23.5	5.2	1.64		0.01		0	MYA
		PALAEOCENE	EOCENE	OLIGOCENE	MIOCENE	PLIOCENE		PLEISTOCENE		HOLOCENE		EPOCH
290	250	200			145							
PERMIAN	TRIASSIC	JURASSIC			CRETACEOUS			TERTIARY		QUATERNARY		PERIOD
		MESOZOIC					CENOZOIC					ERA

The Earth's crust

THE EARTH'S CRUST IS THE SOLID outer shell of the Earth. It includes continental crust (about 40 kilometres thick) and oceanic crust (about six kilometres thick). The crust and the topmost layer of the mantle form the lithosphere. The lithosphere consists of semi-rigid plates that move relative to each other on the underlying asthenosphere (a partly molten layer of the mantle). This process is known as plate tectonics and helps explain continental drift. Where two plates move apart, there are rifts in the crust. In mid-ocean, this movement results in sea-floor spreading and the formation of ocean ridges; on continents, crustal spreading can form rift valleys. When plates move towards each other, one may be subducted beneath (forced under) the other. In mid-ocean, this causes ocean trenches, seismic activity, and arcs of volcanic islands. Where oceanic crust is subducted beneath continental crust or where continents collide, land may be uplifted and mountains formed (see pp. 62–65). Plates may also slide past each other – along the San Andreas fault, for example. Crustal movement on continents may result in earthquakes, while movement under the seabed can lead to tidal waves.

ELEMENTS IN THE EARTH'S CRUST

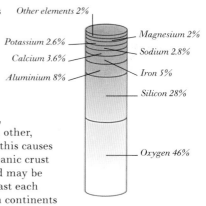

Other elements 2%
Potassium 2.6%
Calcium 3.6%
Aluminium 8%
Magnesium 2%
Sodium 2.8%
Iron 5%
Silicon 28%
Oxygen 46%

FEATURES OF PLATE MOVEMENTS

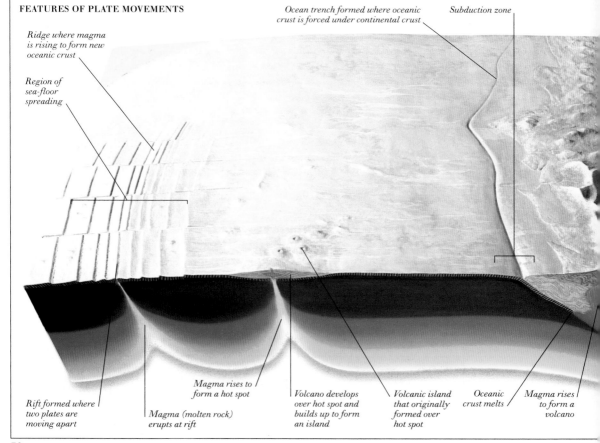

Ridge where magma is rising to form new oceanic crust

Region of sea-floor spreading

Ocean trench formed where oceanic crust is forced under continental crust

Subduction zone

Rift formed where two plates are moving apart

Magma (molten rock) erupts at rift

Magma rises to form a hot spot

Volcano develops over hot spot and builds up to form an island

Volcanic island that originally formed over hot spot

Oceanic crust melts

Magma rises to form a volcano

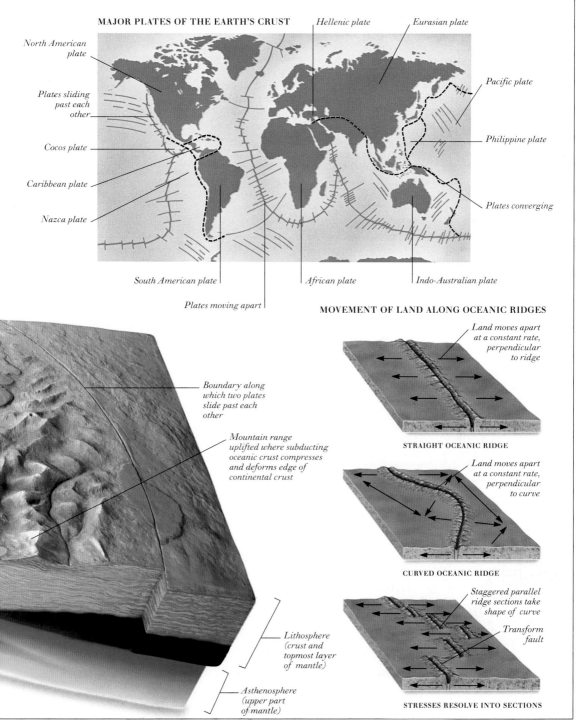

MAJOR PLATES OF THE EARTH'S CRUST

North American plate

Hellenic plate

Eurasian plate

Plates sliding past each other

Pacific plate

Cocos plate

Philippine plate

Caribbean plate

Nazca plate

Plates converging

South American plate

African plate

Indo-Australian plate

Plates moving apart

MOVEMENT OF LAND ALONG OCEANIC RIDGES

Land moves apart at a constant rate, perpendicular to ridge

Boundary along which two plates slide past each other

STRAIGHT OCEANIC RIDGE

Mountain range uplifted where subducting oceanic crust compresses and deforms edge of continental crust

Land moves apart at a constant rate, perpendicular to curve

CURVED OCEANIC RIDGE

Lithosphere (crust and topmost layer of mantle)

Staggered parallel ridge sections take shape of curve

Transform fault

Asthenosphere (upper part of mantle)

STRESSES RESOLVE INTO SECTIONS

Faults and folds

THE CONTINUOUS MOVEMENT of the Earth's crustal plates (see pp. 58–59) can squeeze, stretch, or break rock strata, deforming them and producing faults and folds. A fault is a fracture in a rock along which there is movement of one side relative to the other. The movement can be vertical, horizontal, or oblique (vertical and horizontal). Faults develop when rocks are subjected to compression or tension. They tend to occur in hard, rigid rocks, which are more likely to break than bend. The smallest faults occur in single mineral crystals and are microscopically small, whereas the largest – the Great Rift Valley in Africa, which formed between 5 million and 100,000 years ago – is more than 9,000 kilometres long. A fold is a bend in a rock layer caused by compression. Folds occur in elastic rocks, which tend to bend rather than break. The two main types of fold are anticlines (upfolds) and synclines (downfolds). Folds vary in size from a few millimetres long to folded mountain ranges hundreds of kilometres long, such as the Himalayas (see pp. 62–63) and the Alps, which are repeatedly folding. In addition to faults and folds, other features associated with rock deformations include boudins, mullions, and *en échelon* fractures.

STRUCTURE OF A FOLD

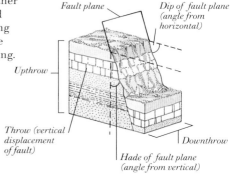

Axial plane

Crest

Limb

Angle of plunge

Hingeline

STRUCTURE OF A FAULT

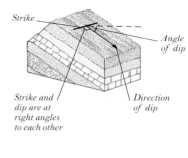

Fault plane

Dip of fault plane (angle from horizontal)

Upthrow

Throw (vertical displacement of fault)

Downthrow

Hade of fault plane (angle from vertical)

STRUCTURE OF A SLOPE

Strike

Angle of dip

Strike and dip are at right angles to each other

Direction of dip

FOLDED ROCK

Steeply dipping limbs

Crest of anticline

Plunge

SECTION THROUGH FOLDED ROCK STRATA THAT HAVE BEEN ERODED

Dipping bed

Anticlinal fold

Monoclinal fold

Mineral-filled fault

Upper Carboniferous Millstone Grit

Lower Carboniferous Limestone

EXAMPLES OF FOLDS

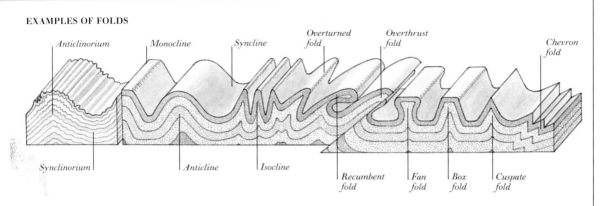

Anticlinorium · Monocline · Syncline · Overturned fold · Overthrust fold · Chevron fold

Synclinorium · Anticline · Isocline · Recumbent fold · Fan fold · Box fold · Cuspate fold

EXAMPLES OF FAULTS

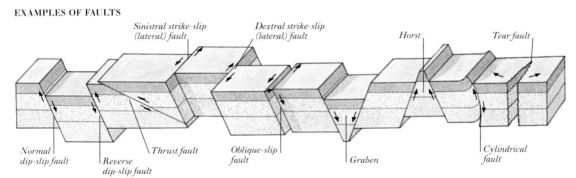

Sinistral strike-slip (lateral) fault · Dextral strike-slip (lateral) fault · Horst · Tear fault

Normal dip-slip fault · Reverse dip-slip fault · Thrust fault · Oblique-slip fault · Graben · Cylindrical fault

SMALL-SCALE ROCK DEFORMATIONS

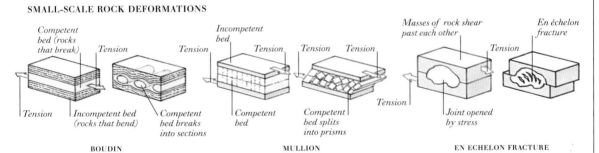

Competent bed (rocks that break) · Tension · Incompetent bed · Tension · Tension · Tension · Masses of rock shear past each other · Tension · En échelon fracture

Tension · Incompetent bed (rocks that bend) · Competent bed breaks into sections · Competent bed · Competent bed splits into prisms · Tension · Joint opened by stress

BOUDIN · **MULLION** · **EN ECHELON FRACTURE**

Horizontal bed · Mineral-filled fault · Dipping bed · Gently folded bed · Mineral-filled fault · Dipping bed

Mineral-filled fault

Upper Carboniferous Millstone Grit · Upper Carboniferous Coal Measures

Mountain building

THE PROCESSES INVOLVED in mountain building – termed orogenesis – occur as a result of the movement of the Earth's crustal plates (see pp. 58–59). There are three main types of mountains: volcanic mountains, fold mountains, and block mountains. Most volcanic mountains have been formed along plate boundaries where plates have come together or moved apart and lava and other debris have been ejected onto the Earth's surface. The lava and debris may have built up to form a dome around the vent of a volcano. Fold mountains are formed where plates push together and cause the rock to buckle upwards. Where oceanic crust meets less dense continental crust, the oceanic crust is forced under the continental crust. The continental crust is buckled by the impact. This is how folded mountain ranges, such as the Appalachian Mountains in North America, were formed. Fold mountains are also formed where two areas of continental crust meet. The Himalayas, for example, began to form when India collided with Asia, buckling the sediments and parts of the oceanic crust between them. Block mountains are formed when a block of land is uplifted between two faults as a result of compression or tension in the Earth's crust (see pp. 60–61). Often, the movement along faults has taken place gradually over millions of years. However, two plates may cause an earthquake by suddenly sliding past each other along a faultline.

BHAGIRATHI PARBAT, HIMALAYAS

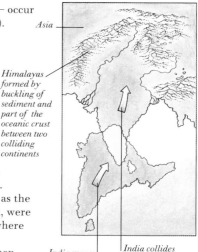

Asia

Himalayas formed by buckling of sediment and part of the oceanic crust between two colliding continents

India moves north

India collides with Asia about 40 million years ago

EXAMPLES OF MOUNTAINS

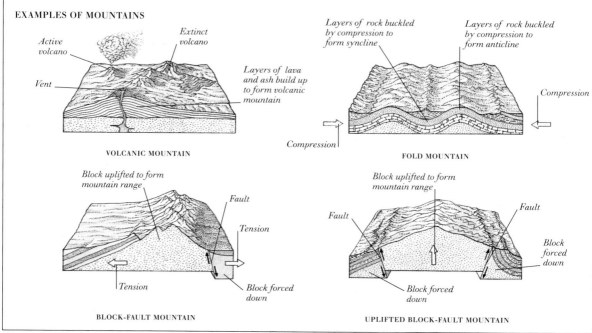

Active volcano

Extinct volcano

Vent

Layers of lava and ash build up to form volcanic mountain

VOLCANIC MOUNTAIN

Layers of rock buckled by compression to form syncline

Layers of rock buckled by compression to form anticline

Compression

Compression

FOLD MOUNTAIN

Block uplifted to form mountain range

Fault

Tension

Tension

Block forced down

BLOCK-FAULT MOUNTAIN

Block uplifted to form mountain range

Fault

Fault

Block forced down

Block forced down

UPLIFTED BLOCK-FAULT MOUNTAIN

STAGES IN THE FORMATION OF THE HIMALAYAS

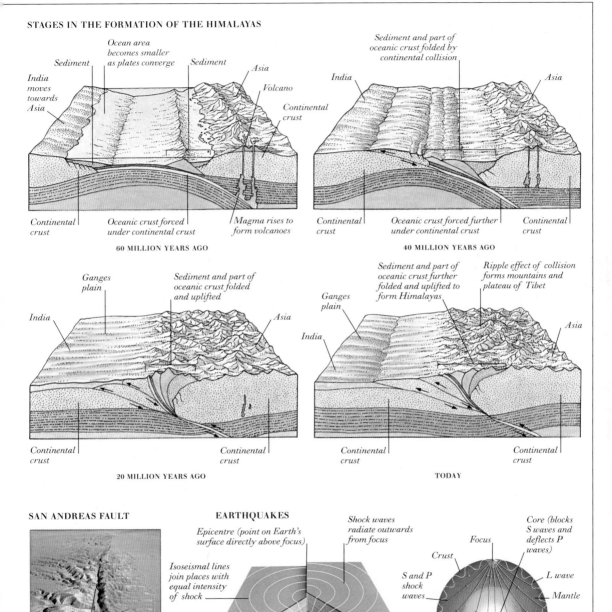

Sediment

India moves towards Asia

Ocean area becomes smaller as plates converge

Sediment

Asia

Volcano

Continental crust

Continental crust

Oceanic crust forced under continental crust

Magma rises to form volcanoes

60 MILLION YEARS AGO

Sediment and part of oceanic crust folded by continental collision

India

Asia

Continental crust

Oceanic crust forced further under continental crust

Continental crust

40 MILLION YEARS AGO

Ganges plain

India

Sediment and part of oceanic crust folded and uplifted

Asia

Continental crust

Continental crust

20 MILLION YEARS AGO

Sediment and part of oceanic crust further folded and uplifted to form Himalayas

Ripple effect of collision forms mountains and plateau of Tibet

Ganges plain

India

Asia

Continental crust

Continental crust

TODAY

SAN ANDREAS FAULT

Faultline along which two plates may slide past each other, causing an earthquake

EARTHQUAKES

Epicentre (point on Earth's surface directly above focus)

Shock waves radiate outwards from focus

Isoseismal lines join places with equal intensity of shock

Focus (point at which earthquake originates)

ANATOMY OF AN EARTHQUAKE

Core (blocks S waves and deflects P waves)

Focus

Crust

S and P shock waves

L wave

Mantle

P wave shadow zone

P wave shadow zone

P wave

PATH OF SHOCK WAVES THROUGH THE EARTH

Precambrian to Devonian periods

WHEN THE EARTH FORMED about 4,600 million years ago, its atmosphere consisted of volcanic gases with little oxygen, making it hostile to most forms of life. One large supercontinent, Gondwana, was situated over the southern polar region, while other smaller continents were spread over the rest of the world. Constant movement of the earth's crustal plates carried continents across the earth's surface. The first primitive life-forms emerged around 3,400 million years ago in shallow, warm seas. The build up of oxygen began to form a shield of ozone around the earth, protecting living organisms from the sun's harmful rays and helping to establish an atmosphere in which life could sustain itself. The first vertebrates appeared about 470 million years ago, during the Ordovician period (510–439 million years ago), the first land plants appeared around 400 million years ago during the Devonian period (409–363 million years ago), and the first land animals about 30 million years later.

MIDDLE ORDOVICIAN POSITIONS OF PRESENT-DAY LAND-MASSES

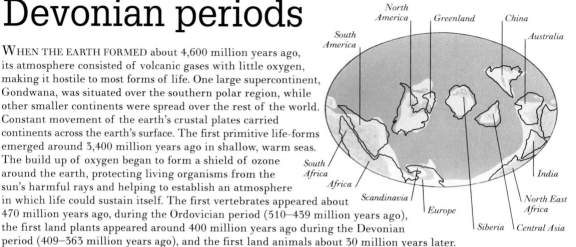

North America
Greenland
China
South America
Australia
South Africa
India
Africa
Scandinavia
North East Africa
Europe
Siberia
Central Asia

EXAMPLES OF PRECAMBRIAN TO DEVONIAN PLANT GROUPS

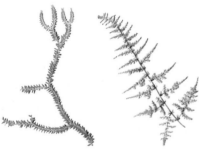

A PRESENT-DAY CLUBMOSS
(*Lycopodium sp.*)

A PRESENT-DAY LAND PLANT
(*Asparagus setaceous*)

FOSSIL OF AN EXTINCT LAND PLANT
(*Cooksonia hemisphaerica*)

FOSSIL OF AN EXTINCT SWAMP PLANT
(*Zosterophyllum llanoveranum*)

EXAMPLES OF PRECAMBRIAN TO DEVONIAN TRILOBITES

ACADAGNOSTUS
Group: Agnostidae
Length: 8 mm (⅓ in)

PHACOPS
Group: Phacopidae
Length: 4.5 cm (1¾ in)

OLENELLUS
Group: Olenellidae
Length: 6 cm (2½ in)

ELRATHIA
Group: Ptychopariidae
Length: 2 cm (¾ in)

THE EARTH DURING THE MIDDLE ORDOVICIAN PERIOD

EXAMPLES OF EARLY MARINE INVERTEBRATES

Siberia

Laurentia

China

Kazakstania

Gondwana

Baltica

FOSSIL NAUTILOID
(Estonioceras perforatum)

FOSSIL BRACHIOPOD
(Dicoelosia bilobata)

TRACE FOSSIL
(Mawsonites spriggi)

FOSSIL GRAPTOLITE
(Monograptus convolutus)

EXAMPLES OF DEVONIAN FISH

RHAMPHODOPSIS
Group: Ptyctodontidae
Length: 15 cm (6 in)

PTERASPIS
Group: Pteraspidae
Length: 25 cm (10 in)

COCCOSTEUS
Group: Coccosteidae
Length: 35 cm (14 in)

BOTHRIOLEPIS
Group: Bothriolepididae
Length: 40 cm (16 in)

CHEIRACANTHUS
Group: Acanthodidae
Length: 30 cm (12 in)

PTERICHTHYODES
Group: Asterolepididae
Length: 15 cm (6 in)

CHEIROLEPIS
Group: Cheirolepidae
Length: 17 cm (6¾ in)

CEPHALASPIS
Group: Cephalaspidae
Length: 22 cm (8¾ in)

65

Carboniferous to Permian periods

THE CARBONIFEROUS PERIOD (363–290 million years ago) takes its name from the thick, carbon-rich layers – now coal – that were produced during this period as swampy tropical forests were repeatedly drowned by shallow seas. The humid climate across northern and equatorial continents throughout Carboniferous times produced the first dense plant cover on Earth. During the early part of this period, the first reptiles appeared. Their development of a waterproof egg with a protective internal structure ended animal life's dependence on an aquatic environment. Towards the end of Carboniferous times, the earth's continents Laurasia and Gondwana collided, resulting in the huge land-mass of Pangaea. Glaciers smothered much of the southern hemisphere during the Permian period (290–245 million years ago), covering Antarctica, parts of Australia, and much of South America, Africa, and India. Ice locked up much of the world's water and large areas of the northern hemisphere experienced a drop in sea-level. Away from the poles, deserts and a hot dry climate predominated. As a result of these conditions, the Permian period ended with the greatest mass extinction of life on earth ever.

LATE CARBONIFEROUS POSITIONS OF PRESENT-DAY LAND-MASSES

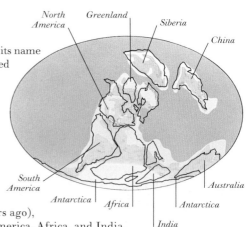

EXAMPLES OF CARBONIFEROUS AND PERMIAN PLANT GROUPS

A PRESENT-DAY FIR
(Abies concolor)

FOSSIL OF AN EXTINCT FERN
(Zeilleria frenzlii)

FOSSIL OF AN EXTINCT HORSETAIL
(Equisetites sp.)

FOSSIL OF AN EXTINCT CLUBMOSS
(Lepidodendron sp.)

EXAMPLES OF CARBONIFEROUS AND PERMIAN TREES

PECOPTERIS
Group: Marattiaceae
Height: 4 m (13 ft)

PARIPTERIS
Group: Medullosaceae
Height: 5 m (16 ft 6 in)

MARIOPTERIS
Group: Lyginopteridales
Height: 5 m (16 ft 6 in)

MEDULLOSA
Group: Medullosaceae
Height: 5 m (16 ft 6 in)

THE EARTH DURING THE LATE CARBONIFEROUS PERIOD

EXAMPLES OF CARBONIFEROUS
AND PERMIAN ANIMALS

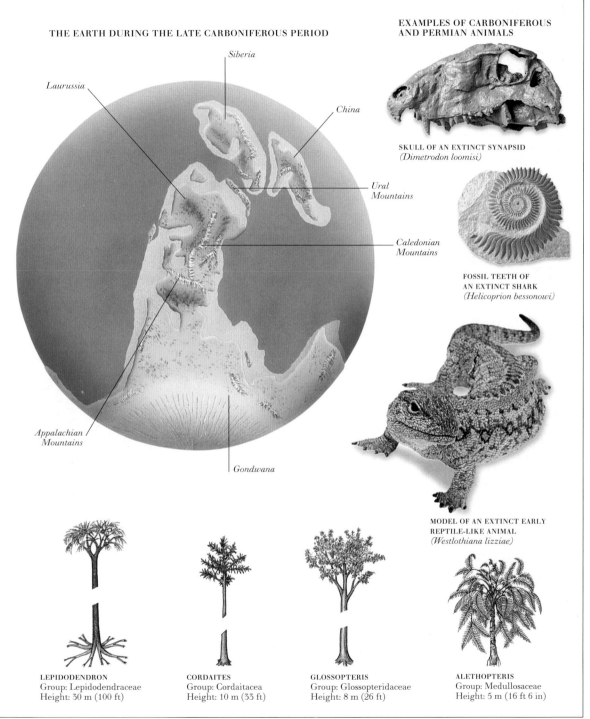

Siberia

Laurussia

China

*Ural
Mountains*

*Caledonian
Mountains*

*Appalachian
Mountains*

Gondwana

SKULL OF AN EXTINCT SYNAPSID
(*Dimetrodon loomisi*)

FOSSIL TEETH OF
AN EXTINCT SHARK
(*Helicoprion bessonowi*)

MODEL OF AN EXTINCT EARLY
REPTILE-LIKE ANIMAL
(*Westlothiana lizziae*)

LEPIDODENDRON
Group: Lepidodendraceae
Height: 30 m (100 ft)

CORDAITES
Group: Cordaitacea
Height: 10 m (33 ft)

GLOSSOPTERIS
Group: Glossopteridaceae
Height: 8 m (26 ft)

ALETHOPTERIS
Group: Medullosaceae
Height: 5 m (16 ft 6 in)

67

Triassic period

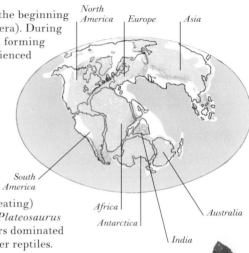

North
America   Europe   Asia

South
America

Africa   Australia

Antarctica

India

THE TRIASSIC PERIOD (250–200 million years ago) marked the beginning of what is known as the Age of the Dinosaurs (the Mesozoic era). During this period, the present-day continents were massed together, forming one huge continent known as Pangaea. This land-mass experienced extremes of climate, with lush green areas around the coast or by lakes and rivers, and arid deserts in the interior. The only forms of plant life were non-flowering plants, such as conifers, ferns, cycads, and ginkgos; flowering plants had not yet evolved. The principal forms of animal life included diverse, often gigantic, amphibians, rhynchosaurs ("beaked lizards"), and primitive crocodilians. Dinosaurs first appeared about 230 million years ago, at the beginning of the Late Triassic period. Among the earliest dinosaurs were the carnivorous (flesh-eating) herrerasaurids, such as *Herrerasaurus* and *Staurikosaurus*. Early herbivorous (plant-eating) dinosaurs first appeared in Late Triassic times and included *Plateosaurus* and *Technosaurus*. By the end of the Triassic period, dinosaurs dominated Pangaea, possibly contributing to the extinction of many other reptiles.

**EXAMPLES OF TRIASSIC
PLANT GROUPS**

**A PRESENT-DAY
CYCAD**
(*Cycas revoluta*)

A PRESENT-DAY GINKGO
(*Ginkgo biloba*)

A PRESENT-DAY CONIFER
(*Araucaria araucana*)

**FOSSIL OF AN
EXTINCT FERN**
(*Pachypteris sp.*)

**FOSSIL LEAF OF AN
EXTINCT CYCAD**
(*Cycas sp.*)

EXAMPLES OF TRIASSIC DINOSAURS

MELANOROSAURUS
Group: Melanorosauridae
Length: 12.2 m (40 ft)

MUSSAURUS
Group: Sauropodomorpha
Length: 2–3 m (6 ft 6 in–10 ft)

HERRERASAURUS
Group: Herrerasauridae
Length: 3 m (10 ft)

PISANOSAURUS
Group: Ornithischia
Length: 90 cm (3 ft)

THE EARTH DURING THE TRIASSIC PERIOD

EXAMPLES OF TRIASSIC ANIMALS

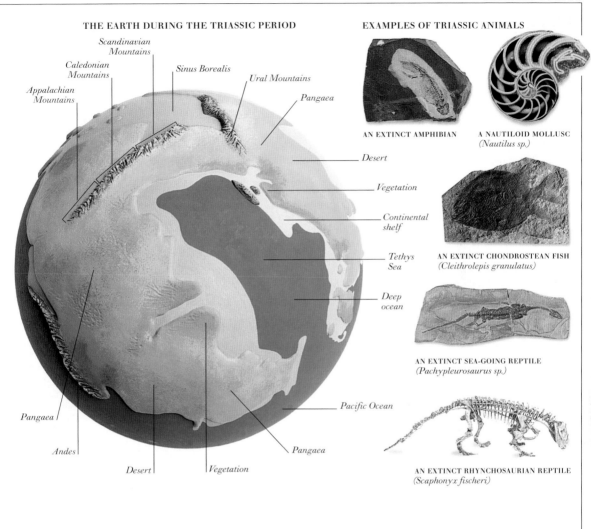

Scandinavian
Mountains

Caledonian
Mountains

Sinus Borealis

Appalachian
Mountains

Ural Mountains

Pangaea

Desert

Vegetation

Continental
shelf

Tethys
Sea

Deep
ocean

Pacific Ocean

Pangaea

Andes

Desert

Vegetation

Pangaea

AN EXTINCT AMPHIBIAN

A NAUTILOID MOLLUSC
(Nautilus sp.)

AN EXTINCT CHONDROSTEAN FISH
(Cleithrolepis granulatus)

AN EXTINCT SEA-GOING REPTILE
(Pachypleurosaurus sp.)

AN EXTINCT RHYNCHOSAURIAN REPTILE
(Scaphonyx fischeri)

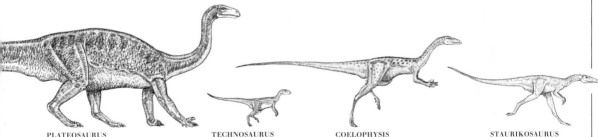

PLATEOSAURUS
Group: Plateosauridae
Length: 7.9 m (26 ft)

TECHNOSAURUS
Group: Ornithischia
Length: 1 m (3 ft 3 in)

COELOPHYSIS
Group: Coelophysidae
Length: 3 m (10 ft)

STAURIKOSAURUS
Group: Herrerasauridae
Length: 2 m (6 ft 6 in)

Jurassic period

THE JURASSIC PERIOD, the middle part of the Mesozoic era, lasted from 199 to 145 million years ago. During Jurassic times, the land-mass of Pangaea broke up into the continents of Gondwana and Laurasia, and sea-levels rose, flooding areas of lower land. The Jurassic climate was warm and moist. Plants such as ginkgos, horsetails, and conifers thrived, and giant redwood trees appeared, as did the first flowering plants. The abundance of plant food coincided with the proliferation of herbivorous (plant-eating) dinosaurs, such as the large sauropods (e.g., *Diplodocus*) and stegosaurs (e.g., *Stegosaurus*). Carnivorous (flesheating) dinosaurs, such as *Compsognathus* and *Allosaurus*, also flourished by hunting the many animals that existed – among them other dinosaurs. Further Jurassic animals included shrew-like mammals, and pterosaurs (flying reptiles), as well as plesiosaurs and ichthyosaurs (both marine reptiles).

JURASSIC POSITIONS OF PRESENT-DAY LAND-MASSES

North America
Europe
Arabia
Asia
Australia
South America
Africa
India
Antarctica

EXAMPLES OF JURASSIC PLANT GROUPS

A PRESENT-DAY FERN
(*Dicksonia antarctica*)

A PRESENT-DAY HORSETAIL
(*Equisetum arvense*)

A PRESENT-DAY CONIFER
(*Taxus baccata*)

FOSSIL LEAF OF AN EXTINCT CONIFER
(*Taxus sp.*)

FOSSIL LEAF OF AN EXTINCT REDWOOD
(*Sequoiadendron affinis*)

EXAMPLES OF JURASSIC DINOSAURS

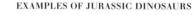

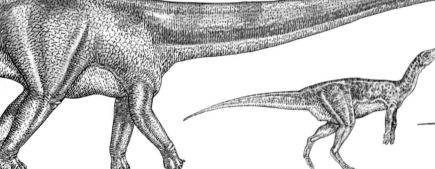

DIPLODOCUS
Group: Diplodocidae
Length: 26.8 m (88 ft)

CAMPTOSAURUS
Group: Iguanodontia
Length: 4.9–7 m (16–23 ft)

DRYOSAURUS
Group: Dryosauridae
Length: 3–4 m (10–13 ft)

THE EARTH DURING THE JURASSIC PERIOD

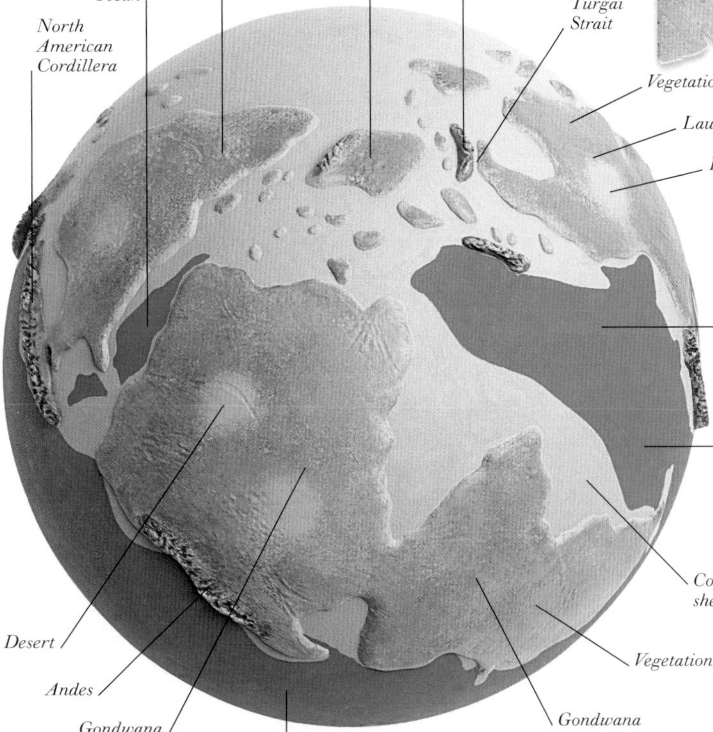

EXAMPLES OF JURASSIC ANIMALS

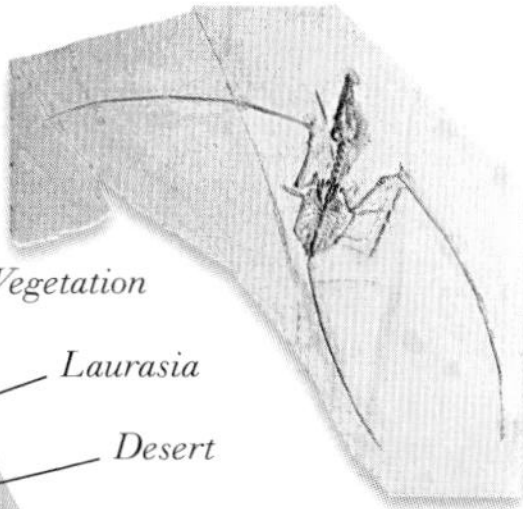

Laurasia

Laurasia

North Atlantic
Ocean

North
American
Cordillera

Ural Mountains

Turgai
Strait

Vegetation

Laurasia

Desert

Tethys Sea

Deep
ocean

Continental
shelf

Desert

Vegetation

Andes

Gondwana

Gondwana

Pacific Ocean

AN EXTINCT PTEROSAUR
(*Rhamphorhynchus sp.*)

**AN EXTINCT
BELEMNITE MOLLUSC**
(*Belemnoteuthis sp.*)

**AN EXTINCT
RHYNCHOSAURIAN REPTILE**
(*Homeosaurus pulchellus*)

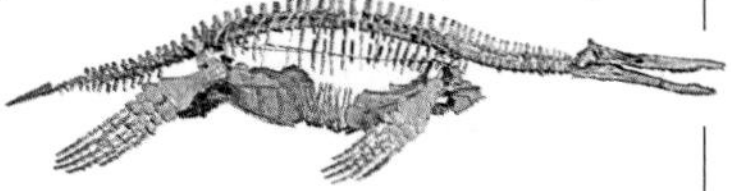

AN EXTINCT PLESIOSAUR
(*Peloneustes philarcus*)

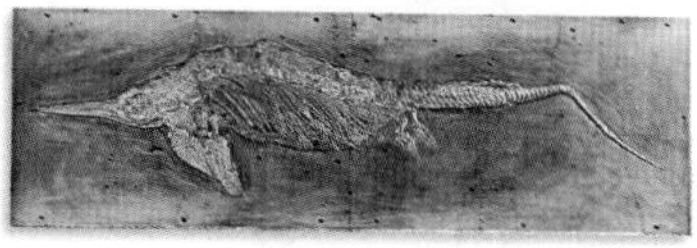

AN EXTINCT ICHTHYOSAUR
(*Stenopterygius megacephalus*)

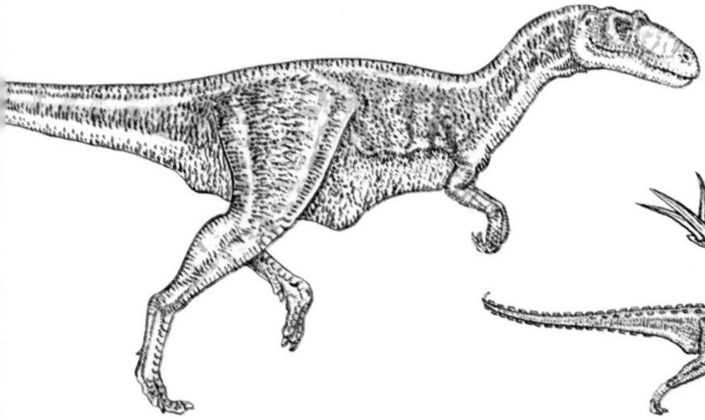

ALLOSAURUS
Group: Allosauroidea
Length: 11 m (36 ft)

SCELIDOSAURUS
Group: Thyreophora
Length: 4 m (13 ft)

STEGOSAURUS
Group: Stegosauridae
Length: 9.1 m (30 ft)

Cretaceous period

THE MESOZOIC ERA ENDED WITH the Cretaceous period, which lasted from 146 to 65 million years ago. During this period, Gondwana and Laurasia were breaking up into smaller land-masses that more closely resembled the modern continents. The climate remained mild and moist but the seasons became more marked. Flowering plants, including deciduous trees, replaced many cycads, seed ferns, and conifers. Animal species became more varied, with the evolution of new mammals, insects, fish, crustaceans, and turtles. Dinosaurs evolved into a wide variety of species during Cretaceous times; more than half of all known dinosaurs – including *Iguanodon*, *Deinonychus*, *Tyrannosaurus*, and *Hypsilophodon* – lived during this period. At the end of the Cretaceous period, however, most dinosaurs became extinct. The reason for this mass extinction is unknown but it is thought to have been caused by climatic changes due to either a catastrophic meteor impact with the Earth or extensive volcanic eruptions.

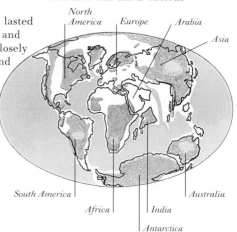

CRETACEOUS POSITIONS OF PRESENT-DAY LAND-MASSES

North America — Europe — Arabia — Asia — South America — Africa — India — Antarctica — Australia

EXAMPLES OF CRETACEOUS PLANT GROUPS

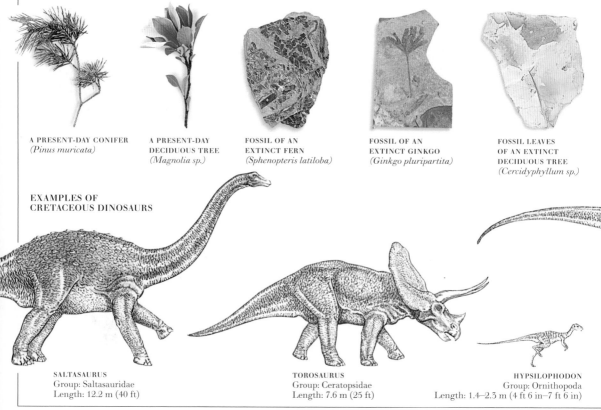

A PRESENT-DAY CONIFER
(*Pinus muricata*)

A PRESENT-DAY DECIDUOUS TREE
(*Magnolia sp.*)

FOSSIL OF AN EXTINCT FERN
(*Sphenopteris latiloba*)

FOSSIL OF AN EXTINCT GINKGO
(*Ginkgo pluripartita*)

FOSSIL LEAVES OF AN EXTINCT DECIDUOUS TREE
(*Cercidyphyllum sp.*)

EXAMPLES OF CRETACEOUS DINOSAURS

SALTASAURUS
Group: Saltasauridae
Length: 12.2 m (40 ft)

TOROSAURUS
Group: Ceratopsidae
Length: 7.6 m (25 ft)

HYPSILOPHODON
Group: Ornithopoda
Length: 1.4–2.3 m (4 ft 6 in–7 ft 6 in)

THE EARTH DURING THE CRETACEOUS PERIOD

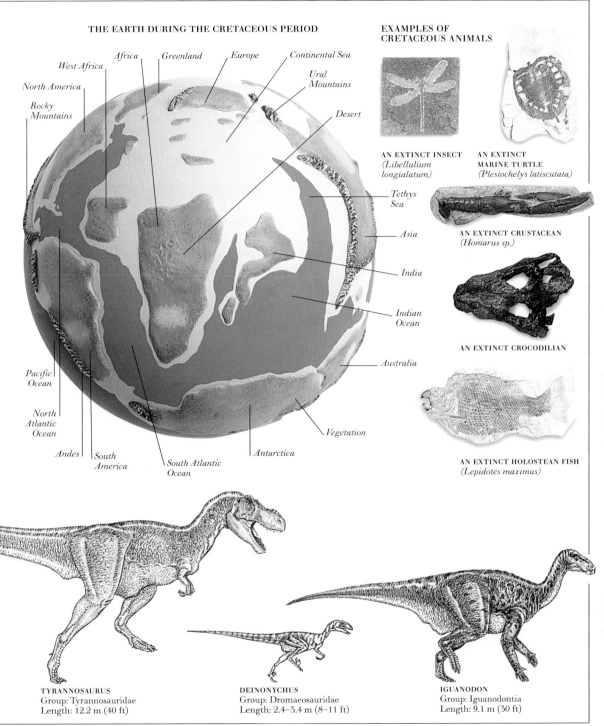

North America
West Africa
Africa
Greenland
Europe
Continental Sea
Ural Mountains
Rocky Mountains
Desert
Tethys Sea
Asia
India
Indian Ocean
Australia
Pacific Ocean
North Atlantic Ocean
Andes
South America
South Atlantic Ocean
Antarctica
Vegetation

EXAMPLES OF CRETACEOUS ANIMALS

AN EXTINCT INSECT
(*Libellulium longialatum*)

AN EXTINCT MARINE TURTLE
(*Plesiochelys latiscutata*)

AN EXTINCT CRUSTACEAN
(*Homarus* sp.)

AN EXTINCT CROCODILIAN

AN EXTINCT HOLOSTEAN FISH
(*Lepidotes maximus*)

TYRANNOSAURUS
Group: Tyrannosauridae
Length: 12.2 m (40 ft)

DEINONYCHUS
Group: Dromaeosauridae
Length: 2.4–3.4 m (8–11 ft)

IGUANODON
Group: Iguanodontia
Length: 9.1 m (30 ft)

73

Tertiary period

TERTIARY POSITIONS OF PRESENT-DAY LAND-MASSES

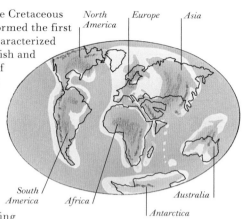

North America
Europe
Asia
South America
Africa
Australia
Antarctica

FOLLOWING THE DEMISE OF THE DINOSAURS at the end of the Cretaceous period, the Tertiary period (65–1.6 million years ago), which formed the first part of the Cenozoic era (65 million years ago–present), was characterized by a huge expansion of mammal life. Placental mammals nourish and maintain the young in the mother's uterus; only a few groups of placental mammals existed during Cretaceous times, compared with several tens of groups during the Tertiary period. One of these tens included the early human (see pp.108–109), *Ardipithecus*, which appeared in Africa. By the beginning of the Tertiary period, the continents had almost reached their present position. The Tethys Sea, which had separated the northern continents from Africa and India, began to close up, forming the Mediterranean Sea and allowing the migration of terrestrial animals between Africa and western Europe. India's collision with Asia led to the formation of the Himalayas. During the middle part of the Tertiary period, the forest-dwelling and browsing mammals were replaced by mammals such as the horses, better suited to grazing the open savannahs that began to dominate. Repeated cool periods throughout the Tertiary period established the Antarctic as an icy island continent.

EXAMPLES OF TERTIARY PLANT GROUPS

A PRESENT-DAY OAK
(Quercus palustris)

A PRESENT-DAY BIRCH
(Betula grossa)

FOSSIL LEAF OF AN EXTINCT BIRCH
(Betulites sp.)

FOSSILIZED STEM OF AN EXTINCT PALM
(Palmoxylon sp.)

EXAMPLES OF TERTIARY ANIMAL GROUPS

HYAENODON
Group: Hyaenodontidae
Length: 2 m (6 ft 6 in)

TITANOHYRAX
Group: Pliohyracidae
Length: 2 m (6 ft 6 in)

PHORUSRHACOS
Group: Phorusrhacidae
Length: 1.5 m (5 ft)

SAMOTHERIUM
Group: Giraffidae
Length: 3 m (10 ft)

THE EARTH DURING THE TERTIARY PERIOD

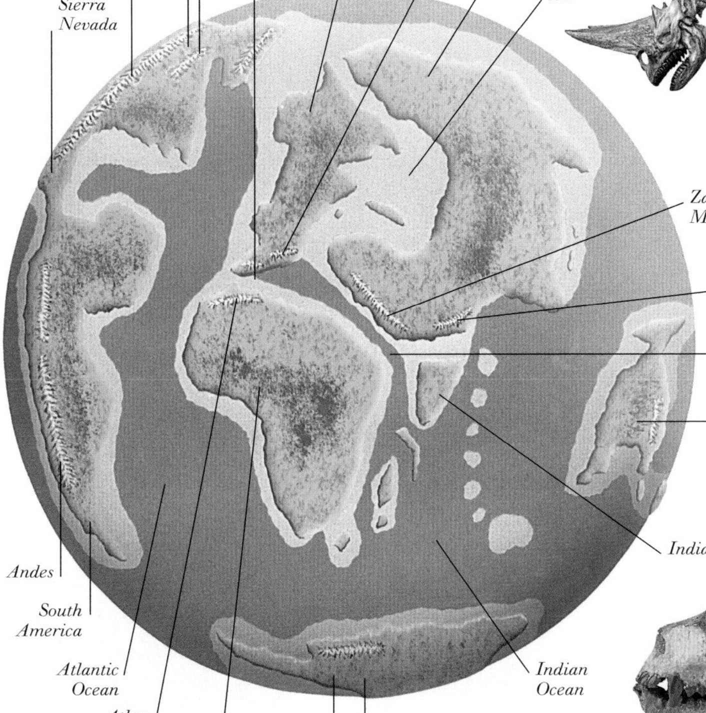

North America
Rocky Mountains
Sierra Nevada
Appalachian Mountains
Pyrenees
Europe
Alps
Asia
Continental sea
Zagros Mountains
Himalayas
Tethys Sea
Australia
India
Andes
South America
Atlantic Ocean
Atlas Mountains
Africa
Antarctica
Vegetation
Indian Ocean

EXAMPLES OF TERTIARY ANIMALS

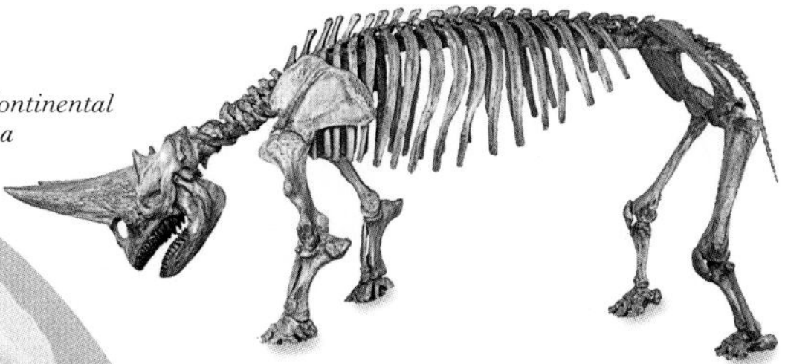

AN EXTINCT MAMMAL
(*Arsinoitherium*)

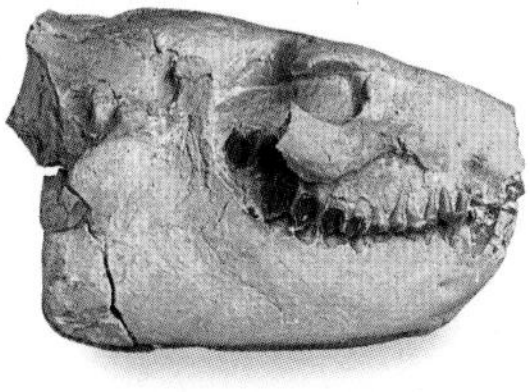

AN EXTINCT MAMMAL
(*Merycoidodon culbertsonii*)

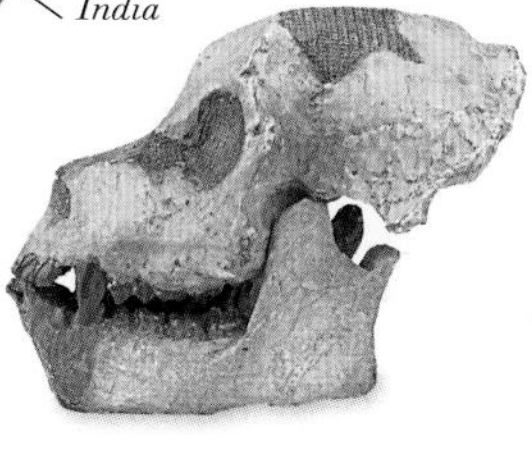

AN EXTINCT PRIMATE
(*Aegyptopithecus sp.*)

AN EXTINCT GASTROPOD MOLLUSC
(*Ecphora quadricostata*)

MAMMUT
Group: Mammutidae
Length: 2.5 m (8 ft)

TETRALOPHODON
Group: Gomphotheriidae
Length: 2.5 m (8 ft)

Quaternary period

THE QUATERNARY PERIOD (1.6 million years ago–present) forms the second part of the Cenozoic era (65 million years ago–present): it has been characterized by alternating cold (glacial) and warm (interglacial) periods. During cold periods, ice sheets and glaciers have formed repeatedly on northern and southern continents. The cold environments in North America and Eurasia, and to a lesser extent in southern South America and parts of Australia, have caused the migration of many life forms towards the Equator. Only the specialized ice age mammals such as *Mammuthus* and *Coelodonta*, with their thick wool and fat insulation, were suited to life in very cold climates. Humans developed throughout the Pleistocene period (1.6 million–10,000 years ago) in Africa and migrated northward into Europe and Asia. Modern humans, *Homo sapiens*, lived on the cold European continent 30,000 years ago and hunted other mammals. The end of the last ice age and the climatic changes that occurred about 10,000 years ago brought extinction to many Pleistocene mammals, but enabled humans to flourish.

QUATERNARY POSITIONS OF PRESENT-DAY LAND-MASSES

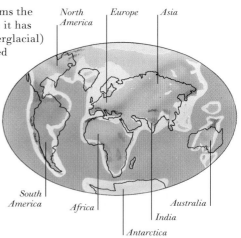

North America

Europe

Asia

South America

Africa

India

Antarctica

Australia

EXAMPLES OF QUATERNARY PLANT GROUPS

A PRESENT-DAY BIRCH
(*Betula lenta*)

A PRESENT-DAY SWEEETGUM
(*Liquidambar styraciflua*)

FOSSIL LEAF OF A SWEETGUM
(*Liquidambar europeanum*)

FOSSIL LEAF OF A BIRCH
(*Betula sp.*)

EXAMPLES OF QUATERNARY ANIMAL GROUPS

PROCOPTODON
Group: Macropodidae
Length: 3 m (10 ft)

DIPROTODON
Group: Diprotodontidae
Length: 3 m (10 ft)

TOXODON
Group: Toxodontidae
Length: 3 m (10 ft)

MAMMUTHUS
Group: Elephantidae
Length: 3 m (10 ft)

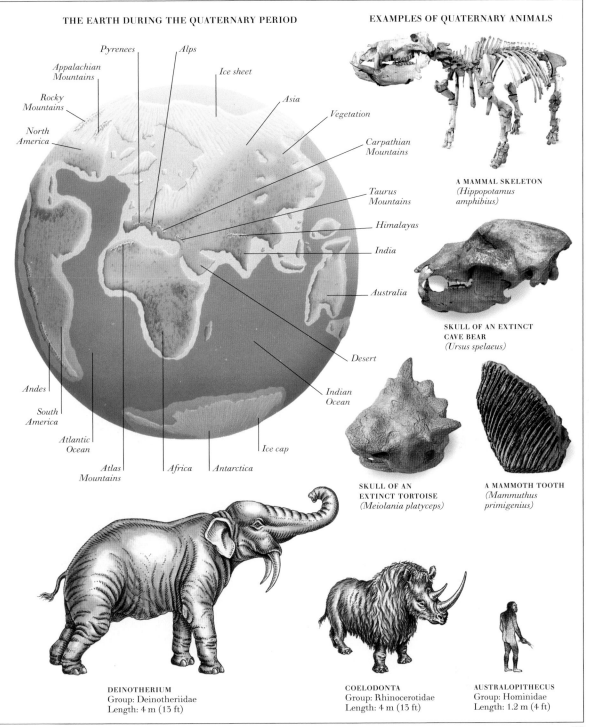

THE EARTH DURING THE QUATERNARY PERIOD

Pyrenees

Alps

Appalachian
Mountains

Ice sheet

Rocky
Mountains

Asia

North
America

Vegetation

Carpathian
Mountains

Taurus
Mountains

Himalayas

India

Australia

Andes

South
America

Desert

Atlantic
Ocean

Indian
Ocean

Atlas
Mountains

Africa

Antarctica

Ice cap

EXAMPLES OF QUATERNARY ANIMALS

A MAMMAL SKELETON
(Hippopotamus
amphibius)

**SKULL OF AN EXTINCT
CAVE BEAR**
(Ursus spelaeus)

**SKULL OF AN
EXTINCT TORTOISE**
(Meiolania platyceps)

A MAMMOTH TOOTH
(Mammuthus
primigenius)

DEINOTHERIUM
Group: Deinotheriidae
Length: 4 m (13 ft)

COELODONTA
Group: Rhinocerotidae
Length: 4 m (13 ft)

AUSTRALOPITHECUS
Group: Hominidae
Length: 1.2 m (4 ft)

Early signs of life

FOR ALMOST A THOUSAND MILLION YEARS after its formation, there
was no known life on Earth. The first simple, sea-dwelling organic
structures appeared about 3,500 million years ago; they may have
formed when certain chemical molecules joined together.
Prokaryotes, single-celled micro-organisms such as blue-green
algae, were able to photosynthesize (see pp. 138–139), and thus
produce oxygen. A thousand million years later, sufficient
oxygen had built up in the earth's atmosphere to allow
multicellular organisms to proliferate in the Precambrian
seas (before 570 million years ago). Soft-bodied jellyfish,
corals, and seaworms flourished about 700 million years
ago. Trilobites, the first animals with hard body frames,
developed during the Cambrian period (570–510 million
years ago). However, it was not until the beginning of the
Devonian period (409–363 million years ago) that early
land plants, such as *Asteroxylon*, formed a water-
retaining cuticle, which ended their dependence on an
aquatic environment. About 360 million years ago, the first
amphibians (see pp. 80–81) crawled onto the land,
although they probably still returned to the water to lay
their soft eggs. By the time the first reptiles and synapsids
appeared late in the Carboniferous, animals with
backbones had become fully independent of water.

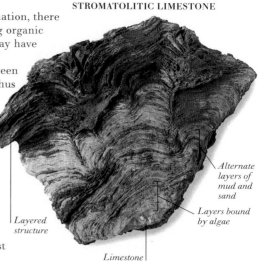

STROMATOLITIC LIMESTONE

*Alternate
layers of
mud and
sand*

*Layers bound
by algae*

*Layered
structure*

Limestone

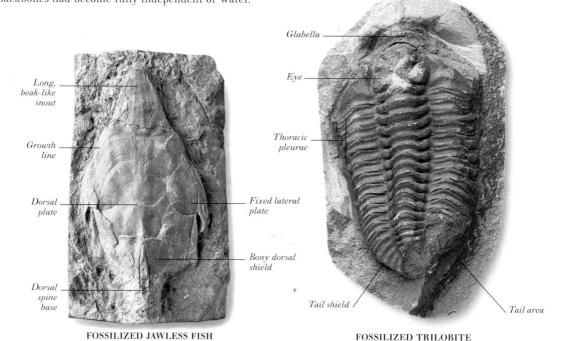

*Long,
beak-like
snout*

*Growth
line*

*Dorsal
plate*

*Dorsal
spine
base*

Glabella

Eye

*Thoracic
pleurae*

*Fixed lateral
plate*

*Bony dorsal
shield*

Tail shield

Tail area

FOSSILIZED JAWLESS FISH

FOSSILIZED TRILOBITE

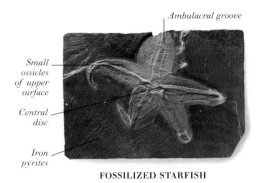

Ambulacral groove

Small
ossicles
of upper
surface

Central
disc

Iron
pyrites

FOSSILIZED STARFISH

Row of
ossicles

Broad disc

**UPPER SURFACE OF
FOSSILIZED STARFISH**

Row of
ossicles

Short
arm

**LOWER SURFACE OF
FOSSILIZED STARFISH**

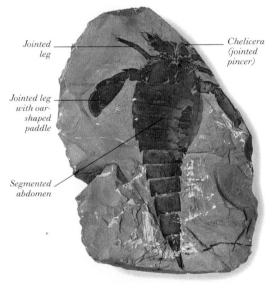

Jointed
leg

Chelicera
(jointed
pincer)

Jointed leg
with oar-
shaped
paddle

Segmented
abdomen

UNDERSIDE OF FOSSILIZED EURYPTERID

Telson (tail
spine)

Abdominal
segments

Shell contains eight
somites (thoracic
segments)

Hingeless,
bivalved
shell

FOSSIL OF AN EXTINCT SHRIMP

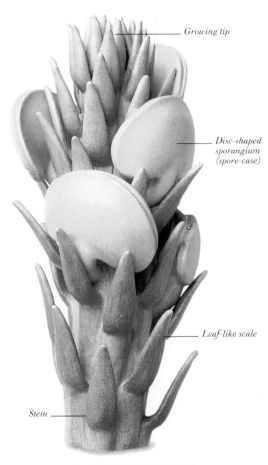

Growing tip

Disc-shaped
sporangium
(spore-case)

Leaf-like scale

Stem

RECONSTRUCTION OF ASTEROXYLON

Amphibians and reptiles

THE EARLIEST KNOWN AMPHIBIANS, such as *Acanthostega* and *Ichthyostega*, lived about 363 million years ago at the end of the Devonian period (409–363 million years ago). Their limbs may have evolved from the muscular fins of lungfish-like creatures. These fish can use their fins to push themselves along the bottom of lakes and some can breathe at the water's surface. While amphibians (see pp. 182–183) can exist on land, they are dependent on a wet environment because their skin does not retain moisture and most species must return to the water to lay their eggs. Evolving from amphibians, reptiles (see pp. 184–187) first appeared during the Carboniferous period (363–290 million years ago): *Westlothiana*, a possible early reptile, lived on land 338 million years ago. The development of the amniotic egg, with an embryo enclosed in its own wet environment (the amnion) and protected by a waterproof shell, freed reptiles from the amphibian's dependence on a wet habitat. A scaly skin protected the reptile from desiccation on land and enabled it to exploit ways of life closed to its amphibian ancestors. Reptiles include the dinosaurs, which came to dominate life on land during the Mesozoic era (245–65 million years ago).

Orbit
Pocket enclosing nostril
Sculpted or pitted bone surface
Spiracle to draw in water
Mandible
Small tooth

FOSSIL SKULL OF ACANTHOSTEGA

Muscular back
Shoulder girdle
Scaly skin
Finned tail
Hip girdle

MODEL OF ICHTHYOSTEGA

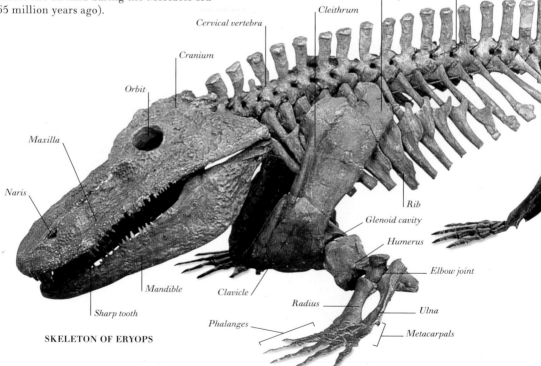

Dorsal vertebra
Scapula
Cleithrum
Cervical vertebra
Cranium
Orbit
Maxilla
Naris
Rib
Glenoid cavity
Humerus
Elbow joint
Mandible
Clavicle
Radius
Ulna
Sharp tooth
Phalanges
Metacarpals

SKELETON OF ERYOPS

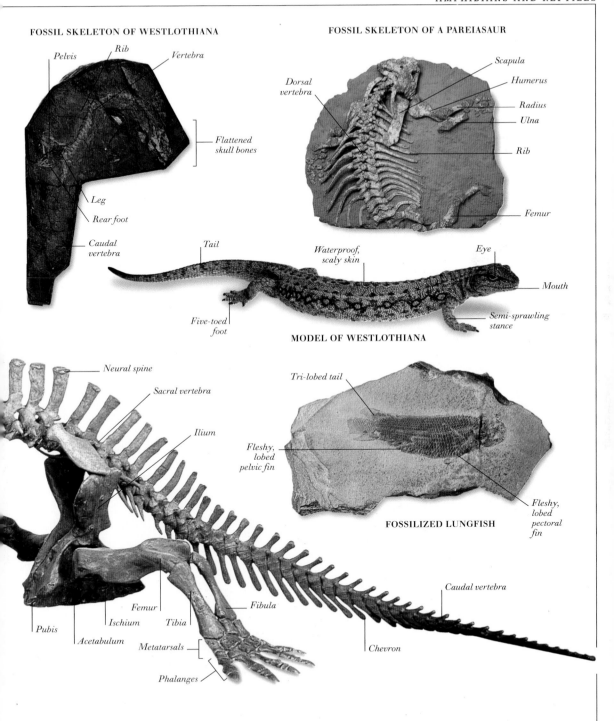

FOSSIL SKELETON OF WESTLOTHIANA

Pelvis

Rib

Vertebra

Flattened
skull bones

Leg

Rear foot

Caudal
vertebra

FOSSIL SKELETON OF A PAREIASAUR

Dorsal
vertebra

Scapula

Humerus

Radius

Ulna

Rib

Femur

Tail

Waterproof,
scaly skin

Eye

Mouth

Five-toed
foot

Semi-sprawling
stance

MODEL OF WESTLOTHIANA

Neural spine

Sacral vertebra

Ilium

Tri-lobed tail

Fleshy,
lobed
pelvic fin

Fleshy,
lobed
pectoral
fin

FOSSILIZED LUNGFISH

Caudal vertebra

Pubis

Acetabulum

Ischium

Femur

Tibia

Metatarsals

Fibula

Chevron

Phalanges

81

The dinosaurs

THE DINOSAURS WERE A LARGE GROUP of reptiles that were the dominant land vertebrates (animals with backbones) for most of the Mesozoic era (245–65 million years ago). They appeared some 230 million years ago and were distinguished from other scaly, egg-laying reptiles by an important feature: dinosaurs had an erect limb stance. This enabled them to keep their bodies well above the ground, unlike the sprawling and semi-sprawling stance of other reptiles. The head of the dinosaur's femur (thigh-bone) fitted into a socket in its pelvis (hip-bone), producing efficient and mobile locomotion. Dinosaurs are categorized into two groups according to the structure of their pelvis: saurischian (lizard-hipped) and ornithischian (bird-hipped) dinosaurs. In the case of most saurischians, the pubis (part of the pelvis) jutted forward, while in ornithischians it slanted back, parallel to the ischium (another part of the pelvis). Dinosaurs ranged in size from smaller than a domestic cat to the biggest land animals ever known. The Dinosauria were the most successful land vertebrates ever, and survived for 165 million years, until most became extinct 65 million years ago.

STRUCTURE OF SAURISCHIAN PELVIS

Ilium

Postacetabular process

Ilio-ischial joint

Ischium

Hook of preacetabular process

Ilio-pubic joint

Acetabulum

Pubis

Pubic foot

GALLIMIMUS
A saurischian dinosaur

POSITION OF PELVIS IN A SAURISCHIAN DINOSAUR

STRUCTURE OF ORNITHISCHIAN PELVIS

Ilium

Postacetabular process

Ilio-ischial joint

Ischium

Preacetabular process

Ilio-pubic joint

Prepubis

Acetabulum

Pubis

HYPSILOPHODON
An ornithischian dinosaur

POSITION OF PELVIS IN AN ORNITHISCHIAN DINOSAUR

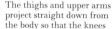

BAROSAURUS
A saurischian dinosaur

COMPARISON OF ANIMAL STANCES

SPRAWLING STANCE
The thighs and upper arms project straight out from the body so that the knees and elbows are bent at right angles.

COMMON IGUANA
(*Iguana iguana*)
A present-day reptile

ERECT STANCE
The thighs and upper arms project straight down from the body so that the knees and elbows are straight.

SEMI-SPRAWLING STANCE
The thighs and upper arms project downwards and outwards so that the knees and elbows are slightly bent.

DWARF CROCODILE
(*Osteolaemus tetraspis*)
A present-day reptile

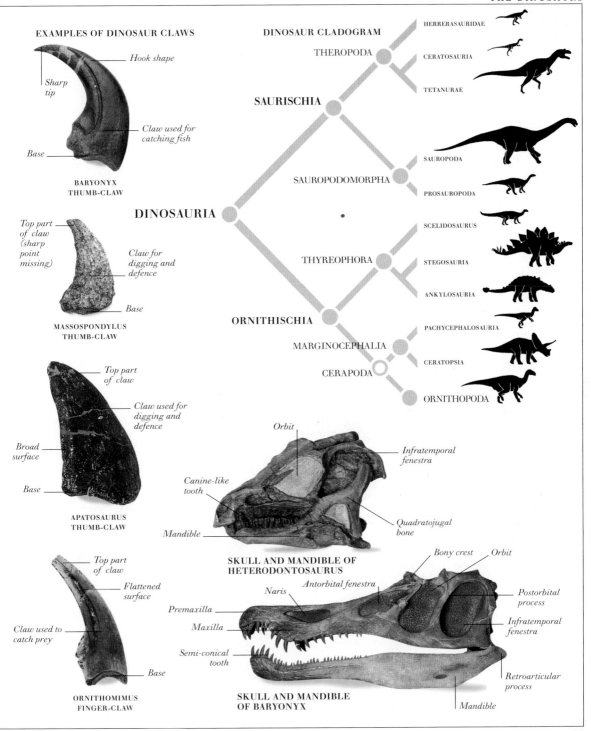

EXAMPLES OF DINOSAUR CLAWS

Hook shape

Sharp tip

Claw used for catching fish

Base

BARYONYX THUMB-CLAW

Top part of claw (sharp point missing)

Claw for digging and defence

Base

MASSOSPONDYLUS THUMB-CLAW

Top part of claw

Claw used for digging and defence

Broad surface

Base

APATOSAURUS THUMB-CLAW

Top part of claw

Flattened surface

Claw used to catch prey

Base

ORNITHOMIMUS FINGER-CLAW

DINOSAUR CLADOGRAM

HERRERASAURIDAE

THEROPODA

CERATOSAURIA

SAURISCHIA

TETANURAE

SAUROPODA

SAUROPODOMORPHA

PROSAUROPODA

DINOSAURIA

SCELIDOSAURUS

THYREOPHORA

STEGOSAURIA

ANKYLOSAURIA

ORNITHISCHIA

PACHYCEPHALOSAURIA

MARGINOCEPHALIA

CERATOPSIA

CERAPODA

ORNITHOPODA

Orbit

Infratemporal fenestra

Canine-like tooth

Quadratojugal bone

Mandible

SKULL AND MANDIBLE OF HETERODONTOSAURUS

Bony crest

Orbit

Antorbital fenestra

Naris

Postorbital process

Premaxilla

Maxilla

Infratemporal fenestra

Semi-conical tooth

Retroarticular process

Mandible

SKULL AND MANDIBLE OF BARYONYX

Theropods 1

AN ENORMOUSLY SUCCESSFUL SUBGROUP of the Saurischia, the bipedal (two-footed) theropods ("beast feet") emerged 230 million years ago in Late Triassic times; the oldest known example comes from South America. Theropods spanned the age of most dinosaurs (230–65 million years ago) and beyond, and included most of the known predatory dinosaurs. The typical theropod had smallish arms with sharp, clawed fingers; powerful jaws lined with sharp teeth; an S-shaped neck; long, muscular hind limbs; and clawed, usually four-toed feet. Many theropods may have been warm-blooded; most were exclusively carnivorous. Theropods ranged from animals no larger than a chicken to huge creatures, such as *Tyrannosaurus* and *Baryonyx*. The group also included ostrich-like omnivores and herbivores with toothless beaks, such as *Struthiomimus* and *Gallimimus*. Birds are dinosaurs and evolved from within a group of tetanuran theropods called maniraptorans. *Archaeopteryx*, small and feathered, was the first known bird and lived alongside other dinosaurs.

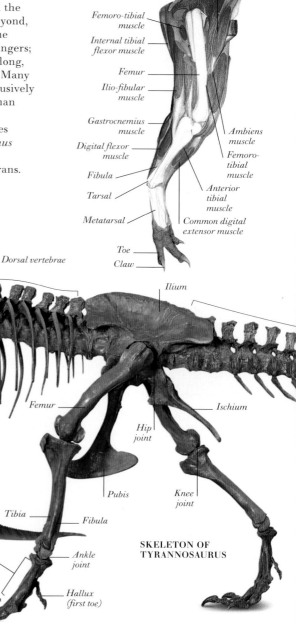

INTERNAL ANATOMY OF ALBERTOSAURUS LEG

Ilio-tibial muscle
Ilio-femoral muscle
Femoro-tibial muscle
Internal tibial flexor muscle
Femur
Ilio-fibular muscle
Gastrocnemius muscle
Digital flexor muscle
Fibula
Tarsal
Metatarsal
Ambiens muscle
Femoro-tibial muscle
Anterior tibial muscle
Common digital extensor muscle
Toe
Claw

SKELETON OF TYRANNOSAURUS

Cranium
Supraoccipital crest
Orbit
Naris
Cervical vertebrae
Dorsal vertebrae
Ilium
Cervical rib
Scapula
Shoulder joint
Mandible
Ulna
Serrated tooth
Phalanges
Metacarpals
Wrist joint
Elbow joint
Coracoid
Rib
Humerus
Femur
Ischium
Hip joint
Pubis
Knee joint
Ankle joint
Fibula
Tibia

EXTERNAL FEATURES OF TYRANNOSAURUS

Naris
Eye
Thigh
Forelimb
Hand
Knee
Ankle
Toe
Claw
Foot
Hind limb
Scaly skin
Tail
Metatarsals
Phalanges
Hallux (first toe)

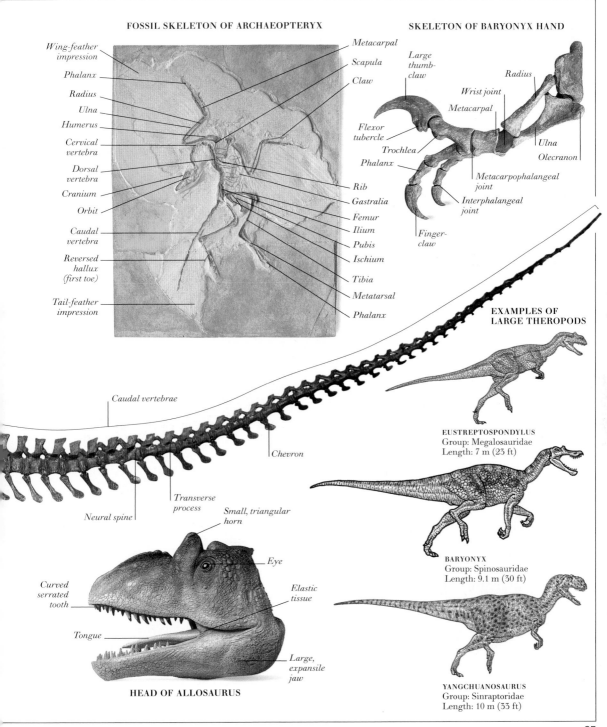

FOSSIL SKELETON OF ARCHAEOPTERYX

Wing-feather impression
Phalanx
Radius
Ulna
Humerus
Cervical vertebra
Dorsal vertebra
Cranium
Orbit
Caudal vertebra
Reversed hallux (first toe)
Tail-feather impression

Metacarpal
Scapula
Claw
Rib
Gastralia
Femur
Ilium
Pubis
Ischium
Tibia
Metatarsal
Phalanx

SKELETON OF BARYONYX HAND

Large thumb-claw
Wrist joint
Metacarpal
Radius
Ulna
Olecranon
Flexor tubercle
Trochlea
Phalanx
Metacarpophalangeal joint
Interphalangeal joint
Finger-claw

EXAMPLES OF LARGE THEROPODS

Caudal vertebrae
Chevron
Transverse process
Neural spine

Small, triangular horn
Eye
Elastic tissue
Curved serrated tooth
Tongue
Large, expansile jaw

HEAD OF ALLOSAURUS

EUSTREPTOSPONDYLUS
Group: Megalosauridae
Length: 7 m (23 ft)

BARYONYX
Group: Spinosauridae
Length: 9.1 m (30 ft)

YANGCHUANOSAURUS
Group: Sinraptoridae
Length: 10 m (33 ft)

Theropods 2

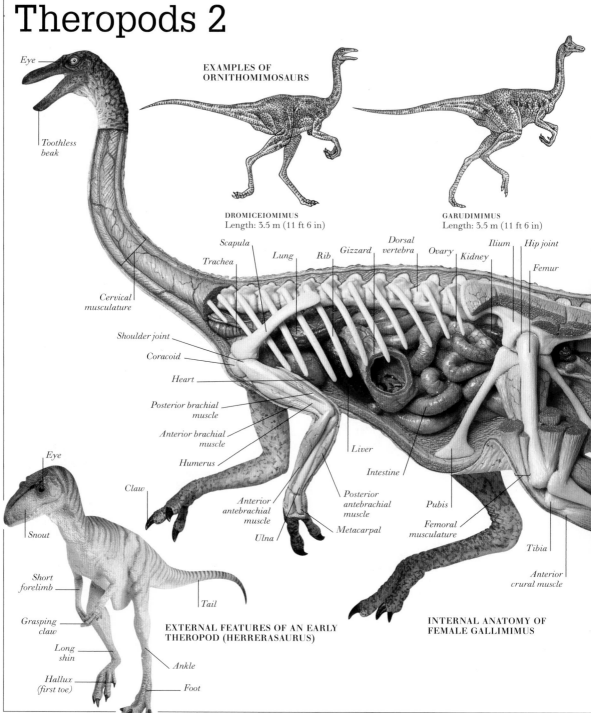

Eye

Toothless beak

EXAMPLES OF ORNITHOMIMOSAURS

DROMICEIOMIMUS
Length: 3.5 m (11 ft 6 in)

GARUDIMIMUS
Length: 3.5 m (11 ft 6 in)

Cervical musculature

Scapula

Trachea

Lung

Rib

Gizzard

Dorsal vertebra

Ovary

Kidney

Ilium

Hip joint

Femur

Shoulder joint

Coracoid

Heart

Posterior brachial muscle

Anterior brachial muscle

Humerus

Claw

Liver

Anterior antebrachial muscle

Posterior antebrachial muscle

Intestine

Pubis

Femoral musculature

Tibia

Anterior crural muscle

Ulna

Metacarpal

Eye

Snout

Short forelimb

Grasping claw

Long shin

Hallux (first toe)

Tail

Ankle

Foot

EXTERNAL FEATURES OF AN EARLY THEROPOD (HERRERASAURUS)

INTERNAL ANATOMY OF FEMALE GALLIMIMUS

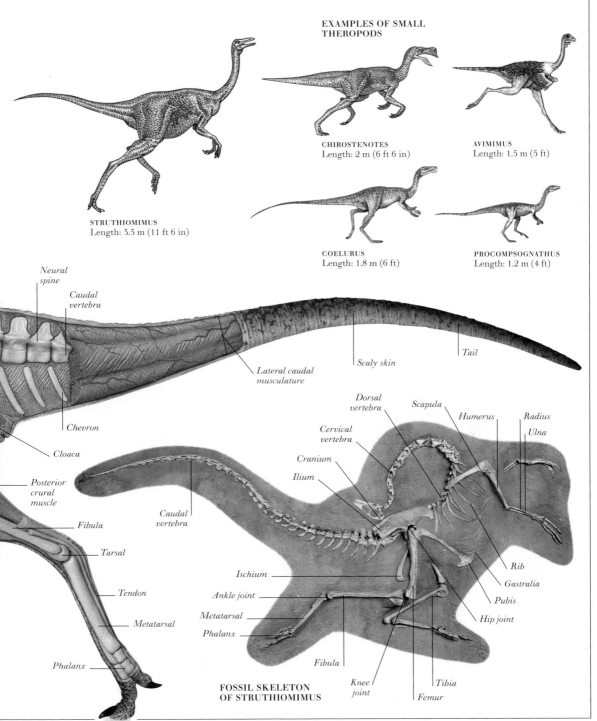

EXAMPLES OF SMALL THEROPODS

CHIROSTENOTES
Length: 2 m (6 ft 6 in)

AVIMIMUS
Length: 1.5 m (5 ft)

STRUTHIOMIMUS
Length: 3.5 m (11 ft 6 in)

COELURUS
Length: 1.8 m (6 ft)

PROCOMPSOGNATHUS
Length: 1.2 m (4 ft)

Neural spine

Caudal vertebra

Lateral caudal musculature

Scaly skin

Tail

Chevron

Cloaca

Dorsal vertebra

Scapula

Humerus

Radius

Ulna

Cervical vertebra

Cranium

Ilium

Posterior crural muscle

Caudal vertebra

Fibula

Tarsal

Rib

Gastralia

Tendon

Pubis

Ischium

Hip joint

Ankle joint

Metatarsal

Metatarsal

Phalanx

Phalanx

Fibula

Knee joint

Tibia

Femur

FOSSIL SKELETON OF STRUTHIOMIMUS

Sauropodomorphs 1

THECODONTOSAURUS

THE SAUROPODOMORPHA ("lizard-feet forms") were herbivorous, usually quadrupedal (four-footed) dinosaurs. A clade within Saurischia, they were characterized by small heads, bulky bodies, and long necks and tails. Sauropodomorphs have often been split into two groups: prosauropods and sauropods. Prosauropods lived from Late Triassic to Early Jurassic times (225–180 million years ago) and included beasts such as the small *Anchisaurus* and one of the first very large dinosaurs, *Plateosaurus*. By Middle Jurassic times (about 165 million years ago), sauropods had replaced prosauropods and spread worldwide. They included the heaviest and longest land animals ever, such as *Diplodocus* and *Brachiosaurus*. Sauropods persisted to the end of the Cretaceous period (65 million years ago). Many of these dinosaurs moved in herds, protected from predatory theropods by their huge bulk and powerful tails, which they could use to lash out at attackers. Sauropodomorphs were the most common large herbivores until Late Jurassic times (about 145 million years ago), and appear to have survived in both southern and northern continents until the end of the Cretaceous period.

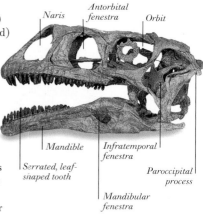

SKULL AND MANDIBLE OF PLATEOSAURUS

Naris

Antorbital fenestra

Orbit

Mandible

Infratemporal fenestra

Serrated, leaf-shaped tooth

Paroccipital process

Mandibular fenestra

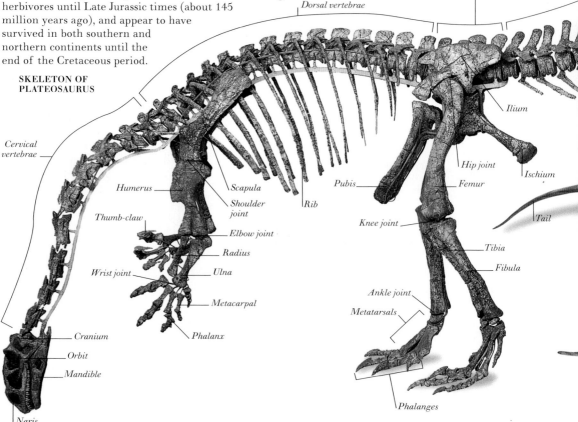

SKELETON OF PLATEOSAURUS

Dorsal vertebrae

Sacral vertebrae

Cervical vertebrae

Ilium

Humerus

Scapula

Shoulder joint

Rib

Pubis

Hip joint

Femur

Ischium

Thumb-claw

Elbow joint

Knee joint

Tail

Radius

Tibia

Wrist joint

Ulna

Fibula

Metacarpal

Ankle joint

Metatarsals

Cranium

Phalanx

Orbit

Mandible

Phalanges

Naris

**THUMB-CLAW OF
MASSOSPONDYLUS**

Top part of
claw (sharp
point missing)

Curved
body of
claw

Base of claw

Caudal
vertebrae

Neural spine

Chevron

Transverse
process

**EXAMPLES OF
PROSAUROPODS**

MASSOSPONDYLUS
Group: Massospondylidae
Length: 5 m (16 ft)

LUFENGOSAURUS
Group: Massospondylidae
Length: 6.1 m (20 ft)

RIOJASAURUS
Group: Riojasauridae
Length: 11 m (36 ft)

MELANOROSAURUS
Group: Melanorosauridae
Length: 7 m (23 ft)

**EXTERNAL FEATURES
OF ANCHISAURUS**

Thigh

Toe

Claw

Forelimb

Hind limb

TOP VIEW OF ANCHISAURUS

Slender snout

Long body

Hip

Scaly skin

Thigh

Tail

Knee

Ankle

Hallux
(first toe)

Foot

Hind limb

Toe

Claw

Naris

Eye

Leaf-
shaped
tooth

Long,
flexible
neck

Shoulder

Forelimb

Elbow

Hand

Large, curved
thumb-claw

Finger

SIDE VIEW OF ANCHISAURUS

Sauropodomorphs 2

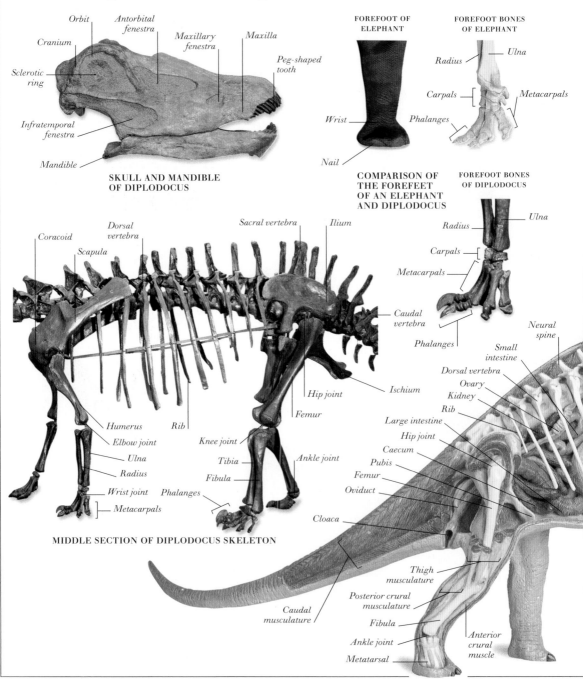

Orbit

Antorbital
fenestra

Cranium

Maxillary
fenestra

Maxilla

Sclerotic
ring

Peg-shaped
tooth

Infratemporal
fenestra

Mandible

**SKULL AND MANDIBLE
OF DIPLODOCUS**

**FOREFOOT OF
ELEPHANT**

Wrist

Nail

**FOREFOOT BONES
OF ELEPHANT**

Radius

Ulna

Carpals

Metacarpals

Phalanges

**COMPARISON OF
THE FOREFEET
OF AN ELEPHANT
AND DIPLODOCUS**

**FOREFOOT BONES
OF DIPLODOCUS**

Radius

Ulna

Carpals

Metacarpals

Phalanges

Coracoid

Dorsal
vertebra

Scapula

Sacral vertebra

Ilium

Caudal
vertebra

Neural
spine

Small
intestine

Dorsal vertebra

Ovary

Kidney

Rib

Large intestine

Hip joint

Caecum

Pubis

Femur

Oviduct

Ischium

Hip joint

Femur

Humerus

Rib

Elbow joint

Ulna

Radius

Wrist joint

Metacarpals

Knee joint

Tibia

Fibula

Phalanges

Ankle joint

Cloaca

MIDDLE SECTION OF DIPLODOCUS SKELETON

Caudal
musculature

Thigh
musculature

Posterior crural
musculature

Fibula

Ankle joint

Metatarsal

Anterior
crural
muscle

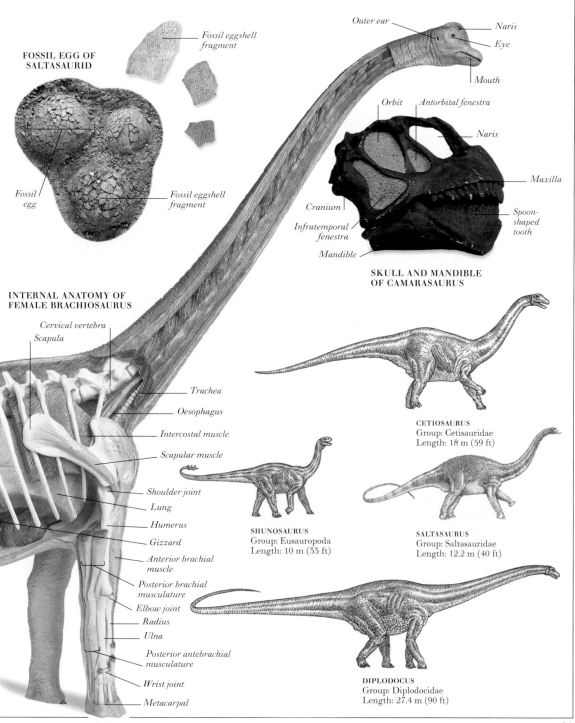

FOSSIL EGG OF SALTASAURID

Fossil eggshell fragment

Fossil egg

Fossil eggshell fragment

Outer ear

Naris

Eye

Mouth

Orbit

Antorbital fenestra

Naris

Maxilla

Cranium

Infratemporal fenestra

Mandible

Spoon-shaped tooth

SKULL AND MANDIBLE OF CAMARASAURUS

INTERNAL ANATOMY OF FEMALE BRACHIOSAURUS

Cervical vertebra

Scapula

Trachea

Oesophagus

Intercostal muscle

Scapular muscle

Shoulder joint

Lung

Humerus

Gizzard

Anterior brachial muscle

Posterior brachial musculature

Elbow joint

Radius

Ulna

Posterior antebrachial musculature

Wrist joint

Metacarpal

CETIOSAURUS
Group: Cetisauridae
Length: 18 m (59 ft)

SHUNOSAURUS
Group: Eusauropoda
Length: 10 m (33 ft)

SALTASAURUS
Group: Saltasauridae
Length: 12.2 m (40 ft)

DIPLODOCUS
Group: Diplodocidae
Length: 27.4 m (90 ft)

Thyreophorans 1

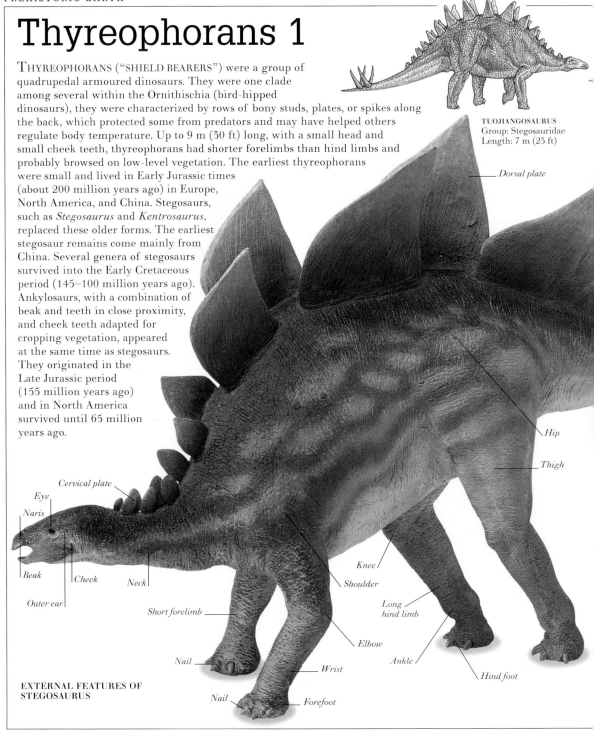

THYREOPHORANS ("SHIELD BEARERS") were a group of
quadrupedal armoured dinosaurs. They were one clade
among several within the Ornithischia (bird-hipped
dinosaurs), they were characterized by rows of bony studs, plates, or spikes along
the back, which protected some from predators and may have helped others
regulate body temperature. Up to 9 m (30 ft) long, with a small head and
small cheek teeth, thyreophorans had shorter forelimbs than hind limbs and
probably browsed on low-level vegetation. The earliest thyreophorans
were small and lived in Early Jurassic times
(about 200 million years ago) in Europe,
North America, and China. Stegosaurs,
such as *Stegosaurus* and *Kentrosaurus*,
replaced these older forms. The earliest
stegosaur remains come mainly from
China. Several genera of stegosaurs
survived into the Early Cretaceous
period (145–100 million years ago).
Ankylosaurs, with a combination of
beak and teeth in close proximity,
and cheek teeth adapted for
cropping vegetation, appeared
at the same time as stegosaurs.
They originated in the
Late Jurassic period
(155 million years ago)
and in North America
survived until 65 million
years ago.

TUOJIANGOSAURUS
Group: Stegosauridae
Length: 7 m (23 ft)

Dorsal plate

Hip

Thigh

Cervical plate

Eye

Naris

Knee

Shoulder

Beak

Cheek

Neck

Long
hind limb

Outer ear

Short forelimb

Elbow

Ankle

Nail

Wrist

Hind foot

**EXTERNAL FEATURES OF
STEGOSAURUS**

Nail

Forefoot

EXAMPLES OF STEGOSAURS

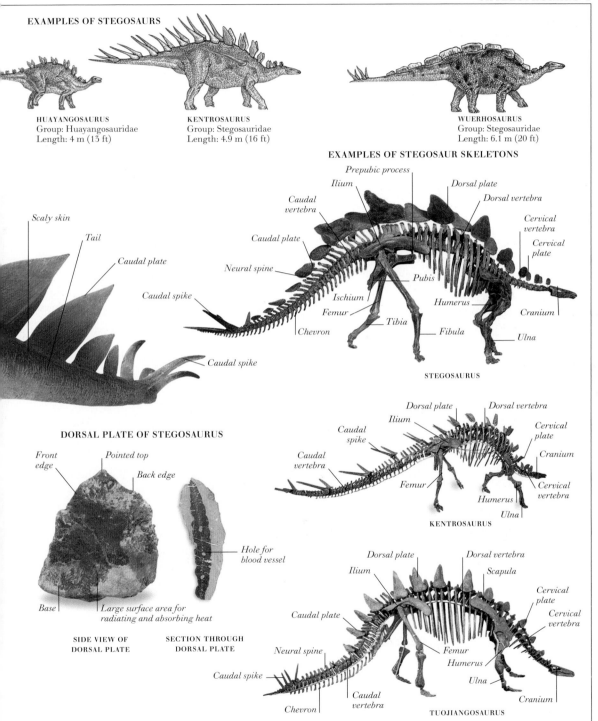

HUAYANGOSAURUS
Group: Huayangosauridae
Length: 4 m (13 ft)

KENTROSAURUS
Group: Stegosauridae
Length: 4.9 m (16 ft)

WUERHOSAURUS
Group: Stegosauridae
Length: 6.1 m (20 ft)

EXAMPLES OF STEGOSAUR SKELETONS

Scaly skin

Tail

Caudal plate

Caudal spike

Caudal spike

Prepubic process

Ilium

Caudal vertebra

Caudal plate

Neural spine

Ischium

Femur

Tibia

Chevron

Dorsal plate

Dorsal vertebra

Cervical vertebra

Cervical plate

Pubis

Humerus

Fibula

Cranium

Ulna

STEGOSAURUS

DORSAL PLATE OF STEGOSAURUS

Front edge

Pointed top

Back edge

Hole for blood vessel

Base

Large surface area for radiating and absorbing heat

SIDE VIEW OF DORSAL PLATE

SECTION THROUGH DORSAL PLATE

Dorsal plate

Ilium

Caudal spike

Caudal vertebra

Dorsal vertebra

Cervical plate

Cranium

Femur

Humerus

Cervical vertebra

Ulna

KENTROSAURUS

Dorsal plate

Ilium

Caudal plate

Neural spine

Caudal spike

Chevron

Caudal vertebra

Dorsal vertebra

Scapula

Cervical plate

Cervical vertebra

Femur

Humerus

Ulna

Cranium

TUOJIANGOSAURUS

Thyreophorans 2

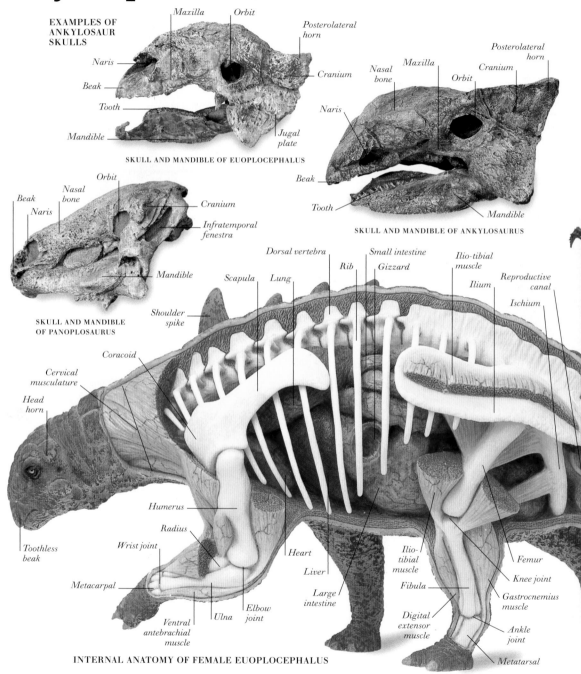

**EXAMPLES OF
ANKYLOSAUR
SKULLS**

Maxilla

Orbit

Posterolateral
horn

Naris

Cranium

Beak

Tooth

Mandible

Jugal
plate

SKULL AND MANDIBLE OF EUOPLOCEPHALUS

Nasal
bone

Maxilla

Cranium

Orbit

Posterolateral
horn

Naris

Beak

Tooth

Mandible

SKULL AND MANDIBLE OF ANKYLOSAURUS

Orbit

Nasal
bone

Cranium

Beak

Naris

Infratemporal
fenestra

Mandible

**SKULL AND MANDIBLE
OF PANOPLOSAURUS**

Dorsal vertebra

Small intestine

Rib

Gizzard

Ilio-tibial
muscle

Ilium

Reproductive
canal

Ischium

Scapula

Lung

Shoulder
spike

Coracoid

Cervical
musculature

Head
horn

Humerus

Radius

Heart

Ilio-
tibial
muscle

Femur

Knee joint

Toothless
beak

Wrist joint

Liver

Fibula

Gastrocnemius
muscle

Metacarpal

Large
intestine

Digital
extensor
muscle

Ankle
joint

Ulna

Elbow
joint

Ventral
antebrachial
muscle

Metatarsal

INTERNAL ANATOMY OF FEMALE EUOPLOCEPHALUS

EXTERNAL FEATURES OF EDMONTONIA

EXAMPLES OF ANKYLOSAURS

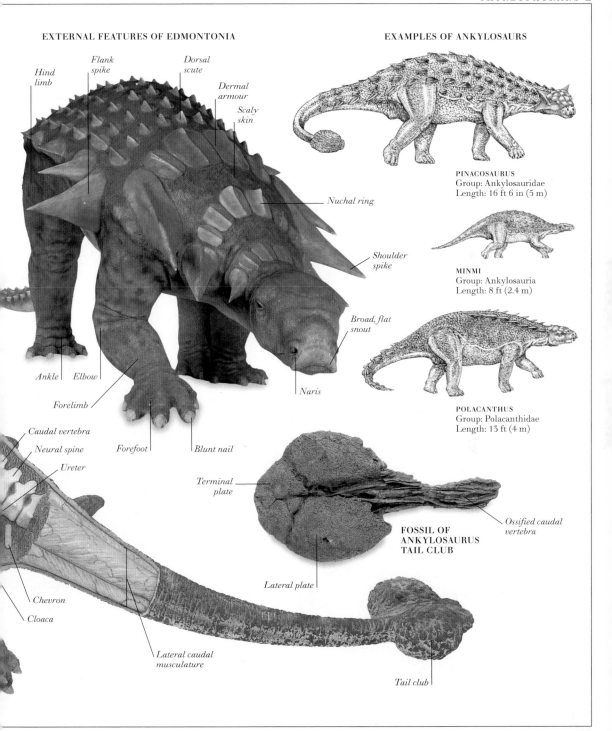

Hind limb

Flank spike

Dorsal scute

Dermal armour

Scaly skin

Nuchal ring

Shoulder spike

Broad, flat snout

Ankle

Elbow

Forelimb

Forefoot

Blunt nail

Naris

Caudal vertebra

Neural spine

Ureter

Chevron

Cloaca

Lateral caudal musculature

Terminal plate

Lateral plate

Ossified caudal vertebra

FOSSIL OF ANKYLOSAURUS TAIL CLUB

Tail club

PINACOSAURUS
Group: Ankylosauridae
Length: 16 ft 6 in (5 m)

MINMI
Group: Ankylosauria
Length: 8 ft (2.4 m)

POLACANTHUS
Group: Polacanthidae
Length: 13 ft (4 m)

Ornithopods 1

ORNITHOPODS ("BIRD FEET") were a group of ornithischian ("bird-hipped") dinosaurs. These bipedal and quadrupedal herbivores had a horny beak, plant-cutting or grinding cheek teeth, and a pelvic and tail region stiffened by bony tendons. They evolved teeth and jaws adapted to pulping vegetation and flourished

IGUANODON TOOTH

from the Middle Jurassic to the Late Cretaceous period (165–65 million years ago) in North America, Europe, Africa, China, Australia, and Antarctica. Some ornithopods were no larger than a dog, while others were immense creatures up to 15 m (49 ft) long. Iguanodonts, an ornithopod group, had a broad, toothless beak at the end of a long snout, large jaws with long rows of ridged, closely packed teeth for grinding vegetation, a bulky body, and a heavy tail. *Iguanodon* and some other iguanodonts had large thumb-spikes that were strong enough to stab attackers. Another group, the hadrosaurs, such as *Gryposaurus* and *Hadrosaurus*, lived in Late Cretaceous times (97–65 million years ago) and with their broad beaks are sometimes known as "duckbills". They were characterized by their deep skulls and closely packed rows of teeth, while some, such as *Corythosaurus* and *Lambeosaurus*, had tall, hollow, bony head crests.

SKELETON OF IGUANODON

Orbit

Cranium

Naris

Mandible

Cervical rib

Cervical vertebra

Scapula

Humerus

Sternal bone

Radius

Ulna

Prepubic process

Femur

Pubis

Tibia

Fibula

Metatarsal

Dorsal vertebra

Sacral vertebra

Caudal vertebra

Neural spine

Ilium

Ischium

Chevron

EXTERNAL FEATURES OF MANTELLISAURUS

Thigh

Heavy, stiff tail

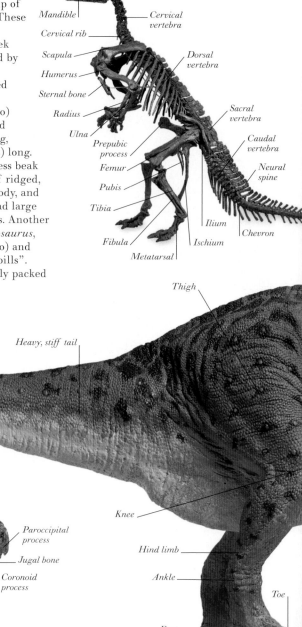

Knee

Hind limb

Ankle

Toe

Foot

Hoof-like nail

SKULL AND MANDIBLE OF YOUNG MANTELLISAURUS

Maxilla

Cheek tooth

Orbit

Cranium

Premaxilla

Paroccipital process

Jugal bone

Coronoid process

Predentary bone

Dentary bone

Mandible

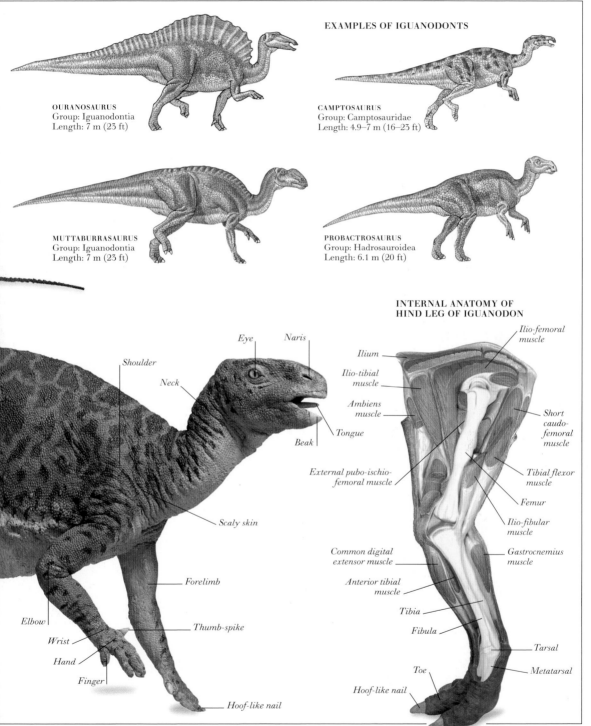

EXAMPLES OF IGUANODONTS

OURANOSAURUS
Group: Iguanodontia
Length: 7 m (23 ft)

CAMPTOSAURUS
Group: Camptosauridae
Length: 4.9–7 m (16–23 ft)

MUTTABURRASAURUS
Group: Iguanodontia
Length: 7 m (23 ft)

PROBACTROSAURUS
Group: Hadrosauroidea
Length: 6.1 m (20 ft)

**INTERNAL ANATOMY OF
HIND LEG OF IGUANODON**

Eye

Naris

Shoulder

Neck

Tongue

Beak

Scaly skin

Forelimb

Elbow

Wrist

Hand

Finger

Thumb-spike

Hoof-like nail

Ilio-femoral muscle

Ilium

Ilio-tibial muscle

Ambiens muscle

Short caudo-femoral muscle

External pubo-ischio-femoral muscle

Tibial flexor muscle

Femur

Ilio-fibular muscle

Common digital extensor muscle

Gastrocnemius muscle

Anterior tibial muscle

Tibia

Fibula

Tarsal

Metatarsal

Toe

Hoof-like nail

Ornithopods 2

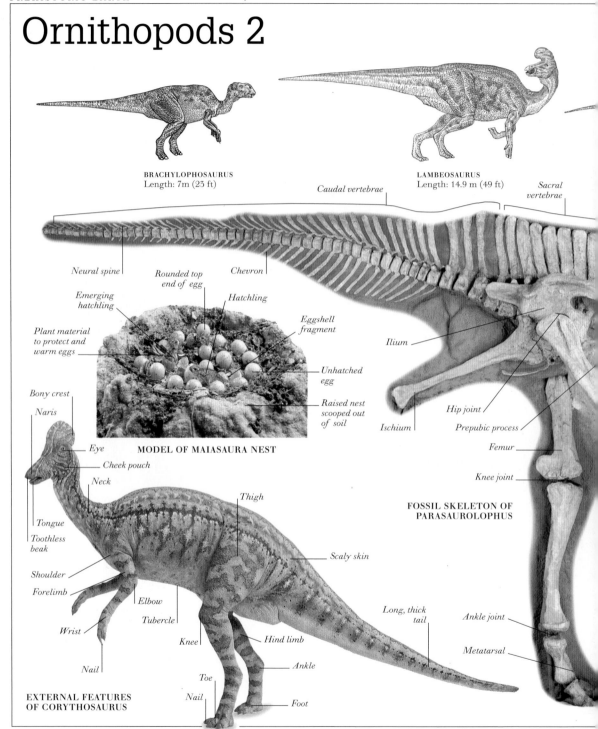

BRACHYLOPHOSAURUS
Length: 7m (23 ft)

LAMBEOSAURUS
Length: 14.9 m (49 ft)

Caudal vertebrae

Sacral vertebrae

Neural spine

Rounded top end of egg

Chevron

Emerging hatchling

Hatchling

Plant material to protect and warm eggs

Eggshell fragment

Ilium

Unhatched egg

Raised nest scooped out of soil

Hip joint

Ischium

Prepubic process

MODEL OF MAIASAURA NEST

Bony crest

Naris

Femur

Eye

Knee joint

Cheek pouch

Neck

Thigh

**FOSSIL SKELETON OF
PARASAUROLOPHUS**

Tongue

Toothless beak

Scaly skin

Shoulder

Forelimb

Elbow

Tubercle

Wrist

Long, thick tail

Ankle joint

Knee

Hind limb

Metatarsal

Nail

Ankle

Toe

**EXTERNAL FEATURES
OF CORYTHOSAURUS**

Nail

Foot

EXAMPLES OF HADROSAURS

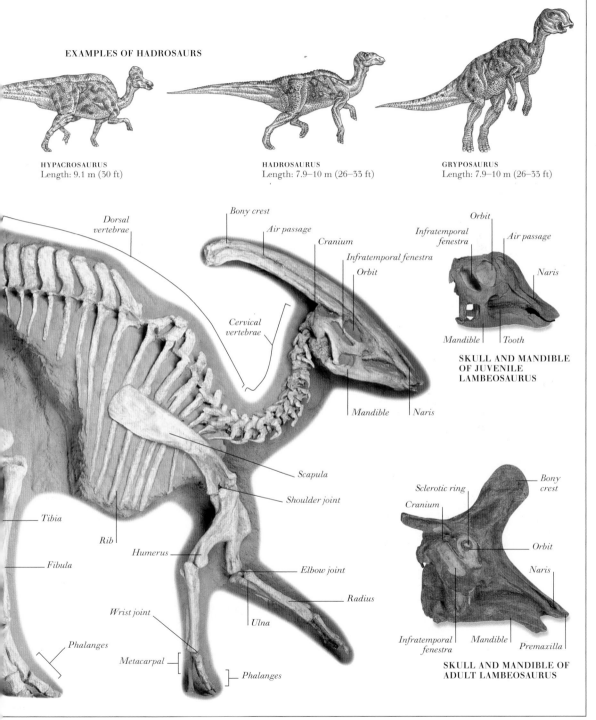

HYPACROSAURUS
Length: 9.1 m (30 ft)

HADROSAURUS
Length: 7.9–10 m (26–33 ft)

GRYPOSAURUS
Length: 7.9–10 m (26–33 ft)

Dorsal
vertebrae

Bony crest

Air passage

Cranium

Infratemporal fenestra

Orbit

Cervical
vertebrae

Mandible

Naris

Scapula

Shoulder joint

Tibia

Rib

Humerus

Elbow joint

Radius

Fibula

Wrist joint

Ulna

Phalanges

Metacarpal

Phalanges

Orbit

Infratemporal
fenestra

Air passage

Naris

Mandible   Tooth

**SKULL AND MANDIBLE
OF JUVENILE
LAMBEOSAURUS**

Sclerotic ring

Bony
crest

Cranium

Orbit

Naris

Infratemporal
fenestra

Mandible

Premaxilla

**SKULL AND MANDIBLE OF
ADULT LAMBEOSAURUS**

Marginocephalians 1

HEAD-BUTTING PRENOCEPHALES

MARGINOCEPHALIA ("margined heads") were a group of bipedal and quadrupedal ornithischian dinosaurs with a narrow shelf or deep, bony frill at the back of the skull. Marginocephalians were probably descended from the same ancestor as the ornithopods and lived in what are now North America, Africa, Asia, and Europe during the Cretaceous period (145–65 million years ago). They were divided into two groups: Pachycephalosauria ("thickheaded lizards"), such as *Pachycephalosaurus* and *Stegoceras*, and Ceratopsia ("horned faces"), such as *Triceratops* and *Psittacosaurus*. The thick skulls of Pachycephalosauria may have protected their brains during possible head-butting contests fought to win territory and mates; their hips and spines may also have been strengthened to withstand the shock. The bony frill of Ceratopsia would have added to their frightening appearance when charging; the neck was strengthened for impact and to support the huge head, with its snipping beak and powerful slicing toothed jaws. A charging ceratopsian would have been a formidable opponent for even the largest predators. Ceratopsians were among the most abundant herbivorous dinosaurs of the Late Cretaceous period (97–65 million years ago).

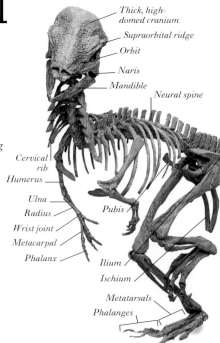

Thick, high-domed cranium
Supraorbital ridge
Orbit
Naris
Mandible
Neural spine
Cervical rib
Humerus
Ulna
Radius
Wrist joint
Metacarpal
Phalanx
Pubis
Ilium
Ischium
Metatarsals
Phalanges

EXAMPLES OF SKULLS OF PACHYCEPHALOSAURS

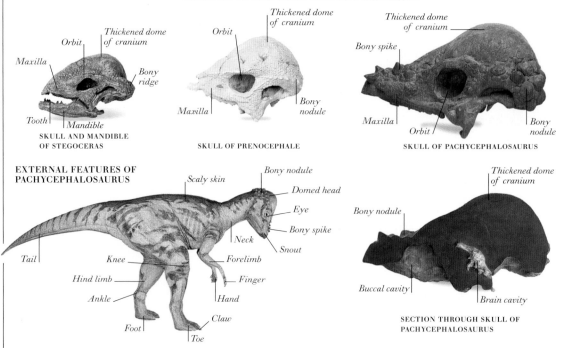

Orbit
Thickened dome of cranium
Maxilla
Bony ridge
Tooth
Mandible

SKULL AND MANDIBLE OF STEGOCERAS

Thickened dome of cranium
Orbit
Maxilla
Bony nodule

SKULL OF PRENOCEPHALE

Thickened dome of cranium
Bony spike
Maxilla
Orbit
Bony nodule

SKULL OF PACHYCEPHALOSAURUS

EXTERNAL FEATURES OF PACHYCEPHALOSAURUS

Scaly skin
Bony nodule
Domed head
Eye
Bony spike
Neck
Snout
Tail
Knee
Forelimb
Finger
Hind limb
Hand
Ankle
Claw
Foot
Toe

Thickened dome of cranium
Bony nodule
Buccal cavity
Brain cavity

SECTION THROUGH SKULL OF PACHYCEPHALOSAURUS

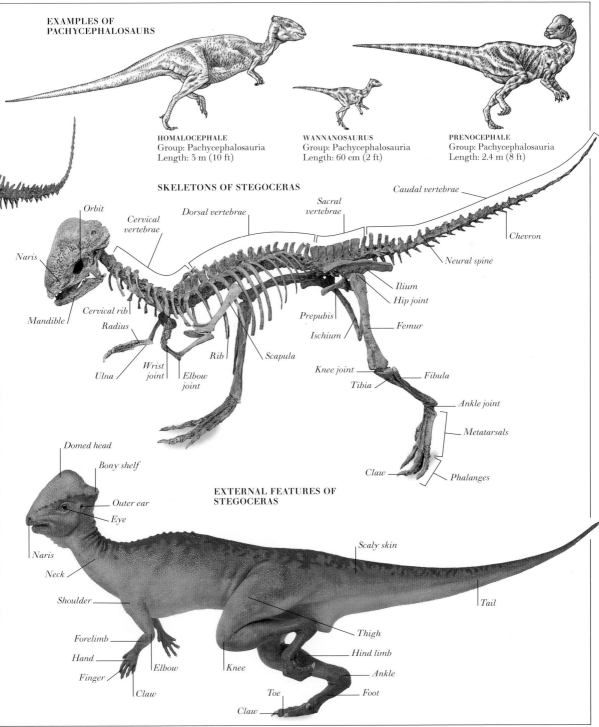

EXAMPLES OF PACHYCEPHALOSAURS

HOMALOCEPHALE
Group: Pachycephalosauria
Length: 3 m (10 ft)

WANNANOSAURUS
Group: Pachycephalosauria
Length: 60 cm (2 ft)

PRENOCEPHALE
Group: Pachycephalosauria
Length: 2.4 m (8 ft)

SKELETONS OF STEGOCERAS

Orbit

Cervical vertebrae

Dorsal vertebrae

Sacral vertebrae

Caudal vertebrae

Naris

Chevron

Neural spine

Mandible

Cervical rib

Ilium

Hip joint

Radius

Prepubis

Femur

Ischium

Ulna

Wrist joint

Elbow joint

Rib

Scapula

Knee joint

Fibula

Tibia

Ankle joint

Metatarsals

Claw

Phalanges

EXTERNAL FEATURES OF STEGOCERAS

Domed head

Bony shelf

Outer ear

Eye

Scaly skin

Naris

Neck

Tail

Shoulder

Forelimb

Thigh

Hand

Hind limb

Finger

Elbow

Knee

Ankle

Claw

Foot

Toe

Claw

101

Marginocephalians 2

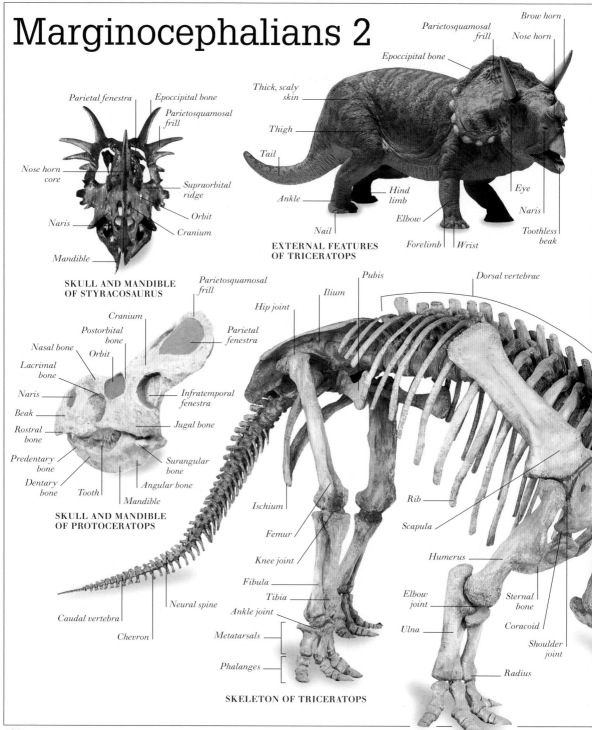

Brow horn

Parietosquamosal frill

Nose horn

Epoccipital bone

Thick, scaly skin

Thigh

Tail

Ankle

Hind limb

Elbow

Nail

Forelimb | **Wrist**

Eye

Naris

Toothless beak

EXTERNAL FEATURES OF TRICERATOPS

Parietal fenestra

Epoccipital bone

Parietosquamosal frill

Nose horn core

Supraorbital ridge

Orbit

Naris

Cranium

Mandible

SKULL AND MANDIBLE OF STYRACOSAURUS

Parietosquamosal frill

Cranium

Postorbital bone

Nasal bone

Orbit

Lacrimal bone

Naris

Beak

Rostral bone

Predentary bone

Dentary bone

Tooth

Mandible

Parietal fenestra

Infratemporal fenestra

Jugal bone

Surangular bone

Angular bone

SKULL AND MANDIBLE OF PROTOCERATOPS

Pubis

Ilium

Hip joint

Dorsal vertebrae

Ischium

Femur

Knee joint

Fibula

Tibia

Ankle joint

Metatarsals

Phalanges

Caudal vertebra

Chevron

Neural spine

Rib

Scapula

Humerus

Elbow joint

Sternal bone

Ulna

Coracoid

Shoulder joint

Radius

SKELETON OF TRICERATOPS

**EXTERNAL FEATURES
OF PSITTACOSAURUS**

Eye

Cheek horn

Beak

Claw

Finger

Scaly skin

Thigh

Forelimb

Elbow

Knee

Claw

Toe

Ankle

Hind limb

Parietosquamosal
frill

Tail

Cranium

Orbit

Brow horn
core

Nose horn
core

Cervical
rib

Naris

Infratemporal
fenestra

Jugal bone

Tooth

Metacarpals

Mandible

Phalanges

Predentary
bone

Rostral bone

EXAMPLES OF CERATOPSIA

PROTOCERATOPS
Group: Protoceratopsidae
Length: 2.7 m (9 ft)

STYRACOSAURUS
Group: Centrosaurinae
Length: 5.5 m (18 ft)

TRICERATOPS
Group: Chasmosaurinae
Length: 9.1 m (30 ft)

PACHYRHINOSAURUS
Group: Centrosaurinae
Length: 5.5 m (18 ft)

LEPTOCERATOPS
Group: Leptoceratopsidae
Length: 2.1 m (7 ft)

Mammals 1

TETRALOPHODON CHEEK TEETH

SINCE THE EXTINCTION of most of the dinosaurs 65 million years ago, mammals (along with birds) have been the dominant vertebrates on land. This class includes terrestrial, aerial, and aquatic forms. Having developed from the therapsids, the first true mammals – small, nocturnal, shrew-like creatures, such as *Megazostrodon*-appeared over 200 million years ago during the Triassic period (250–200 million years ago). Mammals had several features that differed from those of their ancestors: an efficient four-chambered heart allowed these warm-blooded animals to sustain high levels of activity; a covering of hair helped them maintain a constant body temperature; an improved limb structure gave them more efficient locomotion; and the birth of live young and the immediate supply of food from the mother's milk aided their rapid growth. Since the end of the Mesozoic era (65 million years ago), the number of major mammal groups and the abundance of species in each have varied dramatically. For example, the Perissodactyla (the group that includes *Coelodonta* and modern horses) was a common group during the Early Tertiary period (about 54 million years ago). Today, the mammalian groups with the most species include the Rodentia (rats and mice), the Chiroptera (bats), the Primates (monkeys and apes), the Carnivora (bears, cats, and dogs), and the Artiodactyla (cattle, deer, and pigs), while the Proboscidea group, which formerly included many genera, such as *Phiomia*, *Moeritherium*, *Tetralophodon*, and *Mammuthus*, now has only three species of elephant. In Australia and South America, millions of years of continental isolation led to increased diversity of the marsupials, a group of mammals distinct from the placentals (see p. 74) that existed elsewhere.

Long tail aids balance

Insulating hair

Neural spine

Scapula

Cervical vertebra

Humerus

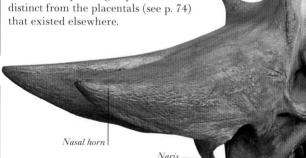

Nasal horn

Naris

Orbit

Premaxilla bone

Mandible

Radius

Ulna

Chisel-edged molar

Metacarpal

Phalanx

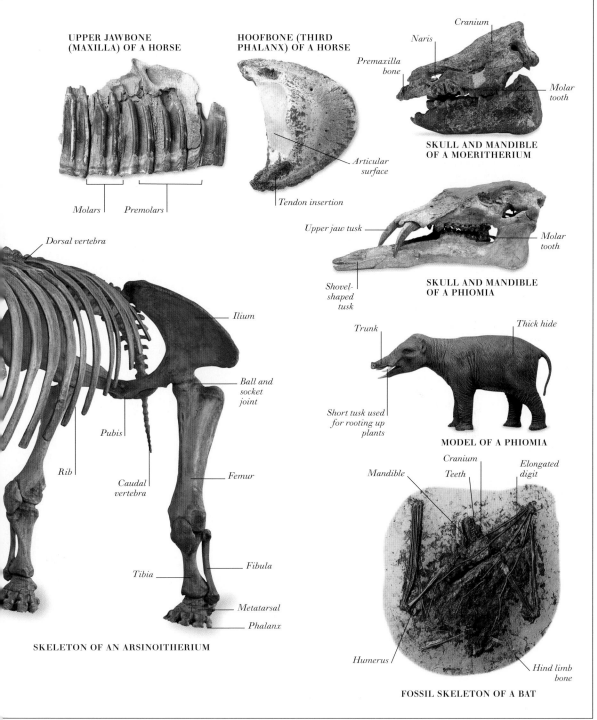

UPPER JAWBONE (MAXILLA) OF A HORSE

Molars

Premolars

HOOFBONE (THIRD PHALANX) OF A HORSE

Articular surface

Tendon insertion

Cranium

Naris

Premaxilla bone

Molar tooth

SKULL AND MANDIBLE OF A MOERITHERIUM

Upper jaw tusk

Molar tooth

Shovel-shaped tusk

SKULL AND MANDIBLE OF A PHIOMIA

Trunk

Thick hide

Short tusk used for rooting up plants

MODEL OF A PHIOMIA

Dorsal vertebra

Ilium

Ball and socket joint

Pubis

Rib

Caudal vertebra

Femur

Tibia

Fibula

Metatarsal

Phalanx

SKELETON OF AN ARSINOITHERIUM

Mandible

Cranium

Teeth

Elongated digit

Humerus

Hind limb bone

FOSSIL SKELETON OF A BAT

105

Mammals 2

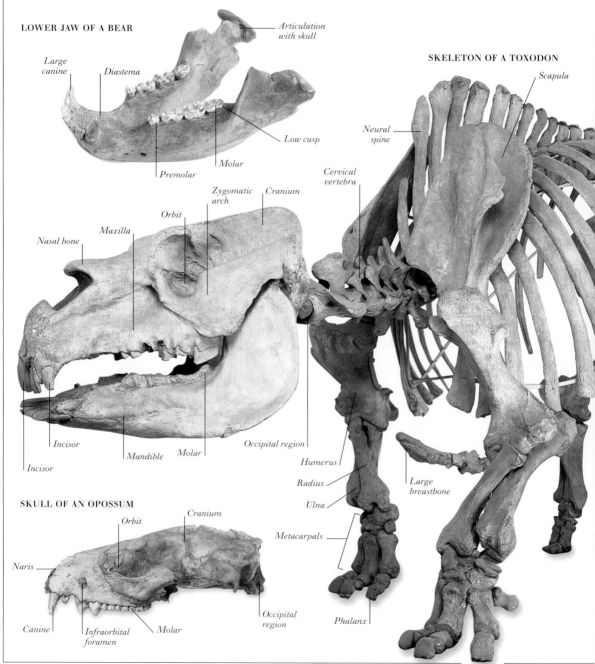

LOWER JAW OF A BEAR

Articulation with skull

Large canine

Diastema

Premolar

Molar

Low cusp

Nasal bone

Maxilla

Orbit

Zygomatic arch

Cranium

Incisor

Incisor

Mandible

Molar

Occipital region

SKULL OF AN OPOSSUM

Orbit

Cranium

Naris

Canine

Infraorbital foramen

Molar

Occipital region

SKELETON OF A TOXODON

Scapula

Neural spine

Cervical vertebra

Humerus

Radius

Ulna

Metacarpals

Phalanx

Large breastbone

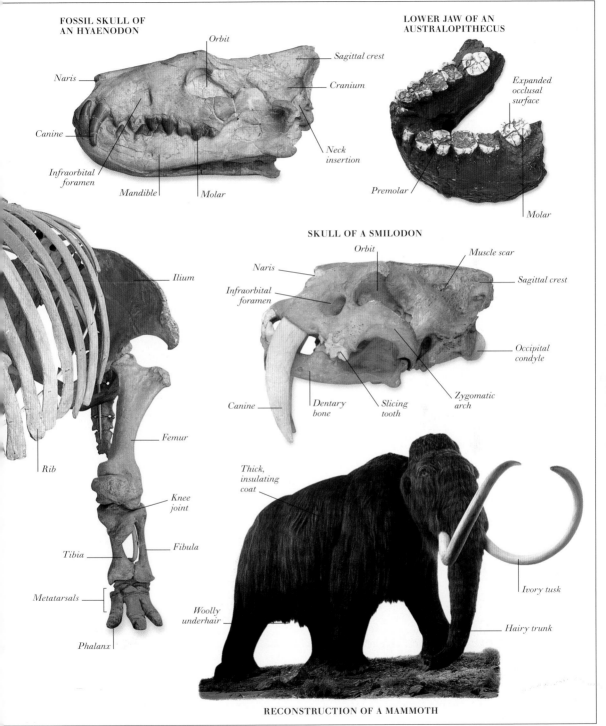

FOSSIL SKULL OF AN HYAENODON

Orbit

Sagittal crest

Naris

Cranium

Canine

Neck insertion

Infraorbital foramen

Mandible

Molar

LOWER JAW OF AN AUSTRALOPITHECUS

Expanded occlusal surface

Premolar

Molar

SKULL OF A SMILODON

Orbit

Muscle scar

Naris

Sagittal crest

Infraorbital foramen

Occipital condyle

Canine

Dentary bone

Slicing tooth

Zygomatic arch

Ilium

Femur

Rib

Knee joint

Thick, insulating coat

Tibia

Fibula

Metatarsals

Ivory tusk

Woolly underhair

Hairy trunk

Phalanx

RECONSTRUCTION OF A MAMMOTH

The first humans

MODERN HUMANS BELONG TO THE MAMMALIAN order of primates
(see pp. 202–203), which originated about 55 million years ago;
primates included the only extant hominid species. The earliest
members of the human clade include *Ardipithecus* ("ground ape")
and *Australopithecus* ("southern ape"), both small-brained intermediates
between apes and humans that were capable of standing and walking
upright. *Homo habilis*, the earliest member of the genus Homo, appeared
at least 2 million years ago. This larger-brained "handy man" began making
tools for hunting. *Homo ergaster* first appeared in Africa about 1.8 million
years ago and spread into Asia about 800,000 years later. Smaller-toothed than
Homo habilis, H. ergaster – followed by Homo erectus – developed fire as a tool,
which enabled it to cook food. Neanderthals, a near relative of modern humans,
originated about 200,000 years ago, and *Homo sapiens* (modern humans) appeared
in Africa about 100,000 years later. The two co-existed for thousands of years, but by
30,000 years ago, *Homo sapiens* had become dominant and the Neanderthals had died
out. Classification of *Homo sapiens* in relation to its ancestors is enormously problematic:
modern humans must be classified not only by bone structure, but also by specific
behaviour – the ability to plan future action; to follow traditions; and to use
symbolic communication, including complex language and the ability to use
and recognize symbols.

**JAWBONE OF AUSTRALOPITHECUS
(SOUTHERN APE)**

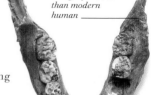

*Larger jawbone
than modern
human*

*Large back
tooth*

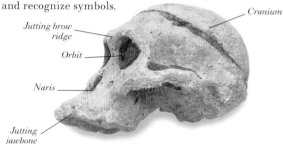

Cranium

*Jutting brow
ridge*

Orbit

Naris

*Jutting
jawbone*

**SKULL OF AUSTRALOPITHECUS
(SOUTHERN APE)**

Orbit

Naris

**SKULL OF HOMO HABILIS
(FIRST MEMBER OF HOMO GENUS)**

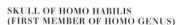

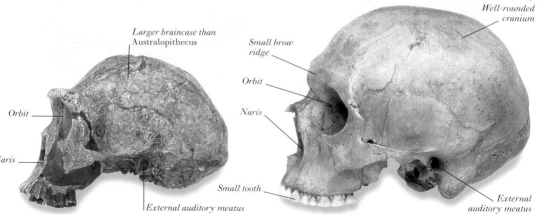

*Larger braincase than
Australopithecus*

*Small brow
ridge*

*Well-rounded
cranium*

Orbit

Orbit

Naris

Naris

Small tooth

External auditory meatus

*External
auditory meatus*

SKULL OF HOMO ERECTUS (UPRIGHT MAN)

SKULL OF HOMO SAPIENS (MODERN HUMAN)

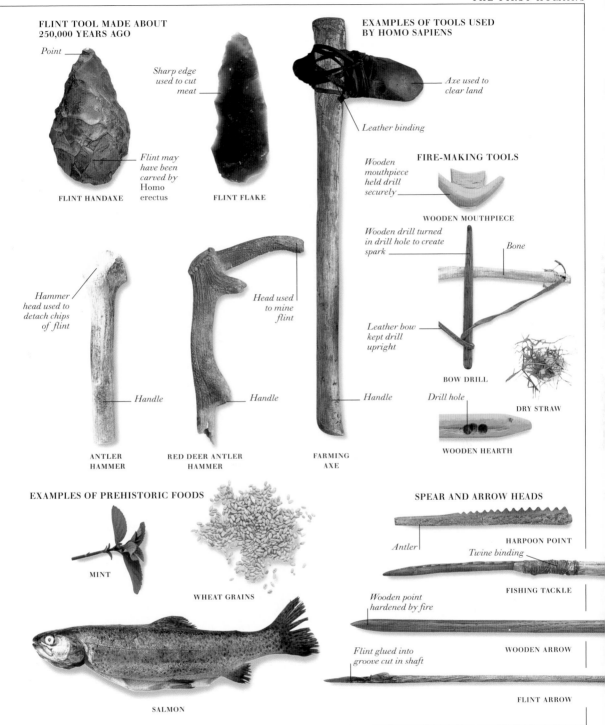

**FLINT TOOL MADE ABOUT
250,000 YEARS AGO**

Point

*Sharp edge
used to cut
meat*

*Flint may
have been
carved by
Homo
erectus*

FLINT HANDAXE

FLINT FLAKE

**EXAMPLES OF TOOLS USED
BY HOMO SAPIENS**

*Axe used to
clear land*

Leather binding

FIRE-MAKING TOOLS

*Wooden
mouthpiece
held drill
securely*

WOODEN MOUTHPIECE

*Wooden drill turned
in drill hole to create
spark*

Bone

*Hammer
head used to
detach chips
of flint*

*Head used
to mine
flint*

*Leather bow
kept drill
upright*

Handle

Handle

Handle

Drill hole

BOW DRILL

DRY STRAW

WOODEN HEARTH

**ANTLER
HAMMER**

**RED DEER ANTLER
HAMMER**

**FARMING
AXE**

EXAMPLES OF PREHISTORIC FOODS

MINT

WHEAT GRAINS

SALMON

SPEAR AND ARROW HEADS

Antler

HARPOON POINT

Twine binding

FISHING TACKLE

*Wooden point
hardened by fire*

WOODEN ARROW

*Flint glued into
groove cut in shaft*

FLINT ARROW

109

PLANTS

Plant variety

Leaf

THERE ARE MORE THAN 300,000 SPECIES of plants.
They show a wide diversity of forms and life-styles, ranging, for example,
from delicate liverworts, adapted for life in a damp habitat, to cacti, capable of surviving
in the desert, and from herbaceous plants, such as corn, which completes its life-cycle in one year,
to the giant redwood tree, which can live for thousands of years. This diversity reflects the adaptations
of plants to survive in a wide range of habitats. This is seen most clearly in the flowering plants (phylum
Angiospermophyta), which are the most numerous, with over 250,000 species, and the most widespread,
being found from the tropics to the poles. Despite their diversity, plants share certain characteristics: typically,
plants are green, and make their food by photosynthesis; and most plants live in or on a substrate, such as
soil, and do not actively move. Algae (kingdom Protista) and fungi (kingdom Fungi) have
some plant-like characteristics and are often studied alongside plants, although they
are not true plants.

GREEN ALGA
Micrograph of desmid
(*Micrasterias sp.*)

FERN
Tree fern
(*Dicksonia antarctica*)

*Pyrenoid
(small protein
body)*

Chloroplast

*Sinus
(division between
two halves of cell)*

Cell wall

*Rachis
(main axis
of pinnate leaf)*

BRYOPHYTE
Moss
(*Bryum sp.*)

*Seta
(stalk)*

Immature capsule

*Petiole
(leaf stalk)*

*Sporophyte
(spore-
producing
plant)*

*Ramentum
(brown scale)*

*Capsule
(site of spore
production)*

*Base of dead
frond (leaf)*

Trunk

"Leaf"

*Adventitious
root*

*Gametophyte
(gamete-producing
plant)*

*Epiphytic
fern growing
at base*

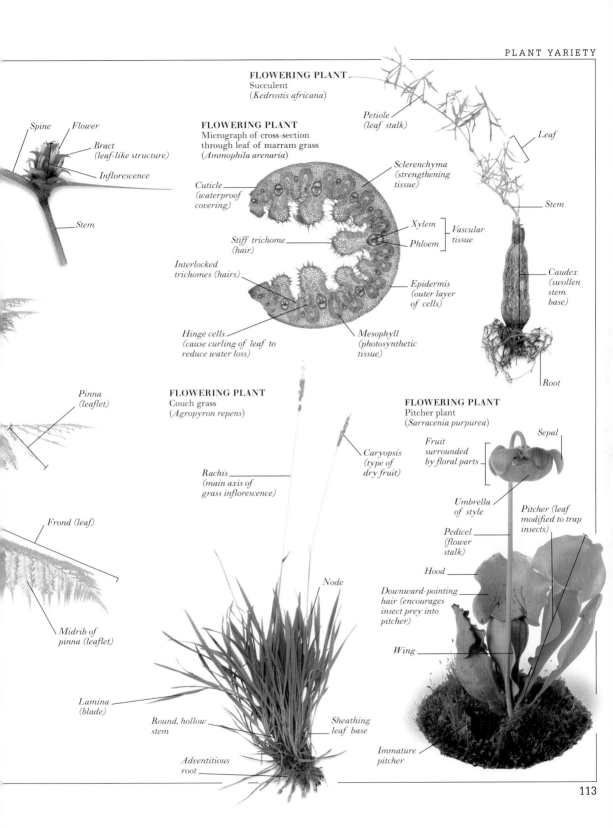

FLOWERING PLANT
Succulent
(*Kedrostis africana*)

Spine

Flower

Bract
(leaf-like structure)

Inflorescence

Stem

Petiole
(leaf stalk)

Leaf

FLOWERING PLANT
Micrograph of cross-section
through leaf of marram grass
(*Ammophila arenaria*)

Cuticle
(waterproof
covering)

Sclerenchyma
(strengthening
tissue)

Stiff trichome
(hair)

Xylem

Phloem

Vascular
tissue

Interlocked
trichomes (hairs)

Epidermis
(outer layer
of cells)

Hinge cells
(cause curling of leaf to
reduce water loss)

Mesophyll
(photosynthetic
tissue)

Stem

Caudex
(swollen
stem
base)

Root

Pinna
(leaflet)

Frond (leaf)

Midrib of
pinna (leaflet)

Lamina
(blade)

FLOWERING PLANT
Couch grass
(*Agropyron repens*)

Rachis
(main axis of
grass inflorescence)

Caryopsis
(type of
dry fruit)

Node

Round, hollow
stem

Adventitious
root

Sheathing
leaf base

FLOWERING PLANT
Pitcher plant
(*Sarracenia purpurea*)

Fruit
surrounded
by floral parts

Sepal

Umbrella
of style

Pedicel
(flower
stalk)

Hood

Pitcher (leaf
modified to trap
insects)

Downward-pointing
hair (encourages
insect prey into
pitcher)

Wing

Immature
pitcher

113

Fungi and lichens

FUNGI WERE ONCE THOUGHT OF AS PLANTS but are now classified as a separate kingdom. This kingdom includes not only the familiar mushrooms, puffballs, stinkhorns, and moulds, but also yeasts, smuts, rusts, and lichens. Most fungi are multicellular, consisting of a mass of thread-like hyphae that together form a mycelium. However, the simpler fungi (e.g., yeasts) are microscopic, single-celled organisms. Typically, fungi reproduce by means of spores. Most fungi feed on dead or decaying matter, or on living organisms. A few fungi obtain their food from plants or algae, with which they have a symbiotic (mutually advantageous) relationship. Lichens are a symbiotic partnership between algae and fungi. Of the six types of lichens the three most common are crustose (flat and crusty), foliose (leafy), and fruticose (shrub-like). Some lichens (e.g., *Cladonia floerkeana*) are a combination of types. Lichens reproduce by means of spores or soredia (powdery vegetative fragments).

EXAMPLES OF FUNGI

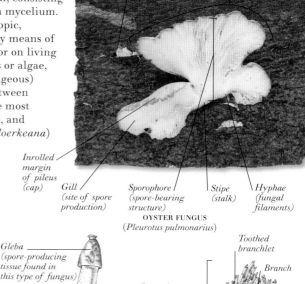

Emerging sporophore (spore-bearing structure)

Pileus (cap) continuous with stipe (stalk)

Bark of dead beech tree

Inrolled margin of pileus (cap)

Gill (site of spore production)

Sporophore (spore-bearing structure)

Stipe (stalk)

Hyphae (fungal filaments)

OYSTER FUNGUS
(*Pleurotus pulmonarius*)

EXAMPLES OF LICHENS

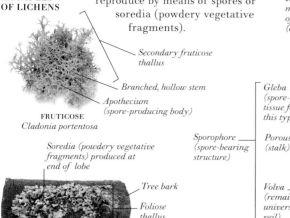

Secondary fruticose thallus

Branched, hollow stem

Apothecium (spore-producing body)

FRUTICOSE
Cladonia portentosa

Soredia (powdery vegetative fragments) produced at end of lobe

Tree bark

Foliose thallus

FOLIOSE
Hypogymnia physodes

Soredia (powdery vegetative fragments) released onto surface of squamulose thallus

Apothecium (spore-producing body)

Basal scale of primary squamulose thallus

Moss

Podetium (granular stalk) of secondary fruticose thallus

SQUAMULOSE (SCALY) AND FRUTICOSE THALLUS
Cladonia floerkeana

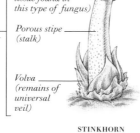

Gleba (spore-producing tissue found in this type of fungus)

Sporophore (spore-bearing structure)

Porous stipe (stalk)

Volva (remains of universal veil)

STINKHORN
(*Phallus impudicus*)

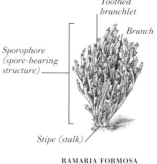

Toothed branchlet

Branch

Sporophore (spore-bearing structure)

Stipe (stalk)

RAMARIA FORMOSA

SECTION THROUGH FOLIOSE LICHEN SHOWING REPRODUCTION BY SOREDIA

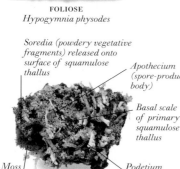

Algal cell

Fungal hypha

Soredium (powdery vegetative fragment involved in propagation) released from lichen

Upper cortex

Algal layer

Medulla of fungal hyphae (mycelium)

Lower cortex

Rhizine (bundle of absorptive hyphae)

Soralium (pore in upper surface of thallus)

Upper surface of thallus

114

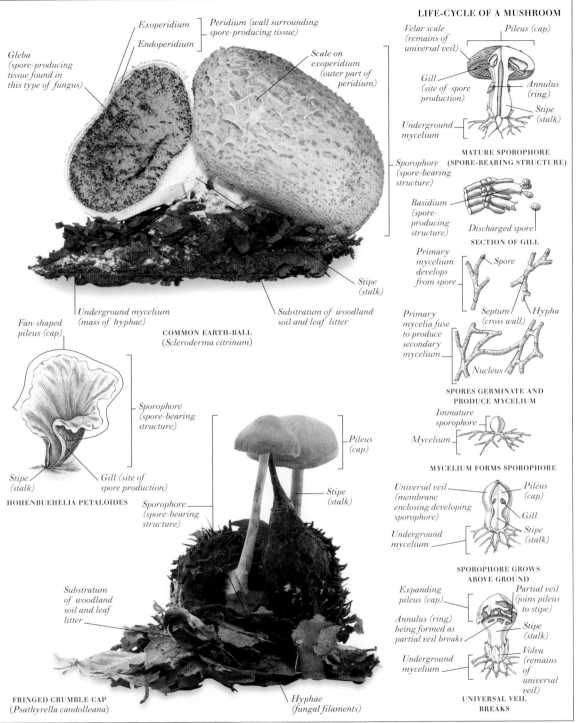

LIFE-CYCLE OF A MUSHROOM

Velar scale
(remains of
universal veil)

Pileus (cap)

Gill
(site of spore
production)

Annulus
(ring)

Stipe
(stalk)

Underground
mycelium

MATURE SPOROPHORE
(SPORE-BEARING STRUCTURE)

Basidium
(spore-
producing
structure)

Discharged spore

SECTION OF GILL

Primary
mycelium
develops
from spore

Spore

Septum
(cross wall)

Hypha

Primary
mycelia fuse
to produce
secondary
mycelium

Nucleus

SPORES GERMINATE AND
PRODUCE MYCELIUM

Immature
sporophore

Mycelium

MYCELIUM FORMS SPOROPHORE

Universal veil
(membrane
enclosing developing
sporophore)

Pileus
(cap)

Gill

Underground
mycelium

Stipe
(stalk)

SPOROPHORE GROWS
ABOVE GROUND

Expanding
pileus (cap)

Partial veil
(joins pileus
to stipe)

Annulus (ring)
being formed as
partial veil breaks

Stipe
(stalk)

Underground
mycelium

Volva
(remains of
universal
veil)

UNIVERSAL VEIL
BREAKS

Exoperidium

Endoperidium

Peridium (wall surrounding
spore-producing tissue)

Scale on
exoperidium
(outer part of
peridium)

Gleba
(spore-producing
tissue found in
this type of fungus)

Sporophore
(spore-bearing
structure)

Stipe
(stalk)

Underground mycelium
(mass of hyphae)

Substratum of woodland
soil and leaf litter

COMMON EARTH-BALL
(Scleroderma citrinum)

Fan-shaped
pileus (cap)

Sporophore
(spore-bearing
structure)

Stipe
(stalk)

Gill (site of
spore production)

HOHENBUEHELIA PETALOIDES

Sporophore
(spore-bearing
structure)

Pileus
(cap)

Stipe
(stalk)

Substratum
of woodland
soil and leaf
litter

Hyphae
(fungal filaments)

FRINGED CRUMBLE CAP
(Psathyrella candolleana)

Algae and seaweeds

ALGAE ARE NOT TRUE PLANTS. They form a diverse group of plant-like organisms that belong to the kingdom Protista. Like plants, algae possess the green pigment chlorophyll and make their own food by photosynthesis (see pp. 138-139). Many algae also possess other pigments by which they can be classified; for example, the brown pigment fucoxanthin is found in the brown algae. Some of the ten phyla of algae are exclusively unicellular (single-celled); others also contain aggregates of cells in filaments or colonies. Three phyla – the Chlorophyta (green algae), Rhodophyta (red algae), and Phaeophyta (brown algae) – contain larger, multicellular, thalloid (flat), marine organisms commonly known as seaweeds. Most algae can reproduce sexually. For example, in the brown seaweed *Fucus vesiculosus*, gametes (sex cells) are produced in conceptacles (chambers) in the receptacles (fertile tips of fronds); after their release into the sea, antherozoids (male gametes) and oospheres (female gametes) fuse; the resulting zygote settles on a rock and develops into a new seaweed.

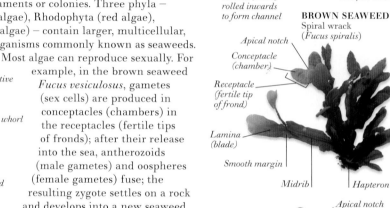

BROWN SEAWEED
Channelled wrack
(*Pelvetia canaliculata*)

Thallus (plant body)

Receptacle (fertile tip of frond)

Apical notch

Hapteron (holdfast)

Margin of lamina (blade) rolled inwards to form channel

BROWN SEAWEED
Spiral wrack
(*Fucus spiralis*)

Apical notch

Conceptacle (chamber)

Receptacle (fertile tip of frond)

Lamina (blade)

Smooth margin

Midrib

Thallus (plant body)

Hapteron (holdfast)

Apical notch

Receptacle (fertile tip of frond)

Conceptacle (chamber) containing reproductive structures

Lamina (blade)

Midrib

RECEPTACLE
Spiral wrack
(*Fucus spiralis*)

EXAMPLES OF ALGAE

Reproductive chamber

Cap

Sterile whorl

Cell wall

Stalk

Rhizoid

GREEN ALGA
Acetabularia sp.

Flagellum

Eyespot

Contractile vacuole

Cytoplasm

Nucleus

Cell wall

Chloroplast

Starch grain

Pyrenoid (small protein body)

GREEN ALGA
Chlamydomonas sp.

Coenobium (colony of cells)

Daughter coenobium

Gelatinous sheath

Biflagellate cell

GREEN ALGA
Volvox sp.

Spine

Cytoplasm

Girdle

Vacuole

Nucleus

Plastid (photosynthetic organelle)

DIATOM
Thalassiosira sp.

BROWN SEAWEED
Oarweed
(*Laminaria digitata*)

Thallus (plant body)

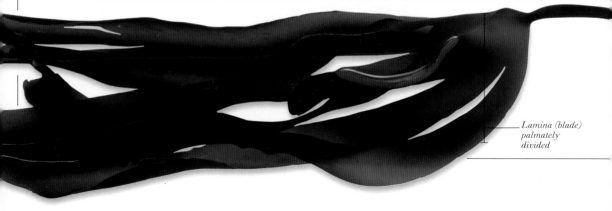

Lamina (blade) palmately divided

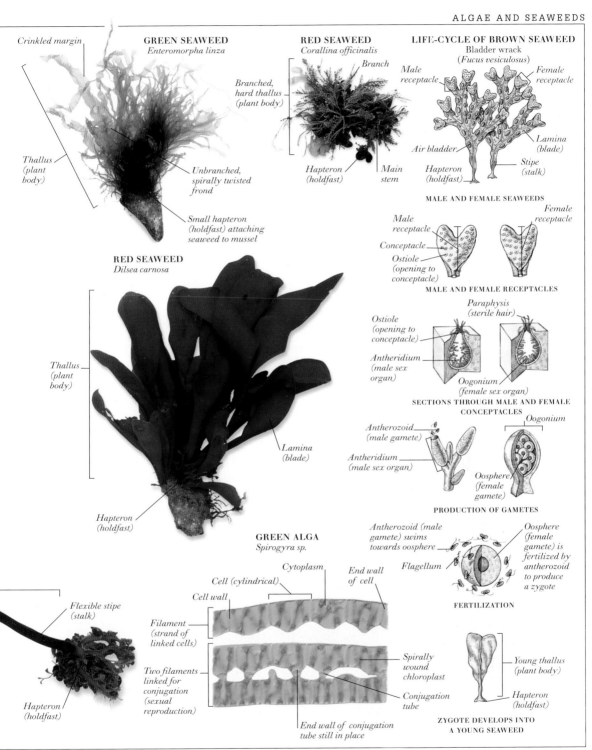

GREEN SEAWEED
Enteromorpha linza

Crinkled margin

Thallus
(plant
body)

Unbranched,
spirally twisted
frond

Small hapteron
(holdfast) attaching
seaweed to mussel

RED SEAWEED
Corallina officinalis

Branch

Branched,
hard thallus
(plant body)

Hapteron
(holdfast)

Main
stem

LIFE-CYCLE OF BROWN SEAWEED
Bladder wrack
(*Fucus vesiculosus*)

Male
receptacle

Female
receptacle

Air bladder

Lamina
(blade)

Hapteron
(holdfast)

Stipe
(stalk)

MALE AND FEMALE SEAWEEDS

Male
receptacle

Female
receptacle

Conceptacle

Ostiole
(opening to
conceptacle)

MALE AND FEMALE RECEPTACLES

Paraphysis
(sterile hair)

Ostiole
(opening to
conceptacle)

Antheridium
(male sex
organ)

Oogonium
(female sex organ)

**SECTIONS THROUGH MALE AND FEMALE
CONCEPTACLES**

Antherozoid
(male gamete)

Oogonium

Antheridium
(male sex organ)

Oosphere
(female
gamete)

PRODUCTION OF GAMETES

RED SEAWEED
Dilsea carnosa

Thallus
(plant
body)

Lamina
(blade)

Hapteron
(holdfast)

Antherozoid (male
gamete) swims
towards oosphere

Flagellum

Oosphere
(female
gamete) is
fertilized by
antherozoid
to produce
a zygote

FERTILIZATION

GREEN ALGA
Spirogyra sp.

Cytoplasm

Cell (cylindrical)

Cell wall

End wall
of cell

Filament
(strand of
linked cells)

Spirally
wound
chloroplast

Two filaments
linked for
conjugation
(sexual
reproduction)

Conjugation
tube

End wall of conjugation
tube still in place

Young thallus
(plant body)

Hapteron
(holdfast)

**ZYGOTE DEVELOPS INTO
A YOUNG SEAWEED**

Flexible stipe
(stalk)

Hapteron
(holdfast)

117

Liverworts and mosses

LIVERWORTS AND MOSSES ARE SMALL, LOW-GROWING PLANTS that belong to the phylum Bryophyta. Bryophytes do not have true stems, leaves, or roots (they are anchored to the ground by rhizoids), nor do they have the vascular tissues (xylem and phloem) that transport water and nutrients in higher plants. With no outer, waterproof cuticle, bryophytes are susceptible to drying out, and most grow in moist habitats. The bryophyte life-cycle has two stages. In stage one, the green plant (gametophyte) produces male and female gametes (sex cells), which fuse to form a zygote. In stage two, the zygote develops into a sporophyte that remains attached to the gametophyte. The sporophyte produces spores, which are released and germinate into new green plants. Liverworts (class Hepaticae) grow horizontally and may be thalloid (flat and ribbon-like) or "leafy". Mosses (class Musci) typically have an upright "stem" with spirally arranged "leaves".

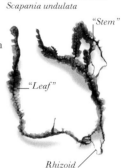

A LEAFY LIVERWORT
Scapania undulata

"Stem"

"Leaf"

Rhizoid

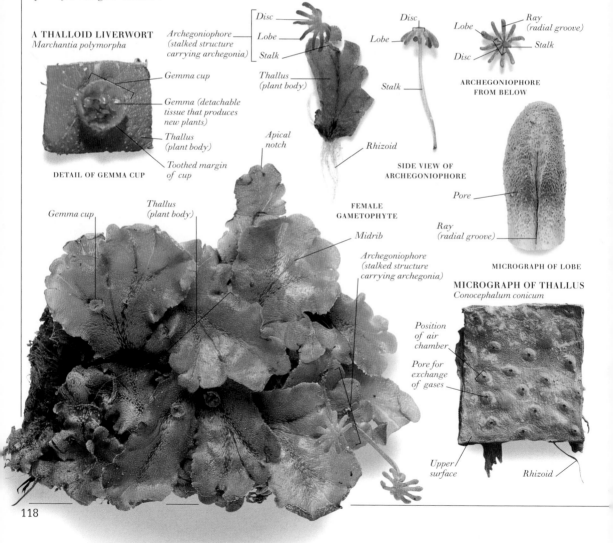

A THALLOID LIVERWORT
Marchantia polymorpha

Gemma cup

Gemma (detachable tissue that produces new plants)

Thallus (plant body)

Toothed margin of cup

DETAIL OF GEMMA CUP

Archegoniophore (stalked structure carrying archegonia)

Disc

Lobe

Stalk

Thallus (plant body)

Apical notch

Rhizoid

Disc

Lobe

Stalk

FEMALE GAMETOPHYTE

Lobe

Disc

Ray (radial groove)

Stalk

ARCHEGONIOPHORE FROM BELOW

SIDE VIEW OF ARCHEGONIOPHORE

Pore

Ray (radial groove)

MICROGRAPH OF LOBE

Gemma cup

Thallus (plant body)

Midrib

Archegoniophore (stalked structure carrying archegonia)

MICROGRAPH OF THALLUS
Conocephalum conicum

Position of air chamber

Pore for exchange of gases

Upper surface

Rhizoid

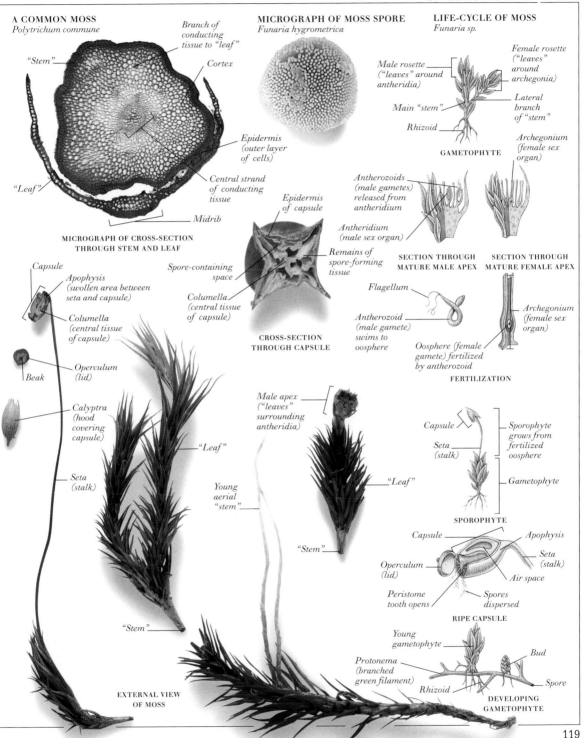

A COMMON MOSS
Polytrichum commune

"Stem"

Branch of conducting tissue to "leaf"

Cortex

Epidermis (outer layer of cells)

Central strand of conducting tissue

"Leaf"

Midrib

MICROGRAPH OF CROSS-SECTION THROUGH STEM AND LEAF

MICROGRAPH OF MOSS SPORE
Funaria hygrometrica

LIFE-CYCLE OF MOSS
Funaria sp.

Male rosette ("leaves" around antheridia)

Female rosette ("leaves" around archegonia)

Main "stem"

Lateral branch of "stem"

Rhizoid

GAMETOPHYTE

Archegonium (female sex organ)

Antherozoids (male gametes) released from antheridium

Antheridium (male sex organ)

SECTION THROUGH MATURE MALE APEX

Archegonium (female sex organ)

SECTION THROUGH MATURE FEMALE APEX

Epidermis of capsule

Spore-containing space

Remains of spore-forming tissue

Columella (central tissue of capsule)

CROSS-SECTION THROUGH CAPSULE

Flagellum

Antherozoid (male gamete) swims to oosphere

Oosphere (female gamete) fertilized by antherozoid

FERTILIZATION

Capsule

Apophysis (swollen area between seta and capsule)

Columella (central tissue of capsule)

Operculum (lid)

Beak

Calyptra (hood covering capsule)

Seta (stalk)

"Leaf"

Young aerial "stem"

Male apex ("leaves" surrounding antheridia)

"Leaf"

"Stem"

"Stem"

EXTERNAL VIEW OF MOSS

Capsule

Seta (stalk)

Sporophyte grows from fertilized oosphere

Gametophyte

SPOROPHYTE

Capsule

Operculum (lid)

Peristome tooth opens

Apophysis

Seta (stalk)

Air space

Spores dispersed

RIPE CAPSULE

Young gametophyte

Protonema (branched green filament)

Rhizoid

Bud

Spore

DEVELOPING GAMETOPHYTE

119

Horsetails, clubmosses, and ferns

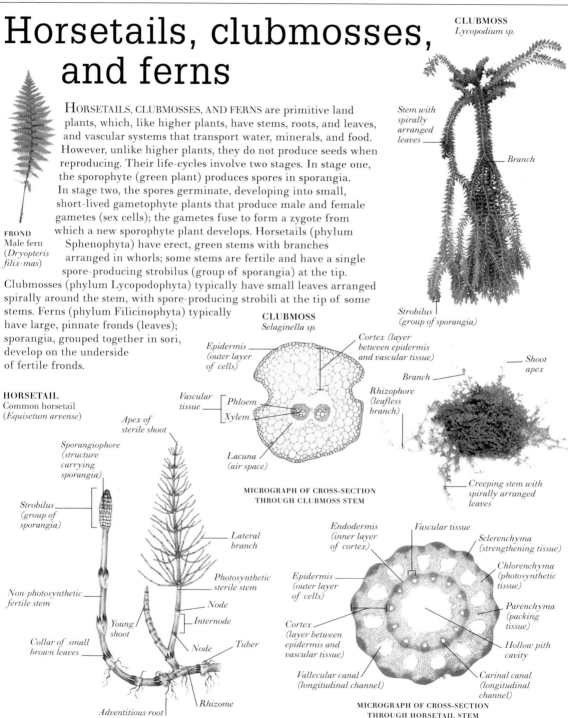

HORSETAILS, CLUBMOSSES, AND FERNS are primitive land plants, which, like higher plants, have stems, roots, and leaves, and vascular systems that transport water, minerals, and food. However, unlike higher plants, they do not produce seeds when reproducing. Their life-cycles involve two stages. In stage one, the sporophyte (green plant) produces spores in sporangia. In stage two, the spores germinate, developing into small, short-lived gametophyte plants that produce male and female gametes (sex cells); the gametes fuse to form a zygote from which a new sporophyte plant develops. Horsetails (phylum Sphenophyta) have erect, green stems with branches arranged in whorls; some stems are fertile and have a single spore-producing strobilus (group of sporangia) at the tip. Clubmosses (phylum Lycopodophyta) typically have small leaves arranged spirally around the stem, with spore-producing strobili at the tip of some stems. Ferns (phylum Filicinophyta) typically have large, pinnate fronds (leaves); sporangia, grouped together in sori, develop on the underside of fertile fronds.

FROND
Male fern
(*Dryopteris filix-mas*)

CLUBMOSS
Lycopodium sp.

Stem with spirally arranged leaves

Branch

Strobilus (group of sporangia)

CLUBMOSS
Selaginella sp.

Epidermis (outer layer of cells)

Cortex (layer between epidermis and vascular tissue)

Vascular tissue
Phloem
Xylem

Lacuna (air space)

MICROGRAPH OF CROSS-SECTION THROUGH CLUBMOSS STEM

Branch

Rhizophore (leafless branch)

Shoot apex

Creeping stem with spirally arranged leaves

HORSETAIL
Common horsetail
(*Equisetum arvense*)

Apex of sterile shoot

Sporangiophore (structure carrying sporangia)

Strobilus (group of sporangia)

Lateral branch

Photosynthetic sterile stem

Node

Internode

Non-photosynthetic fertile stem

Young shoot

Node

Tuber

Collar of small brown leaves

Rhizome

Adventitious root

Endodermis (inner layer of cortex)

Vascular tissue

Sclerenchyma (strengthening tissue)

Chlorenchyma (photosynthetic tissue)

Epidermis (outer layer of cells)

Parenchyma (packing tissue)

Cortex (layer between epidermis and vascular tissue)

Hollow pith cavity

Vallecular canal (longitudinal channel)

Carinal canal (longitudinal channel)

MICROGRAPH OF CROSS-SECTION THROUGH HORSETAIL STEM

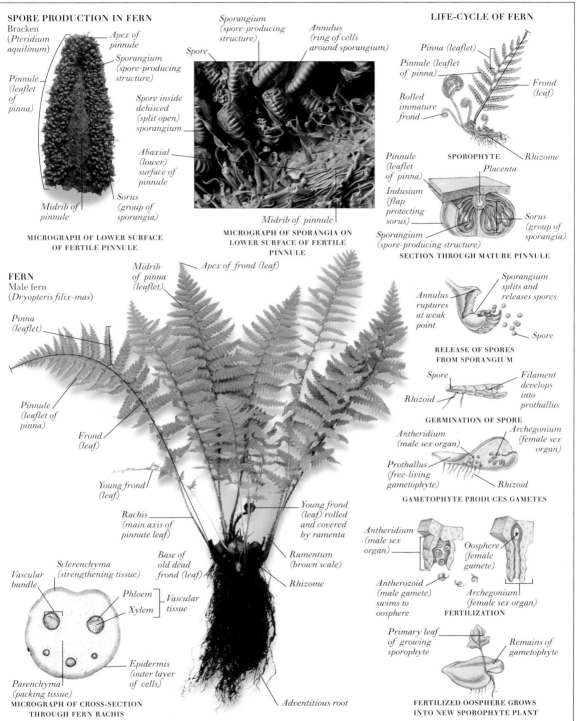

SPORE PRODUCTION IN FERN
Bracken
(*Pteridium aquilinum*)

Apex of pinnule

Sporangium (spore-producing structure)

Pinnule (leaflet of pinna)

Spore inside dehisced (split open) sporangium

Abaxial (lower) surface of pinnule

Midrib of pinnule

Sorus (group of sporangia)

MICROGRAPH OF LOWER SURFACE OF FERTILE PINNULE

Sporangium (spore-producing structure)

Spore

Annulus (ring of cells around sporangium)

Midrib of pinnule

MICROGRAPH OF SPORANGIA ON LOWER SURFACE OF FERTILE PINNULE

LIFE-CYCLE OF FERN

Pinna (leaflet)

Pinnule (leaflet of pinna)

Frond (leaf)

Rolled immature frond

SPOROPHYTE

Rhizome

Pinnule (leaflet of pinna)

Placenta

Indusium (flap protecting sorus)

Sporangium (spore-producing structure)

Sorus (group of sporangia)

SECTION THROUGH MATURE PINNULE

FERN
Male fern
(*Dryopteris filix-mas*)

Midrib of pinna (leaflet)

Apex of frond (leaf)

Pinna (leaflet)

Pinnule (leaflet of pinna)

Frond (leaf)

Young frond (leaf)

Rachis (main axis of pinnate leaf)

Base of old dead frond (leaf)

Young frond (leaf) rolled and covered by ramenta

Ramentum (brown scale)

Rhizome

Vascular bundle

Sclerenchyma (strengthening tissue)

Phloem

Xylem

Vascular tissue

Epidermis (outer layer of cells)

Parenchyma (packing tissue)

MICROGRAPH OF CROSS-SECTION THROUGH FERN RACHIS

Adventitious root

Sporangium splits and releases spores

Annulus ruptures at weak point

Spore

RELEASE OF SPORES FROM SPORANGIUM

Spore

Filament develops into prothallus

Rhizoid

GERMINATION OF SPORE

Antheridium (male sex organ)

Archegonium (female sex organ)

Prothallus (free-living gametophyte)

Rhizoid

GAMETOPHYTE PRODUCES GAMETES

Antheridium (male sex organ)

Oosphere (female gamete)

Antherozoid (male gamete) swims to oosphere

Archegonium (female sex organ)

FERTILIZATION

Primary leaf of growing sporophyte

Remains of gametophyte

FERTILIZED OOSPHERE GROWS INTO NEW SPOROPHYTE PLANT

121

Gymnosperms 1

THE GYMNOSPERMS ARE FOUR RELATED PHYLA of seed-producing
plants; their seeds, however, lack the protective, outer covering
which surrounds the seeds of flowering plants. Typically,
gymnosperms are woody, perennial shrubs or trees, with stems,
leaves, and roots, and a well-developed vascular (transport) system.
The reproductive structures in most gymnosperms are cones: male
cones produce microspores in which male gametes (sex cells) develop;
female cones produce megaspores in which female gametes develop.
Microspores are blown by the wind to female cones, male and female
gametes fuse during fertilization, and a seed develops. The four
gymnosperm phyla are the conifers (phylum Coniferophyta), mostly
tall trees; cycads (phylum Cycadophyta), small palm-like
trees; the ginkgo or maidenhair tree
(phylum Ginkgophyta), a tall tree with
bilobed leaves; and gnetophytes
(phylum Gnetophyta), a diverse
group of plants, mainly shrubs,
but also including the
horizontally growing
welwitschia.

LIFE-CYCLE OF SCOTS PINE
(*Pinus sylvestris*)

Needle
(*foliage
leaf*)

Cone

Ovuliferous scale
(*ovule- then seed-
bearing structure*)

MALE CONES

YOUNG FEMALE CONE

Pollen grain in micropyle
(entrance to ovule)

Ovuliferous
scale

Pollen
grain

Nucleus

Air sac

Ovule
(contains
female
gamete)

POLLINATION

Integument
(outer part
of ovule)

Pollen tube
(carries male
gamete from
pollen grain
to ovum)

Archegonium
(containing
female
gamete)

FERTILIZATION

Seed

Seed

Wing

**MATURE FEMALE CONE AND
WINGED SEED**

SCALE AND SEEDS
Pine
(*Pinus sp.*)

Ovuliferous scale
(*ovule- then seed-
bearing structure*)

Wing of seed
derived from
ovuliferous scale

Wing
scar

Seed

Seed

Seed scar

Point of attachment
to axis of cone

**OVULIFEROUS SCALE FROM
THIRD-YEAR FEMALE CONE**

Microsporangium
(structure in which
pollen grains are
formed)

Microsporophyll
(modified leaf
carrying
microsporangia)

Ovule
(contains
female
gametes)

Bract
scale

Axis
of cone

Scale leaf

Ovuliferous scale
(ovule- then seed-
bearing structure)

Axis
of cone

Ovuliferous
scale
(ovule- then
seed-bearing
structure)

**MICROGRAPH OF LONGITUDINAL
SECTION THROUGH YOUNG
MALE CONE**

**MICROGRAPH OF LONGITUDINAL
SECTION THROUGH SECOND-YEAR
FEMALE CONE**

Plumule
(embryonic
shoot)

Cotyledon
(seed leaf)

Root

**GERMINATION OF
PINE SEEDLING**

WELWITSCHIA
(*Welwitschia mirabilis*)

Frayed end of leaf

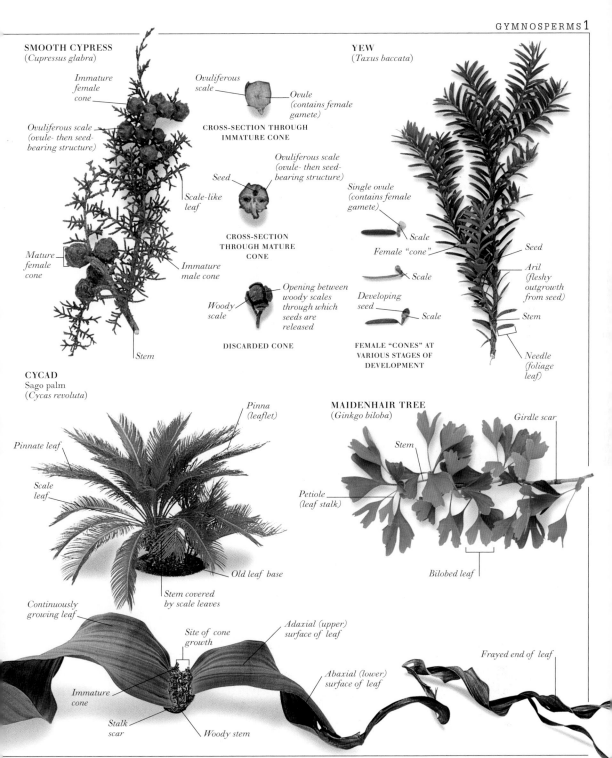

SMOOTH CYPRESS
(*Cupressus glabra*)

Immature female cone

Ovuliferous scale (ovule- then seed-bearing structure)

Mature female cone

Immature male cone

Scale-like leaf

Stem

Ovuliferous scale

Ovule (contains female gamete)

CROSS-SECTION THROUGH IMMATURE CONE

Ovuliferous scale (ovule- then seed-bearing structure)

Seed

CROSS-SECTION THROUGH MATURE CONE

Woody scale

Opening between woody scales through which seeds are released

DISCARDED CONE

YEW
(*Taxus baccata*)

Single ovule (contains female gamete)

Scale

Female "cone"

Scale

Developing seed

Scale

FEMALE "CONES" AT VARIOUS STAGES OF DEVELOPMENT

Seed

Aril (fleshy outgrowth from seed)

Stem

Needle (foliage leaf)

CYCAD
Sago palm
(*Cycas revoluta*)

Pinna (leaflet)

Pinnate leaf

Scale leaf

Old leaf base

Stem covered by scale leaves

MAIDENHAIR TREE
(*Ginkgo biloba*)

Girdle scar

Stem

Petiole (leaf stalk)

Bilobed leaf

Continuously growing leaf

Site of cone growth

Adaxial (upper) surface of leaf

Frayed end of leaf

Abaxial (lower) surface of leaf

Immature cone

Stalk scar

Woody stem

Gymnosperms 2

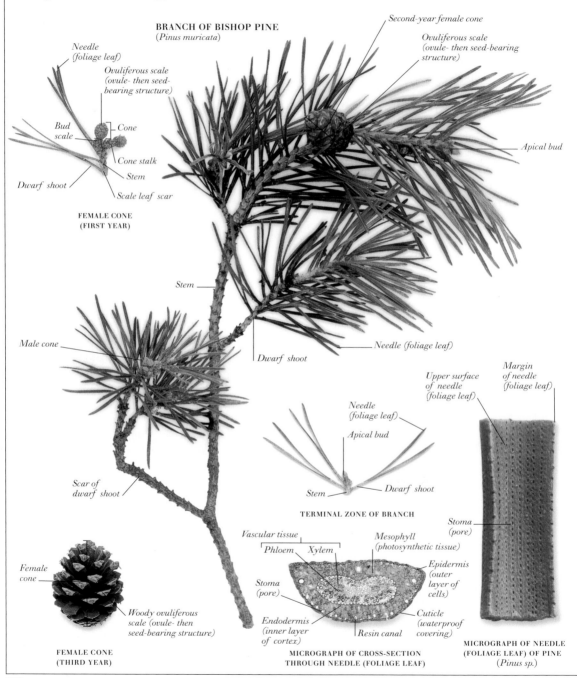

BRANCH OF BISHOP PINE
(Pinus muricata)

Second-year female cone

*Ovuliferous scale
(ovule- then seed-bearing
structure)*

*Needle
(foliage leaf)*

*Ovuliferous scale
(ovule- then seed-
bearing structure)*

*Bud
scale*

Cone

Apical bud

Cone stalk

Stem

Dwarf shoot

Scale leaf scar

**FEMALE CONE
(FIRST YEAR)**

Stem

Needle (foliage leaf)

Male cone

Dwarf shoot

*Margin
of needle
(foliage leaf)*

*Upper surface
of needle
(foliage leaf)*

*Needle
(foliage leaf)*

Apical bud

*Scar of
dwarf shoot*

Stem

Dwarf shoot

TERMINAL ZONE OF BRANCH

*Stoma
(pore)*

Vascular tissue

*Mesophyll
(photosynthetic tissue)*

Phloem *Xylem*

*Female
cone*

*Epidermis
(outer
layer of
cells)*

*Stoma
(pore)*

*Woody ovuliferous
scale (ovule- then
seed-bearing structure)*

*Endodermis
(inner layer
of cortex)*

Resin canal

*Cuticle
(waterproof
covering)*

**MICROGRAPH OF NEEDLE
(FOLIAGE LEAF) OF PINE
*(Pinus sp.)***

**FEMALE CONE
(THIRD YEAR)**

**MICROGRAPH OF CROSS-SECTION
THROUGH NEEDLE (FOLIAGE LEAF)**

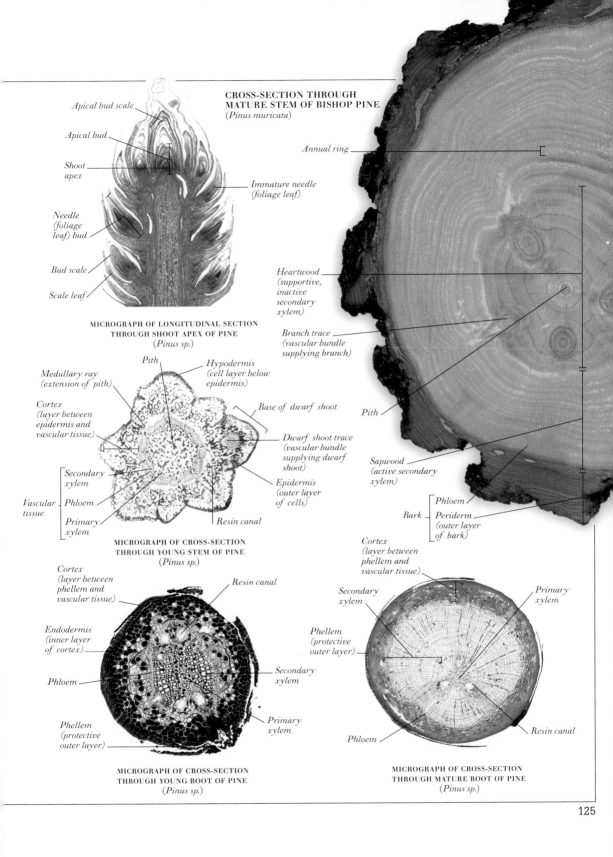

CROSS-SECTION THROUGH MATURE STEM OF BISHOP PINE
(*Pinus muricata*)

Apical bud scale

Apical bud

Shoot apex

Immature needle (foliage leaf)

Needle (foliage leaf) bud

Bud scale

Scale leaf

Annual ring

Heartwood (supportive, inactive secondary xylem)

Branch trace (vascular bundle supplying branch)

Pith

Sapwood (active secondary xylem)

Phloem

Bark — Periderm (outer layer of bark)

MICROGRAPH OF LONGITUDINAL SECTION THROUGH SHOOT APEX OF PINE
(*Pinus sp.*)

Pith

Medullary ray (extension of pith)

Hypodermis (cell layer below epidermis)

Cortex (layer between epidermis and vascular tissue)

Base of dwarf shoot

Secondary xylem

Dwarf shoot trace (vascular bundle supplying dwarf shoot)

Vascular tissue — Phloem

Epidermis (outer layer of cells)

Primary xylem

Resin canal

MICROGRAPH OF CROSS-SECTION THROUGH YOUNG STEM OF PINE
(*Pinus sp.*)

Cortex (layer between phellem and vascular tissue)

Resin canal

Endodermis (inner layer of cortex)

Phloem

Phellem (protective outer layer)

Secondary xylem

Primary xylem

MICROGRAPH OF CROSS-SECTION THROUGH YOUNG ROOT OF PINE
(*Pinus sp.*)

Cortex (layer between phellem and vascular tissue)

Secondary xylem

Primary xylem

Phellem (protective outer layer)

Phloem

Resin canal

MICROGRAPH OF CROSS-SECTION THROUGH MATURE ROOT OF PINE
(*Pinus sp.*)

Monocotyledons and dicotyledons

FLOWERING PLANTS (PHYLUM ANGIOSPERMOPHYTA) are divided into two classes: monocotyledons (class Monocotyledoneae) and dicotyledons (class Dicotyledoneae). Typically, monocotyledons have seeds with one cotyledon (seed leaf); their foliage leaves are narrow with parallel veins; the flower components occur in multiples of three; sepals and petals are indistinguishable and are known as tepals; vascular (transport) tissues are scattered in random bundles throughout the stem; and, since they lack stem cambium (actively dividing cells that produce wood), most monocotyledons are herbaceous (see pp. 128-129). Dicotyledons have seeds with two cotyledons; leaves are broad with a central midrib and branched veins; flower parts occur in multiples of four or five; sepals are generally small and green; petals are large and colourful; vascular bundles are arranged in a ring around the edge of the stem; and, because many dicotyledons possess wood-producing stem cambium, there are woody forms (see pp. 130-131) as well as herbaceous ones.

CROSS-SECTION
THROUGH
MONOCOTYLEDONOUS
LEAF BASES

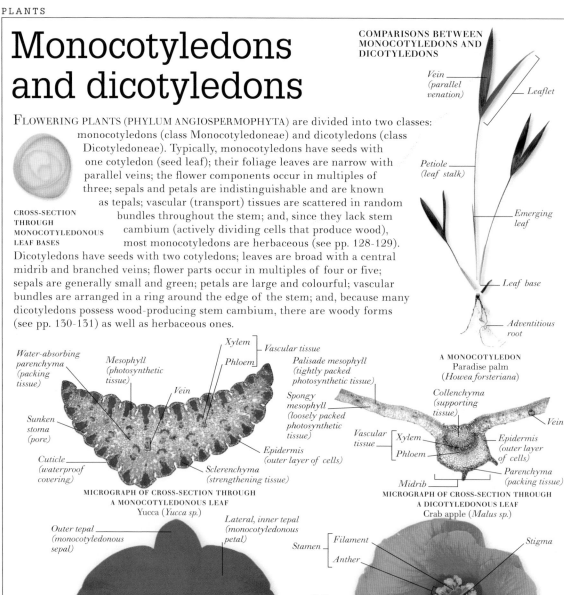

Vein
(parallel
venation)

Leaflet

Petiole
(leaf stalk)

Emerging
leaf

Leaf base

Adventitious
root

A MONOCOTYLEDON
Paradise palm
(*Howea forsteriana*)

Water-absorbing
parenchyma
(packing
tissue)

Mesophyll
(photosynthetic
tissue)

Xylem

Phloem

Vascular tissue

Vein

Sunken
stoma
(pore)

Cuticle
(waterproof
covering)

Epidermis
(outer layer of cells)

Sclerenchyma
(strengthening tissue)

MICROGRAPH OF CROSS-SECTION THROUGH
A MONOCOTYLEDONOUS LEAF
Yucca (*Yucca sp.*)

Palisade mesophyll
(tightly packed
photosynthetic tissue)

Spongy
mesophyll
(loosely packed
photosynthetic
tissue)

Vascular
tissue

Xylem

Phloem

Collenchyma
(supporting
tissue)

Vein

Epidermis
(outer layer
of cells)

Parenchyma
(packing tissue)

Midrib

MICROGRAPH OF CROSS-SECTION THROUGH
A DICOTYLEDONOUS LEAF
Crab apple (*Malus sp.*)

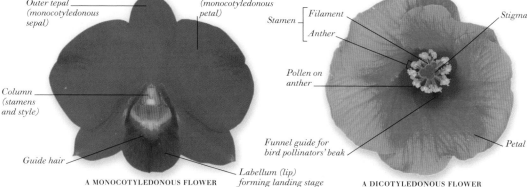

Outer tepal
(monocotyledonous
sepal)

Lateral, inner tepal
(monocotyledonous
petal)

Column
(stamens
and style)

Guide hair

A MONOCOTYLEDONOUS FLOWER
Orchid
(*Phalaenopsis sp.*)

Labellum (lip)
forming landing stage
for pollinator

Stamen

Filament

Anther

Pollen on
anther

Funnel guide for
bird pollinators' beak

Stigma

Petal

A DICOTYLEDONOUS FLOWER
Hibiscus
(*Hibiscus rosa-sinensis*)

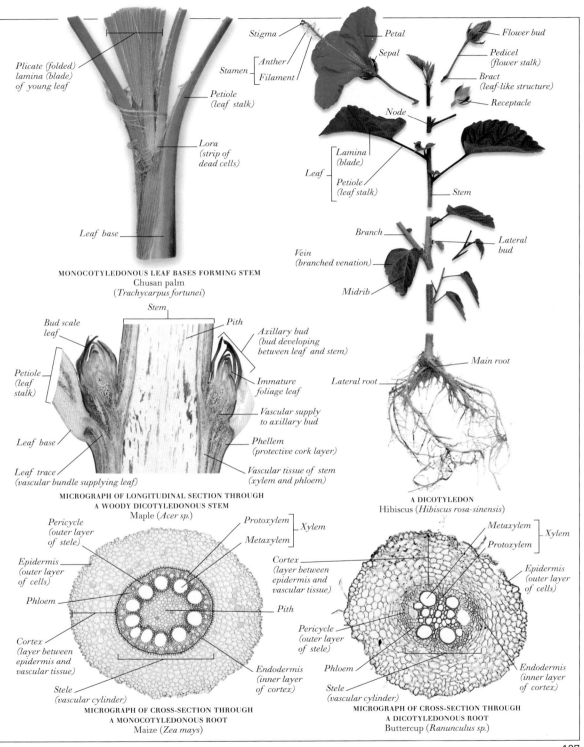

Plicate (folded) lamina (blade) of young leaf

Petiole (leaf stalk)

Lora (strip of dead cells)

Leaf base

MONOCOTYLEDONOUS LEAF BASES FORMING STEM
Chusan palm
(*Trachycarpus fortunei*)

Stigma

Anther

Filament

Stamen

Petal

Sepal

Flower bud

Pedicel (flower stalk)

Bract (leaf-like structure)

Receptacle

Node

Lamina (blade)

Petiole (leaf stalk)

Leaf

Stem

Branch

Lateral bud

Vein (branched venation)

Midrib

Stem

Bud scale leaf

Pith

Petiole (leaf stalk)

Axillary bud (bud developing between leaf and stem)

Immature foliage leaf

Vascular supply to axillary bud

Phellem (protective cork layer)

Leaf base

Leaf trace (vascular bundle supplying leaf)

Vascular tissue of stem (xylem and phloem)

MICROGRAPH OF LONGITUDINAL SECTION THROUGH A WOODY DICOTYLEDONOUS STEM
Maple (*Acer sp.*)

Main root

Lateral root

A DICOTYLEDON
Hibiscus (*Hibiscus rosa-sinensis*)

Pericycle (outer layer of stele)

Protoxylem

Metaxylem

Xylem

Epidermis (outer layer of cells)

Phloem

Cortex (layer between epidermis and vascular tissue)

Stele (vascular cylinder)

Pith

Endodermis (inner layer of cortex)

MICROGRAPH OF CROSS-SECTION THROUGH A MONOCOTYLEDONOUS ROOT
Maize (*Zea mays*)

Cortex (layer between epidermis and vascular tissue)

Metaxylem

Protoxylem

Xylem

Epidermis (outer layer of cells)

Pericycle (outer layer of stele)

Phloem

Stele (vascular cylinder)

Endodermis (inner layer of cortex)

MICROGRAPH OF CROSS-SECTION THROUGH A DICOTYLEDONOUS ROOT
Buttercup (*Ranunculus sp.*)

Herbaceous flowering plants

HERBACEOUS FLOWERING PLANTS TYPICALLY HAVE GREEN, NON-WOODY STEMS, and tend to be relatively short-lived. Many herbaceous plants live for only one or two years. Annuals (e.g., sweet peas) grow from seed, produce flowers and then seeds, and die within a single year. Biennials (e.g., carrots) have a two-year life cycle. In the first year, seeds grow into plants, which produce leaves and store food in underground storage organs; the stems and foliage then die back in winter. In the second year, new stems grow from the storage organs, produce leaves, flowers, and seeds, and then die. Some herbaceous plants (e.g., potatoes) are perennial. They grow back year after year, producing shoots and flowers in spring, storing food in underground tubers or rhizomes during summer, dying back in autumn, and surviving underground during winter.

Young plant forming

Petiole (stalk) of young leaf

Lateral root

Stipule (structure at base of leaf)

Trifoliate leaf

Node

Simple ovate leaflet

Root nodule

Main root

SWEET PEA
(*Lathyrus odoratus*)

STRAWBERRY
(*Fragaria* x *ananassa*)

Runner (creeping stem)

Lateral root scar

Remains of leaves

Stem

Leaf scar

Rib

Lateral root

Tap root

Leaf scar

Leaf base

CARROT
(*Daucus carota*)

Petiole (leaf stalk)

Spine (modified leaf)

Slender rhizome

Stem tuber

Adventitious root

Stem

Simple deltoid leaf

Narrow, succulent leaf

POTATO
(*Solanum tuberosum*)

ROCK STONECROP
(*Sedum rupestre*)

Adventitious root

PARTS OF HERBACEOUS FLOWERING PLANTS

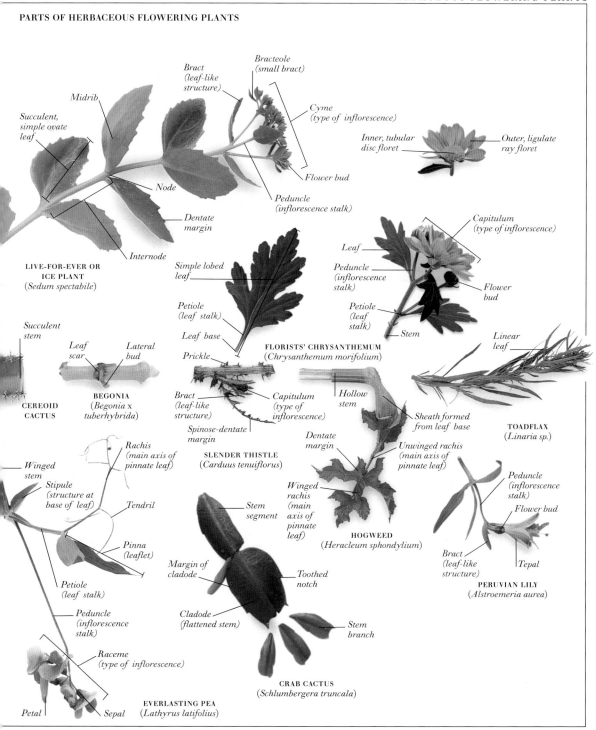

Bract
(leaf-like
structure)

Bracteole
(small bract)

Cyme
(type of inflorescence)

Midrib

Succulent,
simple ovate
leaf

Inner, tubular
disc floret

Outer, ligulate
ray floret

Node

Flower bud

Dentate
margin

Peduncle
(inflorescence stalk)

Internode

**LIVE-FOR-EVER OR
ICE PLANT**
(*Sedum spectabile*)

Capitulum
(type of inflorescence)

Simple lobed
leaf

Leaf

Peduncle
(inflorescence
stalk)

Flower
bud

Succulent
stem

Leaf
scar

Lateral
bud

Petiole
(leaf stalk)

Petiole
(leaf
stalk)

Stem

Linear
leaf

Leaf base

**CEREOID
CACTUS**

BEGONIA
(*Begonia* x
tuberhybrida)

Prickle

FLORISTS' CHRYSANTHEMUM
(*Chrysanthemum morifolium*)

Bract
(leaf-like
structure)

Capitulum
(type of
inflorescence)

Hollow
stem

Sheath formed
from leaf base

TOADFLAX
(*Linaria sp.*)

Spinose-dentate
margin

Dentate
margin

Unwinged rachis
(main axis of
pinnate leaf)

Winged
stem

Rachis
(main axis of
pinnate leaf)

SLENDER THISTLE
(*Carduus tenuiflorus*)

Peduncle
(inflorescence
stalk)

Stipule
(structure at
base of leaf)

Tendril

Stem
segment

Winged
rachis
(main
axis of
pinnate
leaf)

Flower bud

Pinna
(leaflet)

HOGWEED
(*Heracleum sphondylium*)

Bract
(leaf-like
structure)

Tepal

Petiole
(leaf stalk)

Margin of
cladode

Toothed
notch

PERUVIAN LILY
(*Alstroemeria aurea*)

Peduncle
(inflorescence
stalk)

Cladode
(flattened stem)

Stem
branch

Raceme
(type of inflorescence)

Petal

Sepal

EVERLASTING PEA
(*Lathyrus latifolius*)

CRAB CACTUS
(*Schlumbergera truncala*)

Woody flowering plants

WOODY FLOWERING PLANTS ARE PERENNIAL, that is, they continue to grow and reproduce for many years. They have one or more permanent stems above ground, and numerous smaller branches. The stems and branches have a strong woody core that supports the plant and contains vascular tissue for transporting water and nutrients. Outside the woody core is a layer of tough, protective bark, which has lenticels (tiny pores) in it to enable gases to pass through. Woody flowering plants may be shrubs, which have several stems arising from the soil; bushes, which are shrubs with dense branching and foliage; or trees, which typically have a single upright stem (the trunk) that bears branches. Deciduous woody plants (e.g., roses) shed all their leaves once a year and remain leafless during winter. Evergreen woody plants (e.g., ivy) shed their leaves gradually, so retaining full leaf cover throughout the year.

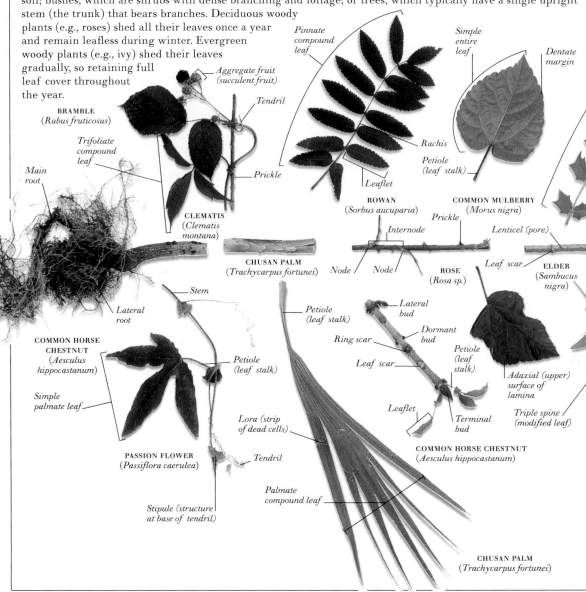

Aggregate fruit
(succulent fruit)

Tendril

BRAMBLE
(*Rubus fruticosus*)

Trifoliate
compound
leaf

Main
root

Prickle

CLEMATIS
(*Clematis
montana*)

Pinnate
compound
leaf

Simple
entire
leaf

Dentate
margin

Rachis

Petiole
(leaf stalk)

Leaflet

ROWAN
(*Sorbus aucuparia*)

COMMON MULBERRY
(*Morus nigra*)

Prickle

Lenticel (pore)

Internode

Node

Node

ROSE
(*Rosa sp.*)

Leaf scar

ELDER
(*Sambucus
nigra*)

CHUSAN PALM
(*Trachycarpus fortunei*)

Stem

Lateral
root

COMMON HORSE
CHESTNUT
(*Aesculus
hippocastanum*)

Simple
palmate leaf

Petiole
(leaf stalk)

Lora (strip
of dead cells)

PASSION FLOWER
(*Passiflora caerulea*)

Tendril

Stipule (structure
at base of tendril)

Petiole
(leaf stalk)

Lateral
bud

Dormant
bud

Ring scar

Leaf scar

Petiole
(leaf
stalk)

Leaflet

Terminal
bud

COMMON HORSE CHESTNUT
(*Aesculus hippocastanum*)

Adaxial (upper)
surface of
lamina

Triple spine
(modified leaf)

Palmate
compound leaf

CHUSAN PALM
(*Trachycarpus fortunei*)

PARTS OF WOODY FLOWERING PLANTS

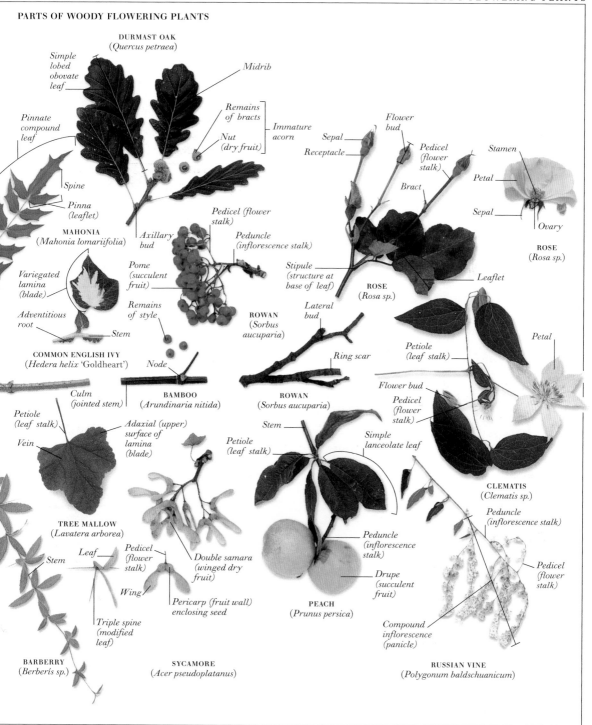

DURMAST OAK
(*Quercus petraea*)

Simple lobed obovate leaf

Midrib

Remains of bracts

Nut (dry fruit)

Immature acorn

Pinnate compound leaf

Spine

Pinna (leaflet)

MAHONIA
(*Mahonia lomariifolia*)

Axillary bud

Pome (succulent fruit)

Pedicel (flower stalk)

Peduncle (inflorescence stalk)

Variegated lamina (blade)

Remains of style

ROWAN
(*Sorbus aucuparia*)

Adventitious root

Stem

COMMON ENGLISH IVY
(*Hedera helix* 'Goldheart')

Node

Lateral bud

Ring scar

ROWAN
(*Sorbus aucuparia*)

Flower bud

Sepal

Receptacle

Pedicel (flower stalk)

Bract

Stipule (structure at base of leaf)

ROSE
(*Rosa sp.*)

Leaflet

Stamen

Petal

Sepal

Ovary

ROSE
(*Rosa sp.*)

Culm (jointed stem)

BAMBOO
(*Arundinaria nitida*)

Petiole (leaf stalk)

Vein

Adaxial (upper) surface of lamina (blade)

TREE MALLOW
(*Lavatera arborea*)

Stem

Leaf

Pedicel (flower stalk)

Wing

Double samara (winged dry fruit)

Pericarp (fruit wall) enclosing seed

Triple spine (modified leaf)

BARBERRY
(*Berberís sp.*)

SYCAMORE
(*Acer pseudoplatanus*)

Stem

Petiole (leaf stalk)

Simple lanceolate leaf

Peduncle (inflorescence stalk)

Drupe (succulent fruit)

PEACH
(*Prunus persica*)

Petiole (leaf stalk)

Petal

Flower bud

Pedicel (flower stalk)

CLEMATIS
(*Clematis sp.*)

Peduncle (inflorescence stalk)

Pedicel (flower stalk)

Compound inflorescence (panicle)

RUSSIAN VINE
(*Polygonum baldschuanicum*)

Roots

ROOTS ARE THE UNDERGROUND PARTS OF PLANTS. They have
three main functions. First, they anchor the plant in the soil.
Second, they absorb water and minerals from the spaces
between soil particles; the roots' absorptive properties are
increased by root hairs, which grow behind the root tip,
allowing maximum uptake of vital substances. Third, the
root is part of the plant's transport system: xylem carries
water and minerals from the roots to the stem and leaves,
and phloem carries nutrients from the leaves to all parts of
the root system. In addition, some roots (e.g., carrots) are food
stores. Roots have an outer epidermis covering a cortex of parenchyma
(packing tissue), and a central cylinder of vascular tissue. This arrangement
helps the roots resist the forces of compression as they grow through the soil.

MICROGRAPH OF PRIMARY ROOT DEVELOPMENT
Cabbage (*Brassica sp.*)

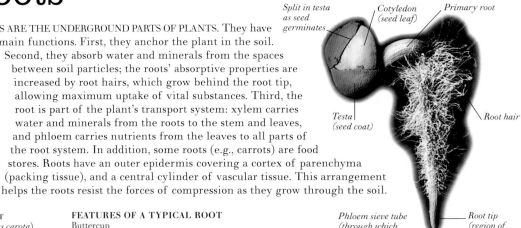

Split in testa
as seed
germinates

Cotyledon
(seed leaf)

Primary root

Testa
(seed coat)

Root hair

CARROT
(*Daucus carota*)

FEATURES OF A TYPICAL ROOT
Buttercup
(*Ranunculus sp.*)

Stele
(vascular cylinder)

Phloem sieve tube
(through which
nutrients are
transported)

Root tip
(region of
cell division)

Pericycle
(outer layer
of stele)

Companion cell
(cell associated
with phloem
sieve tube)

Root hair

Cortex
(layer between
epidermis and
vascular tissue)

Air space
(allowing gas
diffusion in
the root)

Root hair

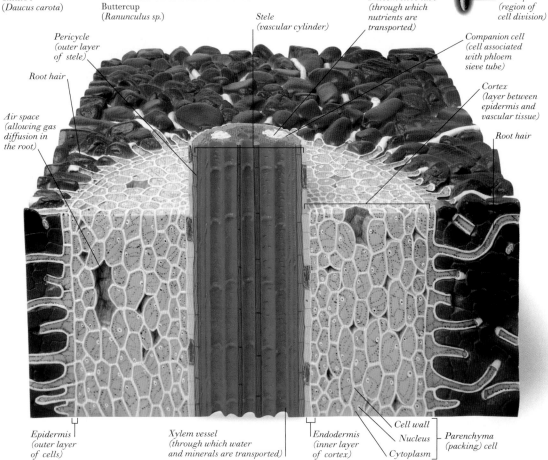

Epidermis
(outer layer
of cells)

Xylem vessel
(through which water
and minerals are transported)

Endodermis
(inner layer
of cortex)

Cell wall

Nucleus

Cytoplasm

Parenchyma
(packing) cell

PRIMARY ROOT AND MICROGRAPHS OF SECTIONS THROUGH ROOTS

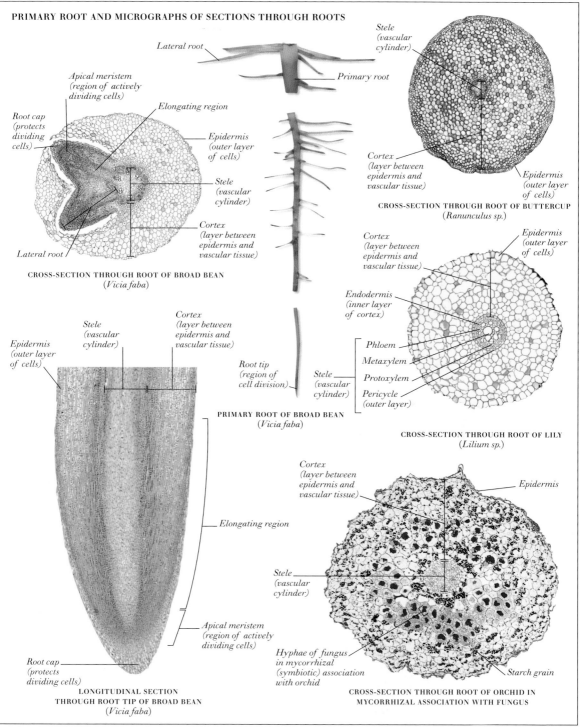

Lateral root

Primary root

Stele
(vascular
cylinder)

Apical meristem
(region of actively
dividing cells)

Elongating region

Root cap
(protects
dividing
cells)

Epidermis
(outer layer
of cells)

Stele
(vascular
cylinder)

Cortex
(layer between
epidermis and
vascular tissue)

Lateral root

CROSS-SECTION THROUGH ROOT OF BROAD BEAN
(*Vicia faba*)

Cortex
(layer between
epidermis and
vascular tissue)

Epidermis
(outer layer
of cells)

CROSS-SECTION THROUGH ROOT OF BUTTERCUP
(*Ranunculus sp.*)

Cortex
(layer between
epidermis and
vascular tissue)

Epidermis
(outer layer
of cells)

Endodermis
(inner layer
of cortex)

Phloem

Metaxylem

Protoxylem

Pericycle
(outer layer)

Stele
(vascular
cylinder)

CROSS-SECTION THROUGH ROOT OF LILY
(*Lilium sp.*)

Stele
(vascular
cylinder)

Cortex
(layer between
epidermis and
vascular tissue)

Epidermis
(outer layer
of cells)

Root tip
(region of
cell division)

Stele
(vascular
cylinder)

PRIMARY ROOT OF BROAD BEAN
(*Vicia faba*)

Elongating region

Apical meristem
(region of actively
dividing cells)

Root cap
(protects
dividing
cells)

**LONGITUDINAL SECTION
THROUGH ROOT TIP OF BROAD BEAN**
(*Vicia faba*)

Cortex
(layer between
epidermis and
vascular tissue)

Epidermis

Stele
(vascular
cylinder)

Hyphae of fungus
in mycorrhizal
(symbiotic) association
with orchid

Starch grain

**CROSS-SECTION THROUGH ROOT OF ORCHID IN
MYCORRHIZAL ASSOCIATION WITH FUNGUS**

133

Stems

T<small>HE STEM IS THE MAIN SUPPORTIVE PART OF A PLANT</small> that grows
above ground. Stems bear leaves (organs of photosynthesis), which
grow at nodes; buds (shoots covered by protective scales), which grow
at the stem tip (apical or terminal buds) and in the angle between a
leaf and the stem (axillary or lateral buds); and flowers (reproductive
structures). The stem forms part of the plant's transport system: xylem
tissue in the stem transports water and minerals from the roots to the
aerial parts of the plant, and phloem tissue transports nutrients
manufactured in the leaves to other parts of the plant. Stem tissues
are also used for storing water and food. Herbaceous (non-woody)
stems have an outer protective epidermis covering a cortex that
consists mainly of parenchyma (packing tissue) but also has some
collenchyma (supporting tissue). The vascular tissue of such stems
is arranged in bundles, each of which consists of xylem, phloem,
and sclerenchyma (strengthening tissue). Woody stems have an outer
protective layer of tough bark, which is perforated with lenticels (pores)
to allow gas exchange. Inside the bark is a ring of secondary phloem,
which surrounds an inner core of secondary xylem.

MICROGRAPH OF LONGITUDINAL SECTION THROUGH APEX OF STEM
Coleus sp.

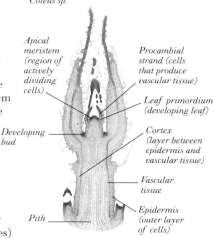

*Apical
meristem
(region of
actively
dividing
cells)*

*Procambial
strand (cells
that produce
vascular tissue)*

*Leaf primordium
(developing leaf)*

*Developing
bud*

*Cortex
(layer between
epidermis and
vascular tissue)*

*Vascular
tissue*

*Epidermis
(outer layer
of cells)*

Pith

YOUNG WOODY STEM
Lime
(Tilia sp.)

EMERGENT BUDS
London plane
(Platanus x acerifolia)

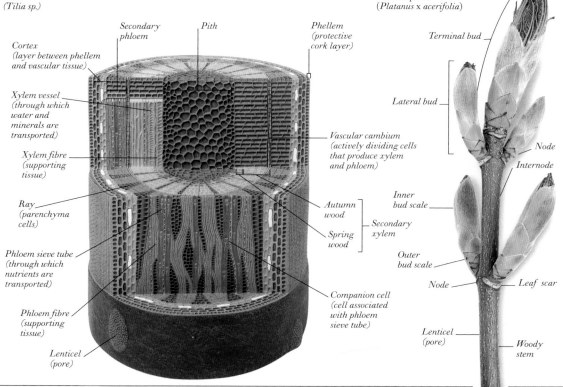

*Secondary
phloem*

Pith

*Phellem
(protective
cork layer)*

*Cortex
(layer between phellem
and vascular tissue)*

*Xylem vessel
(through which
water and
minerals are
transported)*

*Xylem fibre
(supporting
tissue)*

*Ray
(parenchyma
cells)*

*Phloem sieve tube
(through which
nutrients are
transported)*

*Phloem fibre
(supporting
tissue)*

*Lenticel
(pore)*

*Vascular cambium
(actively dividing cells
that produce xylem
and phloem)*

*Autumn
wood*

*Spring
wood*

*Companion cell
(cell associated
with phloem
sieve tube)*

*Young
leaves
emerging*

Terminal bud

Lateral bud

Node

Internode

*Inner
bud scale*

*Secondary
xylem*

*Outer
bud scale*

Node

Leaf scar

*Lenticel
(pore)*

*Woody
stem*

MICROGRAPHS OF CROSS-SECTIONS THROUGH VARIOUS STEMS

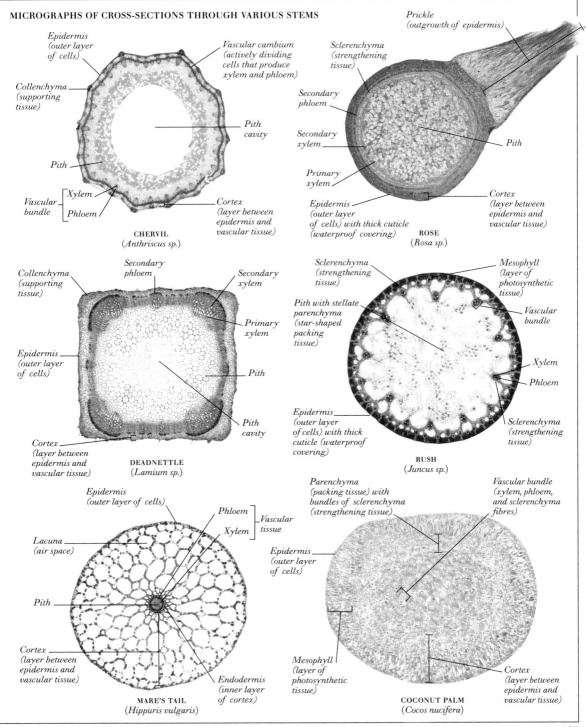

Epidermis
(outer layer
of cells)

Collenchyma
(supporting
tissue)

Pith

Vascular
bundle

Xylem

Phloem

Vascular cambium
(actively dividing
cells that produce
xylem and phloem)

Pith
cavity

Cortex
(layer between
epidermis and
vascular tissue)

CHERVIL
(Anthriscus sp.)

Prickle
(outgrowth of epidermis)

Sclerenchyma
(strengthening
tissue)

Secondary
phloem

Secondary
xylem

Primary
xylem

Epidermis
(outer layer
of cells) with thick
cuticle
(waterproof covering)

Pith

Cortex
(layer between
epidermis and
vascular tissue)

ROSE
(Rosa sp.)

Collenchyma
(supporting
tissue)

Secondary
phloem

Secondary
xylem

Primary
xylem

Epidermis
(outer layer
of cells)

Pith

Pith
cavity

Cortex
(layer between
epidermis and
vascular tissue)

DEADNETTLE
(Lamium sp.)

Sclerenchyma
(strengthening
tissue)

Pith with stellate
parenchyma
(star-shaped
packing
tissue)

Epidermis
(outer layer
of cells) with thick
cuticle (waterproof
covering)

Mesophyll
(layer of
photosynthetic
tissue)

Vascular
bundle

Xylem

Phloem

Sclerenchyma
(strengthening
tissue)

RUSH
(Juncus sp.)

Epidermis
(outer layer of cells)

Lacuna
(air space)

Pith

Cortex
(layer between
epidermis and
vascular tissue)

Phloem

Xylem

Vascular
tissue

Endodermis
(inner layer
of cortex)

MARE'S TAIL
(Hippuris vulgaris)

Parenchyma
(packing tissue) with
bundles of sclerenchyma
(strengthening tissue)

Epidermis
(outer layer
of cells)

Mesophyll
(layer of
photosynthetic
tissue)

Vascular bundle
(xylem, phloem,
and sclerenchyma
fibres)

Cortex
(layer between
epidermis and
vascular tissue)

COCONUT PALM
(Cocos nucifera)

135

Leaves

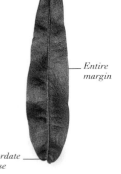

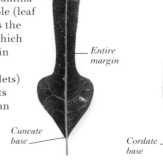

LEAVES ARE THE MAIN SITES OF PHOTOSYNTHESIS (see pp. 138-139) and transpiration (water loss by evaporation) in plants. A typical leaf consists of a thin, flat lamina (blade) supported by a network of veins; a petiole (leaf stalk); and a leaf base, where the petiole joins the stem. Leaves can be classified as simple, in which the lamina is a single unit, or compound, in which the lamina is divided into separate leaflets. Compound leaves may be pinnate, with pinnae (leaflets) on both sides of a rachis (main axis), or palmate, with leaflets arising from a single point at the tip of the petiole. Leaves can be classified further by the overall shape of the lamina, and by the shape of the lamina's apex, margin, and base.

CHECKERBLOOM
(Sidalcea malviflora)

SIMPLE LEAF SHAPES

Subacute apex

Acuminate apex

Entire margin

Entire margin

Cuneate base

Cordate base

PANDURIFORM
Croton
(Codiaeum variegatum)

LANCEOLATE
Sea buckthorn
(Hippophae rhamnoides)

GENERAL LEAF FEATURES

Apex

Lamina (blade)

Midrib

Margin

Lateral vein

Lamina base

Petiole (leaf stalk)

Leaf base

Sweet chestnut
(Castanea sativa)

COMPOUND LEAF SHAPES

Terminal pinna (leaflet)

Emarginate apex

Rachis (main axis of pinnate leaf)

Pinna (leaflet)

Petiolule (leaflet stalk)

Petiole (leaf stalk)

ODD PINNATE
False acacia
(Robinia pseudoacacia)

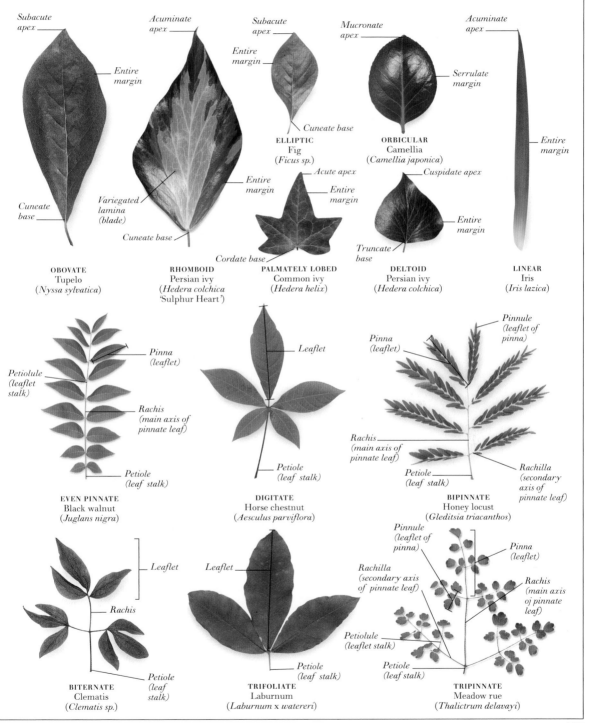

Subacute apex

Entire margin

Cuneate base

OBOVATE
Tupelo
(*Nyssa sylvatica*)

Acuminate apex

Entire margin

Variegated lamina (blade)

Cuneate base

RHOMBOID
Persian ivy
(*Hedera colchica*
'Sulphur Heart')

Subacute apex

Entire margin

Cuneate base

ELLIPTIC
Fig
(*Ficus sp.*)

Acute apex

Entire margin

Cordate base

PALMATELY LOBED
Common ivy
(*Hedera helix*)

Mucronate apex

Serrulate margin

ORBICULAR
Camellia
(*Camellia japonica*)

Cuspidate apex

Entire margin

Truncate base

DELTOID
Persian ivy
(*Hedera colchica*)

Acuminate apex

Entire margin

LINEAR
Iris
(*Iris lazica*)

Pinna (leaflet)

Petiolule (leaflet stalk)

Rachis (main axis of pinnate leaf)

Petiole (leaf stalk)

EVEN PINNATE
Black walnut
(*Juglans nigra*)

Leaflet

Petiole (leaf stalk)

DIGITATE
Horse chestnut
(*Aesculus parviflora*)

Pinnule (leaflet of pinna)

Pinna (leaflet)

Rachis (main axis of pinnate leaf)

Petiole (leaf stalk)

Rachilla (secondary axis of pinnate leaf)

BIPINNATE
Honey locust
(*Gleditsia triacanthos*)

Leaflet

Rachis

Petiole (leaf stalk)

BITERNATE
Clematis
(*Clematis sp.*)

Leaflet

Petiole (leaf stalk)

TRIFOLIATE
Laburnum
(*Laburnum* x *watereri*)

Pinnule (leaflet of pinna)

Rachilla (secondary axis of pinnate leaf)

Petiolule (leaflet stalk)

Petiole (leaf stalk)

Pinna (leaflet)

Rachis (main axis oj pinnate leaf)

TRIPINNATE
Meadow rue
(*Thalictrum delavayi*)

Photosynthesis

PHOTOSYNTHESIS IS THE PROCESS by which plants make their food using sunlight, water, and carbon dioxide. It takes place inside special structures in leaf cells called chloroplasts. The chloroplasts contain chlorophyll, a green pigment that absorbs energy from sunlight. During photosynthesis, the absorbed energy is used to join together carbon dioxide and water to form the sugar glucose, which is the energy source for the whole plant; oxygen, a waste product, is released into the air. Leaves are the main sites of photosynthesis, and have various adaptations for that purpose: flat laminae (blades) provide a large surface for absorbing sunlight; stomata (pores) in the lower surface of the laminae allow gases (carbon dioxide and oxygen) to pass into and out of the leaves; and an extensive network of veins brings water into the leaves and transports the glucose produced by photosynthesis to the rest of the plant.

MICROGRAPH OF LEAF
Lily (*Lilium sp.*)

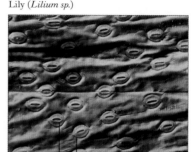

Stoma (pore)

Guard cell (controls opening and closing of stoma)

Lower surface of lamina (blade)

THE PROCESS OF PHOTOSYNTHESIS

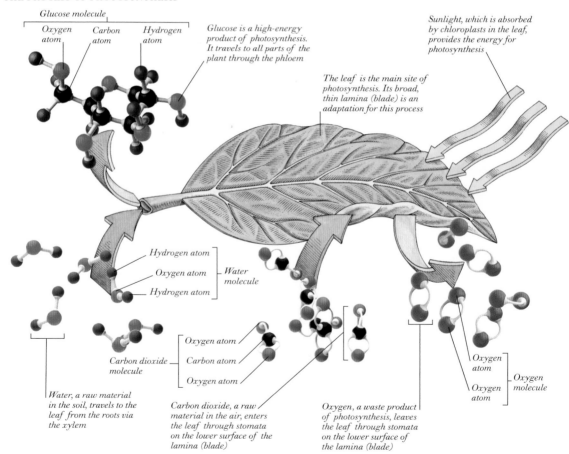

Glucose molecule

Oxygen atom *Carbon atom* *Hydrogen atom*

Glucose is a high-energy product of photosynthesis. It travels to all parts of the plant through the phloem

Sunlight, which is absorbed by chloroplasts in the leaf, provides the energy for photosynthesis

The leaf is the main site of photosynthesis. Its broad, thin lamina (blade) is an adaptation for this process

Hydrogen atom
Oxygen atom — *Water molecule*
Hydrogen atom

Carbon dioxide molecule

Oxygen atom
Carbon atom
Oxygen atom

Oxygen atom
Oxygen molecule
Oxygen atom

Water, a raw material in the soil, travels to the leaf from the roots via the xylem

Carbon dioxide, a raw material in the air, enters the leaf through stomata on the lower surface of the lamina (blade)

Oxygen, a waste product of photosynthesis, leaves the leaf through stomata on the lower surface of the lamina (blade)

CROSS-SECTION THROUGH LEAF
Christmas rose
(*Helleborus niger*)

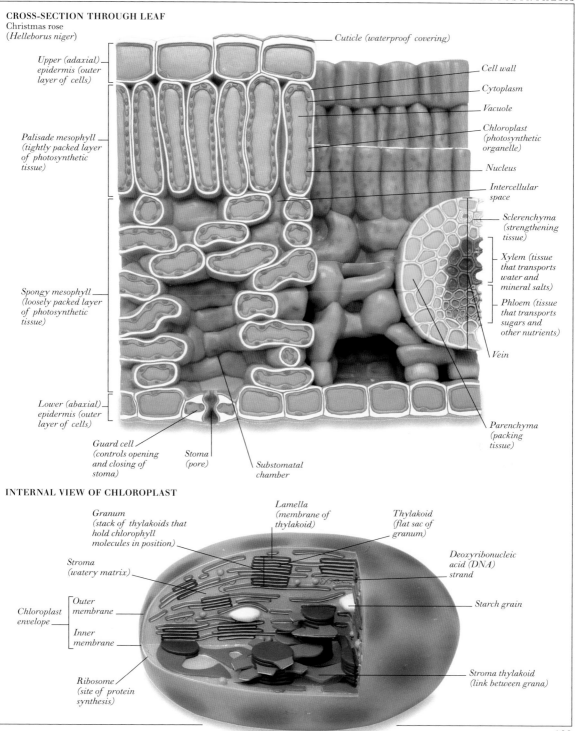

Cuticle (*waterproof covering*)

Upper (*adaxial*)
epidermis (*outer
layer of cells*)

Cell wall

Cytoplasm

Vacuole

Chloroplast
(*photosynthetic
organelle*)

Palisade mesophyll
(*tightly packed layer
of photosynthetic
tissue*)

Nucleus

Intercellular
space

Sclerenchyma
(*strengthening
tissue*)

Xylem (*tissue
that transports
water and
mineral salts*)

Phloem (*tissue
that transports
sugars and
other nutrients*)

Spongy mesophyll
(*loosely packed layer
of photosynthetic
tissue*)

Vein

Lower (*abaxial*)
epidermis (*outer
layer of cells*)

Guard cell
(*controls opening
and closing of
stoma*)

Stoma
(*pore*)

Substomatal
chamber

Parenchyma
(*packing
tissue*)

INTERNAL VIEW OF CHLOROPLAST

Granum
(*stack of thylakoids that
hold chlorophyll
molecules in position*)

Lamella
(*membrane of
thylakoid*)

Thylakoid
(*flat sac of
granum*)

Stroma
(*watery matrix*)

Deoxyribonucleic
acid (DNA)
strand

Chloroplast
envelope

Outer
membrane

Inner
membrane

Starch grain

Ribosome
(*site of protein
synthesis*)

Stroma thylakoid
(*link between grana*)

139

Flowers 1

FLOWERS ARE THE SITES OF SEXUAL REPRODUCTION in flowering plants. Their component parts are arranged in whorls around the receptacle (tip of the flower stalk). The sepals (collectively called the calyx) are outermost; typically small and green, they protect the developing flower. The petals (collectively called the corolla) are typically large and brightly coloured; they are found inside the sepals. In monocotyledonous flowers (see pp. 126-127), sepals and petals are indistinguishable; individually they are called tepals (collectively called the perianth). The petals surround the male and female reproductive structures (androecium and gynoecium). The androecium consists of stamens (male organs); each stamen is made up of a filament (stalk) and anther. The gynoecium has one or more carpels (female organs); each carpel consists of an ovary, style, and stigma. Some flowers (e.g., lily) occur singly on a pedicel (flower stalk); others (e.g., elder, sunflower) are arranged in a group (inflorescence) on a peduncle (inflorescence stalk).

Inner tepal (monocotyledonous petal)
Honey guide
Groove secreting nectar
Filament
Style
Outer tepal (monocotyledonous sepal)
Stigma
Anther

EXTERNAL VIEW

Outer tepal (monocotyledonous sepal)

Inner tepal (monocotyledonous petal)

Honey guide

Tepal scar

Receptacle

Ovary wall

Ovule

Pedicel (flower stalk)

Papilla (fleshy hair)

A MONOCOTYLEDONOUS FLOWER
Lily
(Lilium sp.)

Syncarpous (fused carpels) gynoecium

Ovary

Stigma

Style

Stamen
Anther
Filament

Pollen on anther

Outer tepal sheath

Style

Folded inner tepal (monocotyledonous petal)

Stigma

Ovary

Receptacle

Anther

Pedicel (flower stalk)

Filament

LONGITUDINAL SECTION THROUGH FLOWER BUD

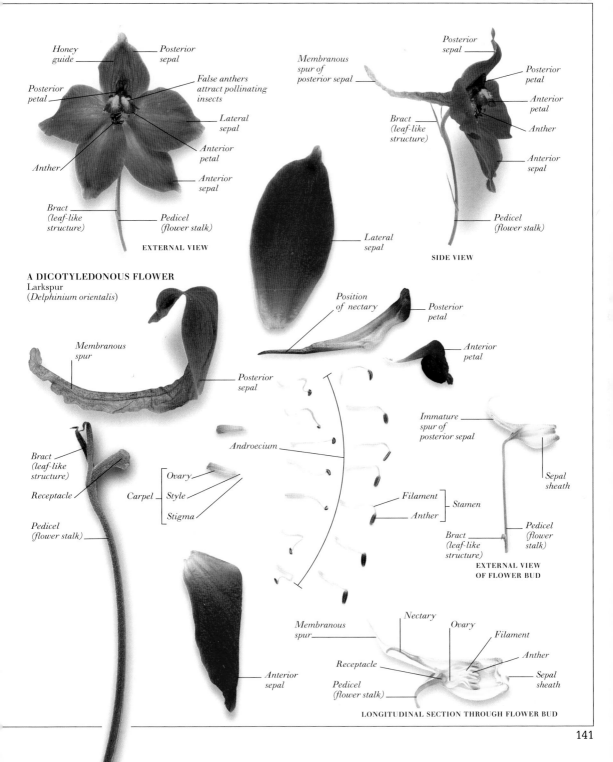

Honey guide

Posterior sepal

Posterior petal

False anthers attract pollinating insects

Lateral sepal

Anterior petal

Anterior sepal

Anther

Bract (leaf-like structure)

Pedicel (flower stalk)

EXTERNAL VIEW

Posterior sepal

Posterior petal

Anterior petal

Anther

Membranous spur of posterior sepal

Bract (leaf-like structure)

Anterior sepal

Pedicel (flower stalk)

SIDE VIEW

A DICOTYLEDONOUS FLOWER
Larkspur
(*Delphinium orientalis*)

Membranous spur

Posterior sepal

Lateral sepal

Position of nectary

Posterior petal

Anterior petal

Androecium

Immature spur of posterior sepal

Sepal sheath

Bract (leaf-like structure)

Receptacle

Carpel { Ovary / Style / Stigma }

Filament

Anther

Stamen

Bract (leaf-like structure)

Pedicel (flower stalk)

Pedicel (flower stalk)

EXTERNAL VIEW OF FLOWER BUD

Anterior sepal

Nectary

Ovary

Filament

Anther

Membranous spur

Receptacle

Sepal sheath

Pedicel (flower stalk)

LONGITUDINAL SECTION THROUGH FLOWER BUD

Flowers 2

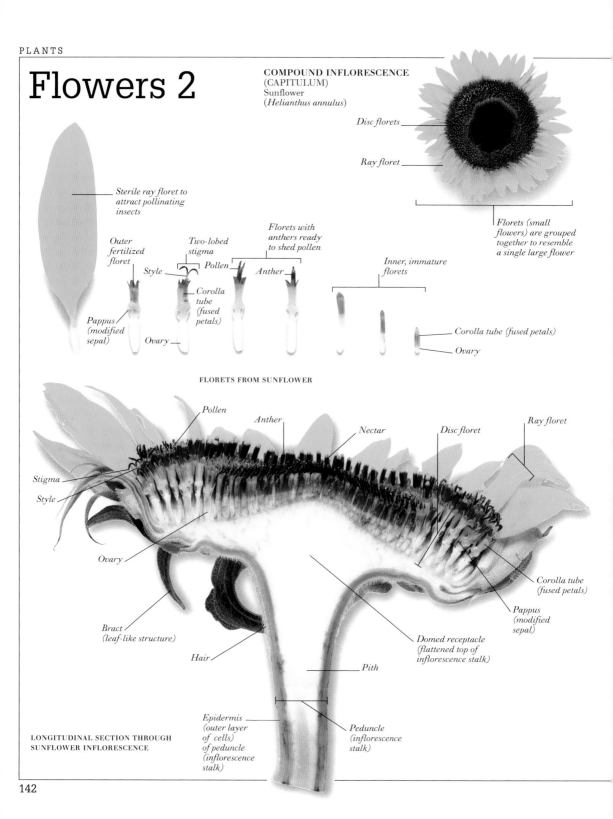

COMPOUND INFLORESCENCE
(CAPITULUM)
Sunflower
(*Helianthus annulus*)

Disc florets

Ray floret

Florets (small flowers) are grouped together to resemble a single large flower

Sterile ray floret to attract pollinating insects

Outer fertilized floret

Two-lobed stigma

Florets with anthers ready to shed pollen

Style

Pollen

Anther

Inner, immature florets

Corolla tube (fused petals)

Pappus (modified sepal)

Ovary

Corolla tube (fused petals)

Ovary

FLORETS FROM SUNFLOWER

Pollen

Anther

Nectar

Disc floret

Ray floret

Stigma

Style

Ovary

Corolla tube (fused petals)

Pappus (modified sepal)

Bract (leaf-like structure)

Hair

Domed receptacle (flattened top of inflorescence stalk)

Pith

Epidermis (outer layer of cells) of peduncle (inflorescence stalk)

Peduncle (inflorescence stalk)

LONGITUDINAL SECTION THROUGH SUNFLOWER INFLORESCENCE

142

ARRANGEMENT OF FLOWERS ON STEM

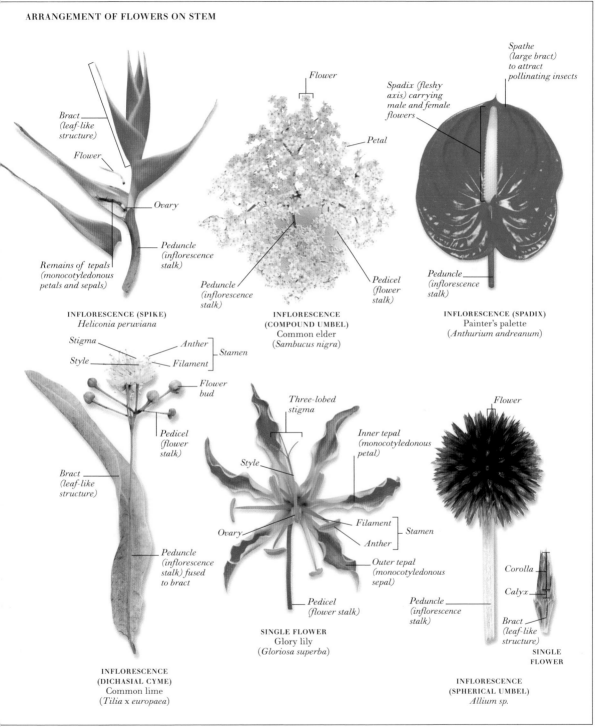

Bract (leaf-like structure)

Flower

Ovary

Remains of tepals (monocotyledonous petals and sepals)

Peduncle (inflorescence stalk)

INFLORESCENCE (SPIKE)
Heliconia peruviana

Flower

Petal

Peduncle (inflorescence stalk)

Pedicel (flower stalk)

INFLORESCENCE (COMPOUND UMBEL)
Common elder
(*Sambucus nigra*)

Spathe (large bract) to attract pollinating insects

Spadix (fleshy axis) carrying male and female flowers

Peduncle (inflorescence stalk)

INFLORESCENCE (SPADIX)
Painter's palette
(*Anthurium andreanum*)

Stigma

Style

Anther

Filament

Stamen

Flower bud

Pedicel (flower stalk)

Bract (leaf-like structure)

Peduncle (inflorescence stalk) fused to bract

INFLORESCENCE (DICHASIAL CYME)
Common lime
(*Tilia x europaea*)

Three-lobed stigma

Inner tepal (monocotyledonous petal)

Style

Ovary

Filament

Anther

Stamen

Outer tepal (monocotyledonous sepal)

Pedicel (flower stalk)

SINGLE FLOWER
Glory lily
(*Gloriosa superba*)

Flower

Peduncle (inflorescence stalk)

Corolla

Calyx

Bract (leaf-like structure)

SINGLE FLOWER

INFLORESCENCE (SPHERICAL UMBEL)
Allium sp.

Pollination

POLLINATION IS THE TRANSFER OF POLLEN (which contains the male sex cells) from an anther (part of the male reproductive organ) to a stigma (part of the female reproductive organ). This process precedes fertilization (see pp. 146-147). Pollination may occur within the same flower (self-pollination), or between flowers on separate plants of the same species (cross-pollination). In most plants, pollination is carried out either by insects (entomophilous pollination) or by the wind (anemophilous pollination). Less commonly, birds, bats, or water are the agents of pollination. Insect-pollinated flowers are typically brightly coloured, scented, and produce nectar, on which insects feed. Such flowers also tend to have patterns that are visible only in ultraviolet light, which many insects can see but which humans cannot. These features attract insects, which become covered with the sticky or hooked pollen grains when they visit one flower, and then transfer the pollen to the next flower they visit. Wind-pollinated flowers are generally small, relatively inconspicuous, and unscented. They produce large quantities of light pollen grains that are easily blown by the wind to other flowers.

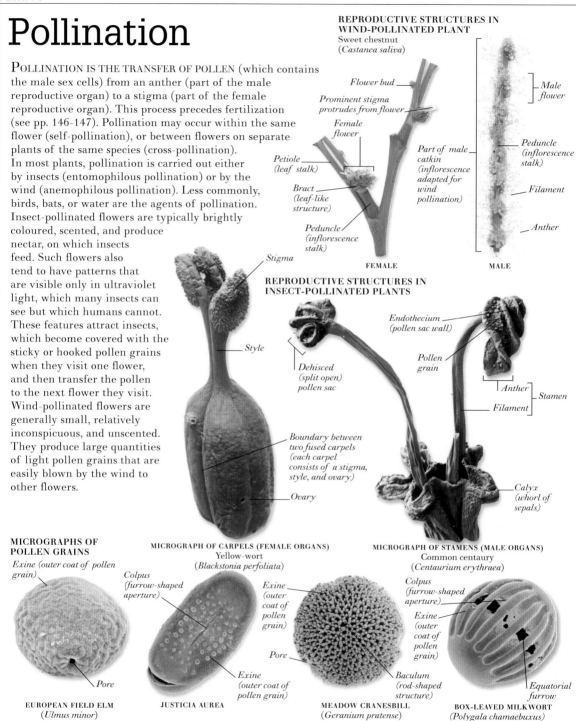

REPRODUCTIVE STRUCTURES IN WIND-POLLINATED PLANT
Sweet chestnut
(*Castanea saliva*)

Flower bud
Prominent stigma protrudes from flower
Female flower
Petiole (leaf stalk)
Bract (leaf-like structure)
Peduncle (inflorescence stalk)

Male flower
Part of male catkin (inflorescence adapted for wind pollination)
Peduncle (inflorescence stalk)
Filament
Anther

FEMALE   MALE

REPRODUCTIVE STRUCTURES IN INSECT-POLLINATED PLANTS

Stigma
Style
Dehisced (split open) pollen sac
Boundary between two fused carpels (each carpel consists of a stigma, style, and ovary)
Ovary

Endothecium (pollen sac wall)
Pollen grain
Anther
Filament
Stamen
Calyx (whorl of sepals)

MICROGRAPHS OF POLLEN GRAINS

Exine (outer coat of pollen grain)
Pore

EUROPEAN FIELD ELM
(*Ulmus minor*)

MICROGRAPH OF CARPELS (FEMALE ORGANS)
Yellow-wort
(*Blackstonia perfoliata*)

Colpus (furrow-shaped aperture)
Exine (outer coat of pollen grain)

JUSTICIA AUREA

Exine (outer coat of pollen grain)
Pore
Baculum (rod-shaped structure)

MEADOW CRANESBILL
(*Geranium pratense*)

MICROGRAPH OF STAMENS (MALE ORGANS)
Common centaury
(*Centaurium erythraea*)

Colpus (furrow-shaped aperture)
Exine (outer coat of pollen grain)
Equatorial furrow

BOX-LEAVED MILKWORT
(*Polygala chamaebuxus*)

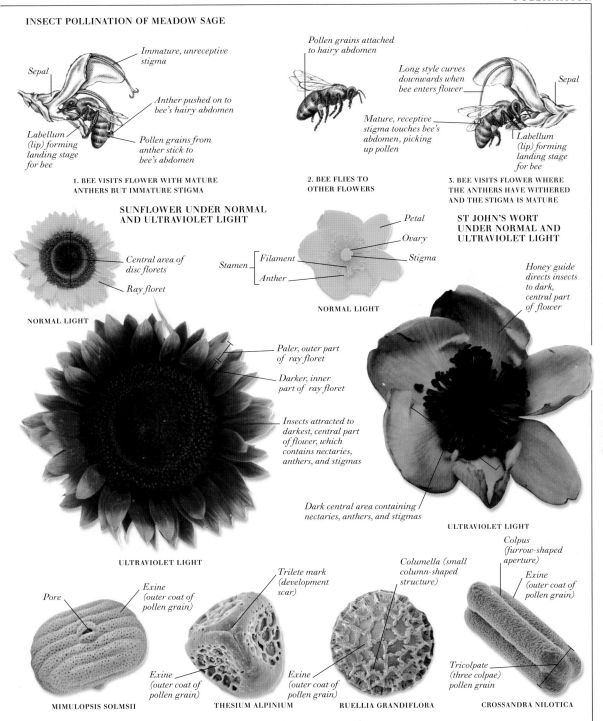

INSECT POLLINATION OF MEADOW SAGE

Immature, unreceptive stigma

Sepal

Anther pushed on to bee's hairy abdomen

Labellum (lip) forming landing stage for bee

Pollen grains from anther stick to bee's abdomen

1. BEE VISITS FLOWER WITH MATURE ANTHERS BUT IMMATURE STIGMA

Pollen grains attached to hairy abdomen

Long style curves downwards when bee enters flower

Sepal

Mature, receptive stigma touches bee's abdomen, picking up pollen

Labellum (lip) forming landing stage for bee

2. BEE FLIES TO OTHER FLOWERS

3. BEE VISITS FLOWER WHERE THE ANTHERS HAVE WITHERED AND THE STIGMA IS MATURE

SUNFLOWER UNDER NORMAL AND ULTRAVIOLET LIGHT

Central area of disc florets

Ray floret

NORMAL LIGHT

Petal

Ovary

Stamen { Filament / Anther }

Stigma

NORMAL LIGHT

ST JOHN'S WORT UNDER NORMAL AND ULTRAVIOLET LIGHT

Honey guide directs insects to dark, central part of flower

Paler, outer part of ray floret

Darker, inner part of ray floret

Insects attracted to darkest, central part of flower, which contains nectaries, anthers, and stigmas

Dark central area containing nectaries, anthers, and stigmas

ULTRAVIOLET LIGHT

ULTRAVIOLET LIGHT

Pore

Exine (outer coat of pollen grain)

Trilete mark (development scar)

Columella (small column-shaped structure)

Colpus (furrow-shaped aperture)

Exine (outer coat of pollen grain)

Exine (outer coat of pollen grain)

Exine (outer coat of pollen grain)

Tricolpate (three colpae) pollen grain

MIMULOPSIS SOLMSII

THESIUM ALPINIUM

RUELLIA GRANDIFLORA

CROSSANDRA NILOTICA

145

Fertilization

FERTILIZATION IS THE FUSION of male and female gametes (sex cells) to produce a zygote (embryo). Following pollination (see pp. 144-145), the pollen grains that contain the male gametes are on the stigma, some distance from the female gamete (ovum) inside the ovule. To enable the gametes to meet, the pollen grain germinates and produces a pollen tube, which grows down and enters the embryo sac (the inner part of the ovule that contains the ovum). Two male gametes, travelling at the tip of the pollen tube, enter the embryo sac. One gamete fuses with the ovum to produce a zygote that will develop into an embryo plant. The other male gamete fuses with two polar nuclei to produce the endosperm, which acts as a food store for the developing embryo. Fertilization also initiates other changes: the integument (outer part of ovule) forms a testa (seed coat) around the embryo and endosperm; the petals fall off; the stigma and style wither; and the ovary wall forms a layer (called the pericarp) around the seed. Together, the pericarp and seed form the fruit, which may be succulent (see pp. 148-149) or dry (see pp. 150-151). In some species (e.g., blackberry), apomixis can occur: the seed develops without fertilization of the ovum by a male gamete but endosperm formation and fruit development take place as in other species.

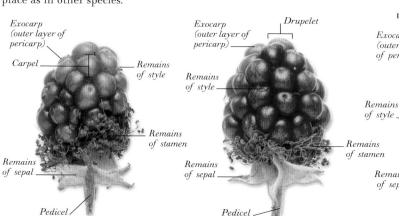

BANANA
(*Musa 'lacatan'*)

DEVELOPMENT OF A SUCCULENT FRUIT
Blackberry
(*Rubus fruticosus*)

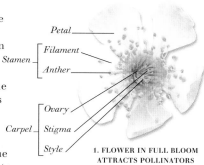

Petal

Stamen ⎰ Filament
⎱ Anther

Carpel ⎰ Ovary
⎱ Stigma
⎱ Style

**1. FLOWER IN FULL BLOOM
ATTRACTS POLLINATORS**

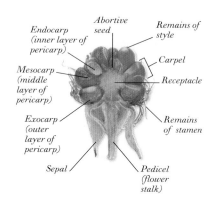

Endocarp
(inner layer of pericarp)

Mesocarp
(middle layer of pericarp)

Exocarp
(outer layer of pericarp)

Sepal

Abortive seed

Remains of style

Carpel

Receptacle

Remains of stamen

Pedicel
(flower stalk)

**4. PERICARP FORMS
FLESH, SKIN, AND A HARD INNER
LAYER (SHOWN IN CROSS-SECTION)**

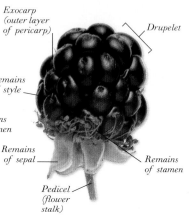

Exocarp
(outer layer of pericarp)

Carpel

Remains of style

Remains of stamen

Remains of sepal

Pedicel
(flower stalk)

**7. MESOCARP (FLESHY PART OF PERICARP)
OF EACH CARPEL STARTS TO
CHANGE COLOUR**

Exocarp
(outer layer of pericarp)

Drupelet

Remains of style

Remains of stamen

Remains of sepal

Pedicel
(flower stalk)

**8. CARPELS MATURE INTO DRUPELETS
(SMALL FLESHY FRUITS WITH SINGLE SEEDS
SURROUNDED BY HARD ENDOCARP)**

Exocarp
(outer layer of pericarp)

Drupelet

Remains of style

Remains of sepal

Remains of stamen

Pedicel
(flower stalk)

**9. MESOCARP OF DRUPELET BECOMES
DARKER AND SWEETER**

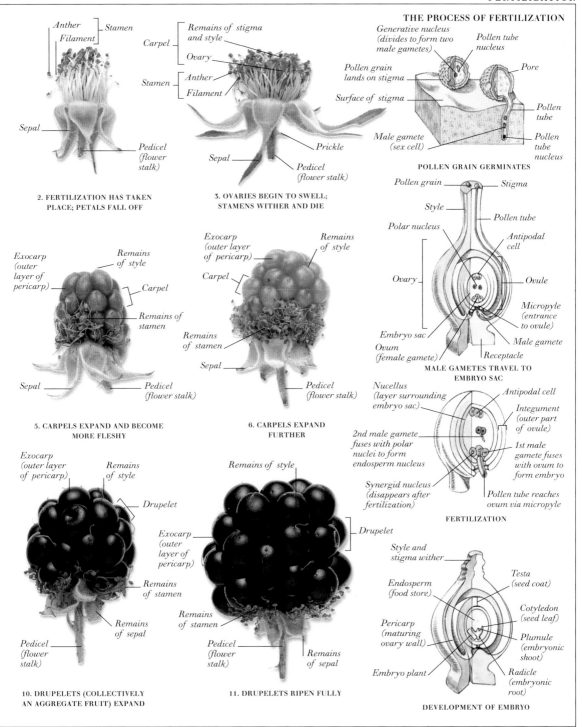

THE PROCESS OF FERTILIZATION

2. FERTILIZATION HAS TAKEN PLACE; PETALS FALL OFF

Anther ⎱ Stamen
Filament ⎰
Sepal
Pedicel (flower stalk)

3. OVARIES BEGIN TO SWELL; STAMENS WITHER AND DIE

Carpel ⎰ Remains of stigma and style / Ovary
Stamen ⎰ Anther / Filament
Sepal
Prickle
Pedicel (flower stalk)

POLLEN GRAIN GERMINATES

Generative nucleus (divides to form two male gametes)
Pollen tube nucleus
Pollen grain lands on stigma
Pore
Surface of stigma
Pollen tube
Male gamete (sex cell)
Pollen tube nucleus

5. CARPELS EXPAND AND BECOME MORE FLESHY

Exocarp (outer layer of pericarp)
Remains of style
Carpel
Remains of stamen
Sepal
Pedicel (flower stalk)

6. CARPELS EXPAND FURTHER

Exocarp (outer layer of pericarp)
Remains of style
Carpel
Remains of stamen
Sepal
Pedicel (flower stalk)

MALE GAMETES TRAVEL TO EMBRYO SAC

Pollen grain
Stigma
Style
Pollen tube
Polar nucleus
Antipodal cell
Ovary
Ovule
Micropyle (entrance to ovule)
Embryo sac
Ovum (female gamete)
Male gamete
Receptacle

10. DRUPELETS (COLLECTIVELY AN AGGREGATE FRUIT) EXPAND

Exocarp (outer layer of pericarp)
Remains of style
Drupelet
Remains of stamen
Remains of sepal
Pedicel (flower stalk)

11. DRUPELETS RIPEN FULLY

Remains of style
Exocarp (outer layer of pericarp)
Drupelet
Remains of stamen
Pedicel (flower stalk)
Remains of sepal

FERTILIZATION

Nucellus (layer surrounding embryo sac)
Antipodal cell
Integument (outer part of ovule)
2nd male gamete fuses with polar nuclei to form endosperm nucleus
1st male gamete fuses with ovum to form embryo
Synergid nucleus (disappears after fertilization)
Pollen tube reaches ovum via micropyle

DEVELOPMENT OF EMBRYO

Style and stigma wither
Testa (seed coat)
Endosperm (food store)
Cotyledon (seed leaf)
Pericarp (maturing ovary wall)
Plumule (embryonic shoot)
Embryo plant
Radicle (embryonic root)

147

Succulent fruits

A FRUIT IS A FULLY DEVELOPED and ripened ovary (seed-producing part of a plant's female reproductive organs). Fruits may be succulent or dry (see pp. 150-151). Succulent fruits are fleshy and brightly coloured, making them attractive to animals, which eat them and so disperse the seeds away from the parent plant. The wall (pericarp) of a succulent fruit has three layers: an outer exocarp, a middle mesocarp, and an inner endocarp. These three layers vary in thickness and texture in different types of fruits and may blend into each other. Succulent fruits can be classed as simple (derived from one ovary) or compound (derived from several ovaries). Simple succulent fruits include berries, which typically have many seeds, and drupes, which typically have a single stone or pip (e.g., cherry and peach). Compound succulent fruits include aggregate fruits, which are formed from many ovaries in one flower, and multiple fruits, which develop from the ovaries of many flowers. Some fruits, known as false fruits or pseudocarps, develop from parts of the flower in addition to the ovaries. For example, the flesh of the apple is formed from the receptacle (the upper end of the flower stalk).

BERRY
Cocoa
(*Theobroma cacao*)

HESPERIDIUM (A TYPE OF BERRY)
Lemon
(*Citrus limon*)

Pedicel
(flower stalk)

Endocarp

Mesocarp

Pedicel
(flower stalk)

Exocarp

Leathery
exocarp

Seed

Oil
gland

Vesicle
(juice
sac)

Remains
of style

Remains
of style

Placenta

**EXTERNAL VIEW
OF FRUIT**

**LONGITUDINAL SECTION
THROUGH FRUIT**

Hilum
(point of
attachment
to ovary)

Embryo

Seed

Carpel
wall

Carpel

Testa
(seed
coat)

Cotyledon
(seed leaf)

Placenta

**EXTERNAL VIEW AND
SECTION THROUGH SEED**

**CROSS-SECTION
THROUGH FRUIT**

SYCONIUM (A TYPE OF FALSE FRUIT)
Fig
(*Ficus carica*)

Remains
of female
flowers

Fleshy infolded
receptacle

Peduncle
(inflorescence
stalk)

Pip (seed
surrounded
by endocarp)

Remains
of male
flowers

Skin

Pore closed
by scales

**EXTERNAL VIEW
OF FRUIT**

**LONGITUDINAL SECTION
THROUGH FRUIT**

FRUIT WITH FLESHY ARIL
Lychee
(*Litchi chinensis*)

Pedicel
(flower stalk)

Pedicel
(flower stalk)

Seed

Aril (fleshy
outgrowth
from seed
stalk)

Pericarp
(fruit wall)

Pericarp
(fruit wall)

Remains
of style

Endocarp

**EXTERNAL VIEW AND
SECTION THROUGH PIP**

Drupelet

Pip

Endocarp

Cotyledon
(seed leaf)

Pedicel
(flower
stalk)

Embryo

Testa
(seed coat)

**EXTERNAL VIEW
OF FRUIT**

**LONGITUDINAL SECTION
THROUGH FRUIT**

**REMAINS OF A SINGLE
FEMALE FLOWER**

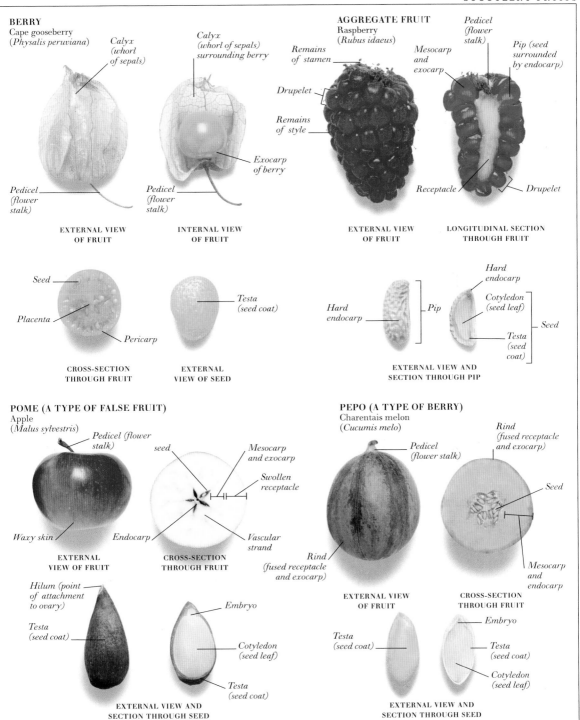

BERRY
Cape gooseberry
(*Physalis peruviana*)

Calyx (whorl of sepals)

Calyx (whorl of sepals) surrounding berry

Pedicel (flower stalk)

Pedicel (flower stalk)

Exocarp of berry

EXTERNAL VIEW OF FRUIT

INTERNAL VIEW OF FRUIT

Seed

Placenta

Pericarp

Testa (seed coat)

CROSS-SECTION THROUGH FRUIT

EXTERNAL VIEW OF SEED

AGGREGATE FRUIT
Raspberry
(*Rubus idaeus*)

Remains of stamen

Drupelet

Remains of style

Pedicel (flower stalk)

Mesocarp and exocarp

Pip (seed surrounded by endocarp)

Receptacle

Drupelet

EXTERNAL VIEW OF FRUIT

LONGITUDINAL SECTION THROUGH FRUIT

Hard endocarp

Pip

Hard endocarp

Cotyledon (seed leaf)

Seed

Testa (seed coat)

EXTERNAL VIEW AND SECTION THROUGH PIP

POME (A TYPE OF FALSE FRUIT)
Apple
(*Malus sylvestris*)

Pedicel (flower stalk)

seed

Mesocarp and exocarp

Swollen receptacle

Waxy skin

Endocarp

Vascular strand

EXTERNAL VIEW OF FRUIT

CROSS-SECTION THROUGH FRUIT

Hilum (point of attachment to ovary)

Testa (seed coat)

Embryo

Cotyledon (seed leaf)

Testa (seed coat)

EXTERNAL VIEW AND SECTION THROUGH SEED

PEPO (A TYPE OF BERRY)
Charentais melon
(*Cucumis melo*)

Pedicel (flower stalk)

Rind (fused receptacle and exocarp)

Seed

Rind (fused receptacle and exocarp)

Mesocarp and endocarp

EXTERNAL VIEW OF FRUIT

CROSS-SECTION THROUGH FRUIT

Testa (seed coat)

Embryo

Testa (seed coat)

Cotyledon (seed leaf)

EXTERNAL VIEW AND SECTION THROUGH SEED

149

Dry fruits

DRY FRUITS HAVE A HARD, DRY PERICARP (fruit wall) around their seeds unlike succulent fruits, which have fleshy pericarps (see pp. 148-149). Dry fruits are divided into three types: dehiscent, in which the pericarp splits open to release the seeds; indehiscent, which do not split open; and schizocarpic, in which the fruit splits but the seeds are not exposed. Dehiscent dry fruits include capsules (e.g., love-in-a-mist), follicles (e.g., delphinium), legumes (e.g., pea), and siliquas (e.g., honesty). Typically, the seeds of dehiscent fruits are dispersed by the wind. Indehiscent dry fruits include nuts (e.g., sweet chestnut), nutlets (e.g., goosegrass), achenes (e.g., strawberry), caryopses (e.g., wheat), samaras (e.g., elm), and cypselas (e.g., dandelion). Some indehiscent dry fruits are dispersed by the wind, assisted by "wings" (e.g., elm) or "parachutes" (e.g., dandelion); others (e.g., goosegrass) have hooked pericarps to aid dispersal on animals' fur. Schizocarpic dry fruits include cremocarps (e.g., hogweed), and double samaras (e.g., sycamore); these are dispersed by the wind.

NUTLET
Goosegrass
(*Galium aparine*)

LEGUME
Pea
(*Pisum sativum*)

Pedicel (flower stalk)
Receptacle
Remains of sepal
Remains of stamen
Placenta
Pericarp (fruit wall)
Remains of style and stigma

EXTERNAL VIEW OF FRUIT

Pedicel (flower stalk)
Receptacle
Remains of sepal
Funicle (stalk attaching seed to placenta)
Pericarp (fruit wall)
Seed
Remains of style and stigma

INTERNAL VIEW OF FRUIT

NUT
Sweet chestnut
(*Castanea sativa*)

Line of splitting between valves of cupule
Peduncle (inflorescence stalk)
Remains of male inflorescence
Nut (indehiscent fruit)
Spiky cupule (husk around fruit formed from bracts)

EXTERNAL VIEW OF FRUIT WITH SURROUNDING CUPULE

Funicle (stalk attaching seed to placenta)
Micropyle (pore for water absorption)
Testa (seed coat)
Cotyledon (seed leaf)
Testa (seed coat)
Radicle (embryonic root)
Plumule (embryonic shoot)

EXTERIOR VIEW AND SECTION THROUGH SEED

ACHENE
Strawberry
(*Fragaria x ananassa*)

Sepal
Pedicel (flower stalk)
Swollen receptacle
Remains of stigma and style
Achene (one-seeded dry fruit)

EXTERNAL VIEW OF FRUIT

Sepal
Pedicel (flower stalk)
Swollen fleshy tissues of receptacle

LONGITUDINAL SECTION THROUGH FRUIT

Remains of stigma
Remains of style
Nut (indehiscent fruit)
Woody pericarp (fruit wall)
Remains of stigma
Remains of style
Embryo
Cotyledon (seed leaf)
Testa (seed coat)
Woody pericarp (fruit wall)

EXTERNAL VIEW AND SECTION THROUGH FRUIT

Pericarp (fruit wall)
Pericarp (fruit wall)
Cotyledon (seed leaf)
Testa (seed coat)

EXTERNAL VIEW AND SECTION THROUGH SEED

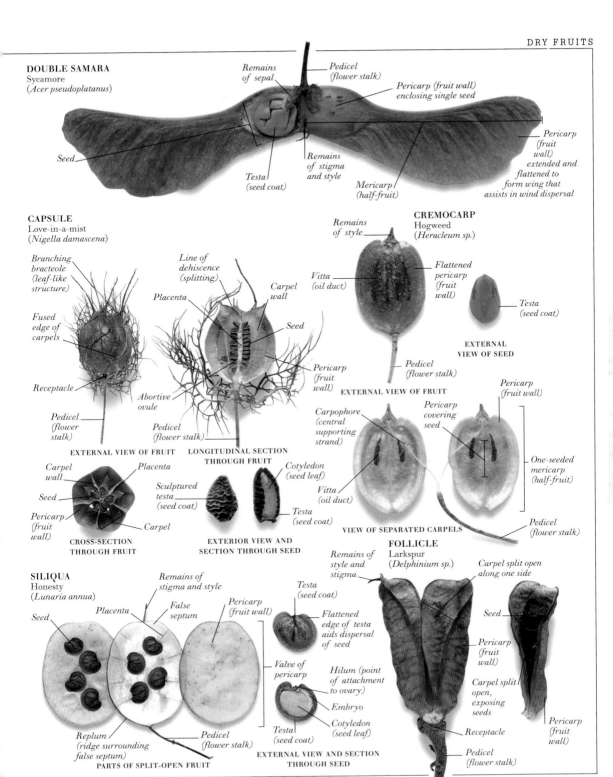

DOUBLE SAMARA
Sycamore
(*Acer pseudoplatanus*)

Remains
of sepal

Pedicel
(flower stalk)

Pericarp (fruit wall)
enclosing single seed

Seed

Remains
of stigma
and style

Testa
(seed coat)

Mericarp
(half-fruit)

Pericarp
(fruit
wall)
extended and
flattened to
form wing that
assists in wind dispersal

CAPSULE
Love-in-a-mist
(*Nigella damascena*)

Branching
bracteole
(leaf-like
structure)

Fused
edge of
carpels

Receptacle

Pedicel
(flower
stalk)

Line of
dehiscence
(splitting)

Placenta

Carpel
wall

Seed

Abortive
ovule

Pedicel
(flower
stalk)

Pericarp
(fruit
wall)

EXTERNAL VIEW OF FRUIT

**LONGITUDINAL SECTION
THROUGH FRUIT**

Carpel
wall

Seed

Pericarp
(fruit
wall)

Placenta

Carpel

**CROSS-SECTION
THROUGH FRUIT**

Sculptured
testa
(seed coat)

Cotyledon
(seed leaf)

Testa
(seed coat)

**EXTERIOR VIEW AND
SECTION THROUGH SEED**

CREMOCARP
Hogweed
(*Heracleum sp.*)

Remains
of style

Vitta
(oil duct)

Flattened
pericarp
(fruit
wall)

Testa
(seed coat)

**EXTERNAL
VIEW OF SEED**

Pedicel
(flower stalk)

EXTERNAL VIEW OF FRUIT

Carpophore
(central
supporting
strand)

Pericarp
covering
seed

Pericarp
(fruit wall)

Vitta
(oil duct)

One-seeded
mericarp
(half-fruit)

Pedicel
(flower stalk)

VIEW OF SEPARATED CARPELS

SILIQUA
Honesty
(*Lunaria annua*)

Seed

Placenta

Remains of
stigma and style

False
septum

Pericarp
(fruit wall)

Replum
(ridge surrounding
false septum)

Pedicel
(flower stalk)

PARTS OF SPLIT-OPEN FRUIT

Valve of
pericarp

FOLLICLE
Larkspur
(*Delphinium sp.*)

Remains of
style and
stigma

Testa
(seed coat)

Flattened
edge of testa
aids dispersal
of seed

Hilum (point
of attachment
to ovary)

Embryo

Testa
(seed coat)

Cotyledon
(seed leaf)

**EXTERNAL VIEW AND SECTION
THROUGH SEED**

Carpel split open
along one side

Seed

Pericarp
(fruit
wall)

Carpel split
open,
exposing
seeds

Receptacle

Pedicel
(flower stalk)

Pericarp
(fruit
wall)

Germination

GERMINATION IS THE GROWTH OF SEEDS INTO SEEDLINGS. It starts when seeds become active below ground, and ends when the first foliage leaves appear above ground. A seed consists of an embryo and its food store, surrounded by a testa (seed coat). The embryo is made up of one or two cotyledons (seed leaves) attached to a central axis. The upper part of the axis consists of an epicotyl, which has a plumule (embryonic shoot) at its tip. The lower part of the axis consists of a hypocotyl and a radicle (embryonic root). After dispersal from the parent plant, the seeds dehydrate and enter a period of dormancy. Following this dormant period, germination begins, provided that the seeds have enough water, oxygen, warmth, and, in some cases, light. In the first stages of germination, the seed takes in water; the embryo starts to use its food store; and the radicle swells, breaks through the testa, and grows downwards. Germination then proceeds in one of two ways, depending on the type of seed. In epigeal germination, the hypocotyl lengthens, pulling the plumule and its protective cotyledons out of the soil. In hypogeal germination, the cotyledons remain below ground and the epicotyl lengthens, pushing the plumule upwards.

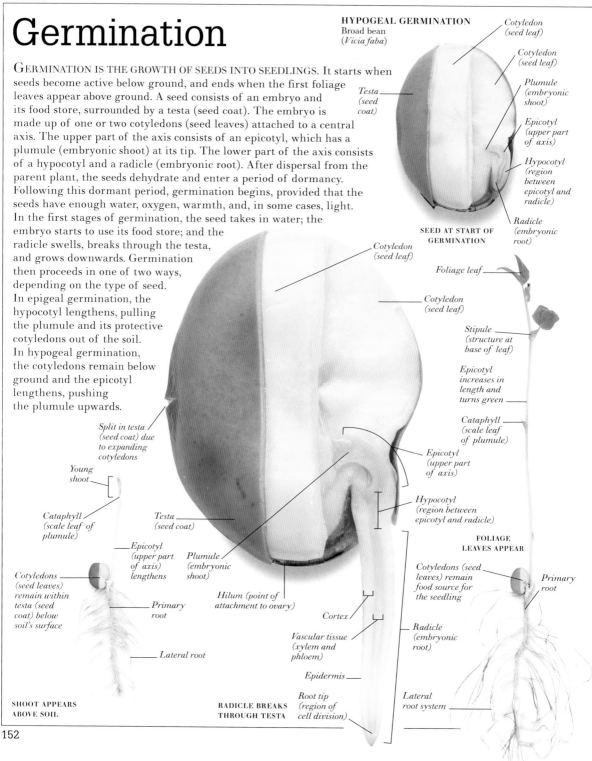

HYPOGEAL GERMINATION
Broad bean
(Vicia faba)

Cotyledon (seed leaf)

Cotyledon (seed leaf)

Plumule (embryonic shoot)

Epicotyl (upper part of axis)

Hypocotyl (region between epicotyl and radicle)

Testa (seed coat)

Radicle (embryonic root)

SEED AT START OF GERMINATION

Cotyledon (seed leaf)

Foliage leaf

Cotyledon (seed leaf)

Stipule (structure at base of leaf)

Epicotyl increases in length and turns green

Cataphyll (scale leaf of plumule)

Epicotyl (upper part of axis)

Hypocotyl (region between epicotyl and radicle)

FOLIAGE LEAVES APPEAR

Cotyledons (seed leaves) remain food source for the seedling

Primary root

Radicle (embryonic root)

Lateral root system

Split in testa (seed coat) due to expanding cotyledons

Young shoot

Cataphyll (scale leaf of plumule)

Testa (seed coat)

Epicotyl (upper part of axis) lengthens

Plumule (embryonic shoot)

Cotyledons (seed leaves) remain within testa (seed coat) below soil's surface

Primary root

Hilum (point of attachment to ovary)

Cortex

Vascular tissue (xylem and phloem)

Epidermis

Root tip (region of cell division)

Lateral root

SHOOT APPEARS ABOVE SOIL

RADICLE BREAKS THROUGH TESTA

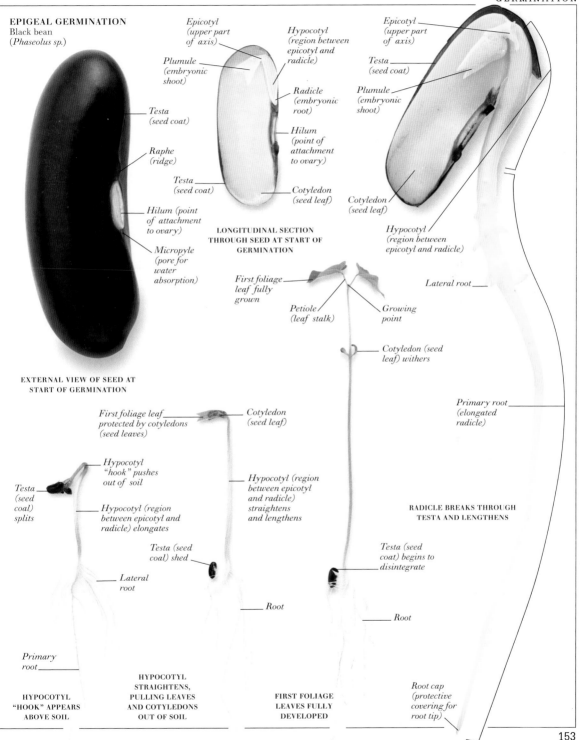

EPIGEAL GERMINATION
Black bean
(*Phaseolus sp.*)

Testa
(seed coat)

Raphe
(ridge)

Hilum (point
of attachment
to ovary)

Micropyle
(pore for
water
absorption)

**EXTERNAL VIEW OF SEED AT
START OF GERMINATION**

Epicotyl
(upper part
of axis)

Plumule
(embryonic
shoot)

Testa
(seed coat)

Testa
(seed coat)

Hypocotyl
(region between
epicotyl and
radicle)

Radicle
(embryonic
root)

Hilum
(point of
attachment
to ovary)

Cotyledon
(seed leaf)

**LONGITUDINAL SECTION
THROUGH SEED AT START OF
GERMINATION**

Epicotyl
(upper part
of axis)

Testa
(seed coat)

Plumule
(embryonic
shoot)

Cotyledon
(seed leaf)

Hypocotyl
(region between
epicotyl and radicle)

Lateral root

Primary root
(elongated
radicle)

**RADICLE BREAKS THROUGH
TESTA AND LENGTHENS**

First foliage
leaf fully
grown

Petiole
(leaf stalk)

Growing
point

Cotyledon (seed
leaf) withers

First foliage leaf
protected by cotyledons
(seed leaves)

Cotyledon
(seed leaf)

Hypocotyl
"hook" pushes
out of soil

Hypocotyl (region
between epicotyl
and radicle)
straightens
and lengthens

Testa
(seed
coal)
splits

Hypocotyl (region
between epicotyl and
radicle) elongates

Testa (seed
coal) shed

Lateral
root

Testa (seed
coat) begins to
disintegrate

Root

Root

Primary
root

**HYPOCOTYL
"HOOK" APPEARS
ABOVE SOIL**

**HYPOCOTYL
STRAIGHTENS,
PULLING LEAVES
AND COTYLEDONS
OUT OF SOIL**

**FIRST FOLIAGE
LEAVES FULLY
DEVELOPED**

Root cap
(protective
covering for
root tip)

153

Vegetative reproduction

ADVENTITIOUS BUD
Mexican hat plant
(*Kalanchoe daigremontiana*)

Apex of leaf

MANY PLANTS CAN PROPAGATE THEMSELVES by vegetative reproduction. In this process, part of a plant separates off, takes root, and grows into a new plant. Vegetative reproduction is a type of asexual reproduction; that is, it involves only one parent, and there is no fusion of gametes (sex cells). Plants use various structures to reproduce vegetatively. Some plants use underground storage organs. Such organs include rhizomes (horizontal, underground stems), the branches of which produce new plants; bulbs (swollen leaf bases) and corms (swollen stems), which produce daughter bulbs or corms that separate off from the parent; and stem tubers (thickened underground stems) and root tubers (swollen adventitious roots), which also separate off from the parent. Other propagative structures include runners and stolons, creeping horizontal stems that take root and produce new plants; bulbils, small bulbs that develop on the stem or in the place of flowers, and then drop off and grow into new plants; and adventitious buds, miniature plants that form on leaf margins before dropping to the ground and growing into mature plants.

CORM
Gladiolus
(*Gladiolus sp.*)

Lamina (blade) of leaf

Leaf margin

Notch in leaf margin containing meristematic (actively dividing) cells

BULBIL IN PLACE OF FLOWER
Orange lily
(*Lilium bulbiferum*)

Scar left by flower

Leaf

Pedicel (flower stalk)

Terminal bud

Adventitious bud (detachable bud with adventitious roots) drops from leaf

Petiole (leaf stalk)

Detachable bulbil formed in place of flower

Internode

STOLON
Ground ivy
(*Glechoma hederacea*)

Parent plant

Node

Stolon (creeping stem)

Peduncle (inflorescence stalk)

Node

Adventitious root of daughter plant

Daughter plant developed from lateral bud

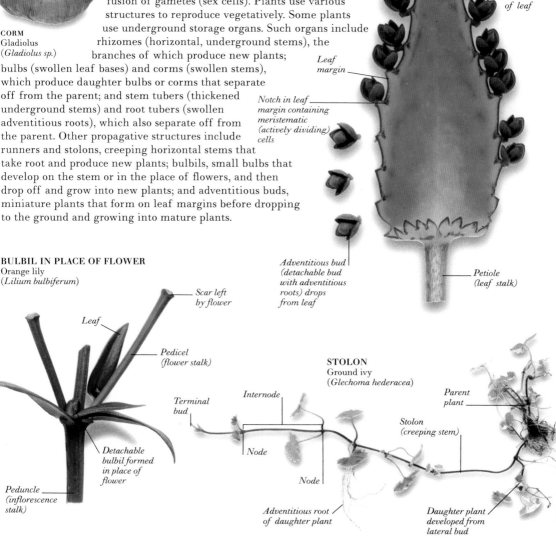

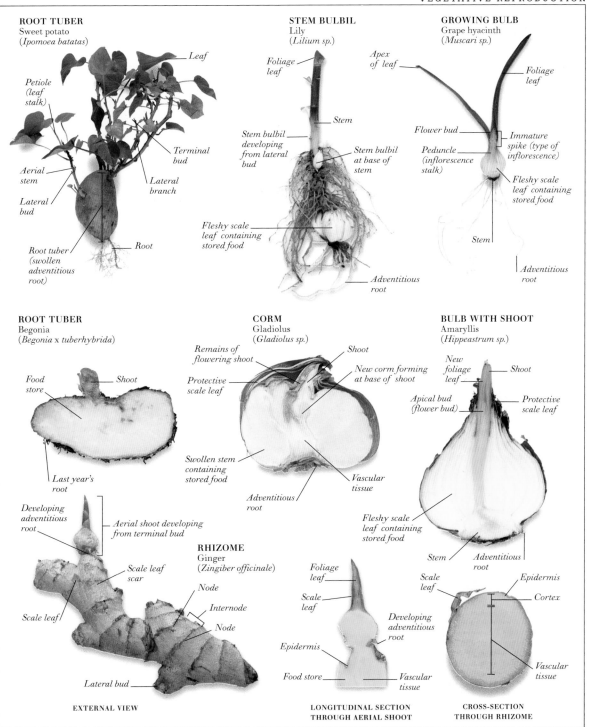

ROOT TUBER
Sweet potato
(*Ipomoea batatas*)

Leaf

Petiole
(leaf
stalk)

Terminal
bud

Aerial
stem

Lateral
branch

Lateral
bud

Root tuber
(swollen
adventitious
root)

Root

STEM BULBIL
Lily
(*Lilium sp.*)

Foliage
leaf

Stem

Stem bulbil
developing
from lateral
bud

Stem bulbil
at base of
stem

Fleshy scale
leaf containing
stored food

Adventitious
root

GROWING BULB
Grape hyacinth
(*Muscari sp.*)

Apex
of leaf

Foliage
leaf

Flower bud

Immature
spike (type of
inflorescence)

Peduncle
(inflorescence
stalk)

Fleshy scale
leaf containing
stored food

Stem

Adventitious
root

ROOT TUBER
Begonia
(*Begonia* x *tuberhybrida*)

Food
store

Shoot

Last year's
root

Developing
adventitious
root

Aerial shoot developing
from terminal bud

Scale leaf
scar

Scale leaf

Lateral bud

EXTERNAL VIEW

CORM
Gladiolus
(*Gladiolus sp.*)

Remains of
flowering shoot

Shoot

Protective
scale leaf

New corm forming
at base of shoot

Swollen stem
containing
stored food

Adventitious
root

Vascular
tissue

RHIZOME
Ginger
(*Zingiber officinale*)

Node

Internode

Node

Foliage
leaf

Scale
leaf

Developing
adventitious
root

Epidermis

Food store

Vascular
tissue

**LONGITUDINAL SECTION
THROUGH AERIAL SHOOT**

BULB WITH SHOOT
Amaryllis
(*Hippeastrum sp.*)

New
foliage
leaf

Shoot

Apical bud
(flower bud)

Protective
scale leaf

Fleshy scale
leaf containing
stored food

Stem

Adventitious
root

Scale
leaf

Epidermis

Cortex

Vascular
tissue

**CROSS-SECTION
THROUGH RHIZOME**

155

Dryland plants

LEAF
SUCCULENT
Lithops sp.

DRYLAND PLANTS (XEROPHYTES) are able to
survive in unfavourable habitats. All are found
in places where little water is available; some
live in high temperatures that cause excessive
loss of water from the leaves. Xerophytes
show a number of adaptations to dry
conditions; these include reduced leaf area,
rolled leaves, sunken stomata, hairs,
spines, and thick cuticles. One group,
succulent plants, stores water in specially
enlarged spongy tissues found in leaves, roots,
or stems. Leaf succulents have enlarged, fleshy,
water-storing leaves. Root succulents have a
large, underground water-storage organ with
short-lived stems and leaves above ground. Stem
succulents are represented by the cacti (family
Cactaceae). Cacti stems are fleshy, green, and
photosynthetic; they are typically ribbed or
covered by tubercles in rows, with leaves
being reduced to spines or entirely absent.

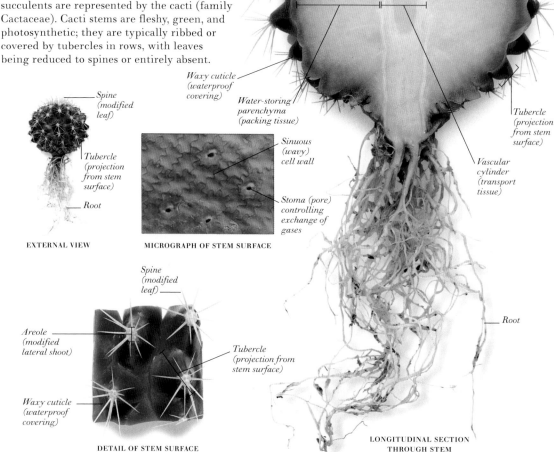

STEM SUCCULENT
Golden barrel cactus
(*Echinocactus grusonii*)

Areole
(modified
lateral shoot)

Trichome
(hair)

Spine
(modified
leaf)

Waxy cuticle
(waterproof
covering)

Water-storing
parenchyma
(packing tissue)

Tubercle
(projection
from stem
surface)

Vascular
cylinder
(transport
tissue)

Spine
(modified
leaf)

Tubercle
(projection
from stem
surface)

Root

EXTERNAL VIEW

Sinuous
(wavy)
cell wall

Stoma (pore)
controlling
exchange of
gases

MICROGRAPH OF STEM SURFACE

Spine
(modified
leaf)

Areole
(modified
lateral shoot)

Tubercle
(projection from
stem surface)

Waxy cuticle
(waterproof
covering)

Root

DETAIL OF STEM SURFACE

**LONGITUDINAL SECTION
THROUGH STEM**

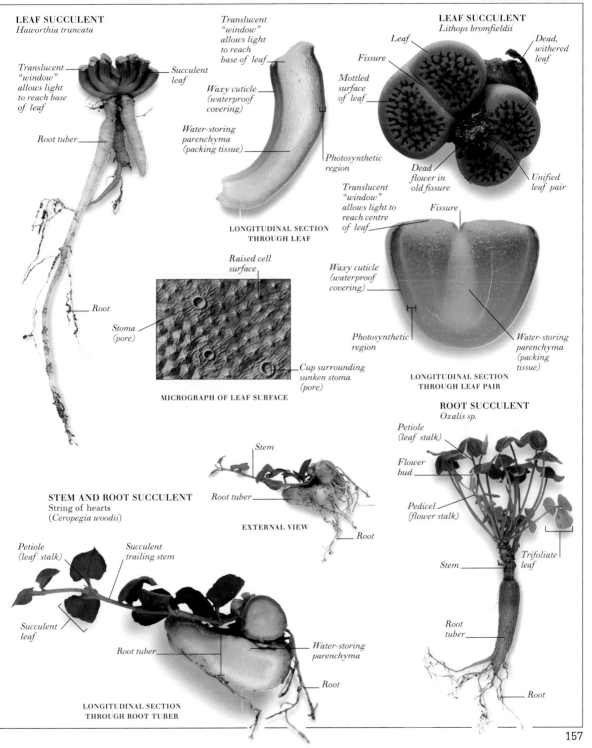

LEAF SUCCULENT
Haworthia truncata

Translucent "window" allows light to reach base of leaf

Succulent leaf

Root tuber

Root

Translucent "window" allows light to reach base of leaf

Waxy cuticle (waterproof covering)

Water-storing parenchyma (packing tissue)

Photosynthetic region

LONGITUDINAL SECTION THROUGH LEAF

Raised cell surface

Stoma (pore)

Cup surrounding sunken stoma (pore)

MICROGRAPH OF LEAF SURFACE

LEAF SUCCULENT
Lithops bromfieldii

Leaf

Fissure

Dead, withered leaf

Mottled surface of leaf

Dead flower in old fissure

Unified leaf pair

Translucent "window" allows light to reach centre of leaf

Fissure

Waxy cuticle (waterproof covering)

Photosynthetic region

Water-storing parenchyma (packing tissue)

LONGITUDINAL SECTION THROUGH LEAF PAIR

ROOT SUCCULENT
Oxalis sp.

Petiole (leaf stalk)

Flower bud

Pedicel (flower stalk)

Stem

Trifoliate leaf

Root tuber

Root

STEM AND ROOT SUCCULENT
String of hearts
(*Ceropegia woodii*)

Stem

Root tuber

Root

EXTERNAL VIEW

Petiole (leaf stalk)

Succulent trailing stem

Succulent leaf

Root tuber

Water-storing parenchyma

Root

LONGITUDINAL SECTION THROUGH ROOT TUBER

157

Wetland plants

WETLAND PLANTS GROW SUBMERGED IN WATER, either partially (e.g., water hyacinth) or completely (e.g., pond weeds), and show various adaptations to this habitat. Typically, there are numerous air spaces inside the stems, leaves, and roots; these aid gas exchange and buoyancy. Submerged parts generally have no cuticle (waterproof covering), enabling the plants to absorb minerals and gases directly from the water; in addition, being supported by the water, they need little of the supportive tissue found in land plants. Stomata, the gas exchange pores, are absent from plants that are completely submerged; in partially submerged plants with floating leaves (e.g., water lilies), stomata are found on the upper leaf surfaces, where they cannot be flooded.

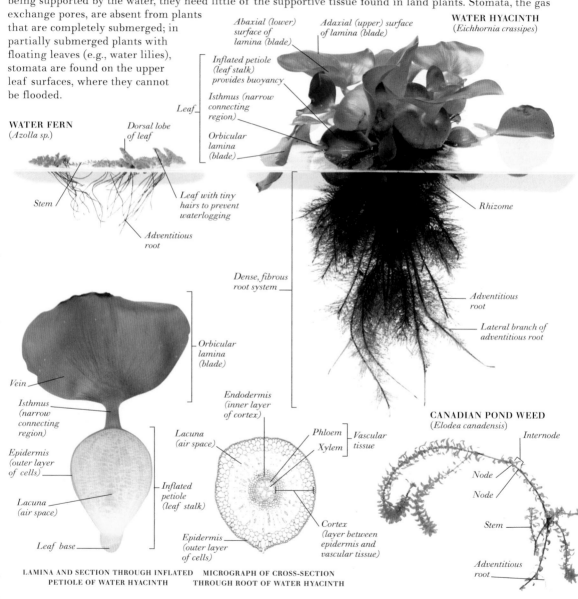

WATER FERN
(*Azolla* sp.)

Dorsal lobe of leaf

Stem

Adventitious root

Leaf with tiny hairs to prevent waterlogging

Abaxial (lower) surface of lamina (blade)

Adaxial (upper) surface of lamina (blade)

WATER HYACINTH
(*Eichhornia crassipes*)

Inflated petiole (leaf stalk) provides buoyancy

Isthmus (narrow connecting region)

Leaf

Orbicular lamina (blade)

Rhizome

Dense, fibrous root system

Adventitious root

Lateral branch of adventitious root

Vein

Isthmus (narrow connecting region)

Epidermis (outer layer of cells)

Lacuna (air space)

Leaf base

Orbicular lamina (blade)

Endodermis (inner layer of cortex)

Lacuna (air space)

Inflated petiole (leaf stalk)

Epidermis (outer layer of cells)

Phloem
Xylem
Vascular tissue

Cortex (layer between epidermis and vascular tissue)

CANADIAN POND WEED
(*Elodea canadensis*)

Internode

Node

Node

Stem

Adventitious root

LAMINA AND SECTION THROUGH INFLATED PETIOLE OF WATER HYACINTH

MICROGRAPH OF CROSS-SECTION THROUGH ROOT OF WATER HYACINTH

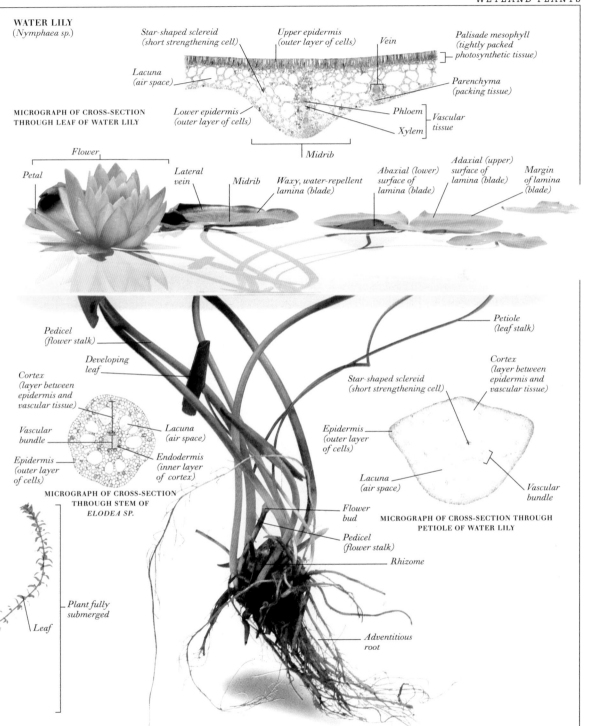

WATER LILY
(*Nymphaea sp.*)

Star-shaped sclereid
(short strengthening cell)

Upper epidermis
(outer layer of cells)

Vein

Palisade mesophyll
(tightly packed
photosynthetic tissue)

Lacuna
(air space)

Parenchyma
(packing tissue)

**MICROGRAPH OF CROSS-SECTION
THROUGH LEAF OF WATER LILY**

Lower epidermis
(outer layer of cells)

Phloem

Xylem

Vascular
tissue

Midrib

Flower

Petal

Lateral
vein

Midrib

Waxy, water-repellent
lamina (blade)

Abaxial (lower)
surface of
lamina (blade)

Adaxial (upper)
surface of
lamina (blade)

Margin
of lamina
(blade)

Pedicel
(flower stalk)

Developing
leaf

Petiole
(leaf stalk)

Cortex
(layer between
epidermis and
vascular tissue)

Star-shaped sclereid
(short strengthening cell)

Cortex
(layer between
epidermis and
vascular tissue)

Cortex
(layer between
epidermis and
vascular tissue)

Vascular
bundle

Lacuna
(air space)

Epidermis
(outer layer
of cells)

Epidermis
(outer layer
of cells)

Endodermis
(inner layer
of cortex)

Lacuna
(air space)

Vascular
bundle

**MICROGRAPH OF CROSS-SECTION
THROUGH STEM OF
ELODEA SP.**

**MICROGRAPH OF CROSS-SECTION THROUGH
PETIOLE OF WATER LILY**

Flower
bud

Pedicel
(flower stalk)

Rhizome

Plant fully
submerged

Leaf

Adventitious
root

159

Carnivorous plants

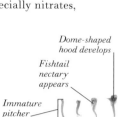

Areola ("window" of transparent tissue)

Fishtail nectary

Wing

Hood

Pitcher

Tubular petiole (leaf stalk)

Areola ("window" of transparent tissue)

CARNIVOROUS (INSECTIVOROUS) PLANTS FEED ON INSECTS and other small animals, in addition to producing food in their leaves by photosynthesis. The nutrients absorbed from trapped insects enable carnivorous plants to thrive in acid, boggy soils that lack essential minerals, especially nitrates, where most other plants could not survive. All carnivorous plants have some leaves modified as traps; many use bright colours and scented nectar to attract prey; and most use enzymes to digest the prey. There are three types of traps. Pitcher plants, such as the monkey cup and cobra lily, have leaves modified as pitcher-shaped pitfall traps, half-filled with water; once lured inside the mouth of the trap, insects lose their footing on the slippery surface, fall into the liquid, and either decompose or are digested. Venus fly traps use a spring-trap mechanism; when an insect touches trigger hairs on the inner surfaces of the leaves, the two lobes of the trap snap shut. Butterworts and sundews entangle prey by sticky droplets on the leaf surface, while the edges of the leaves slowly curl over to envelop and digest the prey.

Dome-shaped hood develops

Fishtail nectary appears

Immature pitcher

Smooth surface

Nectar roll

Wing

Mouth

Downward pointing hair

DEVELOPMENT OF MODIFIED LEAF IN COBRA LILY

Immature trap

Interlocked teeth

Closed trap

VENUS FLY TRAP
(*Dionaea muscipula*)

Red colour of trap attracts insects

Phyllode (flattened petiole)

Summer petiole (leaf stalk)

Nectary zone (glands secrete nectar)

Digestive zone (glands secrete digestive enzymes)

Tooth

Lobe of trap

Midrib (hinge of trap)

Trigger hair

Spring petiole (leaf stalk)

Trap (twin-lobed leaf blade)

Inner surface of trap

Sensory hinge

Trigger hair

Digestive gland

MICROGRAPH OF LOBE OF VENUS FLY TRAP

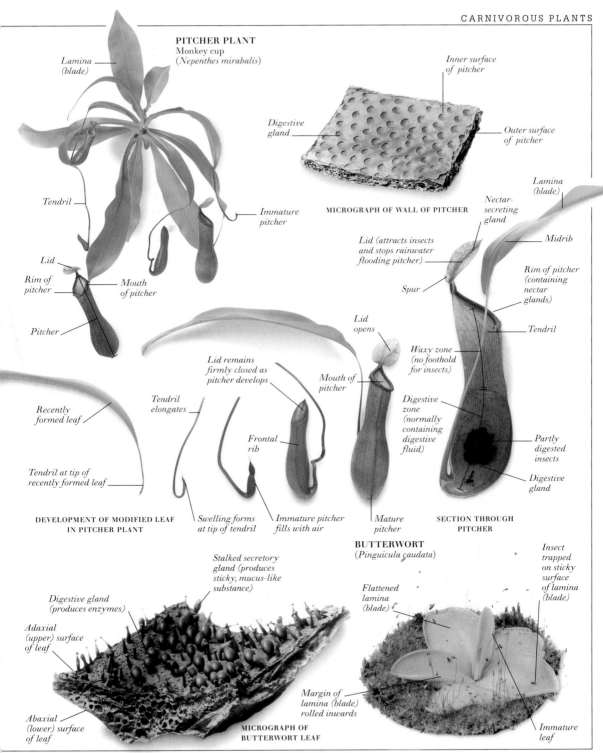

PITCHER PLANT
Monkey cup
(*Nepenthes mirabalis*)

Lamina
(blade)

Tendril

Lid

Rim of
pitcher

Mouth
of pitcher

Pitcher

Immature
pitcher

Inner surface
of pitcher

Digestive
gland

Outer surface
of pitcher

MICROGRAPH OF WALL OF PITCHER

Lamina
(blade)

Nectar-
secreting
gland

Midrib

Lid (attracts insects
and stops rainwater
flooding pitcher)

Spur

Rim of pitcher
(containing
nectar
glands)

Tendril

Recently
formed leaf

Tendril at tip of
recently formed leaf

Tendril
elongates

Lid remains
firmly closed as
pitcher develops

Frontal
rib

Swelling forms
at tip of tendril

Immature pitcher
fills with air

Lid
opens

Mouth of
pitcher

Waxy zone
(no foothold
for insects)

Digestive
zone
(normally
containing
digestive
fluid)

Mature
pitcher

Partly
digested
insects

Digestive
gland

**DEVELOPMENT OF MODIFIED LEAF
IN PITCHER PLANT**

**SECTION THROUGH
PITCHER**

BUTTERWORT
(*Pinguicula çaudata*)

Stalked secretory
gland (produces
sticky, mucus-like
substance)

Digestive gland
(produces enzymes)

Adaxial
(upper) surface
of leaf

Abaxial
(lower) surface
of leaf

Flattened
lamina
(blade)

Insect
trapped
on sticky
surface
of lamina
(blade)

Margin of
lamina (blade)
rolled inwards

Immature
leaf

**MICROGRAPH OF
BUTTERWORT LEAF**

Epiphytic and parasitic plants

EPIPHYTIC AND PARASITIC PLANTS GROW ON OTHER LIVING PLANTS. Typically, epiphytic plants are not rooted in the soil; instead, they live above ground level on the stems and branches of other plants. Epiphytes obtain water from trapped rainwater and from moisture in the air, and minerals from organic matter that has accumulated on the surface of the plant on which they are growing. Like other green plants, epiphytes produce their food by photosynthesis. Epiphytes include tropical orchids and bromeliads (air plants), and some mosses that live in temperate regions. Parasitic plants obtain all their nutrient requirements from the host plants on which they grow. The parasites produce haustoria, root-like organs that penetrate the stem or roots of the host and grow inwards to merge with the host's vascular tissue, from which the parasite extracts water, minerals, and manufactured nutrients. As they have no need to produce their own food, parasitic plants lack chlorophyll, the green photosynthetic pigment, and they have no foliage leaves. Partial parasitic plants (e.g., mistletoe) obtain water and minerals from the host plant but have green leaves and stems and are therefore able to produce their own food by photosynthesis.

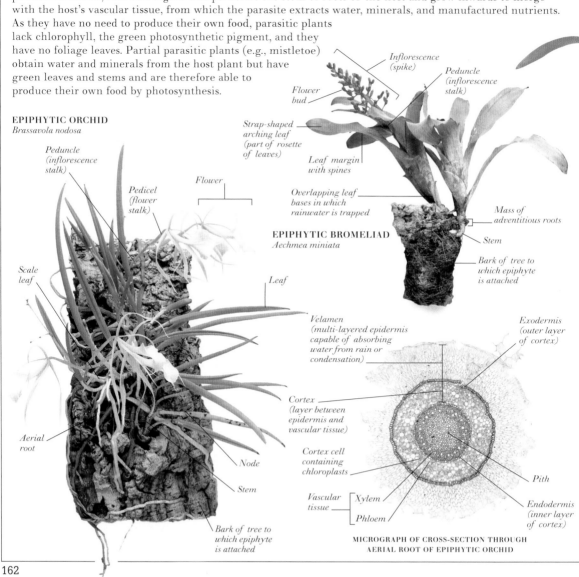

EPIPHYTIC ORCHID
Brassavola nodosa

Peduncle
(inflorescence
stalk)

Pedicel
(flower
stalk)

Flower

Scale
leaf

Aerial
root

Node

Stem

Bark of tree to
which epiphyte
is attached

Inflorescence
(spike)

Peduncle
(inflorescence
stalk)

Flower
bud

Strap-shaped
arching leaf
(part of rosette
of leaves)

Leaf margin
with spines

Overlapping leaf
bases in which
rainwater is trapped

EPIPHYTIC BROMELIAD
Aechmea miniata

Mass of
adventitious roots

Stem

Bark of tree to
which epiphyte
is attached

Leaf

Velamen
(multi-layered epidermis
capable of absorbing
water from rain or
condensation)

Cortex
(layer between
epidermis and
vascular tissue)

Cortex cell
containing
chloroplasts

Vascular
tissue

Xylem

Phloem

Exodermis
(outer layer
of cortex)

Pith

Endodermis
(inner layer
of cortex)

**MICROGRAPH OF CROSS-SECTION THROUGH
AERIAL ROOT OF EPIPHYTIC ORCHID**

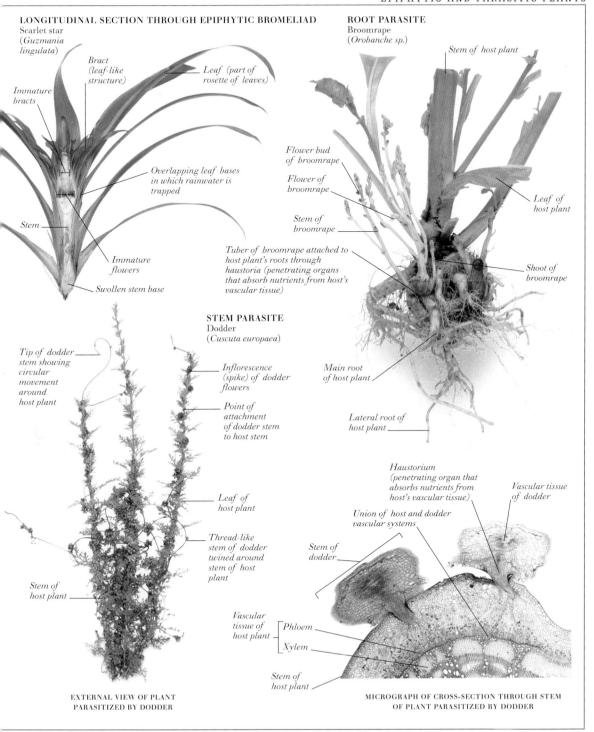

LONGITUDINAL SECTION THROUGH EPIPHYTIC BROMELIAD
Scarlet star
(*Guzmania
lingulata*)

*Bract
(leaf-like
structure)*

*Leaf (part of
rosette of leaves)*

*Immature
bracts*

*Overlapping leaf bases
in which rainwater is
trapped*

Stem

*Immature
flowers*

Swollen stem base

ROOT PARASITE
Broomrape
(*Orobanche sp.*)

Stem of host plant

*Flower bud
of broomrape*

*Flower of
broomrape*

*Stem of
broomrape*

*Leaf of
host plant*

*Tuber of broomrape attached to
host plant's roots through
haustoria (penetrating organs
that absorb nutrients from host's
vascular tissue)*

*Shoot of
broomrape*

*Main root
of host plant*

*Lateral root of
host plant*

STEM PARASITE
Dodder
(*Cuscuta europaea*)

*Tip of dodder
stem showing
circular
movement
around
host plant*

*Inflorescence
(spike) of dodder
flowers*

*Point of
attachment
of dodder stem
to host stem*

*Leaf of
host plant*

*Thread-like
stem of dodder
twined around
stem of host
plant*

*Stem of
host plant*

*Haustorium
(penetrating organ that
absorbs nutrients from
host's vascular tissue)*

*Vascular tissue
of dodder*

*Union of host and dodder
vascular systems*

*Stem of
dodder*

*Vascular
tissue of
host plant*

Phloem

Xylem

*Stem of
host plant*

**EXTERNAL VIEW OF PLANT
PARASITIZED BY DODDER**

**MICROGRAPH OF CROSS-SECTION THROUGH STEM
OF PLANT PARASITIZED BY DODDER**

163

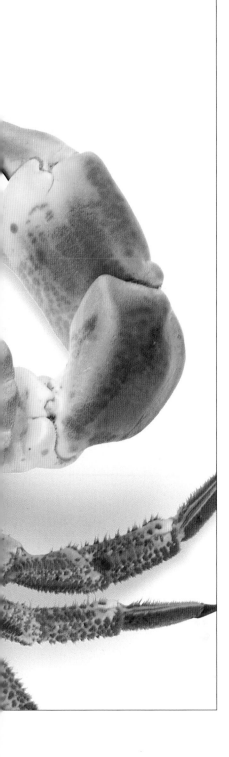

ANIMALS

Sponges, jellyfish, and sea anemones

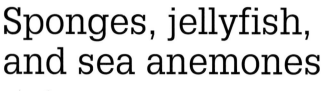

SPONGES ARE MAINLY MARINE animals that make up the phylum Porifera. They are among the simplest of all animals, having no tissues or organs. Their bodies consist of two layers of cells separated by a jelly-like layer (mesohyal) that is strengthened by mineral spicules or protein fibres. The body is perforated by a system of pores and water channels called the aquiferous system. Special cells (choanocytes) with whip-like structures (flagella) draw water through the aquiferous system, thereby bringing tiny food particles to the sponge's cells. Jellyfish (class Scyphozoa), sea anemones (class Anthozoa), and corals (also class Anthozoa) belong to the phylum Cnidaria, also known as Coelenterata. More complex than sponges, coelenterates have simple tissues, such as nervous tissue; a radially symmetrical body; and a mouth surrounded by tentacles with unique stinging cells (cnidocytes).

INTERNAL ANATOMY OF A SPONGE

Amoebocyte

Osculum (excurrent pore)

Choanocyte (collar cell)

Ostium (incurrent pore)

Porocyte (pore cell)

Mesohyal

Spongocoel (atrium; paragaster)

Spicule

Pinacocyte (epidermal cell)

Ostium (incurrent pore)

SKELETON OF A SPONGE

Protein matrix

Pore

EXTERNAL FEATURES OF A SEA ANEMONE

Tentacle

EXAMPLES OF SEA ANEMONES

JEWEL ANEMONE
(Corynactis viridis)

PARASITIC ANEMONE
(Calliactis parasitica)

PLUMOSE ANEMONE
(Metridium senile)

MEDITERRANEAN SEA ANEMONE
(Condylactis sp.)

GREEN SNAKELOCK ANEMONE
(Anemonia viridis)

BEADLET ANEMONE
(Actinia equina)

GHOST ANEMONE
(Actinothoe sphyrodeta)

Sagartia elegans

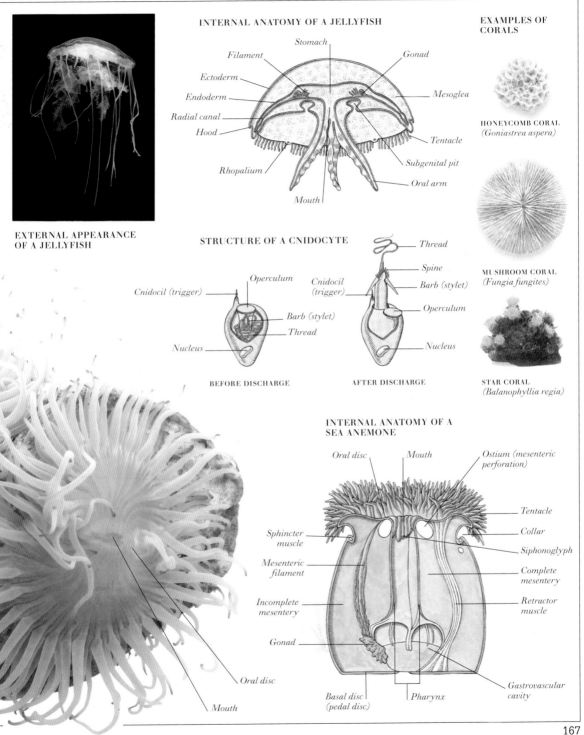

EXTERNAL APPEARANCE OF A JELLYFISH

INTERNAL ANATOMY OF A JELLYFISH

Stomach

Filament

Gonad

Ectoderm

Endoderm

Mesoglea

Radial canal

Hood

Tentacle

Rhopalium

Subgenital pit

Oral arm

Mouth

EXAMPLES OF CORALS

HONEYCOMB CORAL
(*Goniastrea aspera*)

MUSHROOM CORAL
(*Fungia fungites*)

STAR CORAL
(*Balanophyllia regia*)

STRUCTURE OF A CNIDOCYTE

Operculum

Thread

Cnidocil (trigger)

Spine

Cnidocil (trigger)

Barb (stylet)

Barb (stylet)

Operculum

Thread

Nucleus

Nucleus

BEFORE DISCHARGE

AFTER DISCHARGE

INTERNAL ANATOMY OF A SEA ANEMONE

Oral disc

Mouth

Ostium (mesenteric perforation)

Tentacle

Sphincter muscle

Collar

Mesenteric filament

Siphonoglyph

Complete mesentery

Incomplete mesentery

Retractor muscle

Gonad

Oral disc

Mouth

Basal disc (pedal disc)

Pharynx

Gastrovascular cavity

167

Insects

PUPA (CHRYSALIS)

THE WORD INSECT REFERS to small invertebrate creatures, especially those with bodies divided into sections. Insects, including beetles, ants, bees, butterflies, and moths, belong to various orders in the class Insecta, which is a division of the phylum Arthropoda. Features common to all insects are an exoskeleton (external skeleton); three pairs of jointed legs; three body sections (head, thorax, and abdomen); and one pair of sensory antennae. Beetles (order Coleoptera) are the biggest group of insects, with about 300,000 species (about 30 per cent of all known insects). They have a pair of hard elytra (wing cases), which are modified front wings. The principal function of the elytra is to protect the hind wings, which are used for flying. Ants, together with bees and wasps, form the order Hymenoptera, which contains about 200,000 species. This group is characterized by a marked narrowing between the thorax and abdomen. Butterflies and moths form the order Lepidoptera, which has about 150,000 species. They have wings covered with tiny scales, hence the name of their order (Lepidoptera means "scale wings"). The separation of lepidopterans into butterflies and moths is largely artificial as there are no features that categorically distinguish one group from the other. In general, however, most butterflies fly by day, whereas most moths are night-flyers. Some insects, including butterflies and moths, undergo complete metamorphosis (transformation) during their life-cycle. A butterfly metamorphoses from an egg to a larva (caterpillar), then to a pupa (chrysalis), and finally to an imago (adult).

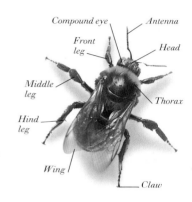

EXAMPLES OF INSECTS

Compound eye · Antenna · Front leg · Head · Middle leg · Thorax · Hind leg · Wing · Claw

BUMBLEBEE

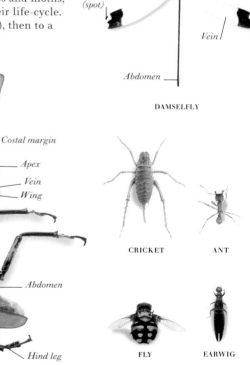

Compound eye · Stigma (spot) · Vein · Abdomen

DAMSELFLY

EXTERNAL FEATURES OF A BEETLE

Elytron · Tarsus · Claw · Tibia · Pedicel · Costal margin · Femur · Apex · Flagellum · Trochanter · Vein · Wing · Mandible · Scape · Coxa · Labrum · Labial palp · Compound eye · Head · Abdomen · Prothorax · Mesothorax · Front leg · Scutellum · Hind leg · Metathorax · Middle leg

CRICKET

ANT

FLY

EARWIG

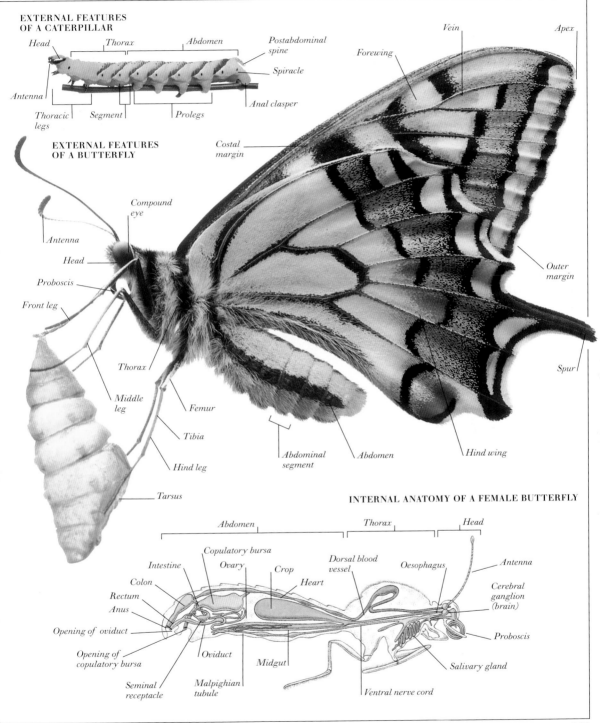

**EXTERNAL FEATURES
OF A CATERPILLAR**

Head

Thorax

Abdomen

Postabdominal
spine

Spiracle

Antenna

Anal clasper

Thoracic
legs

Segment

Prolegs

**EXTERNAL FEATURES
OF A BUTTERFLY**

Vein

Apex

Forewing

Costal
margin

Compound
eye

Antenna

Head

Proboscis

Front leg

Outer
margin

Thorax

Middle
leg

Femur

Tibia

Spur

Hind leg

Tarsus

Abdominal
segment

Abdomen

Hind wing

INTERNAL ANATOMY OF A FEMALE BUTTERFLY

Abdomen

Thorax

Head

Copulatory bursa

Intestine

Ovary

Crop

Dorsal blood
vessel

Oesophagus

Antenna

Colon

Heart

Cerebral
ganglion
(brain)

Rectum

Anus

Proboscis

Opening of oviduct

Opening of
copulatory bursa

Oviduct

Midgut

Salivary gland

Seminal
receptacle

Malpighian
tubule

Ventral nerve cord

Arachnids

THE CLASS ARACHNIDA INCLUDES SPIDERS (order Araneae) and scorpions (order Scorpiones). The class is part of the phylum Arthropoda, which also includes insects and crustaceans.

Spiders and scorpions are characterized by having four pairs of walking legs; a pair of pincer-like mouthparts called chelicerae; another pair of frontal appendages called pedipalps, which are sensory in spiders but used for grasping in scorpions; and a body divided into two sections (a combined head and thorax called a cephalothorax or prosoma, and an abdomen or opisthosoma). Unlike other arthropods, spiders and scorpions lack antennae. Spiders and scorpions are carnivorous. Spiders poison prey by biting with the fanged chelicerae, scorpions by stinging with the end of the metasoma (tail).

MEXICAN TRUE RED-LEGGED TARANTULA
(Euathlus emilia)

INTERNAL ANATOMY OF A FEMALE SPIDER

EXTERNAL FEATURES OF A SCORPION

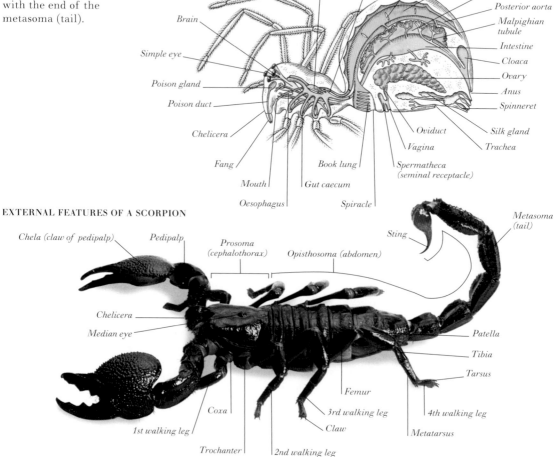

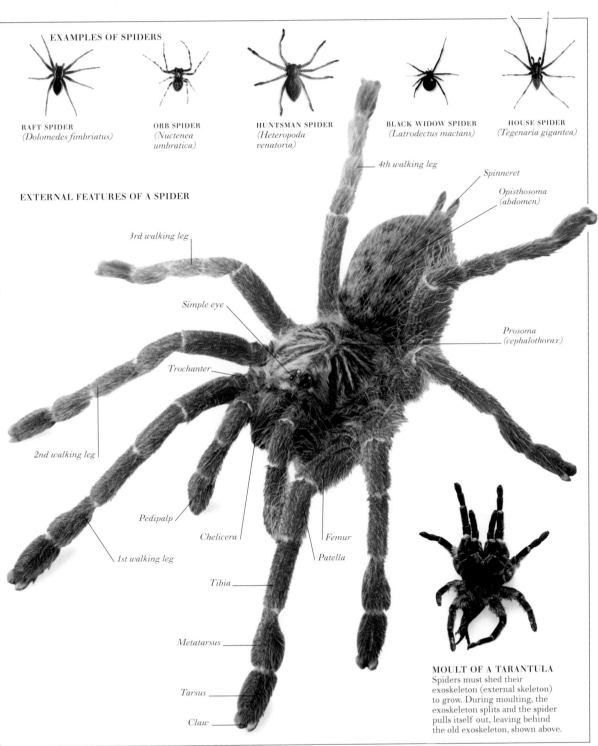

EXAMPLES OF SPIDERS

RAFT SPIDER
(*Dolomedes fimbriatus*)

ORB SPIDER
(*Nuctenea umbratica*)

HUNTSMAN SPIDER
(*Heteropoda venatoria*)

BLACK WIDOW SPIDER
(*Latrodectus mactans*)

HOUSE SPIDER
(*Tegenaria gigantea*)

EXTERNAL FEATURES OF A SPIDER

4th walking leg

Spinneret

Opisthosoma
(abdomen)

3rd walking leg

Simple eye

Prosoma
(cephalothorax)

Trochanter

2nd walking leg

Pedipalp

Chelicera

Femur

Patella

1st walking leg

Tibia

Metatarsus

Tarsus

Claw

MOULT OF A TARANTULA

Spiders must shed their
exoskeleton (external skeleton)
to grow. During moulting, the
exoskeleton splits and the spider
pulls itself out, leaving behind
the old exoskeleton, shown above.

171

Crustaceans

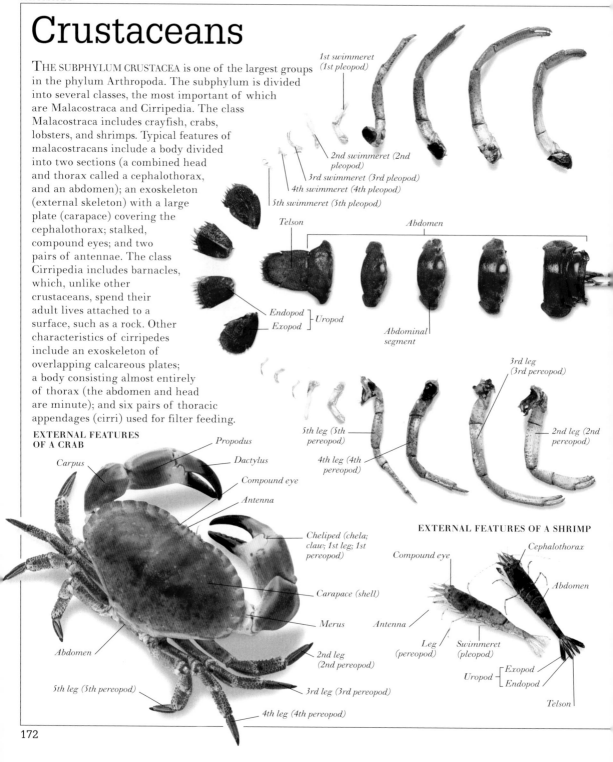

THE SUBPHYLUM CRUSTACEA is one of the largest groups in the phylum Arthropoda. The subphylum is divided into several classes, the most important of which are Malacostraca and Cirripedia. The class Malacostraca includes crayfish, crabs, lobsters, and shrimps. Typical features of malacostracans include a body divided into two sections (a combined head and thorax called a cephalothorax, and an abdomen); an exoskeleton (external skeleton) with a large plate (carapace) covering the cephalothorax; stalked, compound eyes; and two pairs of antennae. The class Cirripedia includes barnacles, which, unlike other crustaceans, spend their adult lives attached to a surface, such as a rock. Other characteristics of cirripedes include an exoskeleton of overlapping calcareous plates; a body consisting almost entirely of thorax (the abdomen and head are minute); and six pairs of thoracic appendages (cirri) used for filter feeding.

1st swimmeret (1st pleopod)

2nd swimmeret (2nd pleopod)

3rd swimmeret (3rd pleopod)

4th swimmeret (4th pleopod)

5th swimmeret (5th pleopod)

Telson

Abdomen

Endopod
Exopod — Uropod

Abdominal segment

3rd leg (3rd pereopod)

2nd leg (2nd pereopod)

5th leg (5th pereopod)

4th leg (4th pereopod)

EXTERNAL FEATURES OF A CRAB

Carpus

Propodus

Dactylus

Compound eye

Antenna

Cheliped (chela; claw; 1st leg; 1st pereopod)

Carapace (shell)

Merus

Abdomen

2nd leg (2nd pereopod)

3rd leg (3rd pereopod)

5th leg (5th pereopod)

4th leg (4th pereopod)

EXTERNAL FEATURES OF A SHRIMP

Cephalothorax

Abdomen

Compound eye

Antenna

Leg (pereopod)

Swimmeret (pleopod)

Uropod — Exopod
Endopod

Telson

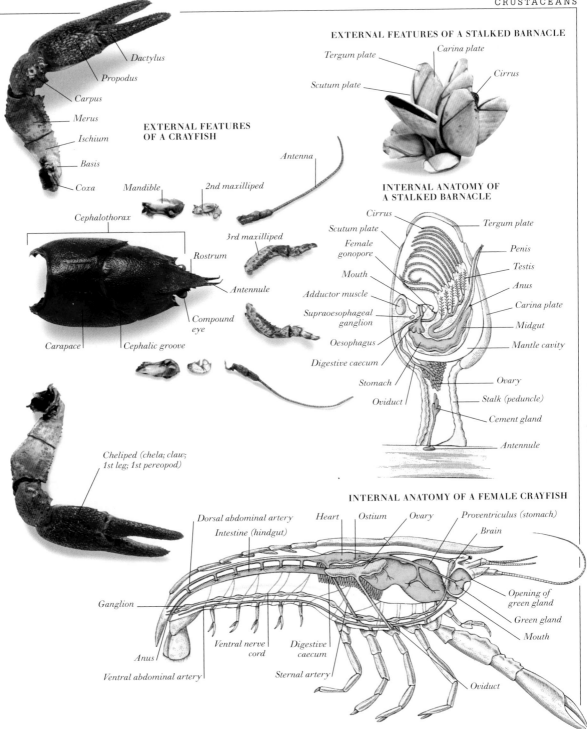

EXTERNAL FEATURES OF A STALKED BARNACLE

Tergum plate

Carina plate

Scutum plate

Cirrus

EXTERNAL FEATURES OF A CRAYFISH

Dactylus

Propodus

Carpus

Merus

Ischium

Basis

Coxa

Mandible

2nd maxilliped

Antenna

Cephalothorax

3rd maxilliped

Rostrum

Antennule

Compound eye

Carapace

Cephalic groove

Cheliped (chela; claw; 1st leg; 1st pereopod)

INTERNAL ANATOMY OF A STALKED BARNACLE

Cirrus

Scutum plate

Tergum plate

Female gonopore

Penis

Mouth

Testis

Adductor muscle

Anus

Supraoesophageal ganglion

Carina plate

Midgut

Oesophagus

Mantle cavity

Digestive caecum

Stomach

Ovary

Oviduct

Stalk (peduncle)

Cement gland

Antennule

INTERNAL ANATOMY OF A FEMALE CRAYFISH

Dorsal abdominal artery

Heart

Ostium

Ovary

Proventriculus (stomach)

Intestine (hindgut)

Brain

Ganglion

Opening of green gland

Green gland

Mouth

Anus

Ventral nerve cord

Digestive caecum

Ventral abdominal artery

Sternal artery

Oviduct

173

Starfish and sea urchins

STARFISH, SEA URCHINS, AND THEIR relatives (including feather stars, brittle stars, basket stars, sea daisies, sea lilies, and sea cucumbers) make up the phylum Echinodermata. A unique feature of echinoderms is the water vascular system, which consists of a series of water-filled canals from which protrude thousands of tiny tube feet. The tube feet may be used for movement, feeding, or respiration. Other features include pentaradiate symmetry (that is, the body can be divided into five parts radiating from the centre); no head; a diffuse, decentralized nervous system that lacks a brain; and no excretory organs. Typically, echinoderms also have an endoskeleton (internal skeleton) consisting of hard calcite ossicles embedded in the body wall and often bearing protruding spines or tubercles. The ossicles may fit together to form a test (as in sea urchins) or remain separate (as in sea cucumbers).

EXTERNAL FEATURES OF A STARFISH (UPPER, OR ABORAL, SURFACE)

Disc

Madreporite

Spine

Arm

INTERNAL ANATOMY OF A STARFISH

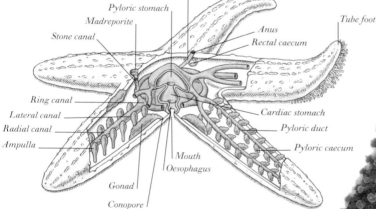

Rectum

Pyloric stomach

Madreporite

Stone canal

Anus

Rectal caecum

Tube foot

Ring canal

Lateral canal

Radial canal

Ampulla

Cardiac stomach

Pyloric duct

Pyloric caecum

Mouth

Oesophagus

Gonad

Conopore

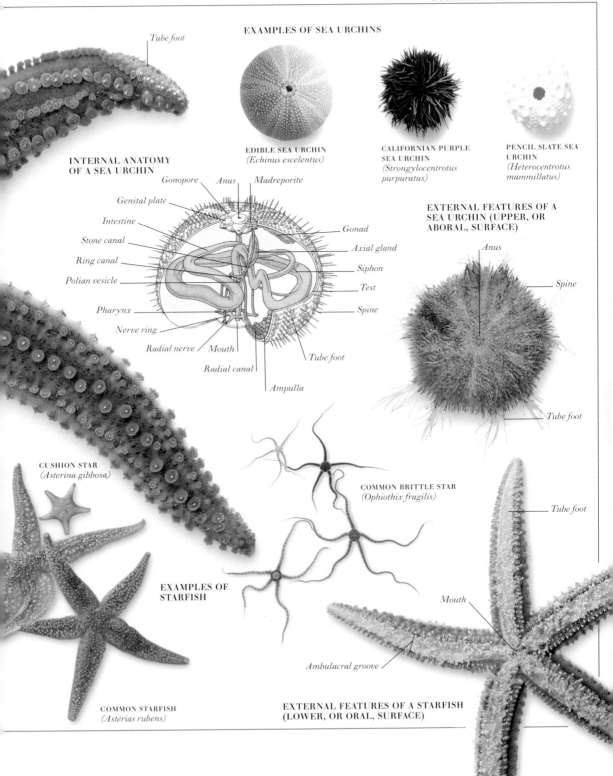

Tube foot

EXAMPLES OF SEA URCHINS

EDIBLE SEA URCHIN
(*Echinus escelentus*)

**CALIFORNIAN PURPLE
SEA URCHIN**
(*Strongylocentrotus
purpuratus*)

**PENCIL SLATE SEA
URCHIN**
(*Heterocentrotus
mammillatus*)

**INTERNAL ANATOMY
OF A SEA URCHIN**

Gonopore   *Anus*   *Madreporite*

Genital plate

Intestine

Stone canal

Ring canal

Polian vesicle

Pharynx

Nerve ring

Radial nerve   *Mouth*

Radial canal

Ampulla

Gonad

Axial gland

Siphon

Test

Spine

Tube foot

**EXTERNAL FEATURES OF A
SEA URCHIN (UPPER, OR
ABORAL, SURFACE)**

Anus

Spine

Tube foot

CUSHION STAR
(*Asterina gibbosa*)

COMMON BRITTLE STAR
(*Ophiothix fragilis*)

Tube foot

**EXAMPLES OF
STARFISH**

Mouth

Ambulacral groove

COMMON STARFISH
(*Asterias rubens*)

**EXTERNAL FEATURES OF A STARFISH
(LOWER, OR ORAL, SURFACE)**

Molluscs

THE PHYLUM MOLLUSCA (MOLLUSCS) is a large group of animals that includes octopuses, snails, and scallops. Octopuses and their relatives – including squid and cuttlefish – form the class Cephalopoda. Cephalopods typically have a head with a radula (a file-like feeding organ) and beak; a well-developed nervous system; sucker-bearing tentacles; a muscular mantle (part of the body wall) that can expel water through the siphon, enabling movement by jet propulsion; and a small shell or no shell. Snails and their relatives – including slugs, limpets, and abalones – make up the class Gastropoda. Gastropods typically have a coiled external shell, although some, such as slugs, have a small internal shell or no shell; a flat foot; and a head with tentacles and a radula. Scallops and their relatives – including clams, mussels, and oysters – make up the class Bivalvia (also called Pelecypoda). Features of bivalves include a shell with two halves (valves); large gills that are used for breathing and filter feeding; and no radula.

EXTERNAL FEATURES OF A SCALLOP

Upper valve (shell)   Mantle   Ocellus (eye)

Lower valve (shell)   Shell rib   Sensory tentacle

Sensory tentacle   Ventral margin of shell   Shell rib

Anterior wing of shell

Umbo

Dorsal margin of shell

Posterior wing of shell

INTERNAL ANATOMY OF AN OCTOPUS

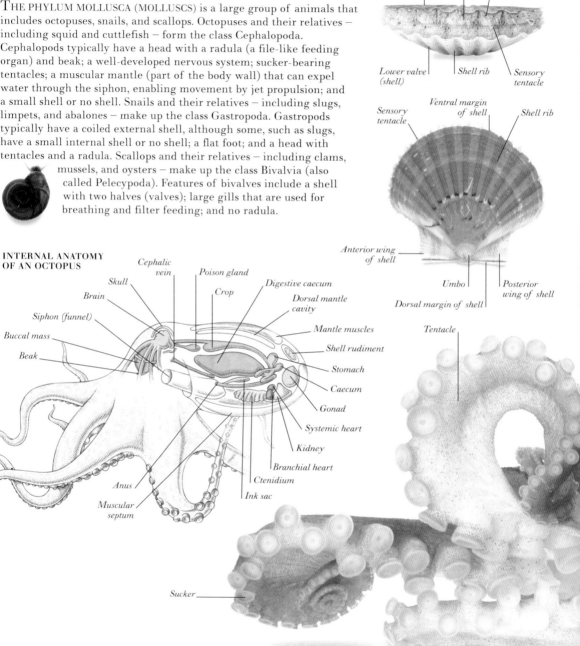

Cephalic vein
Poison gland
Skull
Crop
Brain
Digestive caecum
Dorsal mantle cavity
Siphon (funnel)
Buccal mass
Mantle muscles
Beak
Shell rudiment
Stomach
Caecum
Gonad
Systemic heart
Kidney
Branchial heart
Ctenidium
Ink sac
Anus
Muscular septum
Sucker

Tentacle

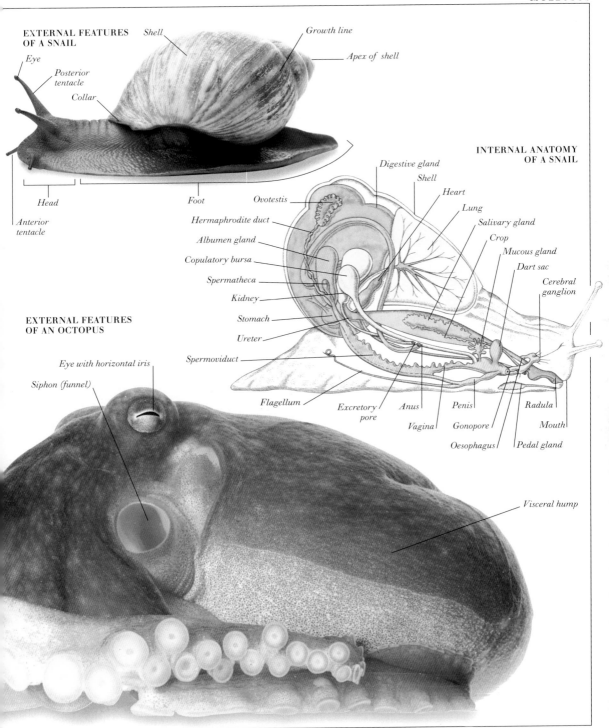

EXTERNAL FEATURES OF A SNAIL

Shell

Growth line

Apex of shell

Eye

Posterior tentacle

Collar

Head

Foot

Anterior tentacle

INTERNAL ANATOMY OF A SNAIL

Digestive gland

Shell

Heart

Lung

Salivary gland

Crop

Mucous gland

Dart sac

Cerebral ganglion

Ovotestis

Hermaphrodite duct

Albumen gland

Copulatory bursa

Spermatheca

Kidney

Stomach

Ureter

Spermoviduct

Flagellum

Excretory pore

Anus

Vagina

Penis

Gonopore

Oesophagus

Radula

Mouth

Pedal gland

EXTERNAL FEATURES OF AN OCTOPUS

Eye with horizontal iris

Siphon (funnel)

Visceral hump

177

Sharks and jawless fish

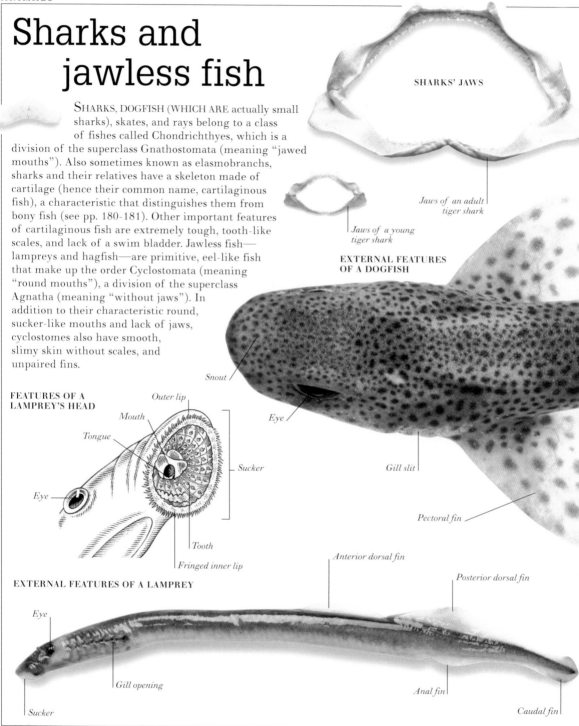

SHARKS, DOGFISH (WHICH ARE actually small sharks), skates, and rays belong to a class of fishes called Chondrichthyes, which is a division of the superclass Gnathostomata (meaning "jawed mouths"). Also sometimes known as elasmobranchs, sharks and their relatives have a skeleton made of cartilage (hence their common name, cartilaginous fish), a characteristic that distinguishes them from bony fish (see pp. 180-181). Other important features of cartilaginous fish are extremely tough, tooth-like scales, and lack of a swim bladder. Jawless fish—lampreys and hagfish—are primitive, eel-like fish that make up the order Cyclostomata (meaning "round mouths"), a division of the superclass Agnatha (meaning "without jaws"). In addition to their characteristic round, sucker-like mouths and lack of jaws, cyclostomes also have smooth, slimy skin without scales, and unpaired fins.

SHARKS' JAWS

Jaws of an adult tiger shark

Jaws of a young tiger shark

EXTERNAL FEATURES OF A DOGFISH

Snout

Eye

Gill slit

Pectoral fin

FEATURES OF A LAMPREY'S HEAD

Outer lip

Mouth

Tongue

Eye

Sucker

Tooth

Fringed inner lip

EXTERNAL FEATURES OF A LAMPREY

Eye

Gill opening

Sucker

Anterior dorsal fin

Posterior dorsal fin

Anal fin

Caudal fin

178

EXAMPLES OF CARTILAGINOUS FISH

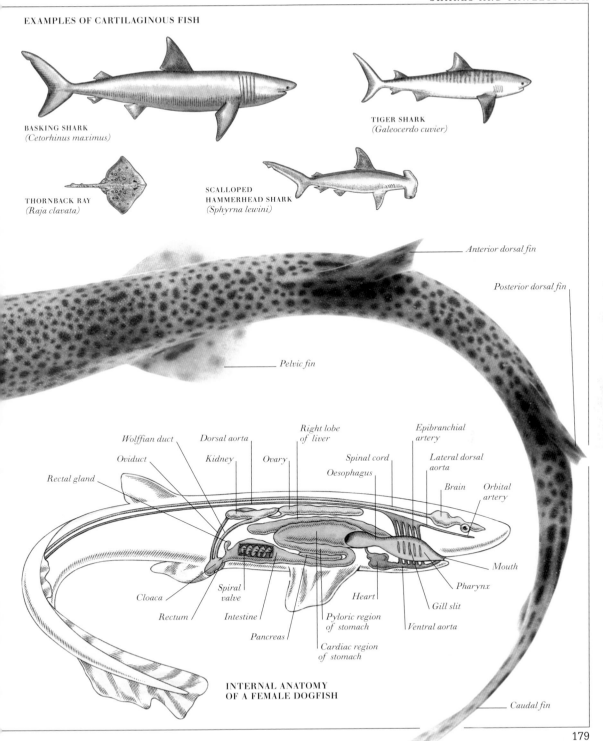

BASKING SHARK
(Cetorhinus maximus)

TIGER SHARK
(Galeocerdo cuvier)

THORNBACK RAY
(Raja clavata)

**SCALLOPED
HAMMERHEAD SHARK**
(Sphyrna lewini)

Anterior dorsal fin

Posterior dorsal fin

Pelvic fin

Wolffian duct

Dorsal aorta

Right lobe
of liver

Epibranchial
artery

Oviduct

Kidney

Ovary

Spinal cord

Lateral dorsal
aorta

Rectal gland

Oesophagus

Brain

Orbital
artery

Mouth

Cloaca

Spiral
valve

Heart

Pharynx

Rectum

Intestine

Pyloric region
of stomach

Gill slit

Pancreas

Ventral aorta

Cardiac region
of stomach

Caudal fin

**INTERNAL ANATOMY
OF A FEMALE DOGFISH**

Bony fish

BONY FISH, SUCH AS CARP, TROUT, SALMON, perch, and cod, are by far the best known and largest group of fish, with more than 20,000 species (over 95 per cent of all known fish). As their name suggests, bony fish have skeletons made of bone, in contrast to the cartilaginous skeletons of sharks, jawless fish, and their relatives (see pp. 178-179). Other typical features of bony fish include a swim bladder, which functions as a variable-buoyancy organ, enabling a fish to remain effortlessly at whatever depth it is swimming; relatively thin, bone-like scales; a flap (called an operculum) covering the gills; and paired pelvic and pectoral fins. Scientifically, bony fish belong to the class Osteichthyes, which is a division of the superclass Gnathostomata (meaning "jawed mouths").

HOW FISH BREATHE

Fish "breathe" by extracting oxygen from water through their gills. Water is sucked in through the mouth; simultaneously, the opercula close to prevent the water from escaping. The mouth is then closed, and muscles in the walls of the mouth, pharynx, and opercular cavity contract to pump the water inside over the gills and out through the opercula. Some fish rely on swimming with their mouths open to keep water flowing over the gills.

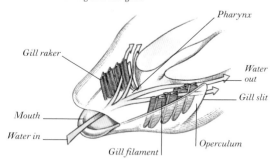

Pharynx

Gill raker

Water out

Gill slit

Mouth

Water in

Gill filament

Operculum

EXAMPLES OF BONY FISH

MANDARINFISH
(Synchiropus splendidus)

ANGLERFISH
(Caulophryne jordani)

LIONFISH
(Pterois volitans)

OCEANIC SEAHORSE
(Hippocampus kuda)

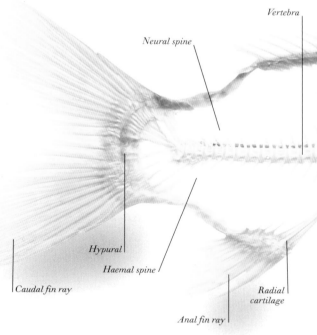

Vertebra

Neural spine

Hypural

Haemal spine

Caudal fin ray

Anal fin ray

Radial cartilage

STURGEON
(Acipenser sturio)

SNOWFLAKE MORAY EEL
(Echidna nebulosa)

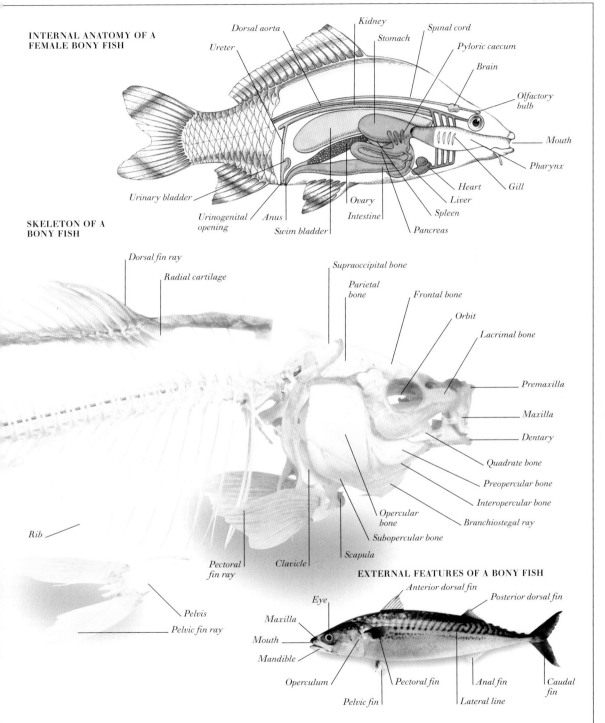

INTERNAL ANATOMY OF A FEMALE BONY FISH

Dorsal aorta
Ureter
Kidney
Stomach
Spinal cord
Pyloric caecum
Brain
Olfactory bulb
Mouth
Pharynx
Gill
Heart
Liver
Spleen
Pancreas
Intestine
Ovary
Swim bladder
Anus
Urinogenital opening
Urinary bladder

SKELETON OF A BONY FISH

Dorsal fin ray
Radial cartilage
Supraoccipital bone
Parietal bone
Frontal bone
Orbit
Lacrimal bone
Premaxilla
Maxilla
Dentary
Quadrate bone
Preopercular bone
Interopercular bone
Branchiostegal ray
Opercular bone
Subopercular bone
Scapula
Clavicle
Pectoral fin ray
Rib
Pelvis
Pelvic fin ray

EXTERNAL FEATURES OF A BONY FISH

Anterior dorsal fin
Posterior dorsal fin
Eye
Maxilla
Mouth
Mandible
Operculum
Pelvic fin
Pectoral fin
Anal fin
Lateral line
Caudal fin

181

Amphibians

THE CLASS AMPHIBIA INCLUDES FROGS and toads (which make up the order Anura), and newts and salamanders (which make up the order Urodela). Amphibians typically have moist, scaleless, hairless skin; lungs; and are cold-blooded. They also undergo complete metamorphosis, from eggs laid in water through various water-living larval stages (such as tadpoles) to land-living adults. Typical features of adult frogs and toads include a squat body with no tail; long, powerful hind legs; and large, often bulging, eyes. Adult newts and salamanders typically have a long body with a well-developed tail; and relatively short, equal-sized legs. However, newts and salamanders show considerable variation; for example, in some species the adults have minute legs, external gills rather than lungs, and spend their entire lives in water.

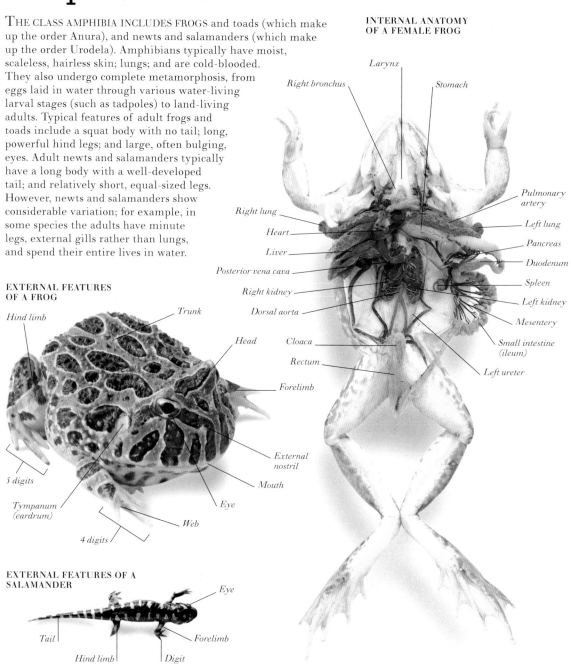

INTERNAL ANATOMY OF A FEMALE FROG

Larynx
Right bronchus
Stomach
Pulmonary artery
Right lung
Left lung
Heart
Pancreas
Liver
Duodenum
Posterior vena cava
Spleen
Right kidney
Left kidney
Dorsal aorta
Mesentery
Cloaca
Small intestine (ileum)
Rectum
Left ureter

EXTERNAL FEATURES OF A FROG

Hind limb
Trunk
Head
Forelimb
5 digits
External nostril
Tympanum (eardrum)
Mouth
Eye
Web
4 digits

EXTERNAL FEATURES OF A SALAMANDER

Eye
Tail
Forelimb
Hind limb
Digit

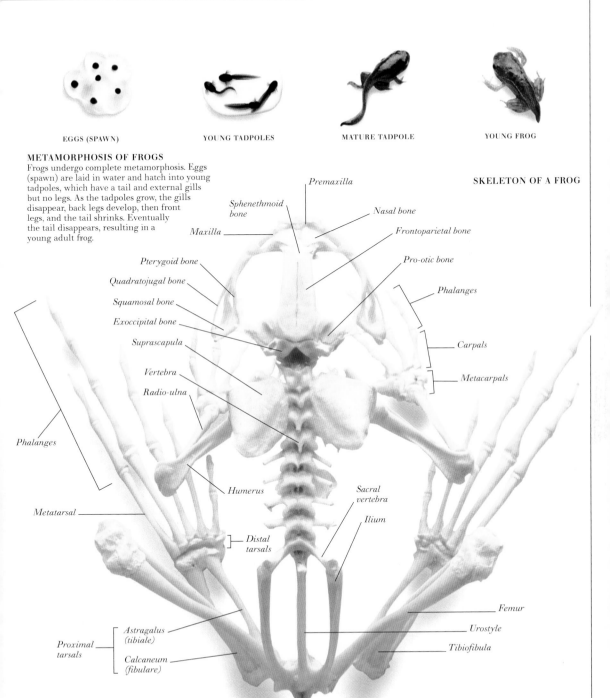

EGGS (SPAWN) YOUNG TADPOLES MATURE TADPOLE YOUNG FROG

METAMORPHOSIS OF FROGS

Frogs undergo complete metamorphosis. Eggs (spawn) are laid in water and hatch into young tadpoles, which have a tail and external gills but no legs. As the tadpoles grow, the gills disappear, back legs develop, then front legs, and the tail shrinks. Eventually the tail disappears, resulting in a young adult frog.

SKELETON OF A FROG

Premaxilla

Sphenethmoid bone

Nasal bone

Maxilla

Frontoparietal bone

Pterygoid bone

Pro-otic bone

Quadratojugal bone

Phalanges

Squamosal bone

Exoccipital bone

Suprascapula

Carpals

Vertebra

Metacarpals

Radio-ulna

Phalanges

Humerus

Metatarsal

Sacral vertebra

Ilium

Distal tarsals

Proximal tarsals

Astragalus (tibiale)

Calcaneum (fibulare)

Femur

Urostyle

Tibiofibula

Ischium

Lizards and snakes

LIZARDS AND SNAKES BELONG to the order Squamata, a division of the class Reptilia. Characteristic reptilian features include scaly skin, lungs, and cold-bloodedness. Most reptiles lay leathery-shelled eggs, although some hatch the eggs inside their bodies and give birth to live young. Lizards belong to the suborder Lacertilia. Typically, they have long tails, and shed their skin in several pieces. Many lizards can regenerate a tail if it is lost; some can change colour; and some are limbless. Snakes make up the suborder Ophidia (also called Serpentes). All snakes have long, limbless bodies; can dislocate their lower jaw to swallow large prey; and have eyelids that are joined together to form a single transparent covering over the front of the eye. Most snakes shed their skin in a single piece. Constrictor snakes kill their prey by squeezing; venomous snakes poison their prey.

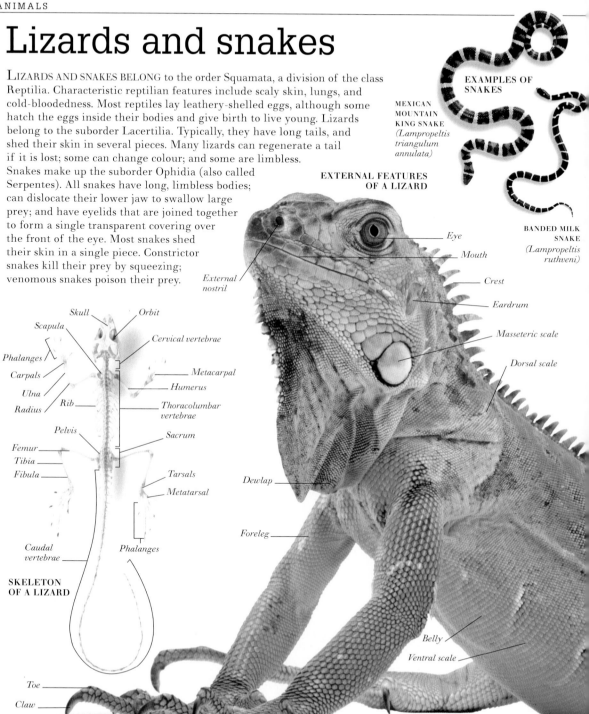

EXAMPLES OF SNAKES

MEXICAN MOUNTAIN KING SNAKE (*Lampropeltis triangulum annulata*)

BANDED MILK SNAKE (*Lampropeltis ruthveni*)

EXTERNAL FEATURES OF A LIZARD

Eye

Mouth

Crest

Eardrum

Masseteric scale

Dorsal scale

External nostril

Dewlap

Foreleg

Belly

Ventral scale

SKELETON OF A LIZARD

Skull

Orbit

Scapula

Cervical vertebrae

Phalanges

Metacarpal

Carpals

Humerus

Ulna

Radius

Rib

Thoracolumbar vertebrae

Pelvis

Sacrum

Femur

Tibia

Fibula

Tarsals

Metatarsal

Caudal vertebrae

Phalanges

Toe

Claw

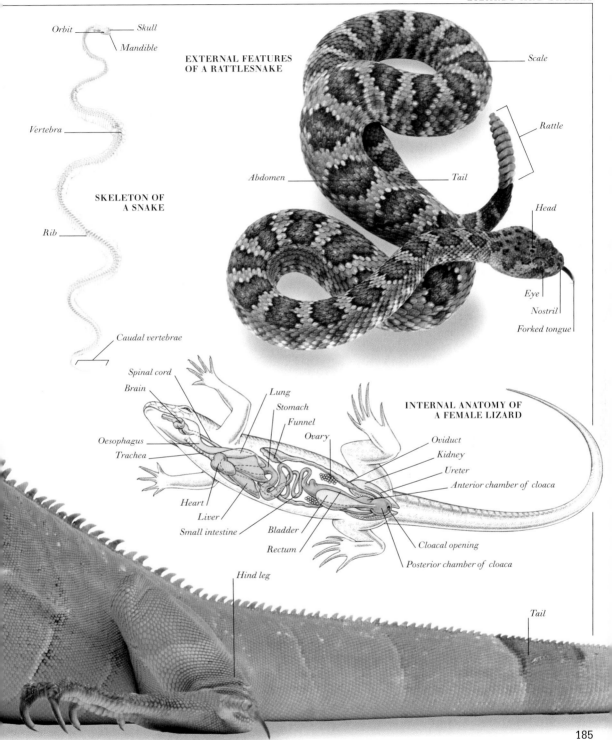

Orbit

Skull

Mandible

**EXTERNAL FEATURES
OF A RATTLESNAKE**

Scale

Vertebra

Rattle

Abdomen

Tail

Head

**SKELETON OF
A SNAKE**

Rib

Eye

Nostril

Forked tongue

Caudal vertebrae

Spinal cord

Brain

Lung

Stomach

Funnel

Ovary

**INTERNAL ANATOMY OF
A FEMALE LIZARD**

Oesophagus

Oviduct

Trachea

Kidney

Ureter

Anterior chamber of cloaca

Heart

Liver

Small intestine

Bladder

Rectum

Cloacal opening

Posterior chamber of cloaca

Hind leg

Tail

185

Crocodilians and turtles

GHARIAL
(Gavialis gangeticus)

CROCODILIANS AND TURTLES BELONG to different orders in the class Reptilia. The order Crocodilia includes crocodiles, alligators, caimans, and gharials. Typically, crocodilians are carnivores (flesh-eaters), and have a long snout, sharp teeth for gripping prey, and hard, square scales. All crocodilians are adapted to living on land and in water: they have four strong legs for moving on land; a powerful tail for swimming; and their eyes and nostrils are high on the head so that they stay above water while the rest of the body is submerged. The order Chelonia includes marine turtles, terrapins (freshwater turtles), and tortoises (land turtles). Characteristically, chelonians have a short, broad body encased in a bony shell with an outer horny covering, into which the head and limbs can be withdrawn; and a horny beak instead of teeth.

NILE CROCODILE
(Crocodylus niloticus)

AMERICAN ALLIGATOR
(Alligator mississippiensis)

SKELETON OF A CROCODILE

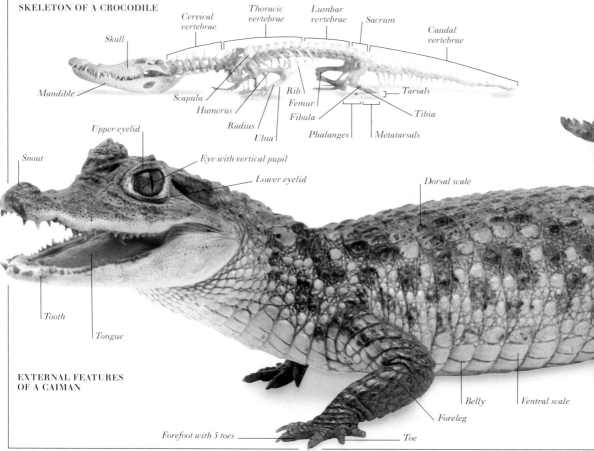

Cervical vertebrae

Thoracic vertebrae

Lumbar vertebrae

Sacrum

Caudal vertebrae

Skull

Mandible

Scapula

Humerus

Radius

Ulna

Rib

Femur

Fibula

Phalanges

Metatarsals

Tibia

Tarsals

Upper eyelid

Eye with vertical pupil

Lower eyelid

Dorsal scale

Snout

Tooth

Tongue

Belly

Ventral scale

Foreleg

EXTERNAL FEATURES OF A CAIMAN

Forefoot with 5 toes

Toe

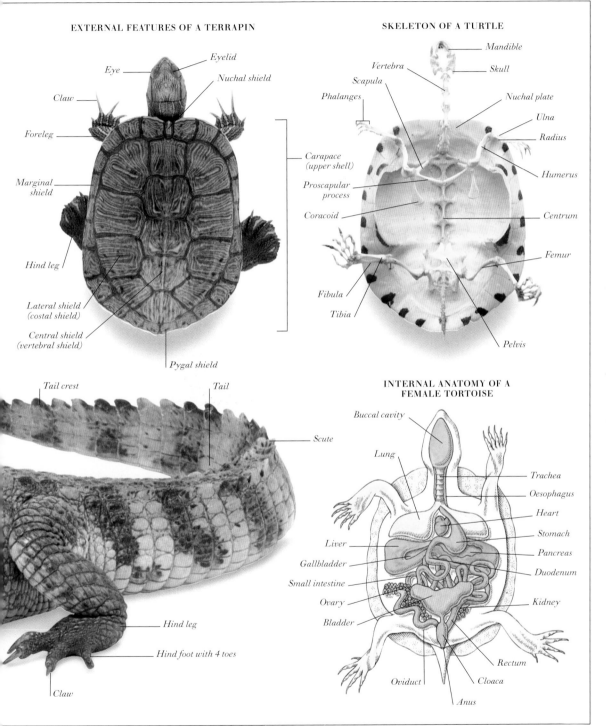

EXTERNAL FEATURES OF A TERRAPIN

Eyelid
Eye
Nuchal shield
Claw
Foreleg
Marginal shield
Hind leg
Carapace (upper shell)
Lateral shield (costal shield)
Central shield (vertebral shield)
Pygal shield

SKELETON OF A TURTLE

Mandible
Vertebra
Skull
Scapula
Phalanges
Nuchal plate
Ulna
Radius
Humerus
Carapace (upper shell)
Proscapular process
Coracoid
Centrum
Femur
Fibula
Tibia
Pelvis

Tail crest
Tail
Scute
Hind leg
Hind foot with 4 toes
Claw

INTERNAL ANATOMY OF A FEMALE TORTOISE

Buccal cavity
Lung
Trachea
Oesophagus
Heart
Stomach
Liver
Pancreas
Gallbladder
Duodenum
Small intestine
Ovary
Kidney
Bladder
Rectum
Cloaca
Oviduct
Anus

187

Birds 1

BIRDS MAKE UP THE CLASS AVES. There are more than 9,000 species, almost all of which can fly (the only flightless birds are penguins, ostriches, rheas, cassowaries, and kiwis). The ability to fly is reflected in the typical bird features: forelimbs modified as wings; a streamlined body; and hollow bones to reduce weight. All birds lay hard-shelled eggs, which the parents incubate. Birds' beaks and feet vary according to diet and way of life. Beaks range from general-purpose types suitable for a mixed diet (those of thrushes, for example), to types specialized for particular foods (such as the large, curved, sieving beaks of flamingos). Feet range from the webbed "paddles" of ducks, to the talons of birds of prey. Plumage also varies widely, and in many species the male is brightly coloured for courtship display whereas the female is drab.

EXTERNAL FEATURES OF A BIRD

Forehead

Eye

Crown

Nostril

Nape

Upper mandible

Beak

Lower mandible

Chin

Throat

EXAMPLES OF BIRDS

MALE TUFTED DUCK
(*Aythya fuligula*)

Minor coverts

Lesser wing coverts

Median wing coverts

Greater wing coverts
(major coverts)

Secondary flight feathers
(secondary remiges)

Primary flight feathers
(primary remiges)

WHITE STORK
(*Ciconia ciconia*)

Breast

Belly

Flank

Thigh

Claw

Under tail coverts

Tarsus

Toe

Tail feathers (retrices)

MALE OSTRICH
(*Struthio camelus*)

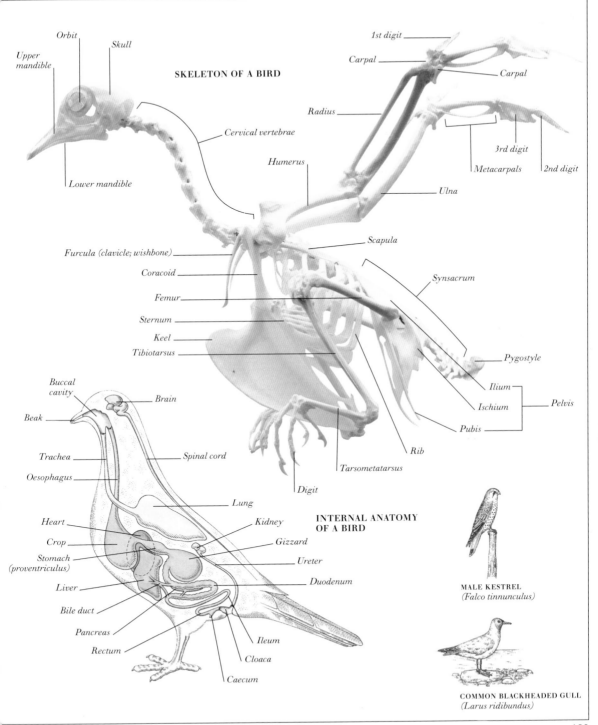

SKELETON OF A BIRD

Orbit

Skull

Upper mandible

Lower mandible

1st digit

Carpal

Carpal

Radius

3rd digit

Metacarpals

2nd digit

Ulna

Cervical vertebrae

Humerus

Scapula

Synsacrum

Furcula (clavicle; wishbone)

Coracoid

Femur

Sternum

Keel

Tibiotarsus

Pygostyle

Ilium

Ischium

Pelvis

Pubis

Rib

Tarsometatarsus

Digit

INTERNAL ANATOMY OF A BIRD

Buccal cavity

Brain

Beak

Trachea

Spinal cord

Oesophagus

Lung

Heart

Kidney

Crop

Gizzard

Stomach (proventriculus)

Ureter

Liver

Duodenum

Bile duct

Pancreas

Rectum

Ileum

Cloaca

Caecum

MALE KESTREL
(Falco tinnunculus)

COMMON BLACKHEADED GULL
(Larus ridibundus)

Birds 2

EXAMPLES OF BIRDS' FEET

KITTIWAKE
(Rissa tridactyla)
The webbed feet are
adapted for paddling
through water.

LITTLE GREBE
(Tachybaptus ruficollis)
The lobed, flattened feet
are adapted for swimming
underwater.

TAWNY OWL
(Strix aluco)
The clawed feet are adapted
for gripping prey.

EXAMPLES OF BIRDS' BEAKS

KING VULTURE
(Sarcorhamphus papa)
The hooked beak is adapted
for pulling apart flesh.

GREATER FLAMINGO
(Phoenicopterus ruber)
In the living bird, the large,
curved beak contains a
cartilaginous "sieve" for
filtering food particles
from water.

MISTLE THRUSH
(Turdus viscivorus)
The general-purpose beak is
suitable for a wide range of
animal and plant foods.

BLUE-AND-YELLOW MACAW
(Ara ararauna)
The broad, powerful, hooked beak
is adapted for crushing seeds and
eating fruit.

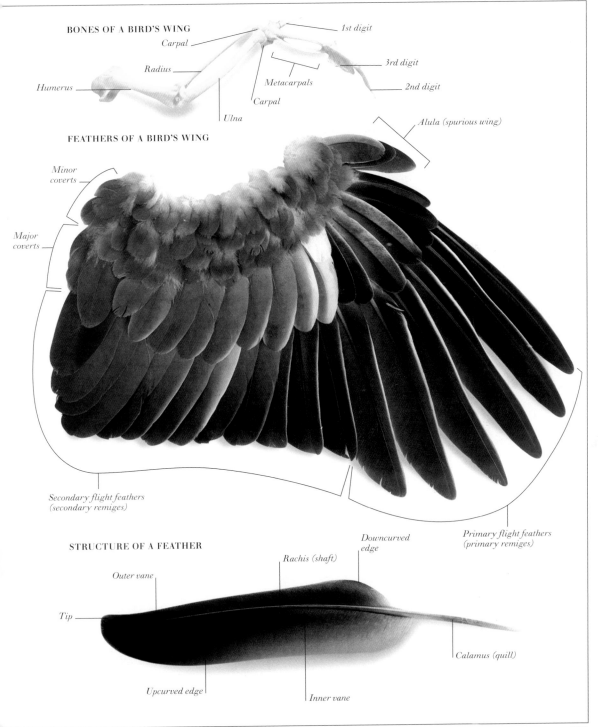

BONES OF A BIRD'S WING

1st digit
Carpal
Radius
Humerus
Metacarpals
Carpal
Ulna
3rd digit
2nd digit
Alula (spurious wing)

FEATHERS OF A BIRD'S WING

Minor coverts

Major coverts

Secondary flight feathers (secondary remiges)

Primary flight feathers (primary remiges)

STRUCTURE OF A FEATHER

Downcurved edge
Rachis (shaft)
Outer vane
Tip
Calamus (quill)
Upcurved edge
Inner vane

Eggs

AN EGG IS A SINGLE CELL, produced by the female, with the capacity to develop into a new individual. Development may take place inside the mother's body (as in most mammals) or outside, in which case the egg has a protective covering such as a shell. Egg yolk nourishes the growing young. Eggs developing inside the mother generally have little yolk, because the young are nourished from her body. Eggs developing outside may also have little yolk if they are produced by animals whose young go through a larval stage (such as a caterpillar) that feeds itself while developing into the adult form. The shelled eggs of birds and reptiles contain enough yolk to sustain the young until it hatches into a juvenile version of the adult.

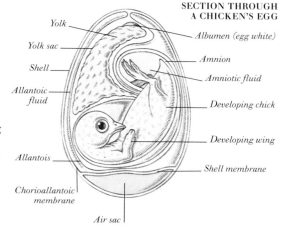

SECTION THROUGH A CHICKEN'S EGG

Yolk
Yolk sac
Shell
Allantoic fluid
Albumen (egg white)
Amnion
Amniotic fluid
Developing chick
Developing wing
Allantois
Shell membrane
Chorioallantoic membrane
Air sac

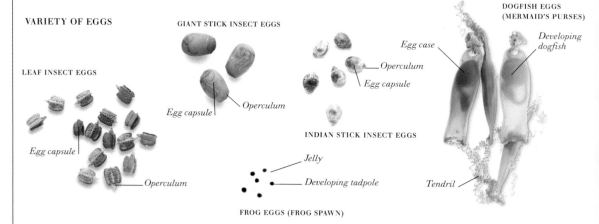

VARIETY OF EGGS

GIANT STICK INSECT EGGS

LEAF INSECT EGGS

Egg capsule
Operculum

Egg capsule
Operculum

Operculum
Egg capsule

INDIAN STICK INSECT EGGS

Jelly
Developing tadpole

FROG EGGS (FROG SPAWN)

DOGFISH EGGS (MERMAID'S PURSES)

Egg case
Developing dogfish
Tendril

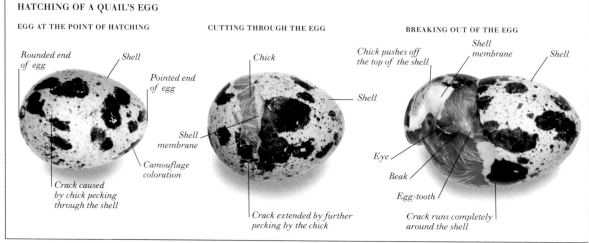

HATCHING OF A QUAIL'S EGG

EGG AT THE POINT OF HATCHING

Rounded end of egg
Shell
Pointed end of egg
Shell membrane
Camouflage coloration
Crack caused by chick pecking through the shell

CUTTING THROUGH THE EGG

Chick
Shell
Crack extended by further pecking by the chick

BREAKING OUT OF THE EGG

Chick pushes off the top of the shell
Shell membrane
Shell
Eye
Beak
Egg-tooth
Crack runs completely around the shell

EXAMPLES OF BIRDS' EGGS

BEE HUMMINGBIRD
(Calypte helenae)

GREATER BLACKBACKED GULL
(Larus marinus)

BALTIMORE ORIOLE
(Icterus galbula)

WILLOW GROUSE
(Lagopus lagopus)

COMMON TERN
(Sterna hirundo)

CARRION CROW
(Corvus corone)

CHAFFINCH
(Fringilla coelebs)

OSTRICH
(Struthio camelus)

EMERGING FROM THE EGG

Eye

Beak

Egg-tooth

Chick heaves itself
out of the egg

Tympanum (eardrum)

Shell

Wet down

Remains of egg membranes
(amnion and allantois)

THE NEWLY HATCHED CHICK

Eye

Beak

Egg-tooth

Nostril

Tympanum
(eardrum)

Chick is dry
about an hour
after hatching

Dry down

Toe

Claw

Leg

Eggshell

193

Carnivores

THE MAMMALIAN ORDER CARNIVORA includes cats, dogs, bears, raccoons, pandas, weasels, badgers, skunks, otters, civets, mongooses, and hyenas. The order's name is derived from the fact that most of its members are carnivores (flesheaters). Typical carnivore features therefore reflect a hunting life-style: speed and agility; sharp claws and well-developed canine teeth for holding and killing prey; carnassial teeth (cheek teeth) for cutting flesh; and forward-facing eyes for good distance judgment. However, some members of the order – bears, badgers, and foxes, for example – have a more mixed diet, and a few are entirely herbivorous (plant-eating), notably pandas. Such animals have no carnassial teeth and tend to be slower-moving than pure flesh-eaters.

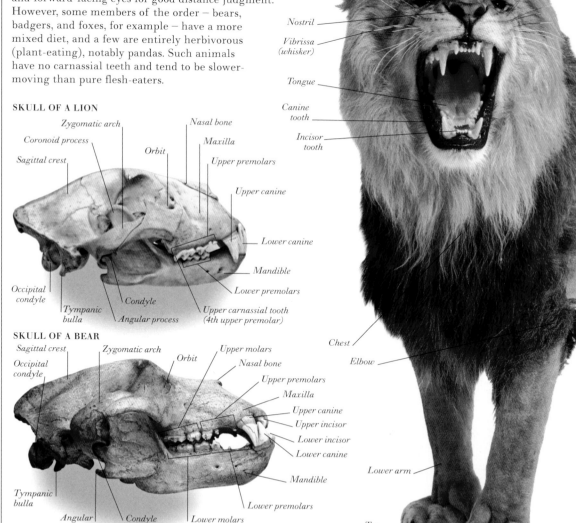

EXTERNAL FEATURES OF A MALE LION

- Nose
- Eye
- Mane
- Nostril
- Vibrissa (whisker)
- Tongue
- Canine tooth
- Incisor tooth
- Chest
- Elbow
- Lower arm
- Toe

SKULL OF A LION

- Zygomatic arch
- Coronoid process
- Sagittal crest
- Orbit
- Nasal bone
- Maxilla
- Upper premolars
- Upper canine
- Lower canine
- Mandible
- Lower premolars
- Occipital condyle
- Tympanic bulla
- Condyle
- Angular process
- Upper carnassial tooth (4th upper premolar)

SKULL OF A BEAR

- Sagittal crest
- Zygomatic arch
- Occipital condyle
- Orbit
- Upper molars
- Nasal bone
- Upper premolars
- Maxilla
- Upper canine
- Upper incisor
- Lower incisor
- Lower canine
- Mandible
- Tympanic bulla
- Angular process
- Condyle
- Lower molars
- Lower premolars

EXAMPLES OF CARNIVORES

ALSATIAN DOG
(Canis familiaris)

MANED WOLF
(Chrysocyon brachyurus)

RACCOON
(Procyon lotor)

AMERICAN BLACK BEAR
(Ursus americanus)

SKELETON OF A DOMESTIC CAT

INTERNAL ANATOMY OF A MALE DOMESTIC CAT

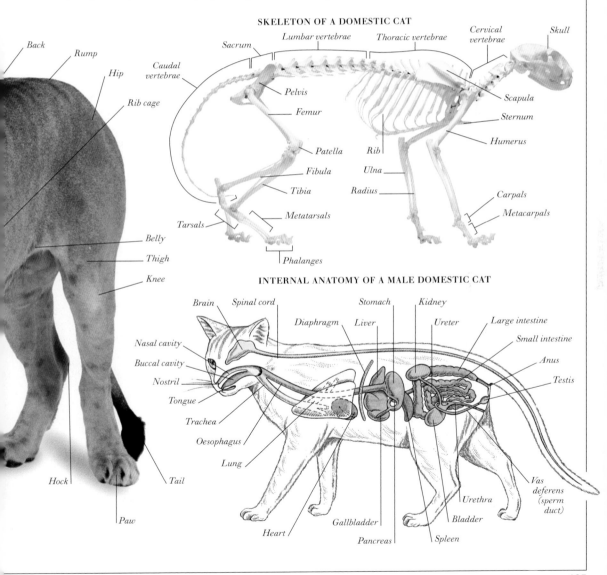

Back
Rump
Hip
Rib cage
Belly
Thigh
Knee
Hock
Paw
Tail

Sacrum
Lumbar vertebrae
Thoracic vertebrae
Cervical vertebrae
Skull
Caudal vertebrae
Pelvis
Femur
Scapula
Sternum
Humerus
Patella
Rib
Ulna
Fibula
Radius
Tibia
Carpals
Metacarpals
Tarsals
Metatarsals
Phalanges

Brain
Spinal cord
Stomach
Kidney
Diaphragm
Liver
Ureter
Large intestine
Small intestine
Nasal cavity
Anus
Buccal cavity
Testis
Nostril
Tongue
Trachea
Oesophagus
Lung
Vas deferens (sperm duct)
Urethra
Heart
Gallbladder
Bladder
Pancreas
Spleen

Rabbits and rodents

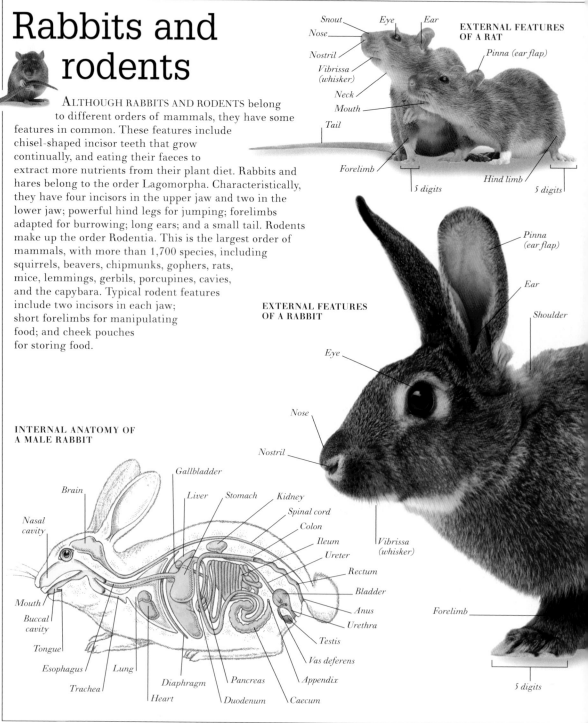

ALTHOUGH RABBITS AND RODENTS belong to different orders of mammals, they have some features in common. These features include chisel-shaped incisor teeth that grow continually, and eating their faeces to extract more nutrients from their plant diet. Rabbits and hares belong to the order Lagomorpha. Characteristically, they have four incisors in the upper jaw and two in the lower jaw; powerful hind legs for jumping; forelimbs adapted for burrowing; long ears; and a small tail. Rodents make up the order Rodentia. This is the largest order of mammals, with more than 1,700 species, including squirrels, beavers, chipmunks, gophers, rats, mice, lemmings, gerbils, porcupines, cavies, and the capybara. Typical rodent features include two incisors in each jaw; short forelimbs for manipulating food; and cheek pouches for storing food.

EXTERNAL FEATURES OF A RAT

Snout
Eye
Ear
Pinna (ear flap)
Nose
Nostril
Vibrissa (whisker)
Neck
Mouth
Tail
Forelimb
5 digits
Hind limb
5 digits

EXTERNAL FEATURES OF A RABBIT

Pinna (ear flap)
Ear
Shoulder
Eye
Nose
Nostril
Vibrissa (whisker)
Forelimb
5 digits

INTERNAL ANATOMY OF A MALE RABBIT

Brain
Gallbladder
Liver
Stomach
Kidney
Spinal cord
Colon
Ileum
Ureter
Rectum
Bladder
Anus
Urethra
Testis
Vas deferens
Appendix
Caecum
Duodenum
Pancreas
Heart
Diaphragm
Lung
Trachea
Esophagus
Tongue
Buccal cavity
Mouth
Nasal cavity

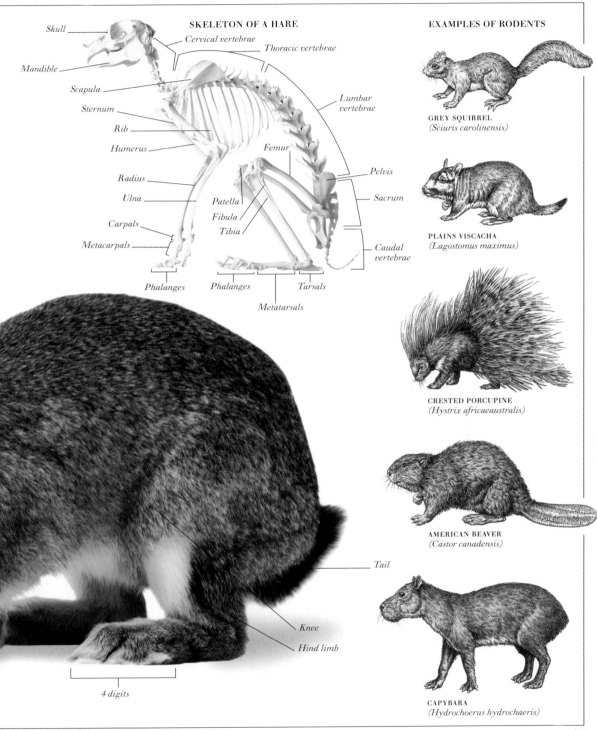

SKELETON OF A HARE

Skull

Cervical vertebrae

Thoracic vertebrae

Mandible

Scapula

Lumbar vertebrae

Sternum

Rib

Humerus

Femur

Radius

Pelvis

Ulna

Patella

Sacrum

Carpals

Fibula

Tibia

Metacarpals

Caudal vertebrae

Phalanges

Phalanges

Tarsals

Metatarsals

EXAMPLES OF RODENTS

GREY SQUIRREL
(*Sciuris carolinensis*)

PLAINS VISCACHA
(*Lagostomus maximus*)

CRESTED PORCUPINE
(*Hystrix africaeaustralis*)

AMERICAN BEAVER
(*Castor canadensis*)

Tail

Knee

Hind limb

CAPYBARA
(*Hydrochoerus hydrochaeris*)

4 digits

Ungulates

UNGULATES IS A GENERAL TERM FOR a large, varied group of mammals that includes horses, cattle, and their relatives. The ungulates are divided into two orders on the basis of the number of toes. Members of the order Perissodactyla (odd-toed ungulates) have one or three toes. Perissodactyls include horses, asses, and zebras (all of which are one-toed), and rhinoceroses and tapirs (which are three-toed). Members of the order Artiodactyla (even-toed ungulates) have two or four toes. Most artiodactyls have two toes, which are typically encased in hooves to give the so-called cloven hoof. Two-toed, cloven-hoofed artiodactyls include cows and other cattle, sheep, goats, antelopes, deer, and giraffes. The other main two-toed artiodactyls are camels and llamas. Most two-toed artiodactyls are ruminants; that is, they have a four-chambered stomach and chew the cud. The principal four-toed artiodactyls are pigs, peccaries, and hippopotamuses.

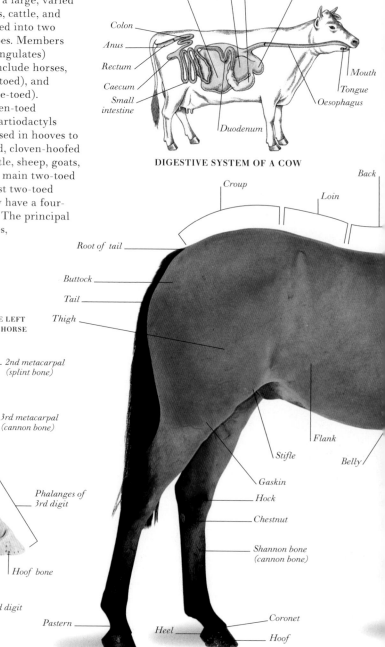

DIGESTIVE SYSTEM OF A COW

COMPARISON OF THE FRONT FEET OF A HORSE AND A COW

SKELETON OF THE LEFT FRONT FOOT OF A HORSE

SKELETON OF THE RIGHT FRONT FOOT OF A COW

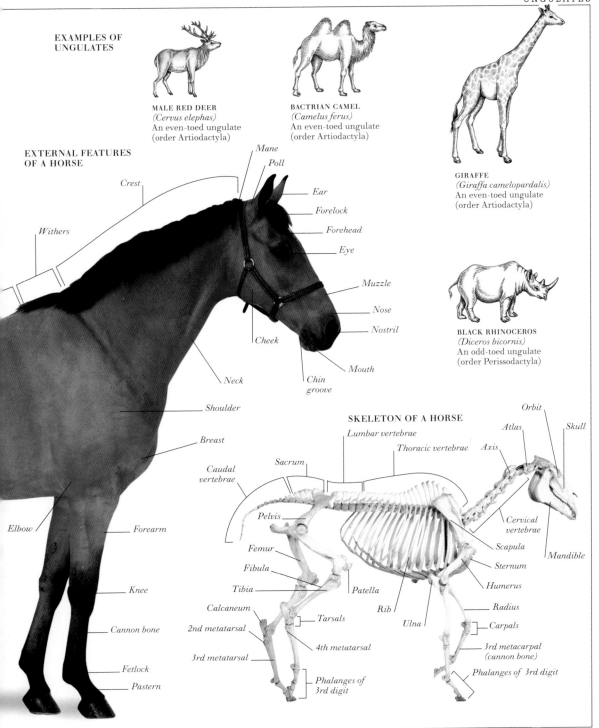

EXAMPLES OF
UNGULATES

MALE RED DEER
(Cervus elephas)
An even-toed ungulate
(order Artiodactyla)

BACTRIAN CAMEL
(Camelus ferus)
An even-toed ungulate
(order Artiodactyla)

GIRAFFE
(Giraffa camelopardalis)
An even-toed ungulate
(order Artiodactyla)

BLACK RHINOCEROS
(Diceros bicornis)
An odd-toed ungulate
(order Perissodactyla)

EXTERNAL FEATURES
OF A HORSE

Crest

Withers

Mane

Poll

Ear

Forelock

Forehead

Eye

Muzzle

Nose

Nostril

Cheek

Mouth

Chin
groove

Neck

Shoulder

Breast

Caudal
vertebrae

Elbow

Forearm

Knee

Cannon bone

Fetlock

Pastern

SKELETON OF A HORSE

Lumbar vertebrae

Thoracic vertebrae

Sacrum

Pelvis

Femur

Fibula

Tibia

Calcaneum

2nd metatarsal

3rd metatarsal

Tarsals

Patella

4th metatarsal

Phalanges of
3rd digit

Rib

Ulna

Sternum

Humerus

Radius

Carpals

3rd metacarpal
(cannon bone)

Phalanges of 3rd digit

Scapula

Cervical
vertebrae

Atlas

Axis

Orbit

Skull

Mandible

199

Elephants

THE TWO SPECIES OF elephants – African and Asian – are the only members of the mammalian order Proboscidea. The bigger African elephant is the largest land animal: a fully grown male may be up to 4 m (13 ft) tall and weigh as much as 7 tonnes (6.9 tons). A fully grown male Asian elephant may be 3.3 m (11 ft) tall and weigh 5.4 tonnes (5.3 tons). The trunk – an extension of the nose and upper lip – is the elephant's other most obvious feature. It is used for manipulating and lifting, feeding, drinking and spraying water, smelling, touching, and producing trumpeting sounds. Other characteristic features include a pair of tusks, used for defence and for crushing vegetation; thick, pillar-like legs and broad feet to support the massive body; and large ear flaps that act as radiators to keep the elephant cool.

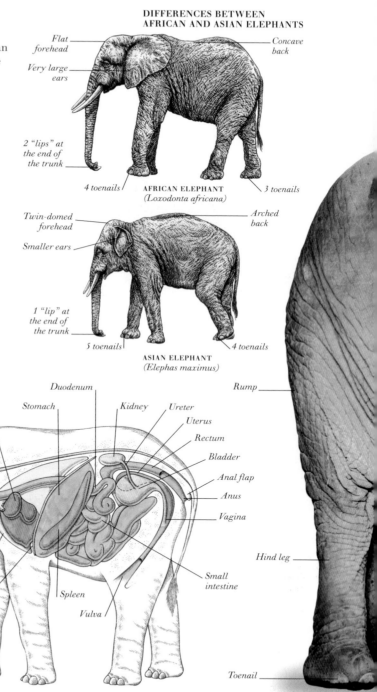

DIFFERENCES BETWEEN AFRICAN AND ASIAN ELEPHANTS

Flat forehead
Very large ears
2 "lips" at the end of the trunk
Concave back
4 toenails
3 toenails

AFRICAN ELEPHANT
(Loxodonta africana)

Twin-domed forehead
Smaller ears
1 "lip" at the end of the trunk
Arched back
5 toenails
4 toenails

ASIAN ELEPHANT
(Elephas maximus)

INTERNAL ANATOMY OF A FEMALE ELEPHANT

Spinal cord
Heart
Brain
Nasal cavity
Buccal cavity
Mouth
Tongue
Tusk
Nasal passage
Epiglottis
Oesophagus
Trachea
Lung
Diaphragm
Nostril

Duodenum
Stomach
Spleen

Kidney
Ureter
Uterus
Rectum
Bladder
Anal flap
Anus
Vagina
Vulva
Small intestine

Rump
Hind leg
Toenail

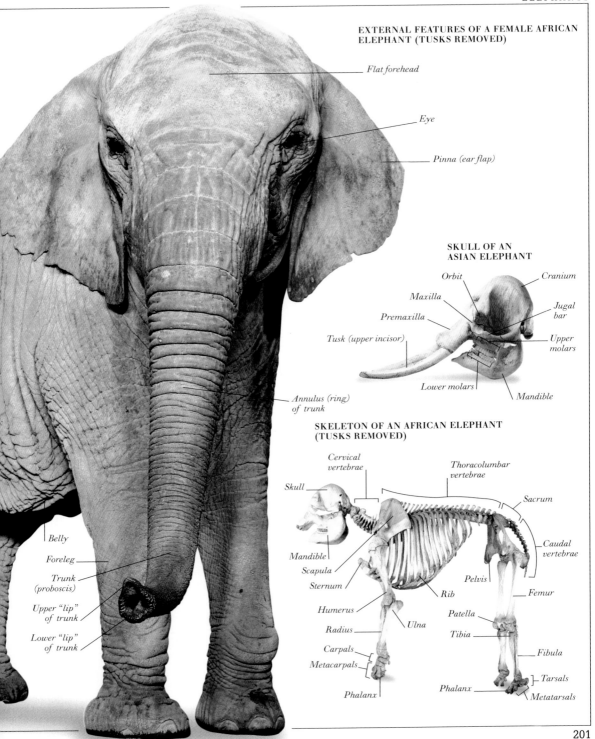

**EXTERNAL FEATURES OF A FEMALE AFRICAN
ELEPHANT (TUSKS REMOVED)**

Flat forehead

Eye

Pinna (ear flap)

**SKULL OF AN
ASIAN ELEPHANT**

Orbit

Cranium

Maxilla

Jugal
bar

Premaxilla

Upper
molars

Tusk (upper incisor)

Lower molars

Mandible

Annulus (ring)
of trunk

**SKELETON OF AN AFRICAN ELEPHANT
(TUSKS REMOVED)**

Cervical
vertebrae

Thoracolumbar
vertebrae

Skull

Sacrum

Belly

Mandible

Caudal
vertebrae

Foreleg

Scapula

Trunk
(proboscis)

Sternum

Pelvis

Rib

Femur

Upper "lip"
of trunk

Humerus

Patella

Radius

Ulna

Tibia

Lower "lip"
of trunk

Carpals

Fibula

Metacarpals

Phalanx

Phalanx

Tarsals

Metatarsals

Primates

THE MAMMALIAN ORDER PRIMATES consists of monkeys, apes, and their relatives (including humans). There are two suborders of primates: Prosimii, the primitive primates, which include lemurs, tarsiers, and lorises; and Anthropoidea, the advanced primates, which include monkeys, apes, and humans. The anthropoids are divided into New World monkeys, Old World monkeys, and hominids. New World monkeys typically have wide-apart nostrils that open to the side; and long tails, which are prehensile (grasping) in some species. This group of monkeys lives in South America, and includes marmosets, tamarins, and howler monkeys. Old World monkeys typically have close-set nostrils that open forwards or downwards; and non-prehensile tails. This group of monkeys lives in Africa and Asia, and includes langurs, mandrills, macaques, and baboons. Hominids typically have large brains, and no tail. This group includes the apes – chimpanzees, gibbons, gorillas, and orangutans – and humans.

INTERNAL ANATOMY OF A FEMALE CHIMPANZEE

Buccal cavity
Tongue
Trachea
Lung
Liver
Pancreas
Small intestine
Caecum
Appendix
Ovary
Uterus
Vagina
Brain
Nasal cavity
Spinal cord
Oesophagus
Heart
Diaphragm
Stomach
Spleen
Large intestine
Rectum
Bladder
Urethra

SKELETON OF A RHESUS MONKEY

Skull
Orbit
Cervical vertebrae
Thoracic vertebrae
Mandible
Clavicle
Scapula
Rib
Humerus
Lumbar vertebrae
Femur
Radius
Sacrum
Ulna
Patella
Tibia
Fibula
Pelvis
Carpals
Metacarpals
Caudal vertebrae
Tarsals
Metatarsals
Phalanges
Phalanges

SKULL OF A CHIMPANZEE

Temporal bone
Suture
Frontal bone
Parietal bone
Supraorbital ridge
Orbit
Occipital bone
Maxilla
Premaxilla
Auditory meatus
Zygomatic arch
Mandible
Molar tooth
Premolar tooth
Incisor tooth
Canine tooth

EXAMPLES OF PRIMATES

RING-TAILED LEMUR
(Lemur catta)
A prosimian

MALE RED HOWLER MONKEY
(Alouatta seniculus)
A New World monkey

MALE MANDRILL
(Mandrillus sphinx)
An Old World monkey

CHIMPANZEE
(Pan troglodytes)
An ape

EXTERNAL FEATURES OF A YOUNG GORILLA

GOLDEN LION TAMARIN
(Leontopithecus rosalia)
A New World monkey

Pinna (ear flap)

Shoulder

Brow ridge

Eye

Nostril

Mouth

Upper arm

Thigh

Forearm

Chest

Elbow

Knee

Lower leg

Hand

Foot

Toe

Finger

Toenail

Dolphins, whales, and seals

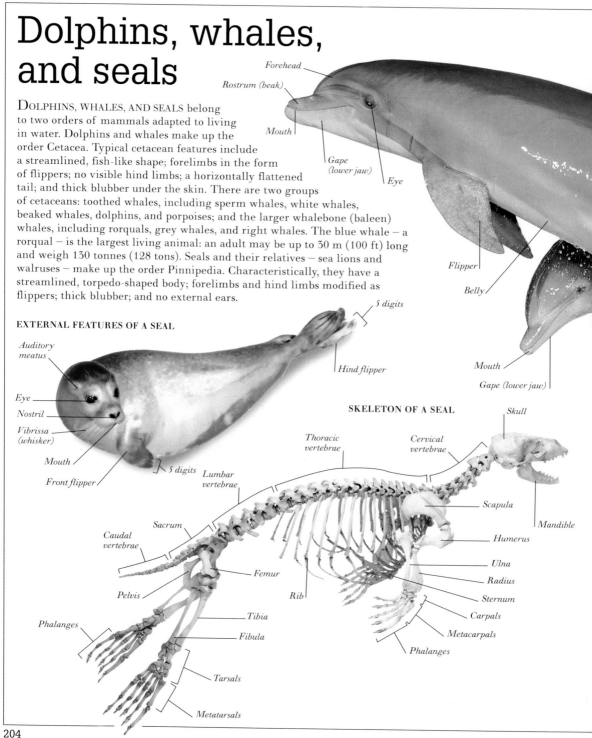

DOLPHINS, WHALES, AND SEALS belong to two orders of mammals adapted to living in water. Dolphins and whales make up the order Cetacea. Typical cetacean features include a streamlined, fish-like shape; forelimbs in the form of flippers; no visible hind limbs; a horizontally flattened tail; and thick blubber under the skin. There are two groups of cetaceans: toothed whales, including sperm whales, white whales, beaked whales, dolphins, and porpoises; and the larger whalebone (baleen) whales, including rorquals, grey whales, and right whales. The blue whale – a rorqual – is the largest living animal: an adult may be up to 30 m (100 ft) long and weigh 130 tonnes (128 tons). Seals and their relatives – sea lions and walruses – make up the order Pinnipedia. Characteristically, they have a streamlined, torpedo-shaped body; forelimbs and hind limbs modified as flippers; thick blubber; and no external ears.

Forehead

Rostrum (beak)

Mouth

Gape (lower jaw)

Eye

Flipper

Belly

Mouth

Gape (lower jaw)

EXTERNAL FEATURES OF A SEAL

5 digits

Hind flipper

Auditory meatus

Eye

Nostril

Vibrissa (whisker)

Mouth

Front flipper

5 digits

SKELETON OF A SEAL

Skull

Thoracic vertebrae

Cervical vertebrae

Lumbar vertebrae

Scapula

Mandible

Humerus

Sacrum

Caudal vertebrae

Femur

Rib

Ulna

Radius

Sternum

Pelvis

Carpals

Metacarpals

Phalanges

Tibia

Fibula

Phalanges

Tarsals

Metatarsals

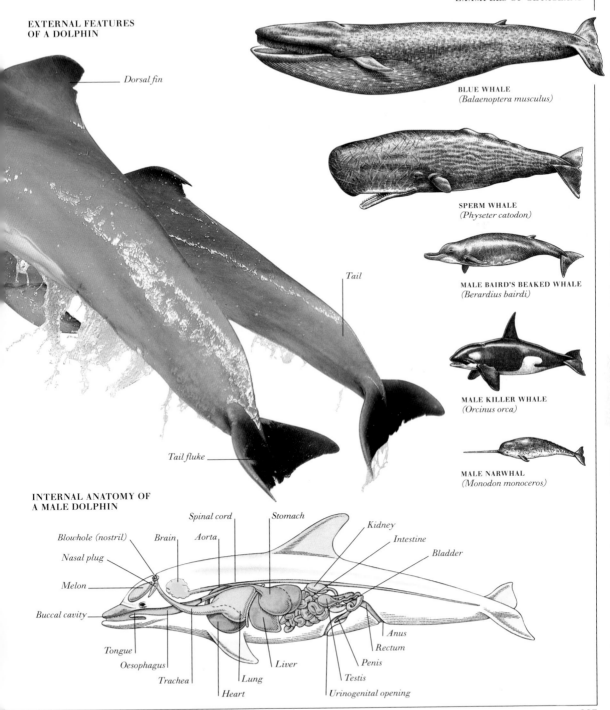

EXAMPLES OF CETACEANS

EXTERNAL FEATURES OF A DOLPHIN

Dorsal fin

Tail

Tail fluke

BLUE WHALE
(Balaenoptera musculus)

SPERM WHALE
(Physeter catodon)

MALE BAIRD'S BEAKED WHALE
(Berardius bairdi)

MALE KILLER WHALE
(Orcinus orca)

MALE NARWHAL
(Monodon monoceros)

INTERNAL ANATOMY OF A MALE DOLPHIN

Blowhole (nostril)

Brain

Spinal cord

Aorta

Stomach

Kidney

Intestine

Bladder

Nasal plug

Melon

Buccal cavity

Tongue

Oesophagus

Trachea

Heart

Lung

Liver

Testis

Urinogenital opening

Penis

Rectum

Anus

205

Marsupials and Monotremes

MARSUPIALS AND MONOTREMES are two orders of mammals that differ from other mammalian groups in the ways that their young develop. The order Marsupalia, the pouched mammals, is made up of kangaroos and their relatives. Typically, marsupials give birth to their young at a very early stage of development. The young then crawls to the mother's pouch (which is on the outside of her abdomen), where it attaches itself to a nipple and remains until fully developed. Most marsupials live in Australia, although the opossums – which are classified as marsupials despite not having a pouch – live in the Americas. The order Monotremata is made up of the platypus and its relatives (the echidnas, or spiny anteaters). The monotremes are primitive mammals that lay eggs, which the mother incubates. The monotremes are found only in Australia and New Guinea.

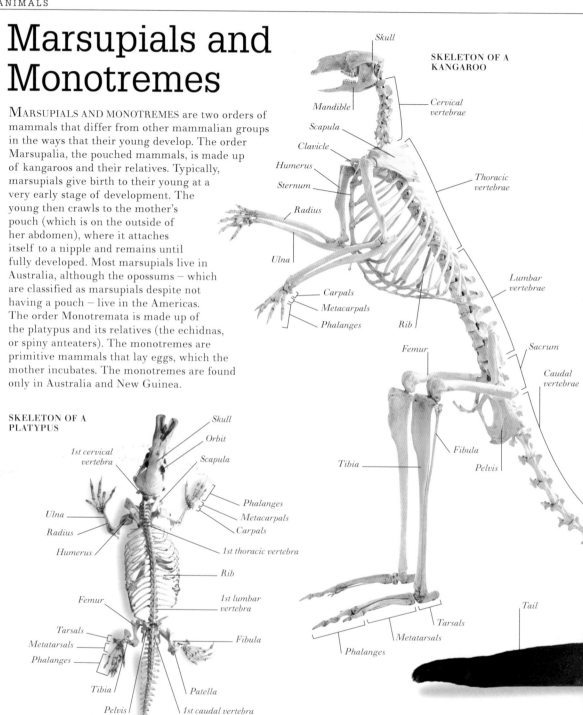

SKELETON OF A KANGAROO

Skull
Mandible
Scapula
Clavicle
Humerus
Sternum
Radius
Ulna
Cervical vertebrae
Thoracic vertebrae
Lumbar vertebrae
Carpals
Metacarpals
Phalanges
Rib
Femur
Sacrum
Caudal vertebrae
Fibula
Pelvis
Tibia
Tarsals
Metatarsals
Phalanges
Tail

SKELETON OF A PLATYPUS

Skull
Orbit
1st cervical vertebra
Scapula
Ulna
Radius
Humerus
Phalanges
Metacarpals
Carpals
1st thoracic vertebra
Rib
1st lumbar vertebra
Femur
Tarsals
Metatarsals
Phalanges
Fibula
Tibia
Patella
Pelvis
1st caudal vertebra

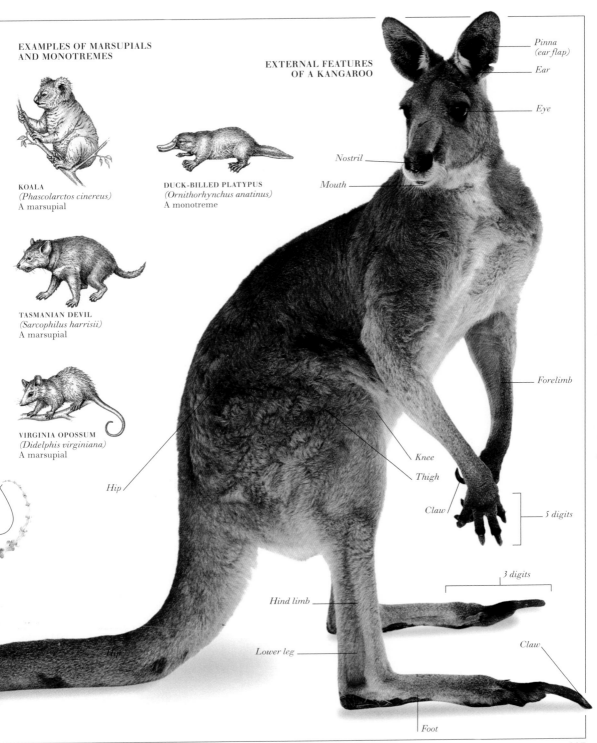

EXAMPLES OF MARSUPIALS AND MONOTREMES

EXTERNAL FEATURES OF A KANGAROO

KOALA
(Phascolarctos cinereus)
A marsupial

DUCK-BILLED PLATYPUS
(Ornithorhynchus anatinus)
A monotreme

TASMANIAN DEVIL
(Sarcophilus harrisii)
A marsupial

VIRGINIA OPOSSUM
(Didelphis virginiana)
A marsupial

Pinna
(ear flap)

Ear

Eye

Nostril

Mouth

Forelimb

Knee

Thigh

Claw

5 digits

3 digits

Hip

Hind limb

Lower leg

Claw

Hip

Foot

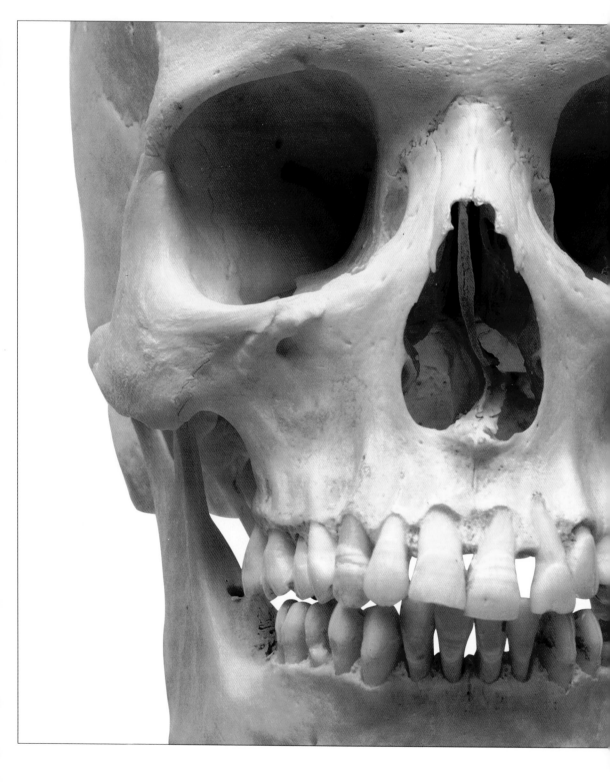

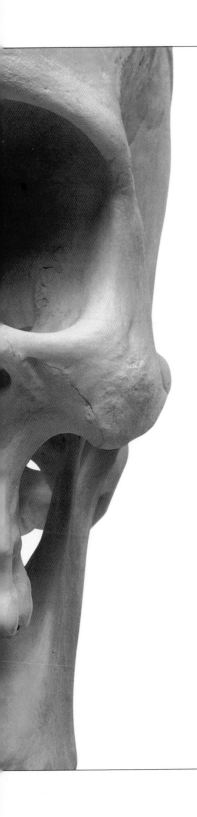

THE HUMAN BODY

Body features

ALTHOUGH THERE IS enormous
variation between the external
appearances of humans, all bodies
contain the same basic features.
The outward form of the
human body depends on the
size of the skeleton, the shape
of the muscles, the thickness
of the fat layer beneath
the skin, the elasticity or
sagginess of the skin, and
the person's age and sex.
Males tend to be taller than
females, with broader
shoulders, more body hair,
and a different pattern of fat
deposits under the skin; the
female body tends to be
less muscular and has
a shallower and wider
pelvis to allow
for childbirth.

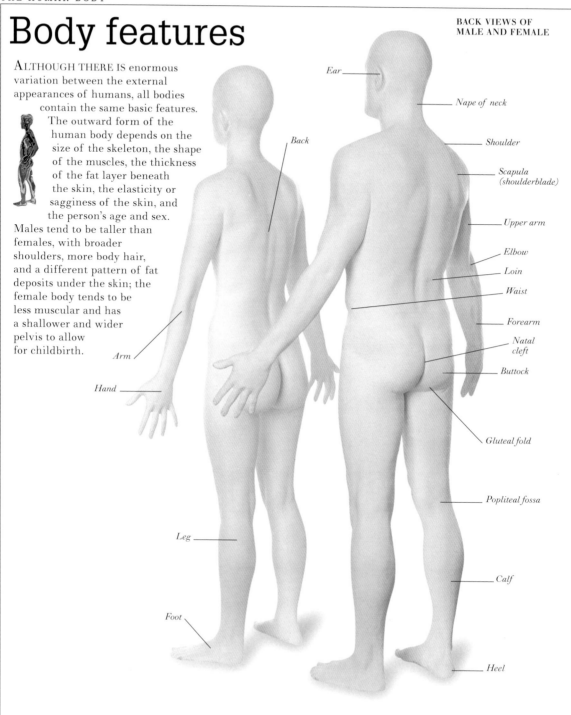

Ear

Nape of neck

Shoulder

Scapula
(shoulderblade)

Upper arm

Back

Elbow

Loin

Waist

Forearm

Natal
cleft

Arm

Buttock

Hand

Gluteal fold

Popliteal fossa

Leg

Calf

Foot

Heel

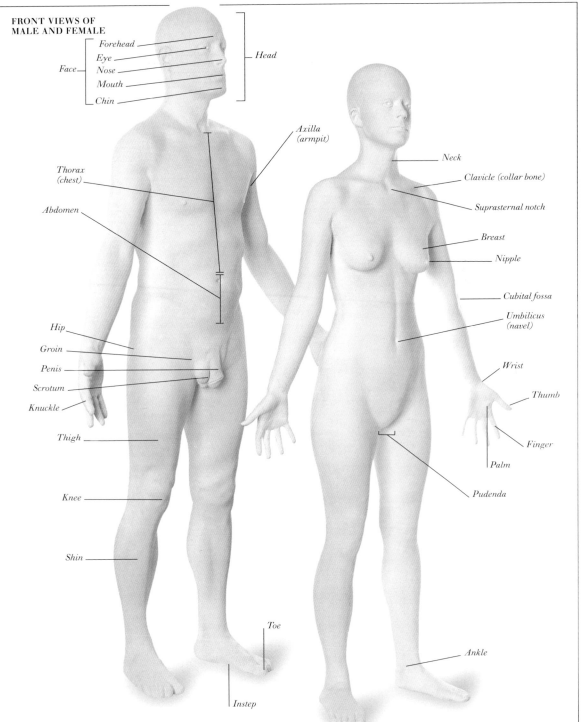

**FRONT VIEWS OF
MALE AND FEMALE**

Face —
— Forehead
— Eye
— Nose
— Mouth
— Chin

— Head

Axilla
(armpit)

Neck

Clavicle (collar bone)

Suprasternal notch

Thorax
(chest)

Breast

Nipple

Abdomen

Cubital fossa

Umbilicus
(navel)

Hip

Groin

Penis

Scrotum

Knuckle

Wrist

Thumb

Finger

Palm

Thigh

Pudenda

Knee

Shin

Toe

Ankle

Instep

Head

IN A NEWBORN BABY, the head accounts for one-quarter of the total body length; by adulthood, the proportion has reduced to one-eighth. Contained in the head are the body's main sense organs: eyes, ears, olfactory nerves that detect smells, and the taste buds of the tongue. Signals from these organs pass to the body's great coordination centre: the brain, housed in the protective, bony dome of the skull. Hair on the head insulates against heat loss, and adult males also grow thick facial hair. The face has three important openings: two nostrils through which air passes, and the mouth, which takes in nourishment and helps form speech. Although all heads are basically similar, differences in the size, shape, and colour of features produce an infinite variety of appearances.

SIDE VIEW OF EXTERNAL FEATURES OF HEAD

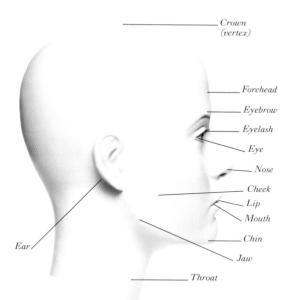

- Crown (vertex)
- Forehead
- Eyebrow
- Eyelash
- Eye
- Nose
- Cheek
- Lip
- Mouth
- Chin
- Jaw
- Ear
- Throat

SECTION THROUGH HEAD

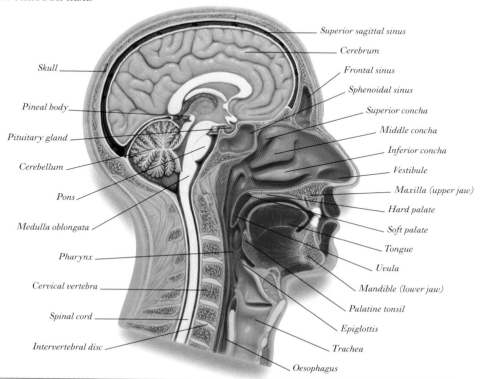

- Superior sagittal sinus
- Cerebrum
- Skull
- Frontal sinus
- Sphenoidal sinus
- Pineal body
- Superior concha
- Middle concha
- Pituitary gland
- Inferior concha
- Cerebellum
- Vestibule
- Pons
- Maxilla (upper jaw)
- Hard palate
- Medulla oblongata
- Soft palate
- Tongue
- Pharynx
- Uvula
- Cervical vertebra
- Mandible (lower jaw)
- Spinal cord
- Palatine tonsil
- Epiglottis
- Intervertebral disc
- Trachea
- Oesophagus

**FRONT VIEW OF EXTERNAL
FEATURES OF HEAD**

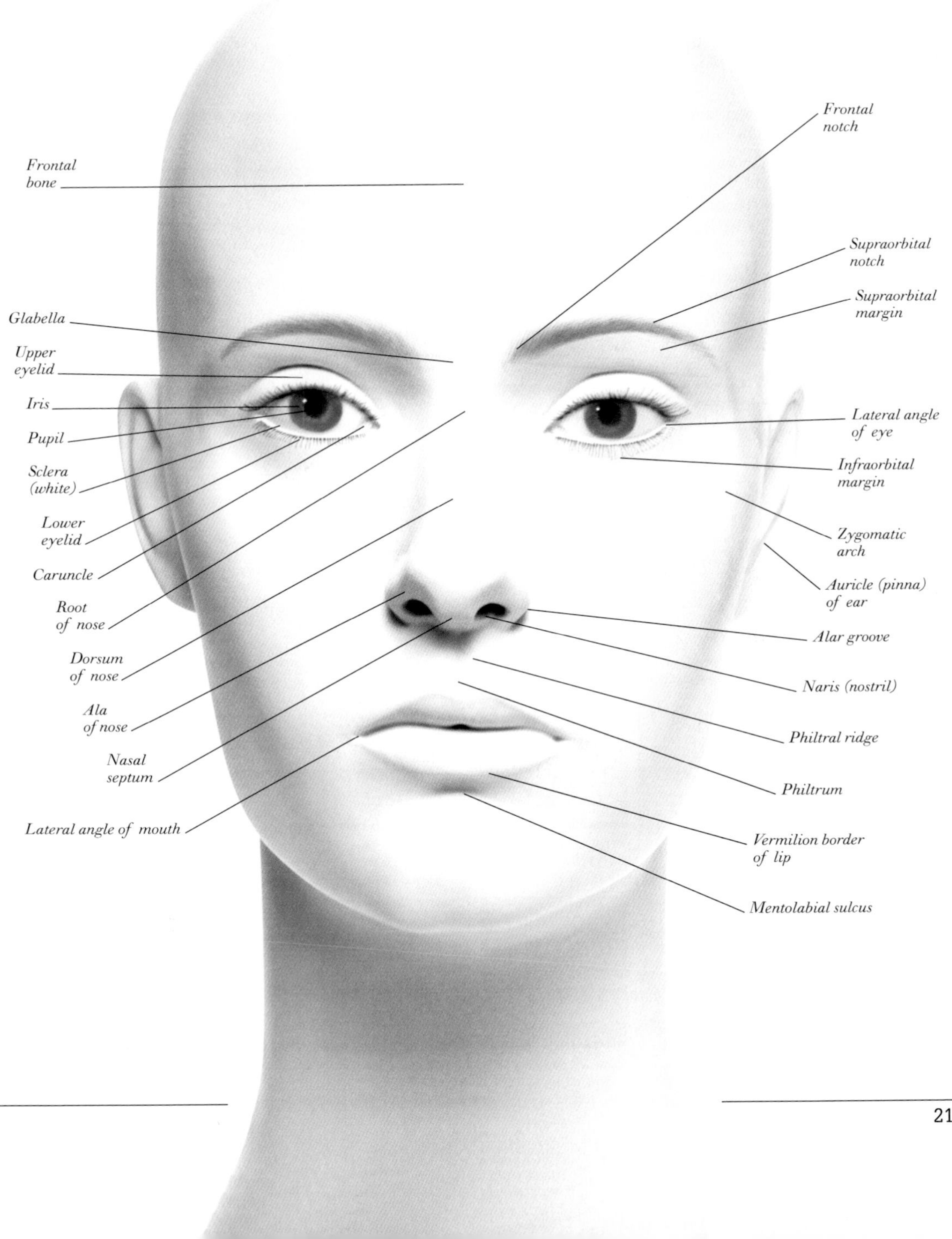

Frontal
notch

Frontal
bone

Supraorbital
notch

Supraorbital
margin

Glabella

Upper
eyelid

Iris

Pupil

Lateral angle
of eye

Sclera
(white)

Infraorbital
margin

Lower
eyelid

Zygomatic
arch

Caruncle

Auricle (pinna)
of ear

Root
of nose

Alar groove

Dorsum
of nose

Naris (nostril)

Ala
of nose

Philtral ridge

Nasal
septum

Philtrum

Lateral angle of mouth

Vermilion border
of lip

Mentolabial sulcus

Body organs

ALL THE VITAL BODY ORGANS except for the brain are enclosed within the trunk or torso (the body apart from the head and limbs). The trunk contains two large cavities separated by a muscular sheet called the diaphragm. The upper cavity, known as the thorax or chest cavity, contains the heart and lungs. The lower cavity, called the abdominal cavity, contains the stomach, intestines, liver, and pancreas, which all play a role in digesting food. Also within the trunk are the kidneys and bladder, which are part of the urinary system, and the reproductive organs, which hold the seeds of new human life. Modern imaging techniques, such as contrast X-rays and different types of scans, make it possible to see and study body organs without the need to cut through their protective coverings of skin, fat, muscle, and bone.

MAJOR INTERNAL STRUCTURES

Thyroid gland

Larynx

Heart

Right lung

Left lung

Diaphragm

Liver

Stomach

Large intestine

Small intestine

Greater omentum

IMAGING THE BODY

SCINTIGRAM OF
HEART CHAMBERS

ANGIOGRAM OF
RIGHT LUNG

CONTRAST X-RAY OF
GALLBLADDER

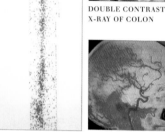

SCINTIGRAM OF
NERVOUS SYSTEM

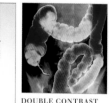

DOUBLE CONTRAST
X-RAY OF COLON

ULTRASOUND SCAN
OF TWINS IN UTERUS

ANGIOGRAM OF
KIDNEYS

ANGIOGRAM OF
ARTERIES OF HEAD

CT SCAN THROUGH
FEMALE CHEST

THERMOGRAM OF
CHEST REGION

ANGIOGRAM OF
ARTERIES OF HEART

MRI SCAN THROUGH
HEAD AT EYE LEVEL

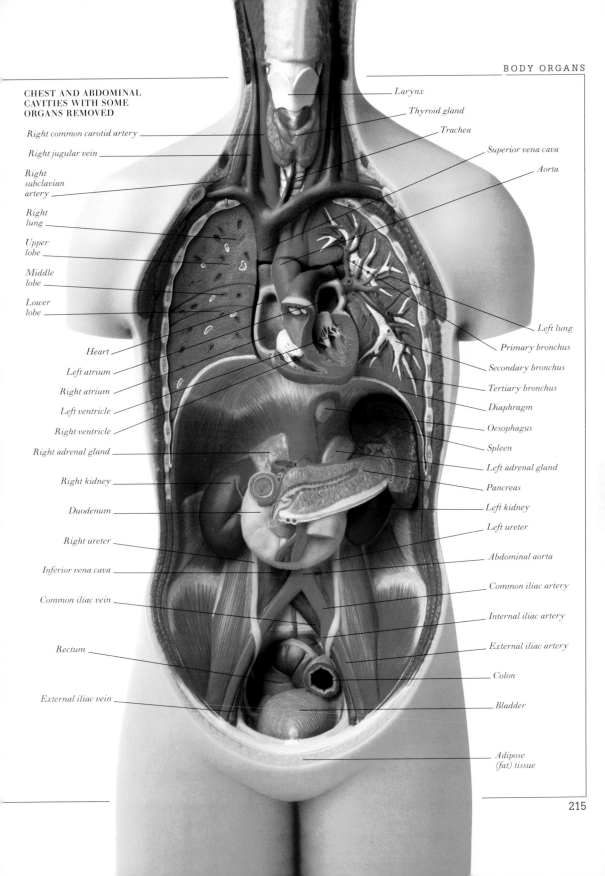

CHEST AND ABDOMINAL
CAVITIES WITH SOME
ORGANS REMOVED

Right common carotid artery

Right jugular vein

*Right
subclavian
artery*

*Right
lung*

*Upper
lobe*

*Middle
lobe*

*Lower
lobe*

Heart

Left atrium

Right atrium

Left ventricle

Right ventricle

Right adrenal gland

Right kidney

Duodenum

Right ureter

Inferior vena cava

Common iliac vein

Rectum

External iliac vein

Larynx

Thyroid gland

Trachea

Superior vena cava

Aorta

Left lung

Primary bronchus

Secondary bronchus

Tertiary bronchus

Diaphragm

Oesophagus

Spleen

Left adrenal gland

Pancreas

Left kidney

Left ureter

Abdominal aorta

Common iliac artery

Internal iliac artery

External iliac artery

Colon

Bladder

*Adipose
(fat) tissue*

215

Body cells

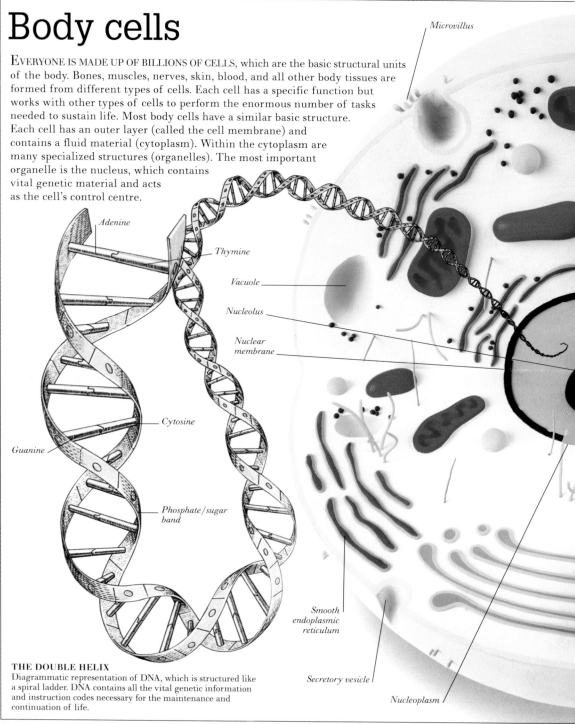

EVERYONE IS MADE UP OF BILLIONS OF CELLS, which are the basic structural units of the body. Bones, muscles, nerves, skin, blood, and all other body tissues are formed from different types of cells. Each cell has a specific function but works with other types of cells to perform the enormous number of tasks needed to sustain life. Most body cells have a similar basic structure. Each cell has an outer layer (called the cell membrane) and contains a fluid material (cytoplasm). Within the cytoplasm are many specialized structures (organelles). The most important organelle is the nucleus, which contains vital genetic material and acts as the cell's control centre.

Microvillus

Adenine

Thymine

Vacuole

Nucleolus

Nuclear membrane

Cytosine

Guanine

Phosphate / sugar band

Smooth endoplasmic reticulum

Secretory vesicle

Nucleoplasm

THE DOUBLE HELIX
Diagrammatic representation of DNA, which is structured like a spiral ladder. DNA contains all the vital genetic information and instruction codes necessary for the maintenance and continuation of life.

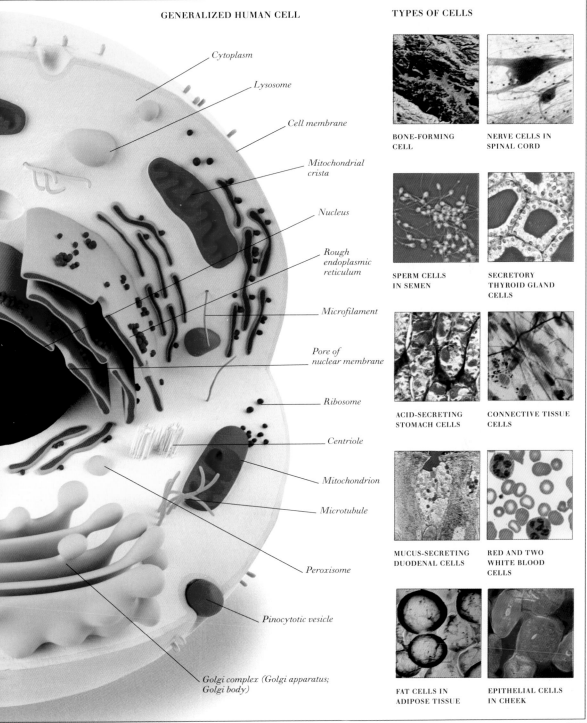

GENERALIZED HUMAN CELL

Cytoplasm

Lysosome

Cell membrane

Mitochondrial crista

Nucleus

Rough endoplasmic reticulum

Microfilament

Pore of nuclear membrane

Ribosome

Centriole

Mitochondrion

Microtubule

Peroxisome

Pinocytotic vesicle

Golgi complex (Golgi apparatus; Golgi body)

TYPES OF CELLS

BONE-FORMING CELL

NERVE CELLS IN SPINAL CORD

SPERM CELLS IN SEMEN

SECRETORY THYROID GLAND CELLS

ACID-SECRETING STOMACH CELLS

CONNECTIVE TISSUE CELLS

MUCUS-SECRETING DUODENAL CELLS

RED AND TWO WHITE BLOOD CELLS

FAT CELLS IN ADIPOSE TISSUE

EPITHELIAL CELLS IN CHEEK

217

Skeleton

THE SKELETON IS A MOBILE FRAMEWORK made up of 206 bones, approximately half of which are in the hands and feet. Although individual bones are rigid, the skeleton as a whole is remarkably flexible and allows the human body a huge range of movement. The skeleton serves as an anchorage for the skeletal muscles, and as a protective cage for the body's internal organs. Female bones are usually smaller and lighter than male bones, and the female pelvis is shallower and has a wider cavity.

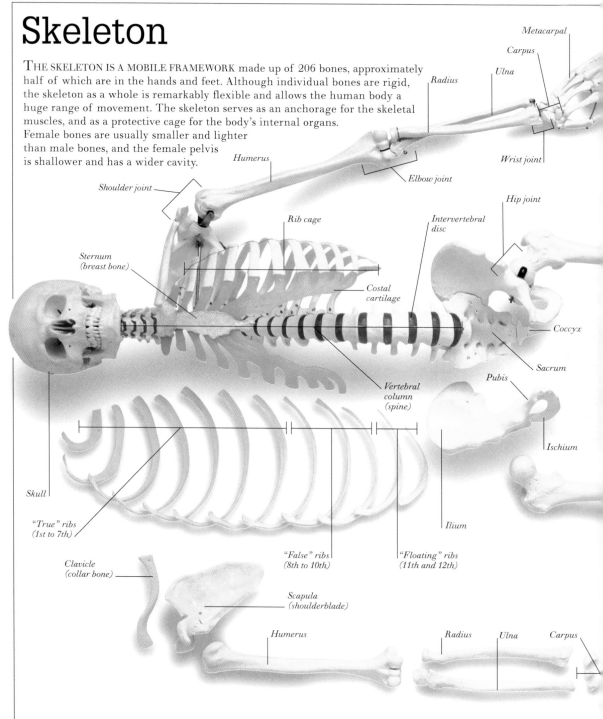

Metacarpal

Carpus

Ulna

Radius

Humerus

Shoulder joint

Elbow joint

Wrist joint

Hip joint

Rib cage

Intervertebral disc

Sternum
(breast bone)

Costal cartilage

Coccyx

Sacrum

Pubis

Vertebral column (spine)

Ischium

Skull

Ilium

"True" ribs
(1st to 7th)

"False" ribs
(8th to 10th)

"Floating" ribs
(11th and 12th)

Clavicle
(collar bone)

Scapula
(shoulderblade)

Humerus

Radius

Ulna

Carpus

Distal phalanx

Middle phalanx

Proximal phalanx

Femur

Patella

Tibia

Fibula

Tarsus

Proximal phalanx

Middle phalanx

Distal phalanx

Knee joint

Ankle joint

Metatarsal

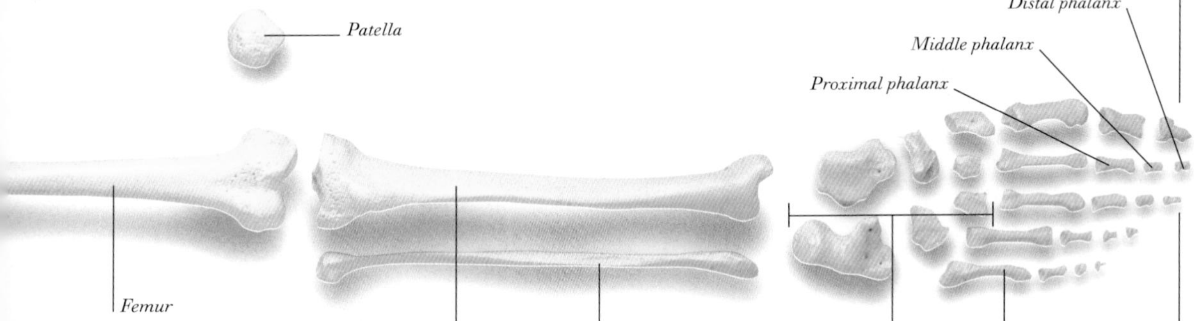

Patella

Distal phalanx

Middle phalanx

Proximal phalanx

Femur

Tibia

Fibula

Tarsus

Metatarsal

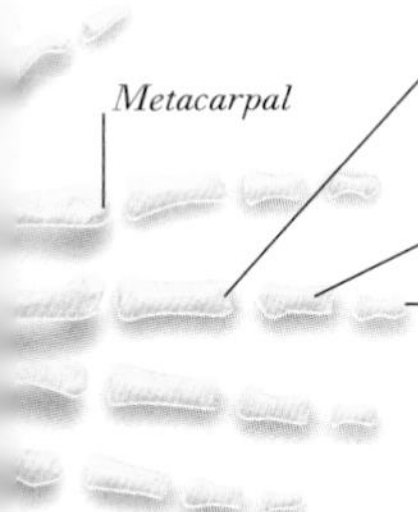

Proximal phalanx

Metacarpal

Middle phalanx

Distal phalanx

Skull

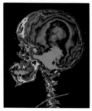

THE SKULL is the most complicated bony structure of the body but every feature serves a purpose. Internally, the main hollow chamber of the skull has three levels that support the brain, with every bump and hollow corresponding to the shape of the brain. Underneath and towards the back of the skull is a large round hole, the foramen magnum, through which the spinal cord passes. To the front of this are many smaller openings through which nerves, arteries, and veins pass to and from the brain. The roof of the skull is formed from four thin, curved bones that are firmly fixed together from the age of about two years. At the front of the skull are the two orbits, which contain the eyeballs, and a central hole for the airway of the nose. The jaw bone hinges on either side at ear level.

RIGHT SIDE VIEW OF A FETAL SKULL

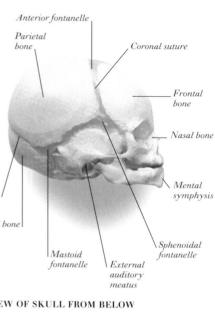

Anterior fontanelle
Parietal bone
Coronal suture
Frontal bone
Nasal bone
Mental symphysis
Lambdoid suture
Occipital bone
Sphenoidal fontanelle
Mastoid fontanelle
External auditory meatus

RIGHT SIDE VIEW OF SKULL

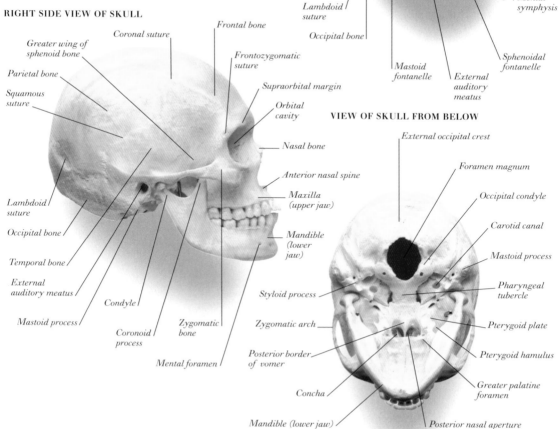

Greater wing of sphenoid bone
Coronal suture
Frontal bone
Frontozygomatic suture
Parietal bone
Squamous suture
Supraorbital margin
Orbital cavity
Nasal bone
Anterior nasal spine
Maxilla (upper jaw)
Mandible (lower jaw)
Lambdoid suture
Occipital bone
Temporal bone
External auditory meatus
Condyle
Mastoid process
Coronoid process
Zygomatic bone
Mental foramen
Styloid process
Zygomatic arch
Posterior border of vomer
Concha
Mandible (lower jaw)

VIEW OF SKULL FROM BELOW

External occipital crest
Foramen magnum
Occipital condyle
Carotid canal
Mastoid process
Pharyngeal tubercle
Pterygoid plate
Pterygoid hamulus
Greater palatine foramen
Posterior nasal aperture

FRONT VIEW OF SKULL

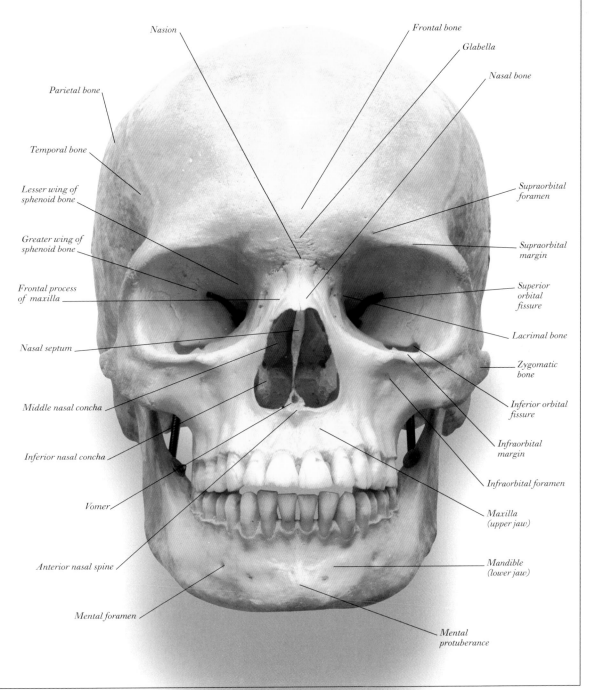

Nasion

Frontal bone

Glabella

Nasal bone

Parietal bone

Temporal bone

Lesser wing of
sphenoid bone

Greater wing of
sphenoid bone

Frontal process
of maxilla

Nasal septum

Middle nasal concha

Inferior nasal concha

Vomer

Anterior nasal spine

Mental foramen

Supraorbital
foramen

Supraorbital
margin

Superior
orbital
fissure

Lacrimal bone

Zygomatic
bone

Inferior orbital
fissure

Infraorbital
margin

Infraorbital foramen

Maxilla
(upper jaw)

Mandible
(lower jaw)

Mental
protuberance

Spine

THE SPINE (OR VERTEBRAL COLUMN) has two main functions:
it serves as a protective surrounding for the delicate spinal
cord and forms the supporting back bone of the skeleton.
The spine consists of 24 separate differently shaped bones
(vertebrae) with a curved, triangular bone (the sacrum) at
the bottom. The sacrum is made up of fused vertebrae; at its
lower end is a small tail-like structure made up of tiny bones
collectively called the coccyx. Between each pair of vertebrae
is a disc of cartilage that cushions the bones during movement.
The top two vertebrae differ in appearance from the others and
work as a pair: the first, called the atlas, rotates around a stout
vertical peg on the second, the axis. This arrangement allows
the skull to move freely up and down, and from side to side.

Cervical vertebrae

Thoracic vertebrae

Lumbar vertebrae

Sacral vertebrae

Coccygeal vertebrae

TYPES OF VERTEBRAE (VIEWED FROM ABOVE)

ATLAS

Anterior arch

Lateral mass with
superior articular facet

Posterior
arch

Anterior
tubercle

Posterior
tubercle

Vertebral
foramen

Transverse
process

Transverse
foramen

AXIS

Facet

Dens

Vertebral foramen

Spinous
process

Lamina

Transverse process
and foramen

CERVICAL VERTEBRA

Body

Anterior
tubercle

Posterior
tubercle

Superior
articular
process

Spinous
process

Vertebral
foramen

Transverse
foramen

SKULL AND SPINE

Skull

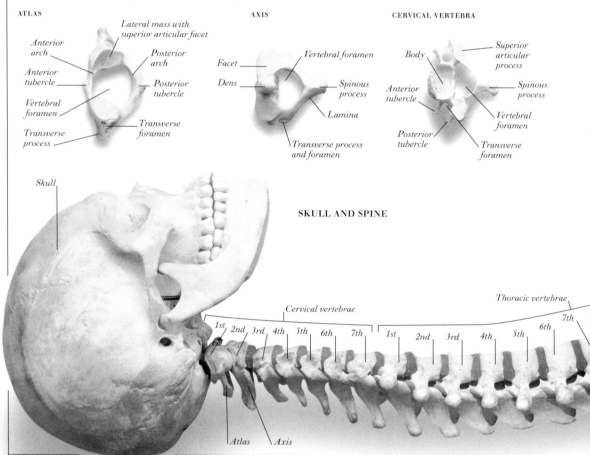

Cervical vertebrae

1st 2nd 3rd 4th 5th 6th 7th

Thoracic vertebrae

1st 2nd 3rd 4th 5th 6th 7th

Atlas Axis

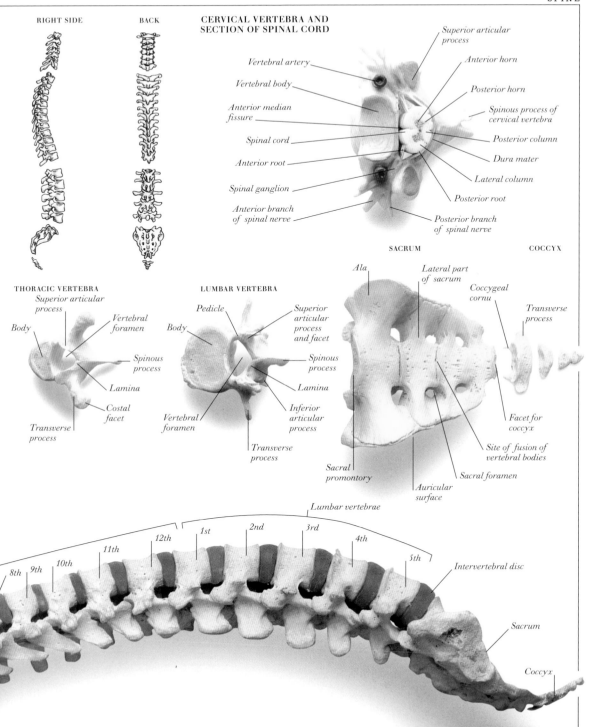

RIGHT SIDE

BACK

CERVICAL VERTEBRA AND SECTION OF SPINAL CORD

Superior articular process

Vertebral artery

Anterior horn

Vertebral body

Posterior horn

Anterior median fissure

Spinous process of cervical vertebra

Spinal cord

Posterior column

Anterior root

Dura mater

Spinal ganglion

Lateral column

Anterior branch of spinal nerve

Posterior root

Posterior branch of spinal nerve

SACRUM

COCCYX

Ala

Lateral part of sacrum

Coccygeal cornu

Transverse process

THORACIC VERTEBRA

Superior articular process

LUMBAR VERTEBRA

Pedicle

Superior articular process and facet

Body

Vertebral foramen

Body

Spinous process

Spinous process

Lamina

Lamina

Transverse process

Inferior articular process

Costal facet

Vertebral foramen

Facet for coccyx

Transverse process

Site of fusion of vertebral bodies

Sacral foramen

Sacral promontory

Auricular surface

Lumbar vertebrae

1st 2nd 3rd 4th 5th

8th 9th 10th 11th 12th

Intervertebral disc

Sacrum

Coccyx

Bones and joints

BONES FORM the body's hard, strong skeletal framework. Each bone has a hard, compact exterior surrounding a spongy, lighter interior. The long bones of the arms and legs, such as the femur (thigh bone), have a central cavity containing bone marrow. Bones are composed chiefly of calcium, phosphorus, and a fibrous substance known as collagen. Bones meet at joints, which are of several different types. For example, the hip is a ball-and-socket joint that allows the femur a wide range of movement, whereas finger joints are simple hinge joints that allow only bending and straightening. Joints are held in place by bands of tissue called ligaments. Movement of joints is facilitated by the smooth hyaline cartilage that covers the bone ends and by the synovial membrane that lines and lubricates the joint.

LIGAMENTS SURROUNDING HIP JOINT

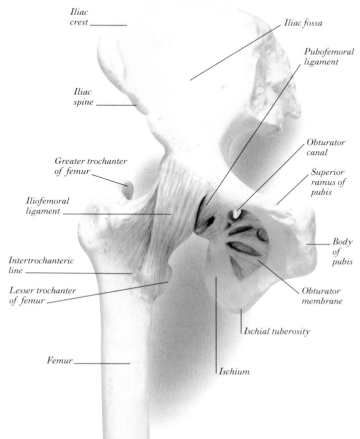

Iliac crest
Iliac fossa
Pubofemoral ligament
Iliac spine
Obturator canal
Greater trochanter of femur
Superior ramus of pubis
Iliofemoral ligament
Body of pubis
Intertrochanteric line
Lesser trochanter of femur
Obturator membrane
Ischial tuberosity
Femur
Ischium

SECTION THROUGH LEFT FEMUR

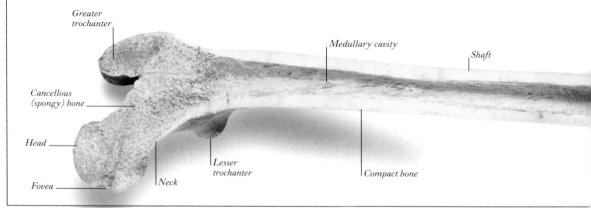

Greater trochanter
Medullary cavity
Shaft
Cancellous (spongy) bone
Head
Lesser trochanter
Compact bone
Fovea
Neck

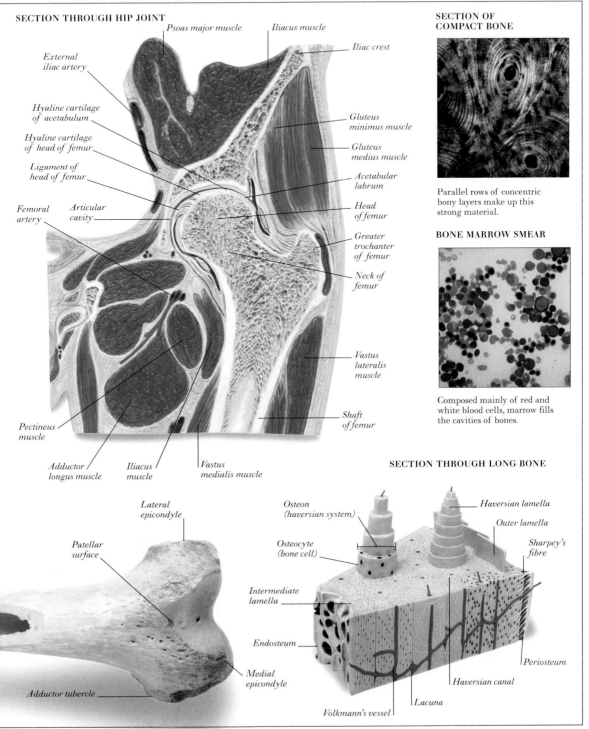

SECTION THROUGH HIP JOINT

- Psoas major muscle
- Iliacus muscle
- Iliac crest
- External iliac artery
- Hyaline cartilage of acetabulum
- Hyaline cartilage of head of femur
- Ligament of head of femur
- Gluteus minimus muscle
- Gluteus medius muscle
- Acetabular labrum
- Femoral artery
- Articular cavity
- Head of femur
- Greater trochanter of femur
- Neck of femur
- Vastus lateralis muscle
- Pectineus muscle
- Adductor longus muscle
- Iliacus muscle
- Vastus medialis muscle
- Shaft of femur

SECTION OF COMPACT BONE

Parallel rows of concentric bony layers make up this strong material.

BONE MARROW SMEAR

Composed mainly of red and white blood cells, marrow fills the cavities of bones.

SECTION THROUGH LONG BONE

- Lateral epicondyle
- Patellar surface
- Medial epicondyle
- Adductor tubercle
- Osteon (haversian system)
- Osteocyte (bone cell)
- Intermediate lamella
- Endosteum
- Volkmann's vessel
- Lacuna
- Haversian lamella
- Outer lamella
- Sharpey's fibre
- Periosteum
- Haversian canal

Muscles 1

THERE ARE THREE MAIN TYPES OF MUSCLE: skeletal muscle (also called voluntary muscle because it can be consciously controlled); smooth muscle (also called involuntary muscle because it is not under voluntary control); and the specialized muscle tissue of the heart. Humans have more than 600 skeletal muscles, which differ in size and shape according to the jobs they do. Skeletal muscles are attached either directly or indirectly (via tendons) to bones, and work in opposing pairs (one muscle in the pair contracts while the other relaxes) to produce body movements as diverse as walking, threading a needle, and an array of facial expressions. Smooth muscles occur in the walls of internal body organs and perform actions such as forcing food through the intestines, contracting the uterus (womb) in childbirth, and pumping blood through the blood vessels.

SOME OTHER MUSCLES IN THE BODY

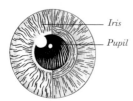

Iris
Pupil

IRIS
The muscle fibres contract and dilate (expand) to alter pupil size.

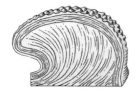

TONGUE
Interlacing layers of muscle allow great mobility.

ILEUM
Opposing muscle layers transport semi-digested food.

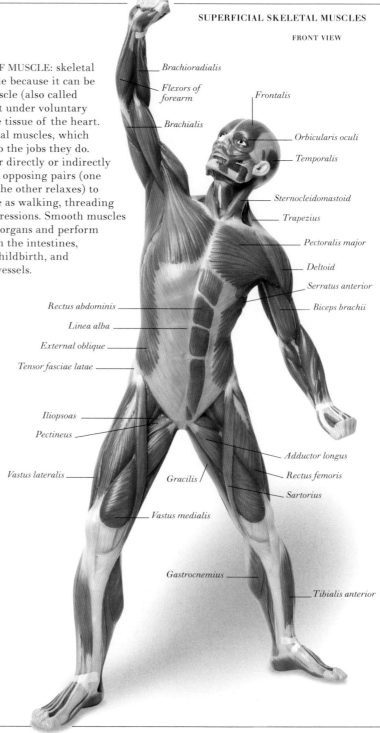

SUPERFICIAL SKELETAL MUSCLES

FRONT VIEW

Brachioradialis

Flexors of forearm

Brachialis

Frontalis

Orbicularis oculi

Temporalis

Sternocleidomastoid

Trapezius

Pectoralis major

Deltoid

Serratus anterior

Biceps brachii

Rectus abdominis

Linea alba

External oblique

Tensor fasciae latae

Iliopsoas

Pectineus

Vastus lateralis

Gracilis

Adductor longus

Rectus femoris

Sartorius

Vastus medialis

Gastrocnemius

Tibialis anterior

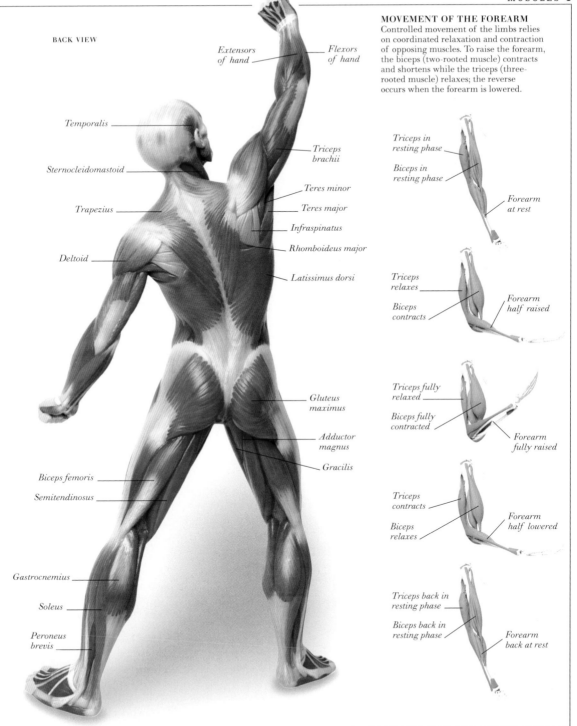

BACK VIEW

Extensors
of hand

Flexors
of hand

Temporalis

Sternocleidomastoid

Trapezius

Deltoid

Triceps
brachii

Teres minor

Teres major

Infraspinatus

Rhomboideus major

Latissimus dorsi

Gluteus
maximus

Adductor
magnus

Gracilis

Biceps femoris

Semitendinosus

Gastrocnemius

Soleus

Peroneus
brevis

MOVEMENT OF THE FOREARM
Controlled movement of the limbs relies
on coordinated relaxation and contraction
of opposing muscles. To raise the forearm,
the biceps (two-rooted muscle) contracts
and shortens while the triceps (three-
rooted muscle) relaxes; the reverse
occurs when the forearm is lowered.

Triceps in
resting phase

Biceps in
resting phase

Forearm
at rest

Triceps
relaxes

Biceps
contracts

Forearm
half raised

Triceps fully
relaxed

Biceps fully
contracted

Forearm
fully raised

Triceps
contracts

Biceps
relaxes

Forearm
half lowered

Triceps back in
resting phase

Biceps back in
resting phase

Forearm
back at rest

Muscles 2

SKELETAL MUSCLE FIBRE

Myofibril

Sarcomere

Motor end plate

Synaptic knob

Nucleus

Sarcoplasmic reticulum

Schwann cell

Sarcolemma

Motor neuron

Endomysium

Node of Ranvier

MUSCLES OF FACIAL EXPRESSION

A single expression is the result of movement of many muscles; the main muscles of expression are shown in action below.

FRONTALIS

CORRUGATOR SUPERCILII

ORBICULARIS ORIS

TYPES OF MUSCLE

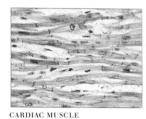

CARDIAC MUSCLE

SKELETAL MUSCLE

SMOOTH MUSCLE

ZYGOMATICUS MAJOR

CONTRACTION OF SKELETAL MUSCLE

RELAXED STATE

CONTRACTED STATE

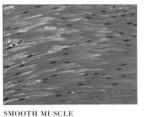

DEPRESSOR ANGULI ORIS

**MUSCLES OF
HEAD AND NECK**

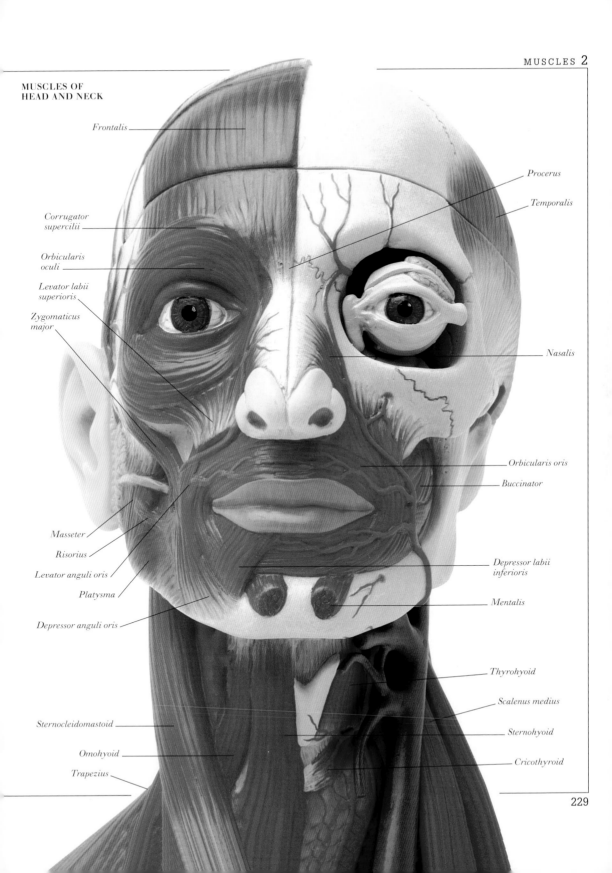

Frontalis

Procerus

Temporalis

Corrugator
supercilii

Orbicularis
oculi

Levator labii
superioris

Zygomaticus
major

Nasalis

Orbicularis oris

Buccinator

Masseter

Risorius

Levator anguli oris

Platysma

Depressor anguli oris

Depressor labii
inferioris

Mentalis

Thyrohyoid

Scalenus medius

Sternocleidomastoid

Omohyoid

Sternohyoid

Cricothyroid

Trapezius

Hands

THE HUMAN HAND is an extremely versatile tool, capable of delicate manipulation as well as powerful gripping actions. The arrangement of its 27 small bones, moved by 37 skeletal muscles that are connected to the bones by tendons, allows a wide range of movements. Our ability to bring the tips of our thumbs and fingers together, combined with the extraordinary sensitivity of our fingertips due to their rich supply of nerve endings, makes our hands uniquely dextrous.

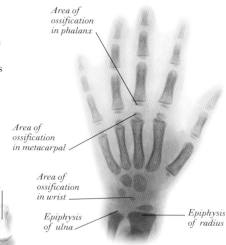

X-RAY OF LEFT HAND OF A YOUNG CHILD

Area of ossification in phalanx

Area of ossification in metacarpal

Area of ossification in wrist

Epiphysis of ulna

Epiphysis of radius

Areas of cartilage in the wrist and at the ends of the finger bones are the sites of growth and have still to ossify.

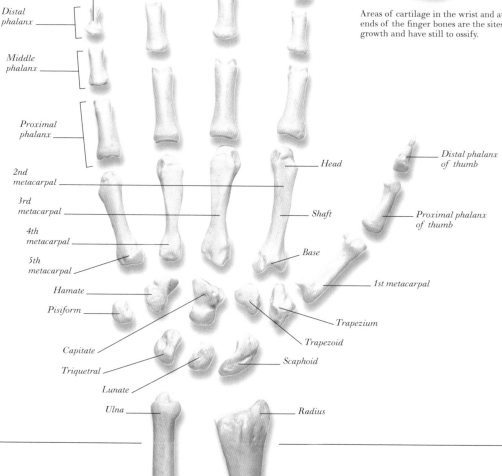

BONES OF HAND

Ring finger

Middle finger

Index finger

Little finger

Distal phalanx

Middle phalanx

Proximal phalanx

2nd metacarpal

3rd metacarpal

4th metacarpal

5th metacarpal

Hamate

Pisiform

Capitate

Triquetral

Lunate

Ulna

Head

Shaft

Base

Distal phalanx of thumb

Proximal phalanx of thumb

1st metacarpal

Trapezium

Trapezoid

Scaphoid

Radius

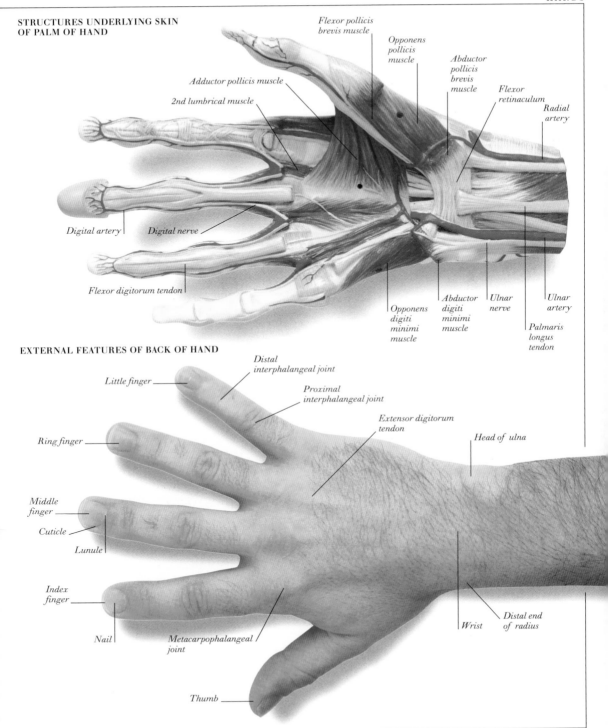

STRUCTURES UNDERLYING SKIN OF PALM OF HAND

Flexor pollicis brevis muscle

Opponens pollicis muscle

Abductor pollicis brevis muscle

Flexor retinaculum

Radial artery

Adductor pollicis muscle

2nd lumbrical muscle

Digital artery

Digital nerve

Flexor digitorum tendon

Opponens digiti minimi muscle

Abductor digiti minimi muscle

Ulnar nerve

Ulnar artery

Palmaris longus tendon

EXTERNAL FEATURES OF BACK OF HAND

Little finger

Distal interphalangeal joint

Proximal interphalangeal joint

Extensor digitorum tendon

Head of ulna

Ring finger

Middle finger

Cuticle

Lunule

Index finger

Nail

Metacarpophalangeal joint

Thumb

Wrist

Distal end of radius

Feet

THE FEET AND TOES are essential elements in body movement. They bear and propel the weight of the body during walking and running, and also help to maintain balance during changes of body position. Each foot has 26 bones, more than 100 ligaments, and 33 muscles, some of which are attached to the lower leg. The heel pad and the arch of the foot act as shock absorbers, providing a cushion against the jolts that occur with every step.

BONES OF FOOT

LIGAMENTS OF FOOT

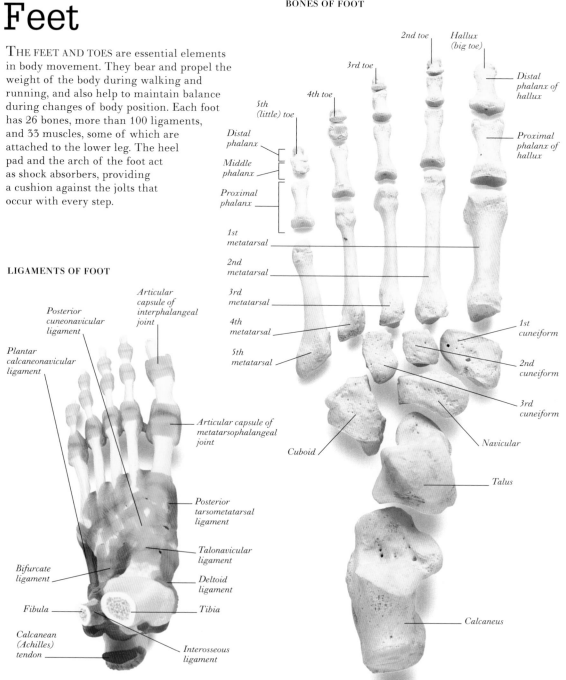

2nd toe

Hallux (big toe)

3rd toe

Distal phalanx of hallux

4th toe

5th (little) toe

Proximal phalanx of hallux

Distal phalanx

Middle phalanx

Proximal phalanx

1st metatarsal

2nd metatarsal

3rd metatarsal

1st cuneiform

4th metatarsal

5th metatarsal

2nd cuneiform

3rd cuneiform

Cuboid

Navicular

Talus

Calcaneus

Posterior cuneonavicular ligament

Articular capsule of interphalangeal joint

Plantar calcaneonavicular ligament

Articular capsule of metatarsophalangeal joint

Posterior tarsometatarsal ligament

Talonavicular ligament

Bifurcate ligament

Deltoid ligament

Fibula

Tibia

Calcanean (Achilles) tendon

Interosseous ligament

STRUCTURES UNDERLYING SKIN OF FOOT

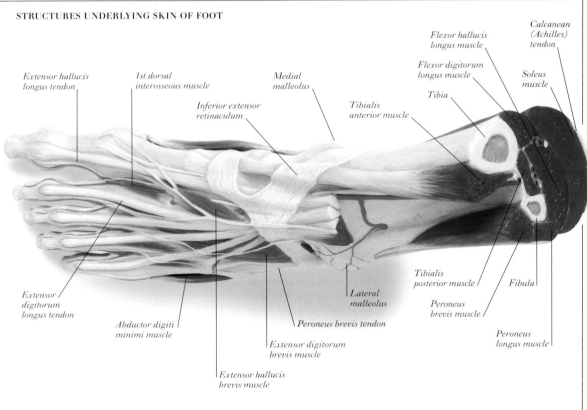

Extensor hallucis
longus tendon

1st dorsal
interosseous muscle

Medial
malleolus

Flexor hallucis
longus muscle

Calcanean
(Achilles)
tendon

Flexor digitorum
longus muscle

Soleus
muscle

Inferior extensor
retinaculum

Tibialis
anterior muscle

Tibia

Extensor
digitorum
longus tendon

Abductor digiti
minimi muscle

Extensor hallucis
brevis muscle

Extensor digitorum
brevis muscle

Peroneus brevis tendon

Lateral
malleolus

Tibialis
posterior muscle

Peroneus
brevis muscle

Fibula

Peroneus
longus muscle

EXTERNAL FEATURES OF FOOT

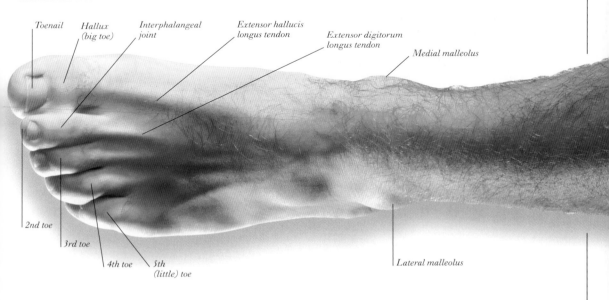

Toenail

Hallux
(big toe)

Interphalangeal
joint

Extensor hallucis
longus tendon

Extensor digitorum
longus tendon

Medial malleolus

2nd toe

3rd toe

4th toe

5th
(little) toe

Lateral malleolus

233

Skin and hair

SKIN IS THE BODY'S LARGEST ORGAN, a waterproof barrier that protects the internal organs against infection, injury, and harmful sun rays. The skin is also an important sensory organ and helps to control body temperature. The outer layer of the skin, known as the epidermis, is coated with keratin, a tough, horny protein that is also the chief constituent of hair and nails. Dead cells are shed from the skin's surface and are replaced by new cells from the base of the epidermis, the region that also produces the skin pigment, melanin. The dermis contains most of the skin's living structures, and includes nerve endings, blood vessels, elastic fibres, sweat glands that cool the skin, and sebaceous glands that produce oil to keep the skin supple. Beneath the dermis lies the subcutaneous tissue (hypodermis), which is rich in fat and blood vessels. Hair shafts grow from hair follicles situated in the dermis and subcutaneous tissue. Hair grows on every part of the skin apart from the palms of the hands and soles of the feet.

SECTION OF HAIR

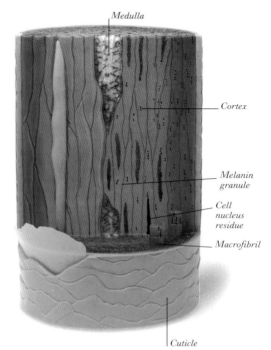

Medulla

Cortex

Melanin granule

Cell nucleus residue

Macrofibril

Cuticle

SECTIONS OF DIFFERENT TYPES OF SKIN

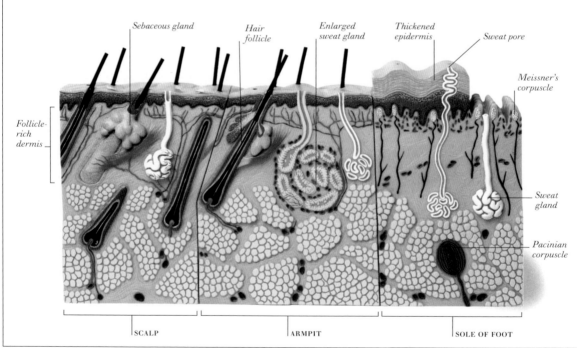

Sebaceous gland

Hair follicle

Enlarged sweat gland

Thickened epidermis

Sweat pore

Meissner's corpuscle

Follicle-rich dermis

Sweat gland

Pacinian corpuscle

SCALP

ARMPIT

SOLE OF FOOT

SECTION OF SKIN

Stratum granulosum

Stratum corneum

Sweat pore

Hair shaft

Sweat duct

Stratum spinosum

Merkel's disc

Stratum basale

Dermal papilla

Epidermis

Free nerve ending

Meissner's corpuscle

Vascular plexus

Nerve fibre

Sebaceous gland

Dermis

Arrector pili muscle

Hair bulb

Papilla

Pacinian corpuscle

Hypodermis

Adipose (fat) tissue

Ruffini corpuscle

Artery

Vein

Sweat gland

Hair follicle

PHOTOMICROGRAPHS OF SKIN AND HAIR

SECTION OF SKIN
The flaky cells at the skin's surface are shed continuously.

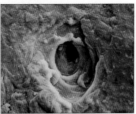

SWEAT PORE
This allows loss of fluid as part of temperature control.

SKIN HAIR
Two hairs pushing through the outer layer of skin.

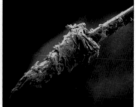

HEAD HAIR
The root and part of the shaft of a hair from the scalp.

235

Brain

THE BRAIN IS THE MAJOR ORGAN of the central nervous
system and the control centre for all the body's voluntary
and involuntary activities. It is also responsible for the
complexities of thought, memory, emotion, and language.
In adults, this complex organ is a mere 1.4 kg (3 lb) in weight,
containing over 10 thousand million nerve cells. Three distinct
regions can easily be seen – the brainstem, the cerebellum,
and the large cerebrum. The brainstem controls vital body
functions, such as breathing and digestion. The cerebellum's
main functions are the maintenance of posture and the
coordination of body movements. The cerebrum, which
consists of the right and left cerebral hemispheres joined
by the corpus callosum, is the site of most conscious and
intelligent activities.

**MRI SCAN OF TRANSVERSE
SECTION THROUGH BRAIN**

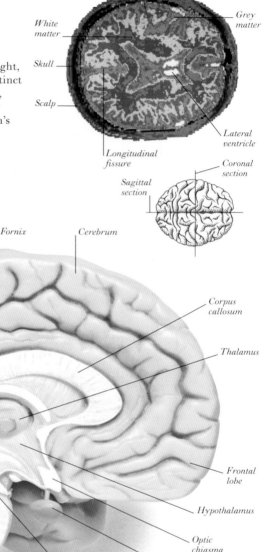

White matter

Skull

Scalp

Grey matter

Lateral ventricle

Longitudinal fissure

Coronal section

Sagittal section

**SAGITTAL SECTION
THROUGH BRAIN**

Central sulcus

Fornix

Cerebrum

Parietal lobe

Parieto-occipital sulucs

Pineal body

Occipital lobe

Aqueduct

Cerebellum

4th ventricle

Spinal cord

Corpus callosum

Thalamus

Frontal lobe

Hypothalamus

Optic chiasma

Pituitary gland

Mesencephalon (midbrain)

Pons

Medulla oblongata

Brainstem

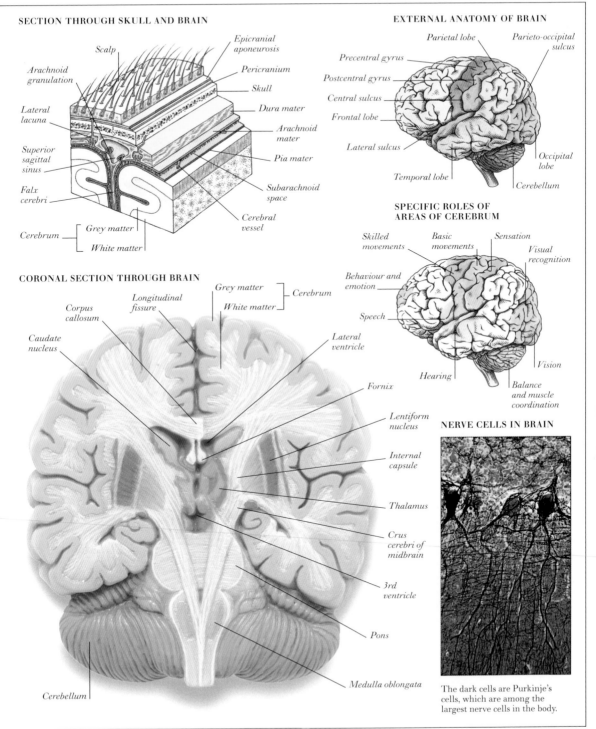

SECTION THROUGH SKULL AND BRAIN

Scalp
Epicranial aponeurosis
Arachnoid granulation
Pericranium
Skull
Dura mater
Lateral lacuna
Arachnoid mater
Superior sagittal sinus
Pia mater
Falx cerebri
Subarachnoid space
Cerebral vessel
Cerebrum — Grey matter
White matter

EXTERNAL ANATOMY OF BRAIN

Parietal lobe
Parieto-occipital sulcus
Precentral gyrus
Postcentral gyrus
Central sulcus
Frontal lobe
Lateral sulcus
Occipital lobe
Temporal lobe
Cerebellum

SPECIFIC ROLES OF AREAS OF CEREBRUM

Skilled movements
Basic movements
Sensation
Visual recognition
Behaviour and emotion
Speech
Hearing
Vision
Balance and muscle coordination

CORONAL SECTION THROUGH BRAIN

Corpus callosum
Longitudinal fissure
Grey matter
White matter — Cerebrum
Caudate nucleus
Lateral ventricle
Fornix
Lentiform nucleus
Internal capsule
Thalamus
Crus cerebri of midbrain
3rd ventricle
Pons
Medulla oblongata
Cerebellum

NERVE CELLS IN BRAIN

The dark cells are Purkinje's cells, which are among the largest nerve cells in the body.

237

Nervous system

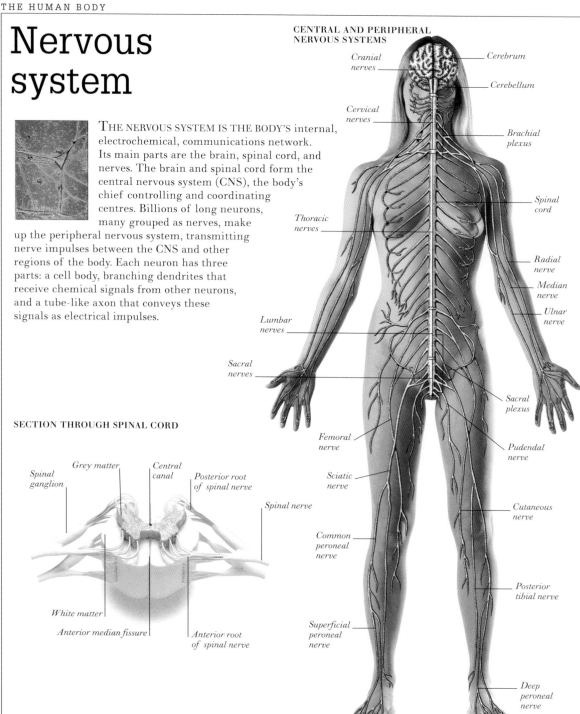

THE NERVOUS SYSTEM IS THE BODY'S internal, electrochemical, communications network. Its main parts are the brain, spinal cord, and nerves. The brain and spinal cord form the central nervous system (CNS), the body's chief controlling and coordinating centres. Billions of long neurons, many grouped as nerves, make up the peripheral nervous system, transmitting nerve impulses between the CNS and other regions of the body. Each neuron has three parts: a cell body, branching dendrites that receive chemical signals from other neurons, and a tube-like axon that conveys these signals as electrical impulses.

CENTRAL AND PERIPHERAL NERVOUS SYSTEMS

Cranial nerves

Cerebrum

Cerebellum

Cervical nerves

Brachial plexus

Spinal cord

Thoracic nerves

Radial nerve

Median nerve

Ulnar nerve

Lumbar nerves

Sacral nerves

Sacral plexus

Femoral nerve

Pudendal nerve

Sciatic nerve

Cutaneous nerve

Common peroneal nerve

Posterior tibial nerve

Superficial peroneal nerve

Deep peroneal nerve

SECTION THROUGH SPINAL CORD

Spinal ganglion

Grey matter

Central canal

Posterior root of spinal nerve

Spinal nerve

White matter

Anterior median fissure

Anterior root of spinal nerve

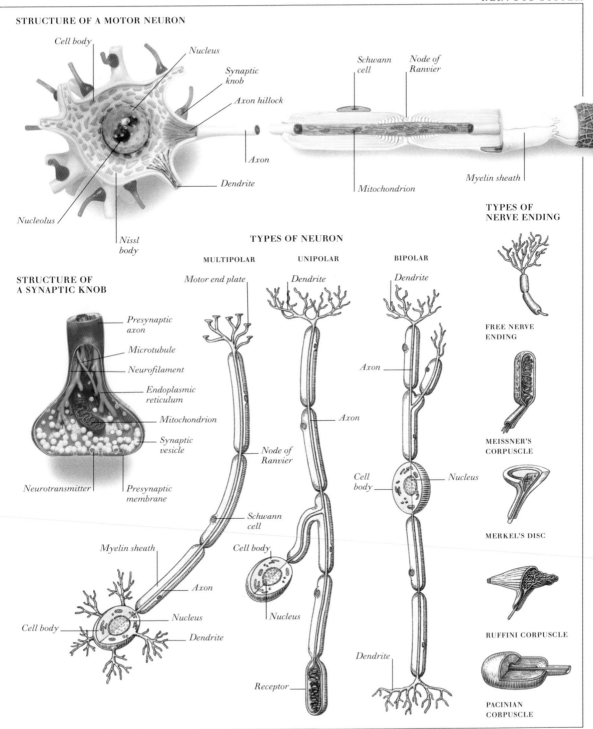

STRUCTURE OF A MOTOR NEURON

Cell body

Nucleus

Synaptic knob

Axon hillock

Axon

Dendrite

Nucleolus

Nissl body

Schwann cell

Node of Ranvier

Mitochondrion

Myelin sheath

STRUCTURE OF A SYNAPTIC KNOB

Presynaptic axon

Microtubule

Neurofilament

Endoplasmic reticulum

Mitochondrion

Synaptic vesicle

Neurotransmitter

Presynaptic membrane

Myelin sheath

Axon

Cell body

Nucleus

Dendrite

TYPES OF NEURON

MULTIPOLAR

Motor end plate

Node of Ranvier

Schwann cell

UNIPOLAR

Dendrite

Axon

Cell body

Nucleus

Receptor

BIPOLAR

Dendrite

Axon

Cell body

Nucleus

Dendrite

TYPES OF NERVE ENDING

FREE NERVE ENDING

MEISSNER'S CORPUSCLE

MERKEL'S DISC

RUFFINI CORPUSCLE

PACINIAN CORPUSCLE

239

Eye

THE EYE IS THE ORGAN OF SIGHT. The two eyeballs, protected within bony sockets called orbits and on the outside by the eyelids, eyebrows, and tear film, are directly connected to the brain by the optic nerves. Each eye is moved by six muscles, which are attached around the eyeball. Light rays entering the eye through the pupil are focused by the cornea and lens to form an image on the retina. The retina contains millions of light-sensitive cells, called rods and cones, which convert the image into a pattern of nerve impulses. These impulses are transmitted along the optic nerve to the brain. Information from the two optic nerves is processed in the brain to produce a single coordinated image.

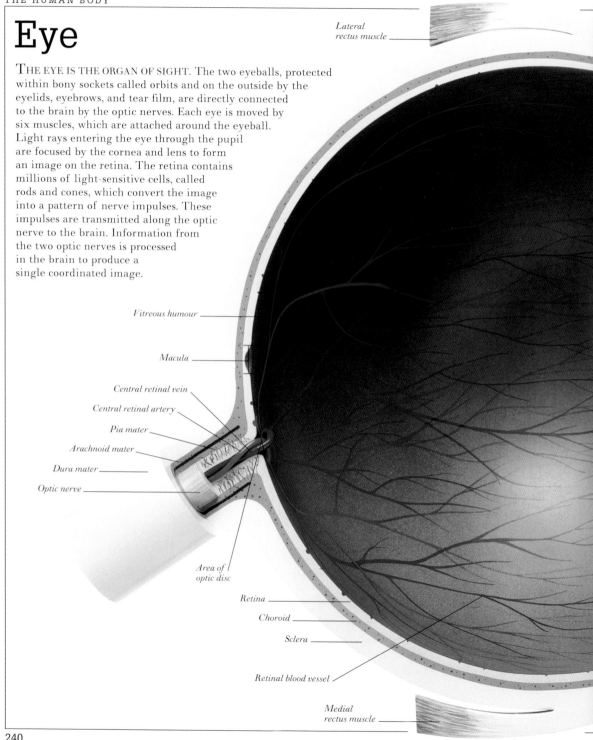

Lateral rectus muscle

Vitreous humour

Macula

Central retinal vein

Central retinal artery

Pia mater

Arachnoid mater

Dura mater

Optic nerve

Area of optic disc

Retina

Choroid

Sclera

Retinal blood vessel

Medial rectus muscle

SECTION THROUGH NOSE, MOUTH, AND THROAT

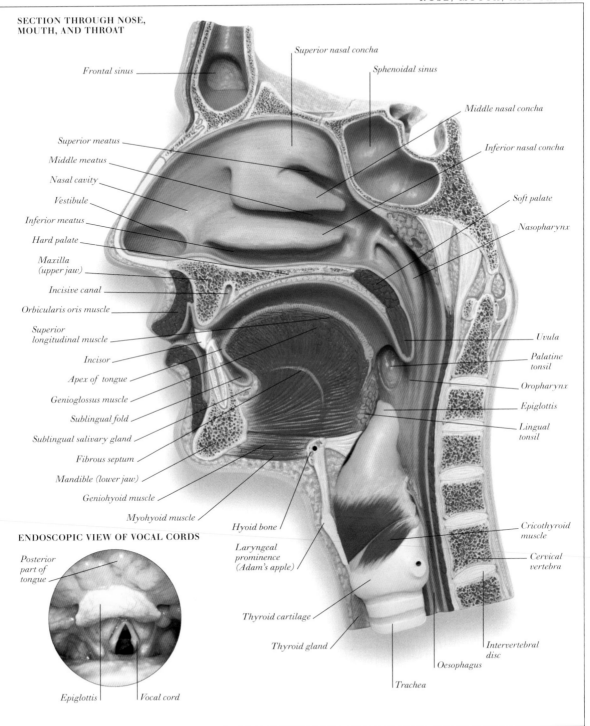

Frontal sinus

Superior nasal concha

Sphenoidal sinus

Middle nasal concha

Superior meatus

Middle meatus

Nasal cavity

Vestibule

Inferior meatus

Hard palate

Maxilla (upper jaw)

Incisive canal

Orbicularis oris muscle

Superior longitudinal muscle

Incisor

Apex of tongue

Genioglossus muscle

Sublingual fold

Sublingual salivary gland

Fibrous septum

Mandible (lower jaw)

Geniohyoid muscle

Myohyoid muscle

Inferior nasal concha

Soft palate

Nasopharynx

Uvula

Palatine tonsil

Oropharynx

Epiglottis

Lingual tonsil

ENDOSCOPIC VIEW OF VOCAL CORDS

Posterior part of tongue

Epiglottis

Vocal cord

Hyoid bone

Laryngeal prominence (Adam's apple)

Thyroid cartilage

Thyroid gland

Trachea

Cricothyroid muscle

Cervical vertebra

Intervertebral disc

Oesophagus

Teeth

THE 20 PRIMARY TEETH (also called deciduous or milk teeth) usually begin to erupt when a baby is about six months old. They start to be replaced by the permanent teeth when the child is about six years old. By the age of 20, most adults have a full set of 32 teeth although the third molars (commonly called wisdom teeth) may never erupt. While teeth help people to speak clearly and give shape to the face, their main function is the chewing of food. Incisors and canines shear and tear the food into pieces; premolars and molars crush and grind it further. Although tooth enamel is the hardest substance in the body, it tends to be eroded and destroyed by acid produced in the mouth during the breakdown of food.

DEVELOPMENT OF TEETH IN A FETUS

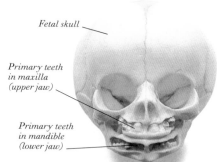

Fetal skull

Primary teeth in maxilla (upper jaw)

Primary teeth in mandible (lower jaw)

FETAL JAWS
By the sixth week of embryonic development areas of thickening occur in each jaw; these areas give rise to tooth buds. By the time the fetus is six months old, enamel has formed on the tooth buds.

DEVELOPMENT OF JAW AND TEETH

Maxilla (upper jaw)

Mandible (lower jaw)

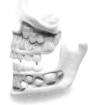

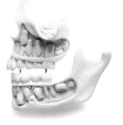

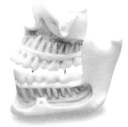

A NEWBORN BABY'S JAWS
The primary teeth can be seen developing in the jaw bones; they begin to erupt around the age of six months.

A FIVE-YEAR-OLD CHILD'S TEETH
There is a full set of 20 erupted primary teeth; the permanent teeth can be seen developing in the upper and lower jaws.

A NINE-YEAR-OLD CHILD'S TEETH
Most of the teeth are primary teeth but the permanent incisors and first molars have now emerged.

AN ADULT'S TEETH
By the age of 20, the full set of 32 permanent teeth (including the wisdom teeth) should be in position.

THE PERMANENT TEETH

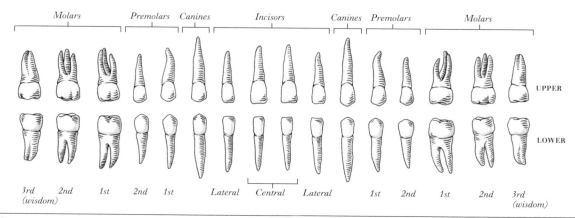

Molars   Premolars   Canines   Incisors   Canines   Premolars   Molars

UPPER

LOWER

3rd (wisdom)   2nd   1st   2nd   1st   Lateral   Central   Lateral   1st   2nd   1st   2nd   3rd (wisdom)

STRUCTURE OF A TOOTH

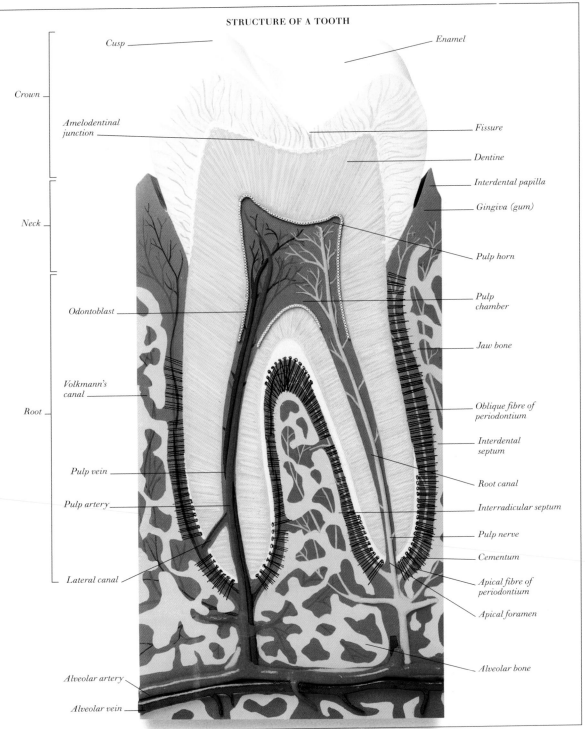

Cusp

Enamel

Crown

Amelodentinal junction

Fissure

Dentine

Interdental papilla

Gingiva (gum)

Neck

Pulp horn

Odontoblast

Pulp chamber

Jaw bone

Volkmann's canal

Root

Oblique fibre of periodontium

Interdental septum

Pulp vein

Root canal

Pulp artery

Interradicular septum

Pulp nerve

Cementum

Lateral canal

Apical fibre of periodontium

Apical foramen

Alveolar bone

Alveolar artery

Alveolar vein

Digestive system

THE DIGESTIVE SYSTEM BREAKS DOWN FOOD into particles so tiny that blood can take nourishment to all parts of the body. The system's main part is a 9 m (30 ft) tube from mouth to rectum; muscles in this alimentary canal force food along. Chewed food first travels through the oesophagus to the stomach, which churns and liquidizes food before it passes through the duodenum, jejunum, and ileum – the three parts of the long, convoluted small intestine. Here, digestive juices from the gallbladder and pancreas break down food particles; many filter out into the blood through tiny fingerlike villi that line the small intestine's inner wall. Undigested food in the colon forms faeces that leave the body through the anus.

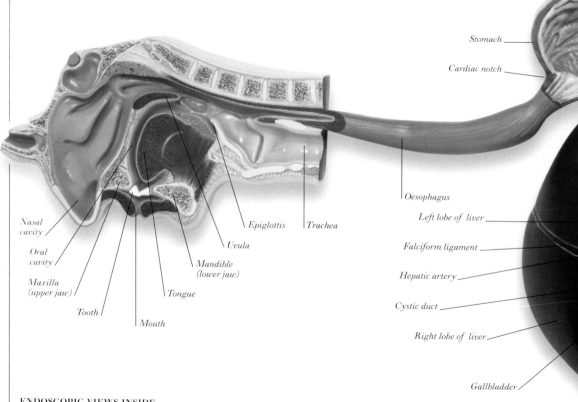

Stomach

Cardiac notch

Oesophagus

Left lobe of liver

Falciform ligament

Hepatic artery

Cystic duct

Right lobe of liver

Gallbladder

Epiglottis | Trachea

Uvula

Mandible (lower jaw)

Tongue

Mouth

Tooth

Maxilla (upper jaw)

Oral cavity

Nasal cavity

ENDOSCOPIC VIEWS INSIDE ALIMENTARY CANAL

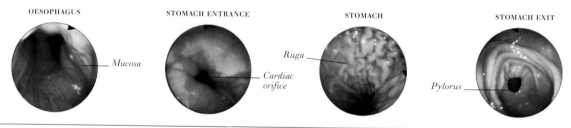

OESOPHAGUS

Mucosa

STOMACH ENTRANCE

Cardiac orifice

STOMACH

Ruga

STOMACH EXIT

Pylorus

ALIMENTARY CANAL

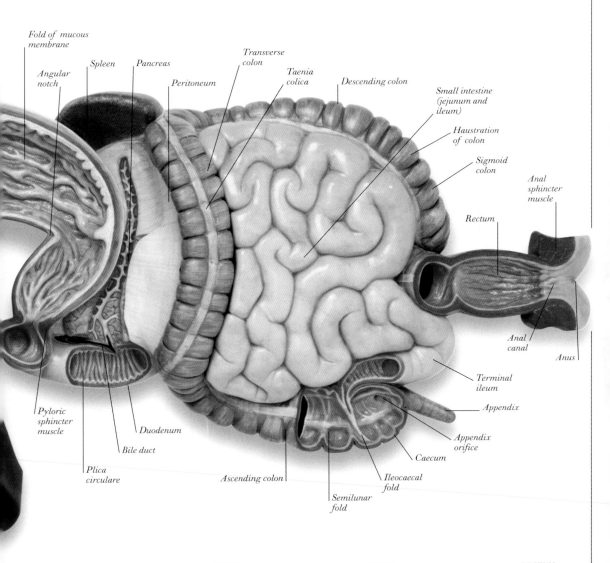

Fold of mucous membrane

Spleen

Pancreas

Transverse colon

Angular notch

Peritoneum

Taenia colica

Descending colon

Small intestine (jejunum and ileum)

Haustration of colon

Sigmoid colon

Anal sphincter muscle

Rectum

Anal canal

Anus

Terminal ileum

Appendix

Appendix orifice

Caecum

Ileocaecal fold

Pyloric sphincter muscle

Duodenum

Bile duct

Plica circulare

Ascending colon

Semilunar fold

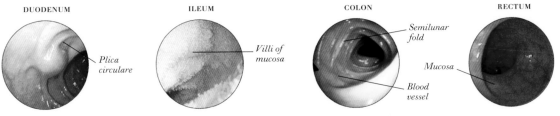

DUODENUM

Plica circulare

ILEUM

Villi of mucosa

COLON

Semilunar fold

Blood vessel

RECTUM

Mucosa

Heart

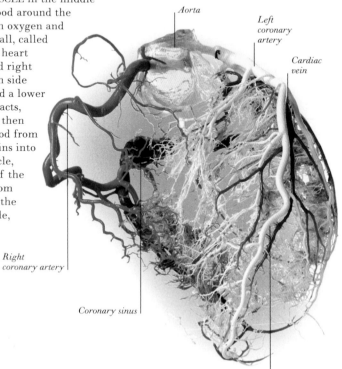

THE HEART IS A HOLLOW MUSCLE in the middle of the chest that pumps blood around the body, supplying cells with oxygen and nutrients. A muscular wall, called the septum, divides the heart lengthways into left and right sides. A valve divides each side into two chambers: an upper atrium and a lower ventricle. When the heart muscle contracts, it squeezes blood through the atria and then through the ventricles. Oxygenated blood from the lungs flows from the pulmonary veins into the left atrium, through the left ventricle, and then out via the aorta to all parts of the body. Deoxygenated blood returning from the body flows from the vena cava into the right atrium, through the right ventricle, and then out via the pulmonary artery to the lungs for reoxygenation. At rest the heart beats between 60 and 80 times a minute; during exercise or at times of stress or excitement the rate may increase to 200 beats a minute.

ARTERIES AND VEINS SURROUNDING HEART

Aorta

Left coronary artery

Cardiac vein

Right coronary artery

Coronary sinus

Main branch of left coronary artery

SECTION THROUGH HEART WALL

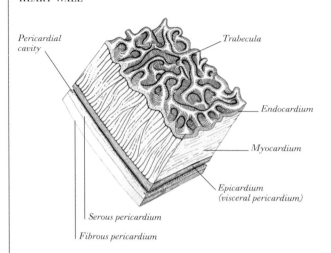

Pericardial cavity

Trabecula

Endocardium

Myocardium

Epicardium (visceral pericardium)

Serous pericardium

Fibrous pericardium

HEARTBEAT SEQUENCE

ATRIAL DIASTOLE

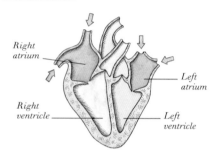

Right atrium

Left atrium

Right ventricle

Left ventricle

Deoxygenated blood enters the right atrium while the left atrium receives oxygenated blood.

STRUCTURE OF HEART

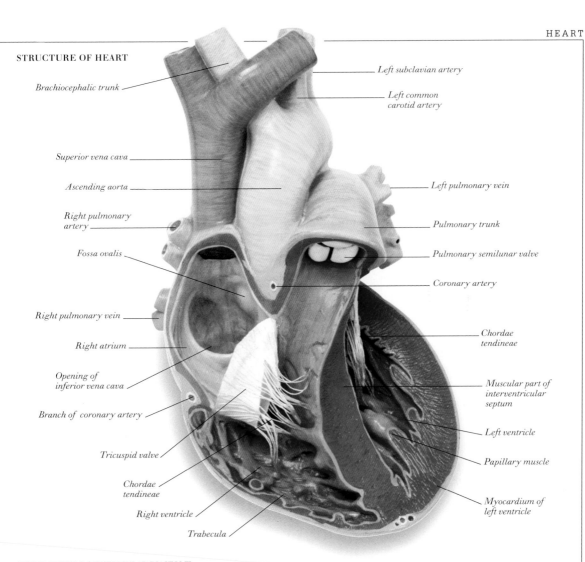

Brachiocephalic trunk

Superior vena cava

Ascending aorta

Right pulmonary artery

Fossa ovalis

Right pulmonary vein

Right atrium

Opening of inferior vena cava

Branch of coronary artery

Tricuspid valve

Chordae tendineae

Right ventricle

Trabecula

Left subclavian artery

Left common carotid artery

Left pulmonary vein

Pulmonary trunk

Pulmonary semilunar valve

Coronary artery

Chordae tendineae

Muscular part of interventricular septum

Left ventricle

Papillary muscle

Myocardium of left ventricle

ATRIAL SYSTOLE (VENTRICULAR DIASTOLE)

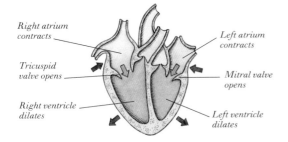

Right atrium contracts

Tricuspid valve opens

Right ventricle dilates

Left atrium contracts

Mitral valve opens

Left ventricle dilates

Left and right atria contract, forcing blood into the relaxed ventricles.

VENTRICULAR SYSTOLE

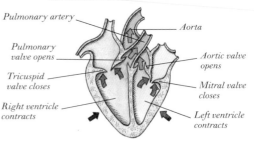

Pulmonary artery

Pulmonary valve opens

Tricuspid valve closes

Right ventricle contracts

Aorta

Aortic valve opens

Mitral valve closes

Left ventricle contracts

Ventricles contract and force blood to the lungs for oxygenation and via the aorta to the rest of the body.

Circulatory system

THE CIRCULATORY SYSTEM consists of the heart and blood vessels, which together maintain a continuous flow of blood around the body. The heart pumps oxygen-rich blood from the lungs to all parts of the body through a network of tubes called arteries, and smaller branches called arterioles. Blood returns to the heart via small vessels called venules, which lead in turn into larger tubes called veins. Arterioles and venules are linked by a network of tiny vessels called capillaries, where the exchange of oxygen and carbon dioxide between blood and body cells takes place. Blood has four main components: red blood cells, white blood cells, platelets, and liquid plasma.

ARTERIAL SYSTEM OF BRAIN

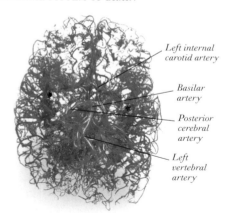

Left internal carotid artery

Basilar artery

Posterior cerebral artery

Left vertebral artery

CIRCULATORY SYSTEM OF HEART AND LUNGS

Superior vena cava

Aorta

Right ventricle

Left ventricle

CIRCULATORY SYSTEM OF LIVER

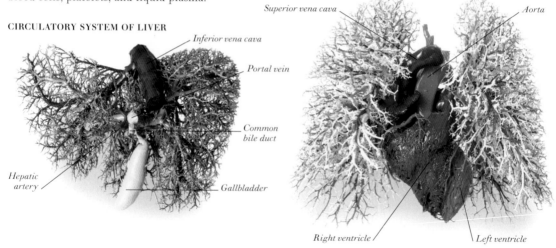

Inferior vena cava

Portal vein

Common bile duct

Hepatic artery

Gallbladder

SECTION OF MAIN ARTERY

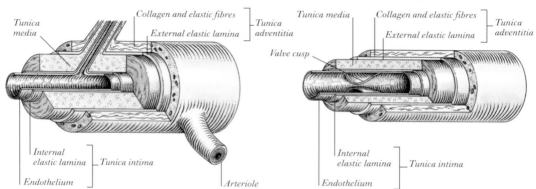

Tunica media

Collagen and elastic fibres

External elastic lamina

Tunica adventitia

Internal elastic lamina

Tunica intima

Endothelium

Arteriole

SECTION OF MAIN VEIN

Tunica media

Collagen and elastic fibres

External elastic lamina

Tunica adventitia

Valve cusp

Internal elastic lamina

Tunica intima

Endothelium

PRINCIPAL ARTERIES AND VEINS OF CIRCULATORY SYSTEM

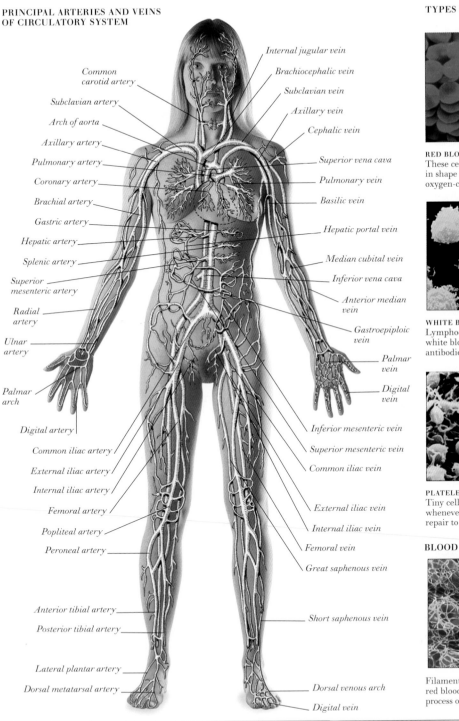

Common carotid artery

Subclavian artery

Arch of aorta

Axillary artery

Pulmonary artery

Coronary artery

Brachial artery

Gastric artery

Hepatic artery

Splenic artery

Superior mesenteric artery

Radial artery

Ulnar artery

Palmar arch

Digital artery

Common iliac artery

External iliac artery

Internal iliac artery

Femoral artery

Popliteal artery

Peroneal artery

Anterior tibial artery

Posterior tibial artery

Lateral plantar artery

Dorsal metatarsal artery

Internal jugular vein

Brachiocephalic vein

Subclavian vein

Axillary vein

Cephalic vein

Superior vena cava

Pulmonary vein

Basilic vein

Hepatic portal vein

Median cubital vein

Inferior vena cava

Anterior median vein

Gastroepiploic vein

Palmar vein

Digital vein

Inferior mesenteric vein

Superior mesenteric vein

Common iliac vein

External iliac vein

Internal iliac vein

Femoral vein

Great saphenous vein

Short saphenous vein

Dorsal venous arch

Digital vein

TYPES OF BLOOD CELLS

RED BLOOD CELLS
These cells are biconcave in shape to maximize their oxygen-carrying capacity.

WHITE BLOOD CELLS
Lymphocytes are the smallest white blood cells; they form antibodies against disease.

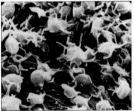

PLATELETS
Tiny cells that are activated whenever blood clotting or repair to vessels is necessary.

BLOOD CLOTTING

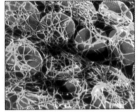

Filaments of fibrin enmesh red blood cells as part of the process of blood clotting.

Respiratory system

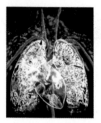

THE RESPIRATORY SYSTEM supplies the oxygen needed by body cells and carries off their carbon dioxide waste. Inhaled air passes via the trachea (windpipe) through two narrower tubes, the bronchi, to the lungs. Each lung comprises many fine, branching tubes called bronchioles that end in tiny clustered chambers called alveoli. Gases cross the thin alveolar walls to and from a network of tiny blood vessels. Intercostal (rib) muscles and the muscular diaphragm below the lungs operate the lungs like bellows, drawing air in and forcing it out at regular intervals.

BRONCHIOLE AND ALVEOLI

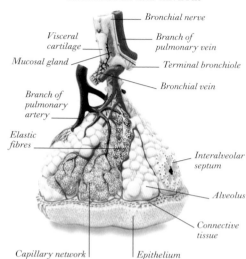

Bronchial nerve

Visceral cartilage

Branch of pulmonary vein

Mucosal gland

Terminal bronchiole

Branch of pulmonary artery

Bronchial vein

Elastic fibres

Interalveolar septum

Alveolus

Connective tissue

Capillary network

Epithelium

SEGMENTS OF BRONCHIAL TREE

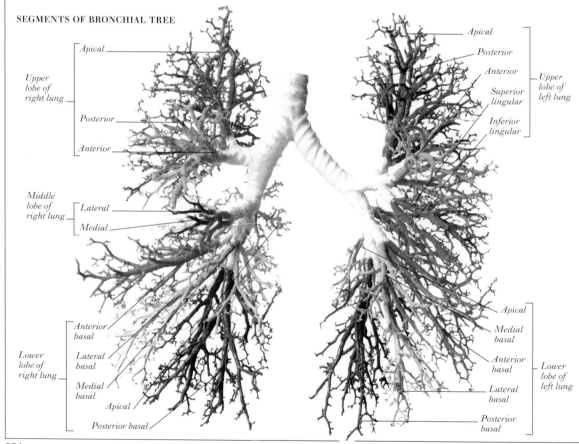

Apical

Upper lobe of right lung

Posterior

Anterior

Middle lobe of right lung

Lateral

Medial

Lower lobe of right lung

Anterior basal

Lateral basal

Medial basal

Apical

Posterior basal

Apical

Posterior

Anterior

Superior lingular

Inferior lingular

Upper lobe of left lung

Apical

Medial basal

Anterior basal

Lateral basal

Posterior basal

Lower lobe of left lung

STRUCTURES OF THORACIC CAVITY

GASEOUS EXCHANGE IN ALVEOLUS

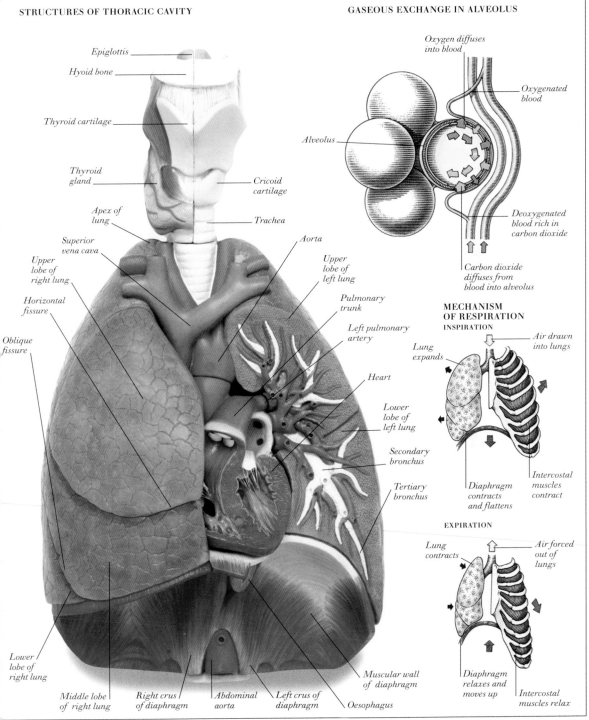

Epiglottis

Hyoid bone

Thyroid cartilage

Thyroid gland

Cricoid cartilage

Apex of lung

Trachea

Superior vena cava

Aorta

Upper lobe of right lung

Upper lobe of left lung

Horizontal fissure

Pulmonary trunk

Oblique fissure

Left pulmonary artery

Heart

Lower lobe of left lung

Secondary bronchus

Tertiary bronchus

Lower lobe of right lung

Middle lobe of right lung

Right crus of diaphragm

Abdominal aorta

Left crus of diaphragm

Oesophagus

Muscular wall of diaphragm

Oxygen diffuses into blood

Oxygenated blood

Alveolus

Deoxygenated blood rich in carbon dioxide

Carbon dioxide diffuses from blood into alveolus

MECHANISM OF RESPIRATION

INSPIRATION

Lung expands

Air drawn into lungs

Diaphragm contracts and flattens

Intercostal muscles contract

EXPIRATION

Lung contracts

Air forced out of lungs

Diaphragm relaxes and moves up

Intercostal muscles relax

Urinary system

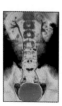

THE URINARY SYSTEM FILTERS WASTE PRODUCTS from the blood and removes them from the body via a system of tubes. Blood is filtered in the two kidneys, which are fist-sized, bean-shaped organs. The renal arteries carry blood to the kidneys; the renal veins remove blood after filtering. Each kidney contains about one million tiny units called nephrons. Each nephron is made up of a tubule and a filtering unit called a glomerulus, which consists of a collection of tiny blood vessels surrounded by the hollow Bowman's capsule. The filtering process produces a watery fluid that leaves the kidney as urine. The urine is carried via two tubes called ureters to the bladder, where it is stored until its release from the body through another tube called the urethra.

ARTERIAL SYSTEM OF KIDNEYS

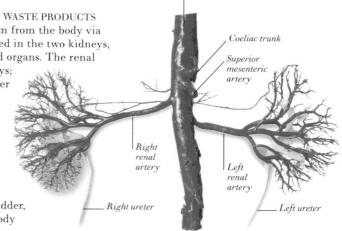

- Aorta
- Coeliac trunk
- Superior mesenteric artery
- Right renal artery
- Left renal artery
- Right ureter
- Left ureter

SECTION THROUGH LEFT KIDNEY

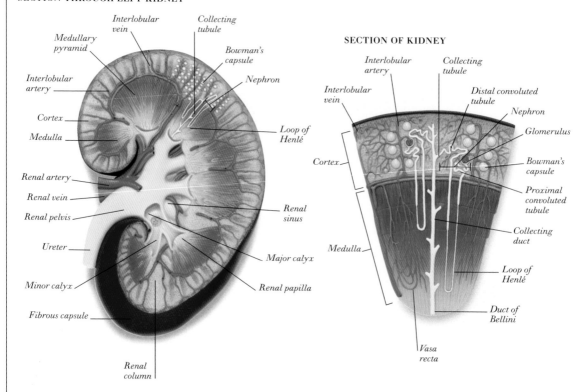

- Medullary pyramid
- Interlobular vein
- Collecting tubule
- Bowman's capsule
- Nephron
- Interlobular artery
- Cortex
- Medulla
- Loop of Henlé
- Renal artery
- Renal vein
- Renal pelvis
- Ureter
- Renal sinus
- Major calyx
- Minor calyx
- Renal papilla
- Fibrous capsule
- Renal column

SECTION OF KIDNEY

- Interlobular artery
- Collecting tubule
- Interlobular vein
- Distal convoluted tubule
- Nephron
- Cortex
- Glomerulus
- Bowman's capsule
- Proximal convoluted tubule
- Collecting duct
- Medulla
- Loop of Henlé
- Duct of Bellini
- Vasa recta

MALE URINARY TRACT

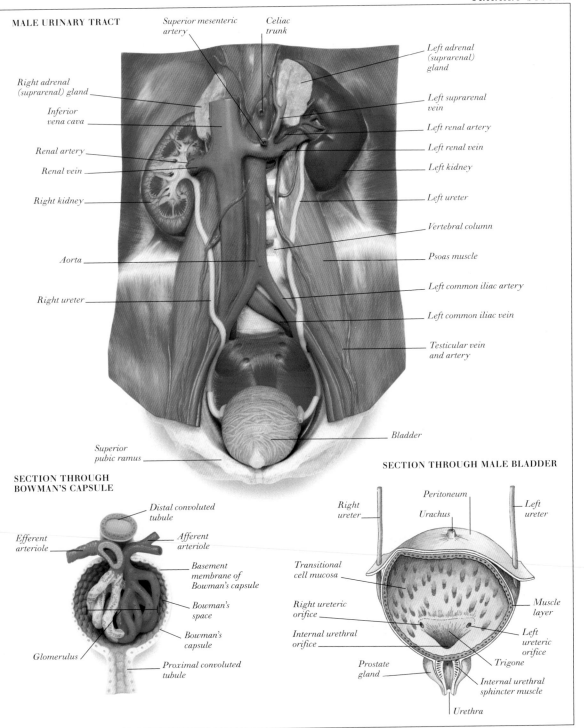

Superior mesenteric artery

Celiac trunk

Left adrenal (suprarenal) gland

Right adrenal (suprarenal) gland

Inferior vena cava

Renal artery

Renal vein

Right kidney

Aorta

Right ureter

Left suprarenal vein

Left renal artery

Left renal vein

Left kidney

Left ureter

Vertebral column

Psoas muscle

Left common iliac artery

Left common iliac vein

Testicular vein and artery

Bladder

Superior pubic ramus

SECTION THROUGH MALE BLADDER

SECTION THROUGH BOWMAN'S CAPSULE

Distal convoluted tubule

Efferent arteriole

Afferent arteriole

Basement membrane of Bowman's capsule

Bowman's space

Bowman's capsule

Glomerulus

Proximal convoluted tubule

Right ureter

Peritoneum

Urachus

Left ureter

Transitional cell mucosa

Right ureteric orifice

Internal urethral orifice

Prostate gland

Muscle layer

Left ureteric orifice

Trigone

Internal urethral sphincter muscle

Urethra

257

Reproductive system

SEX ORGANS LOCATED IN THE PELVIS create new human lives. Each month a ripe egg is released from one of the female's ovaries into a fallopian tube leading to the uterus (womb), a muscular pear-sized organ. A male produces minute tadpole-like sperm in two oval glands called testes. When the male is ready to release sperm into the female's vagina, many millions pass into his urethra and leave his body through the fleshy penis. The sperm travel up through the vagina into the uterus and fallopian tubes, and one sperm may enter and fertilize an egg. The fertilized egg becomes embedded in the uterus wall and starts to grow into a new human being.

SECTION THROUGH OVARY

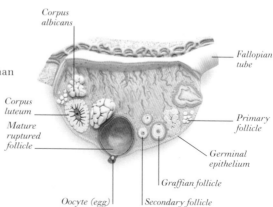

Corpus albicans

Corpus luteum

Mature ruptured follicle

Oocyte (egg)

Fallopian tube

Primary follicle

Germinal epithelium

Graffian follicle

Secondary follicle

SECTION THROUGH FEMALE PELVIC REGION

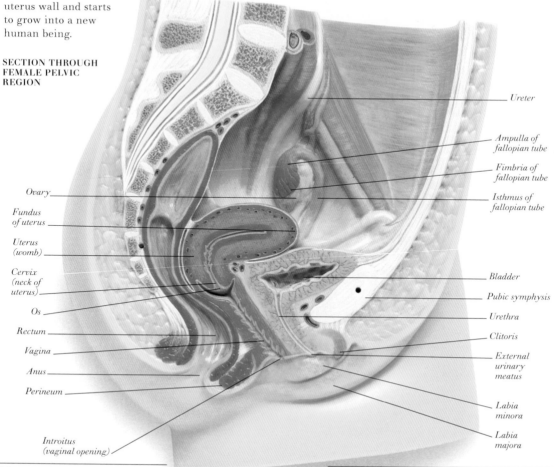

Ovary

Fundus of uterus

Uterus (womb)

Cervix (neck of uterus)

Os

Rectum

Vagina

Anus

Perineum

Introitus (vaginal opening)

Ureter

Ampulla of fallopian tube

Fimbria of fallopian tube

Isthmus of fallopian tube

Bladder

Pubic symphysis

Urethra

Clitoris

External urinary meatus

Labia minora

Labia majora

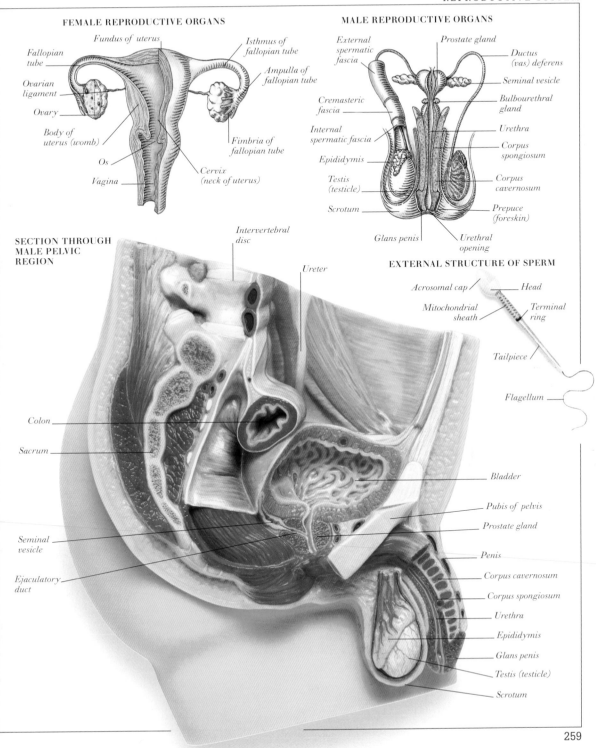

FEMALE REPRODUCTIVE ORGANS

Fallopian tube

Fundus of uterus

Isthmus of fallopian tube

Ampulla of fallopian tube

Ovarian ligament

Ovary

Body of uterus (womb)

Os

Vagina

Cervix (neck of uterus)

Fimbria of fallopian tube

MALE REPRODUCTIVE ORGANS

External spermatic fascia

Prostate gland

Ductus (vas) deferens

Seminal vesicle

Cremasteric fascia

Bulbourethral gland

Internal spermatic fascia

Urethra

Corpus spongiosum

Epididymis

Corpus cavernosum

Testis (testicle)

Prepuce (foreskin)

Scrotum

Glans penis

Urethral opening

SECTION THROUGH MALE PELVIC REGION

Intervertebral disc

Ureter

Colon

Sacrum

Seminal vesicle

Ejaculatory duct

Bladder

Pubis of pelvis

Prostate gland

Penis

Corpus cavernosum

Corpus spongiosum

Urethra

Epididymis

Glans penis

Testis (testicle)

Scrotum

EXTERNAL STRUCTURE OF SPERM

Acrosomal cap

Head

Mitochondrial sheath

Terminal ring

Tailpiece

Flagellum

Development of a baby

A FERTILIZED EGG IS NOURISHED AND PROTECTED as it develops into an embryo and then a fetus during the 40 weeks of pregnancy. The placenta, a mass of blood vessels implanted in the uterus lining, delivers nourishment and oxygen, and removes waste through the umbilical cord. Meanwhile, the fetus lies snugly in its amniotic sac, a bag of fluid that protects it against any sudden jolts. In the last weeks of the pregnancy, the rapidly growing fetus turns head-down: a baby ready to be born.

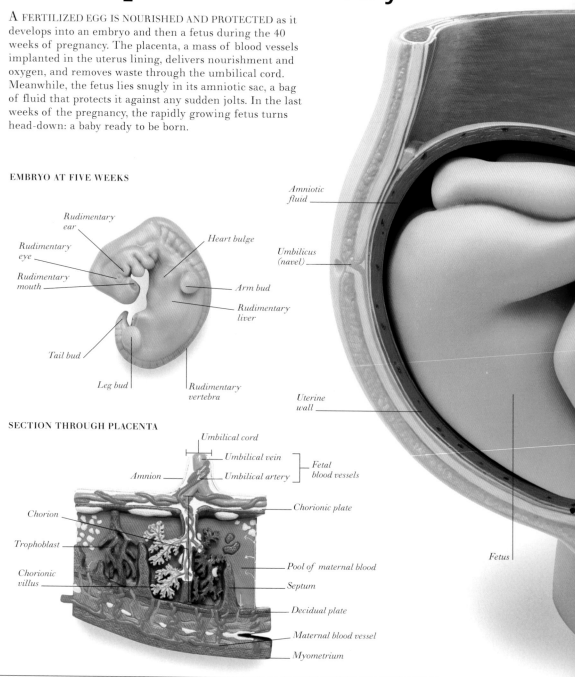

EMBRYO AT FIVE WEEKS

Rudimentary ear

Rudimentary eye

Rudimentary mouth

Heart bulge

Arm bud

Rudimentary liver

Tail bud

Leg bud

Rudimentary vertebra

Amniotic fluid

Umbilicus (navel)

Uterine wall

Fetus

SECTION THROUGH PLACENTA

Umbilical cord

Umbilical vein

Umbilical artery

Fetal blood vessels

Amnion

Chorionic plate

Chorion

Trophoblast

Pool of maternal blood

Chorionic villus

Septum

Decidual plate

Maternal blood vessel

Myometrium

260

SECTION THROUGH PELVIS IN NINTH MONTH OF PREGNANCY

THE DEVELOPING FETUS

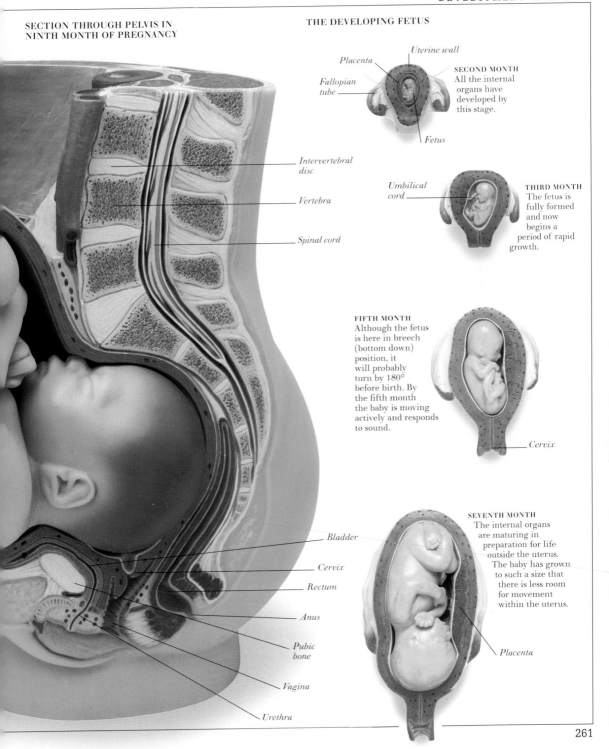

Placenta

Uterine wall

Fallopian tube

Fetus

SECOND MONTH
All the internal organs have developed by this stage.

Intervertebral disc

Vertebra

Spinal cord

Umbilical cord

THIRD MONTH
The fetus is fully formed and now begins a period of rapid growth.

FIFTH MONTH
Although the fetus is here in breech (bottom down) position, it will probably turn by 180° before birth. By the fifth month the baby is moving actively and responds to sound.

Cervix

Bladder

Cervix

Rectum

Anus

Pubic bone

Vagina

Urethra

SEVENTH MONTH
The internal organs are maturing in preparation for life outside the uterus. The baby has grown to such a size that there is less room for movement within the uterus.

Placenta

261

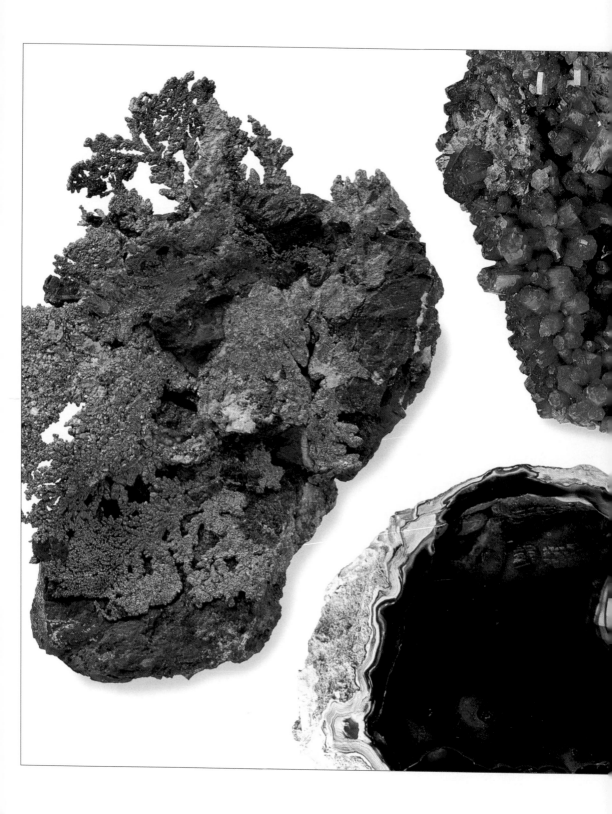

GEOLOGY, GEOGRAPHY, AND METEOROLOGY

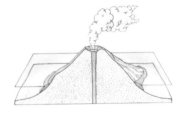

Earth's physical features

MOST OF THE EARTH'S SURFACE (about 70 per cent) is covered with water. The largest single body of water, the Pacific Ocean, alone covers about 30 per cent of the surface. Most of the land is distributed as seven continents; these are (from largest to smallest) Asia, Africa, North America, South America, Antarctica, Europe, and Australasia. The physical features of the land are remarkably varied. Among the most notable are mountain ranges, rivers, and deserts. The largest mountain ranges – the Himalayas in Asia and the Andes in South America – extend for thousands of kilometres. The Himalayas include the world's highest mountain, Mount Everest (8,848 metres). The longest rivers are the River Nile in Africa (6,695 kilometres) and the Amazon River in South America (6,437 kilometres). Deserts cover about 20 per cent of the total land area. The largest is the Sahara, which covers nearly a third of Africa. The Earth's surface features can be represented in various ways. Only a globe can correctly represent areas, shapes, sizes, and directions, because there is always distortion when a spherical surface – the Earth's, for example – is projected on to the flat surface of a map. Each map projection is therefore a compromise: it shows some features accurately but distorts others. Even satellite mapping does not produce completely accurate maps, although they can show physical features with great clarity.

CYLINDRICAL PROJECTION

CYLINDRICAL-PROJECTION MAP

180° 160° 120° 80°

Great Slave Lake
Great Bear Lake
Lake Superior
Greenland
Mackenzie-Peace River
Bering Sea
Hudson Bay
Baffin Island
NORTH AMERICA
Rocky Mountains
Sonoran Desert
Lake Huron
Lake Ontario
Lake Erie
Lake Michigan
Sierra Madre
Chihuahuan Desert
Appalachian Mountains
Gulf of Mexico
ATLANTIC OCEAN
Mississippi-Missouri River
Caribbean Sea
Guiana Highlands
Amazon River
Brazilian Highlands
PACIFIC OCEAN
Andes
Atacama Desert
Gran Chaco
Mato Grosso
Parana River
Pampas
Patagonia

180° 160° 120° 80°

WEST OF GREENWICH MERIDIAN

SATELLITE MAPPING OF THE EARTH

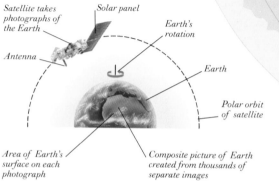

Satellite takes photographs of the Earth
Solar panel
Earth's rotation
Antenna
Earth
Polar orbit of satellite
Area of Earth's surface on each photograph
Composite picture of Earth created from thousands of separate images

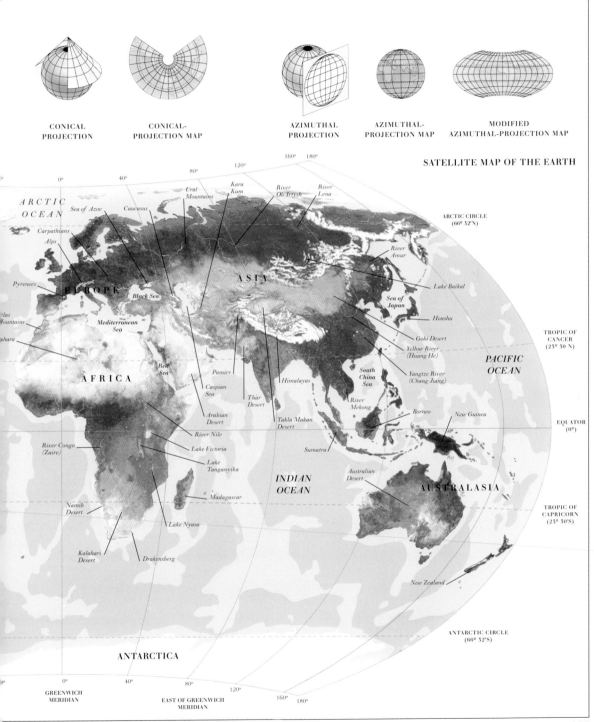

CONICAL
PROJECTION

CONICAL-
PROJECTION MAP

AZIMUTHAL
PROJECTION

AZIMUTHAL-
PROJECTION MAP

MODIFIED
AZIMUTHAL-PROJECTION MAP

SATELLITE MAP OF THE EARTH

ARCTIC
OCEAN

Sea of Azov

Caucasus

*Ural
Mountains*

*Kara
Kum*

*River
Ob-Irtysh*

*River
Lena*

ARCTIC CIRCLE
(66° 32'N)

Carpathians

Alps

EUROPE

Black Sea

A S I A

*River
Amur*

Lake Baikal

Pyrenees

*las
ountains*

*Mediterranean
Sea*

*Sea of
Japan*

Honshu

TROPIC OF
CANCER
(23° 30 N)

ahara

*Red
Sea*

Pamirs

Gobi Desert

*Yellow River
(Huang He)*

PACIFIC
OCEAN

AFRICA

*Caspian
Sea*

*Thar
Desert*

Himalayas

*Yangtze River
(Chang Jiang)*

*Arabian
Desert*

*Takla Makan
Desert*

South
China
Sea

Borneo

New Guinea

EQUATOR
(0°)

River Nile

*River
Mekong*

*River Congo
(Zaire)*

Lake Victoria

Sumatra

*Lake
Tanganyika*

INDIAN
OCEAN

*Australian
Desert*

AUSTRALASIA

Madagascar

*Namib
Desert*

TROPIC OF
CAPRICORN
(23° 30'S)

Lake Nyasa

*Kalahari
Desert*

Drakensberg

New Zealand

ANTARCTIC CIRCLE
(66° 32'S)

ANTARCTICA

0°

40°

80°

120°

160°

180°

The rock cycle

HEXAGONAL BASALT COLUMNS, ICELAND

THE ROCK CYCLE IS A CONTINUOUS PROCESS through which old rocks are transformed into new ones. Rocks can be divided into three main groups: igneous, sedimentary, and metamorphic. Igneous rocks are formed when magma (molten rock) from the Earth's interior cools and solidifies (see pp. 274-275). Sedimentary rocks are formed when sediment (rock particles, for example) becomes compressed and cemented together in a process known as lithification (see pp. 276-277). Metamorphic rocks are formed when igneous, sedimentary, or other metamorphic rocks are changed by heat or pressure (see pp. 274-275). Rocks are added to the Earth's surface by crustal movements and volcanic activity. Once exposed on the surface, the rocks are broken down into rock particles by weathering (see pp. 282-283). The particles are then transported by glaciers, rivers, and wind, and deposited as sediment in lakes, deltas, deserts, and on the ocean floor. Some of this sediment undergoes lithification and forms sedimentary rock. This rock may be thrust back to the surface by crustal movements or forced deeper into the Earth's interior, where heat and pressure transform it into metamorphic rock. The metamorphic rock in turn may be pushed up to the surface or may be melted to form magma. Eventually, the magma cools and solidifies - below or on the surface -forming igneous rock. When the sedimentary, igneous, and metamorphic rocks are exposed once more on the Earth's surface, the cycle begins again.

THE ROCK CYCLE

Igneous rock

Cooling and solidification (crystallization)

Weathering, transport, and deposition

Sediment

Heat and pressure (metamorphism)

Weathering, transport, and deposition

Weathering, transport, and deposition

Compression and cementation (lithification)

Magma

Melting

Heat and pressure (metamorphism)

Metamorphic rock

Sedimentary rock

STAGES IN THE ROCK CYCLE

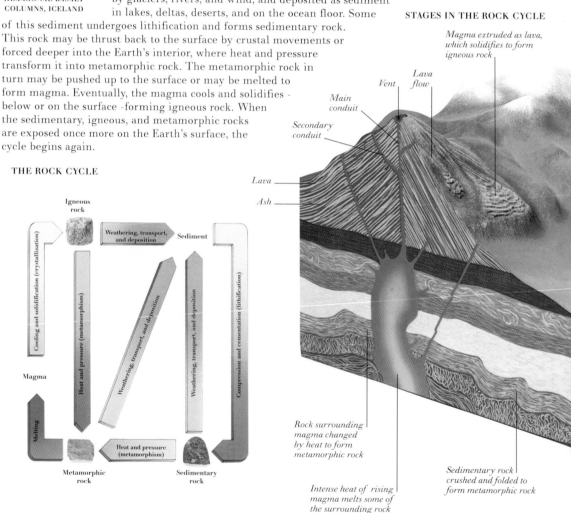

Magma extruded as lava, which solidifies to form igneous rock

Vent

Lava flow

Main conduit

Secondary conduit

Lava

Ash

Rock surrounding magma changed by heat to form metamorphic rock

Intense heat of rising magma melts some of the surrounding rock

Sedimentary rock crushed and folded to form metamorphic rock

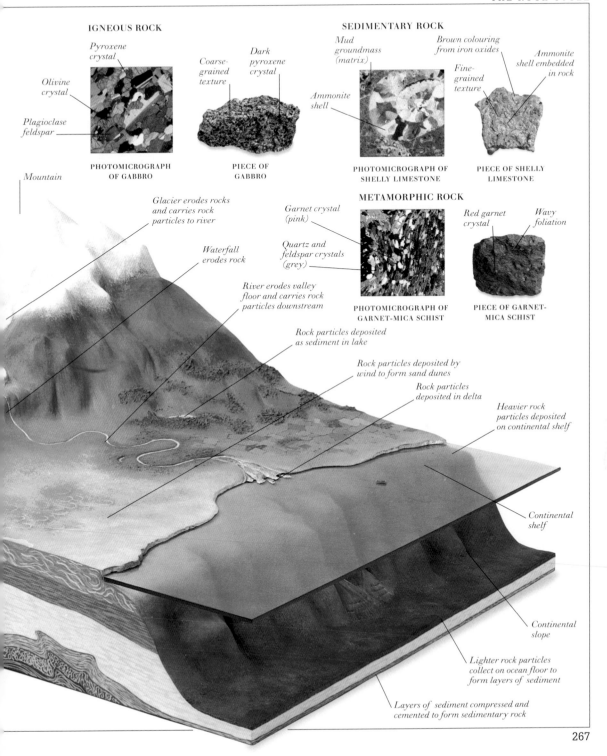

IGNEOUS ROCK

Pyroxene crystal

Olivine crystal

Plagioclase feldspar

PHOTOMICROGRAPH OF GABBRO

Coarse-grained texture

Dark pyroxene crystal

PIECE OF GABBRO

SEDIMENTARY ROCK

Mud groundmass (matrix)

Ammonite shell

Brown colouring from iron oxides

Fine-grained texture

Ammonite shell embedded in rock

PHOTOMICROGRAPH OF SHELLY LIMESTONE

PIECE OF SHELLY LIMESTONE

METAMORPHIC ROCK

Garnet crystal (pink)

Quartz and feldspar crystals (grey)

Red garnet crystal

Wavy foliation

PHOTOMICROGRAPH OF GARNET-MICA SCHIST

PIECE OF GARNET-MICA SCHIST

Mountain

Glacier erodes rocks and carries rock particles to river

Waterfall erodes rock

River erodes valley floor and carries rock particles downstream

Rock particles deposited as sediment in lake

Rock particles deposited by wind to form sand dunes

Rock particles deposited in delta

Heavier rock particles deposited on continental shelf

Continental shelf

Continental slope

Lighter rock particles collect on ocean floor to form layers of sediment

Layers of sediment compressed and cemented to form sedimentary rock

Minerals

A MINERAL IS A NATURALLY OCCURRING SUBSTANCE that has a characteristic chemical composition and specific physical properties, such as habit and streak (see pp. 270-271). A rock, by comparison, is an aggregate of minerals and need not have a specific chemical composition. Minerals are made up of elements (substances that cannot be broken down chemically into simpler substances), each of which can be represented by a chemical symbol. Minerals can be divided into two main groups: native elements and compounds. Native elements are made up of a pure element. Examples include gold (chemical symbol Au), silver (Ag), copper (Cu), and carbon (C); carbon occurs as a native element in two forms, diamond and graphite. Compounds are combinations of two or more elements. For example, sulphides are compounds of sulphur (S) and one or more other elements, such as lead (Pb) in the mineral galena, or antimony (Sb) in the mineral stibnite.

NATIVE ELEMENTS

Dendritic (branching) copper

Limonite groundmass (matrix)

COPPER
(Cu)

SULPHIDES

Cubic galena crystal

GALENA
(PbS)

Prismatic stibnite crystal

Quartz groundmass (matrix)

STIBNITE
(Sb_2S_3)

Perfect octahedral pyrites crystal

Quartz crystal

PYRITES
(FeS_2)

Dendritic (branching) gold

Quartz vein

GOLD
(Au)

White diamond

Kimberlite groundmass (matrix)

DIAMOND
(C)

Hexagonal graphite crystal

GRAPHITE
(C)

OXIDES/HYDROXIDES

Milky quartz groundmass (matrix)

Smoky quartz crystal

SMOKY QUARTZ
(SiO_2)

Rounded bauxite grains in groundmass (matrix)

BAUXITE
$(FeO(OH)$ and $Al_2O_3.2H_2O)$

Mass of specular haematite crystals

SPECULAR HAEMATITE
(Fe_2O_3)

Parallel bands of onyx

ONYX
(SiO_2)

Kidney ore haematite

Specular crystals of haematite

KIDNEY ORE HAEMATITE
(Fe_2O_3)

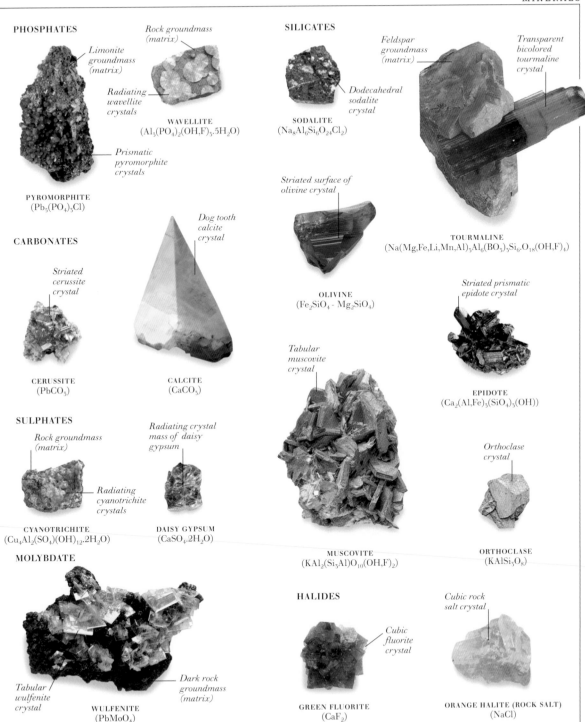

PHOSPHATES

Rock groundmass (matrix)

Limonite groundmass (matrix)

Radiating wavellite crystals

WAVELLITE
$(Al_5(PO_4)_2(OH,F)_5.5H_2O)$

Prismatic pyromorphite crystals

PYROMORPHITE
$(Pb_5(PO_4)_3Cl)$

CARBONATES

Dog tooth calcite crystal

Striated cerussite crystal

CERUSSITE
$(PbCO_3)$

CALCITE
$(CaCO_3)$

SULPHATES

Rock groundmass (matrix)

Radiating crystal mass of daisy gypsum

Radiating cyanotrichite crystals

CYANOTRICHITE
$(Cu_4Al_2(SO_4)(OH)_{12}.2H_2O)$

DAISY GYPSUM
$(CaSO_4.2H_2O)$

MOLYBDATE

Tabular wulfenite crystal

Dark rock groundmass (matrix)

WULFENITE
$(PbMoO_4)$

SILICATES

Feldspar groundmass (matrix)

Transparent bicolored tourmaline crystal

Dodecahedral sodalite crystal

SODALITE
$(Na_8Al_6Si_6O_{24}Cl_2)$

TOURMALINE
$(Na(Mg,Fe,Li,Mn,Al)_3Al_6(BO_3)_3Si_6.O_{18}(OH,F)_4)$

Striated surface of olivine crystal

OLIVINE
$(Fe_2SiO_4 - Mg_2SiO_4)$

Striated prismatic epidote crystal

EPIDOTE
$(Ca_2(Al,Fe)_3(SiO_4)_3(OH))$

Tabular muscovite crystal

Orthoclase crystal

MUSCOVITE
$(KAl_2(Si_3Al)O_{10}(OH,F)_2)$

ORTHOCLASE
$(KAlSi_3O_8)$

HALIDES

Cubic rock salt crystal

Cubic fluorite crystal

GREEN FLUORITE
(CaF_2)

ORANGE HALITE (ROCK SALT)
$(NaCl)$

Mineral features

MINERALS CAN BE IDENTIFIED BY STUDYING features such as fracture, cleavage, crystal system, habit, hardness, colour, and streak. Minerals can break in different ways. If a mineral breaks in an irregular way, leaving rough surfaces, it possesses fracture. If a mineral breaks along well-defined planes of weakness, it possesses cleavage. Specific minerals have distinctive patterns of cleavage; for example, mica cleaves along one plane. Most minerals form crystals, which can be categorized into crystal systems according to their symmetry and number of faces. Within each system, several different but related forms of crystal are possible; for example, a cubic crystal can have six, eight, or twelve sides. A mineral's habit is the typical form taken by an aggregate of its crystals. Examples of habit include botryoidal (like a bunch of grapes) and massive (no definite form). The relative hardness of a mineral may be assessed by testing its resistance to scratching. This property is usually measured using Mohs scale, which increases in hardness from 1 (talc) to 10 (diamond). The colour of a mineral is not a dependable guide to its identity as some minerals have a range of colours. Streak (the colour the powdered mineral makes when rubbed across an unglazed tile) is a more reliable indicator.

CLEAVAGE

Cleavage in one direction

CLEAVAGE ALONG ONE PLANE

Cleavage in three directions, forming a block cube

CLEAVAGE ALONG THREE PLANES

Horizontal cleavage

Vertical cleavage

CLEAVAGE ALONG TWO PLANES

Cleavage in four directions, forming a double-pyramid crystal

CLEAVAGE ALONG FOUR PLANES

CRYSTAL SYSTEMS

Cubic iron pyrites crystal

Tetragonal idocrase crystal

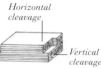

Representation of tetragonal system

TETRAGONAL SYSTEM

CUBIC SYSTEM

Representation of cubic system

Hexagonal beryl crystal

Representation of hexagonal/trigonal system

HEXAGONAL/TRIGONAL SYSTEM

Orthorhombic barytes crystal

Representation of orthorhombic system

ORTHORHOMBIC SYSTEM

FRACTURE

Fire opal with conchoidal (shell-like) fracture

CONCHOIDAL FRACTURE

Nickel-iron with hackly (jagged) fracture

HACKLY FRACTURE

Orpiment with uneven fracture

UNEVEN FRACTURE

Garnierite with splintery fracture

SPLINTERY FRACTURE

Monoclinic selenite crystal

Representation of monoclinic system

MONOCLINIC SYSTEM

Triclinic axinite crystal

Representation of triclinic system

TRICLINIC SYSTEM

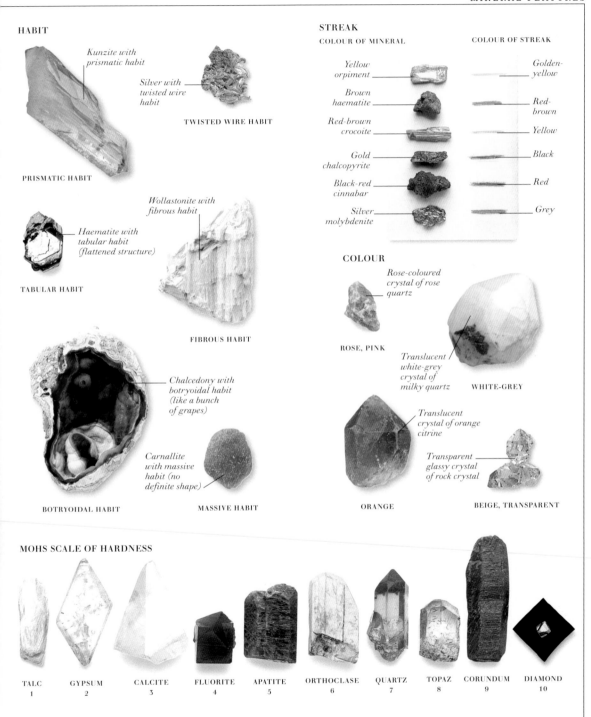

HABIT

Kunzite with prismatic habit

Silver with twisted wire habit

TWISTED WIRE HABIT

PRISMATIC HABIT

Wollastonite with fibrous habit

Haematite with tabular habit (flattened structure)

TABULAR HABIT

FIBROUS HABIT

Chalcedony with botryoidal habit (like a bunch of grapes)

Carnallite with massive habit (no definite shape)

BOTRYOIDAL HABIT

MASSIVE HABIT

STREAK

COLOUR OF MINERAL

Yellow orpiment

Brown haematite

Red-brown crocoite

Gold chalcopyrite

Black-red cinnabar

Silver molybdenite

COLOUR OF STREAK

Golden-yellow

Red-brown

Yellow

Black

Red

Grey

COLOUR

Rose-coloured crystal of rose quartz

ROSE, PINK

Translucent white-grey crystal of milky quartz

WHITE-GREY

Translucent crystal of orange citrine

Transparent glassy crystal of rock crystal

ORANGE

BEIGE, TRANSPARENT

MOHS SCALE OF HARDNESS

TALC	GYPSUM	CALCITE	FLUORITE	APATITE	ORTHOCLASE	QUARTZ	TOPAZ	CORUNDUM	DIAMOND
1	2	3	4	5	6	7	8	9	10

271

Volcanoes

VOLCANOES ARE VENTS OR FISSURES in the Earth's crust through which magma (molten rock that originates from deep beneath the crust) is forced on to the surface as lava. They occur most commonly along the boundaries of crustal plates; most volcanoes lie in a belt called the "Ring of Fire", which runs along the edge of the Pacific Ocean. Volcanoes can be classified according to the violence and frequency of their eruptions.

Non-explosive volcanic eruptions generally occur where crustal plates pull apart. These eruptions produce runny basaltic lava that spreads quickly over a wide area to form relatively flat cones. The most violent eruptions take place where plates collide. Such eruptions produce thick rhyolitic lava and may also blast out clouds of dust and pyroclasts (lava fragments). The lava does not flow far before cooling and therefore builds up steep-sided, conical volcanoes. Some volcanoes produce lava and ash eruptions, which build up composite volcanic cones. Volcanoes that erupt frequently are described as active; those that erupt rarely are termed dormant; and those that have stopped erupting altogether are termed extinct. As well as the volcanoes themselves, other features associated with volcanic regions include geysers, hot mineral springs, solfataras, fumaroles, and bubbling mud pools.

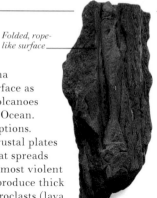

Folded, rope-like surface

PAHOEHOE
(ROPY LAVA)

HORU GEYSER,
NEW ZEALAND

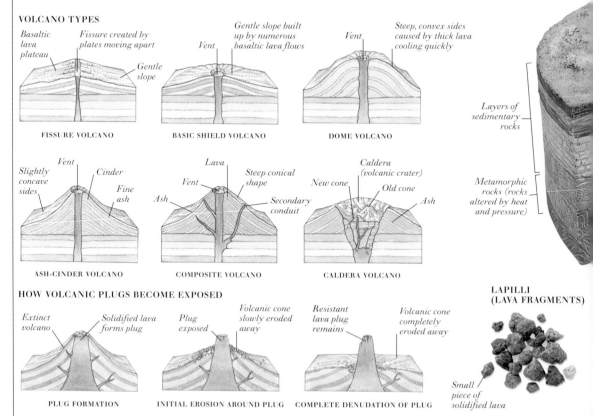

VOLCANO TYPES

Basaltic lava plateau — *Fissure created by plates moving apart* — *Gentle slope*

FISSURE VOLCANO

Gentle slope built up by numerous basaltic lava flows — *Vent*

BASIC SHIELD VOLCANO

Steep, convex sides caused by thick lava cooling quickly — *Vent*

DOME VOLCANO

Slightly concave sides — *Vent* — *Cinder* — *Fine ash*

ASH-CINDER VOLCANO

Lava — *Vent* — *Steep conical shape* — *Ash* — *Secondary conduit*

COMPOSITE VOLCANO

Caldera (volcanic crater) — *New cone* — *Old cone* — *Ash*

CALDERA VOLCANO

Layers of sedimentary rocks

Metamorphic rocks (rocks altered by heat and pressure)

HOW VOLCANIC PLUGS BECOME EXPOSED

Extinct volcano — *Solidified lava forms plug*

PLUG FORMATION

Plug exposed — *Volcanic cone slowly eroded away*

INITIAL EROSION AROUND PLUG

Resistant lava plug remains — *Volcanic cone completely eroded away*

COMPLETE DENUDATION OF PLUG

**LAPILLI
(LAVA FRAGMENTS)**

Small piece of solidified lava

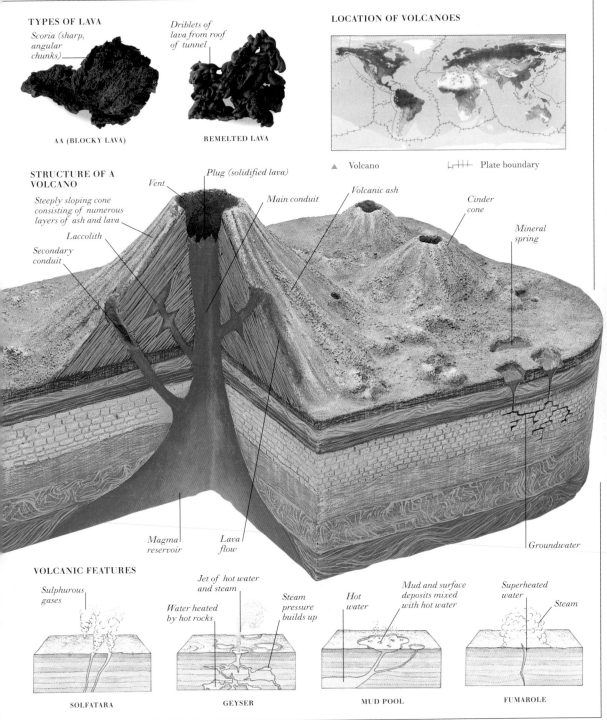

TYPES OF LAVA

Scoria (sharp, angular chunks)

AA (BLOCKY LAVA)

Driblets of lava from roof of tunnel

REMELTED LAVA

LOCATION OF VOLCANOES

▲ Volcano   ⊢⊦⊦⊦ Plate boundary

STRUCTURE OF A VOLCANO

Steeply sloping cone consisting of numerous layers of ash and lava

Laccolith

Secondary conduit

Vent

Plug (solidified lava)

Main conduit

Volcanic ash

Cinder cone

Mineral spring

Magma reservoir

Lava flow

Groundwater

VOLCANIC FEATURES

Sulphurous gases

SOLFATARA

Jet of hot water and steam

Water heated by hot rocks

Steam pressure builds up

GEYSER

Hot water

Mud and surface deposits mixed with hot water

MUD POOL

Superheated water

Steam

FUMAROLE

273

Igneous and metamorphic rocks

IGNEOUS ROCKS ARE FORMED WHEN MAGMA (molten rock that originates from deep beneath the Earth's crust) cools and solidifies. There are two main types of igneous rock: intrusive and extrusive. Intrusive rocks are formed deep underground where magma is forced into cracks or between rock layers to form structures such as sills, dykes, and batholiths. The magma cools slowly to form coarse-grained rocks such as gabbro and pegmatite. Extrusive rocks are formed above the Earth's surface from lava (magma that has been ejected in a volcanic eruption). The molten lava cools quickly, producing fine-grained rocks such as rhyolite and basalt. Metamorphic rocks are those that have been altered by intense heat (contact metamorphism) or extreme pressure (regional metamorphism). Contact metamorphism occurs when rocks are changed by heat from, for example, an igneous intrusion or lava flow. Regional metamorphism occurs when rock is crushed in the middle of a folding mountain range. Metamorphic rocks can be formed from igneous rocks, sedimentary rocks, or even from other metamorphic rocks.

BASALT COLUMNS

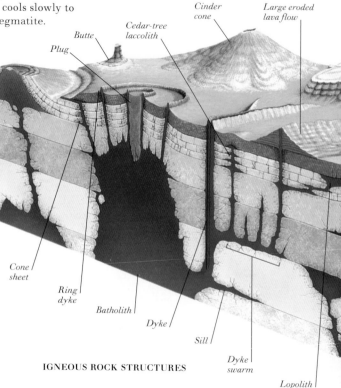

CONTACT METAMORPHISM

Metamorphic aureole (region where contact metamorphism occurs)

Hot igneous intrusion

Limestone

Shale

Marble (metamorphosed limestone)

Slate (metamorphosed shale)

IGNEOUS ROCK STRUCTURES

Cinder cone

Large eroded lava flow

Cedar-tree laccolith

Butte

Plug

Cone sheet

Ring dyke

Batholith

Dyke

Sill

Dyke swarm

Lopolith

REGIONAL METAMORPHISM

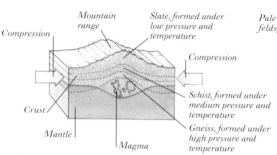

Mountain range

Slate, formed under low pressure and temperature

Compression

Compression

Crust

Schist, formed under medium pressure and temperature

Mantle

Gneiss, formed under high pressure and temperature

Magma

EXAMPLES OF METAMORPHIC ROCKS

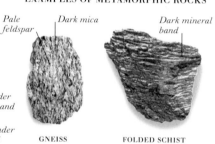

Pale feldspar

Dark mica

Dark mineral band

Pale calcite

GNEISS

FOLDED SCHIST

SKARN

EXAMPLES OF EXTRUSIVE IGNEOUS ROCKS

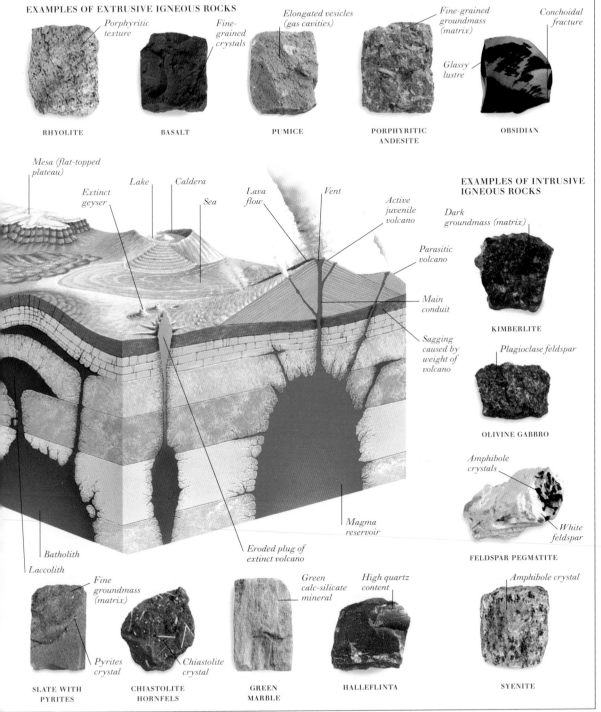

Porphyritic texture

Fine-grained crystals

Elongated vesicles (gas cavities)

Fine-grained groundmass (matrix)

Conchoidal fracture

Glassy lustre

RHYOLITE

BASALT

PUMICE

PORPHYRITIC ANDESITE

OBSIDIAN

Mesa (flat-topped plateau)

Extinct geyser

Lake

Caldera

Sea

Lava flow

Vent

Active juvenile volcano

EXAMPLES OF INTRUSIVE IGNEOUS ROCKS

Dark groundmass (matrix)

Parasitic volcano

Main conduit

Sagging caused by weight of volcano

KIMBERLITE

Plagioclase feldspar

OLIVINE GABBRO

Amphibole crystals

White feldspar

Magma reservoir

FELDSPAR PEGMATITE

Batholith

Laccolith

Eroded plug of extinct volcano

Fine groundmass (matrix)

Green calc-silicate mineral

High quartz content

Amphibole crystal

Pyrites crystal

Chiastolite crystal

SLATE WITH PYRITES

CHIASTOLITE HORNFELS

GREEN MARBLE

HALLEFLINTA

SYENITE

275

Sedimentary rocks

SEDIMENTARY ROCKS ARE FORMED BY THE ACCUMULATION and consolidation of sediments (see pp. 266-267). There are three main types of sedimentary rock. Clastic sedimentary rocks, such as breccia or sandstone, are formed from other rocks that have been broken down into fragments by weathering (see pp. 282-283), which have then been transported and deposited elsewhere. Organic sedimentary rocks – for example, coal (see pp. 280-281) – are derived from plant and animal remains. Chemical sedimentary rocks are formed by chemical processes. For example, rock salt is formed when salt dissolved in water is deposited as the water evaporates. Sedimentary rocks are laid down in layers, called beds or strata. Each new layer is laid down horizontally over older ones. There are usually some gaps in the sequence, called unconformities. These represent periods in which no new sediments were being laid down, or when earlier sedimentary layers were raised above sea level and eroded away.

THE GRAND CANYON, USA

EXAMPLES OF UNCONFORMITIES

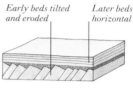

Early beds tilted and eroded   *Later beds horizontal*

ANGULAR UNCONFORMITY

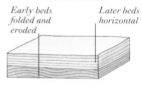

No bedding in early rocks   *Later beds horizontal*

NONCONFORMITY

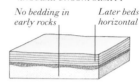

Early beds folded and eroded   *Later beds horizontal*

DISCONFORMITY

SEDIMENTARY LAYERS OF THE GRAND CANYON REGION

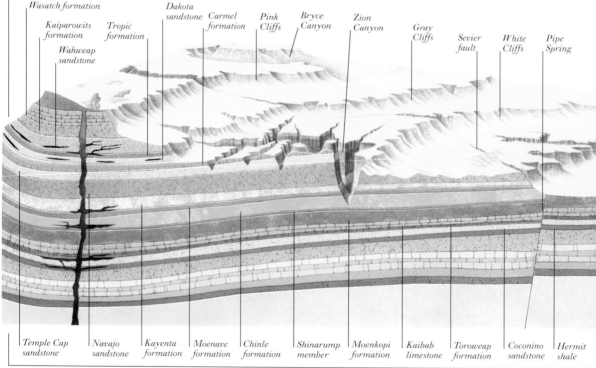

Wasatch formation

Kaiparowits formation

Tropic formation

Wahweap sandstone

Dakota sandstone

Carmel formation

Pink Cliffs

Bryce Canyon

Zion Canyon

Gray Cliffs

Sevier fault

White Cliffs

Pipe Spring

Temple Cap sandstone

Navajo sandstone

Kayenta formation

Moenave formation

Chinle formation

Shinarump member

Moenkopi formation

Kaibab limestone

Toroweap formation

Coconino sandstone

Hermit shale

EXAMPLES OF SEDIMENTARY ROCKS

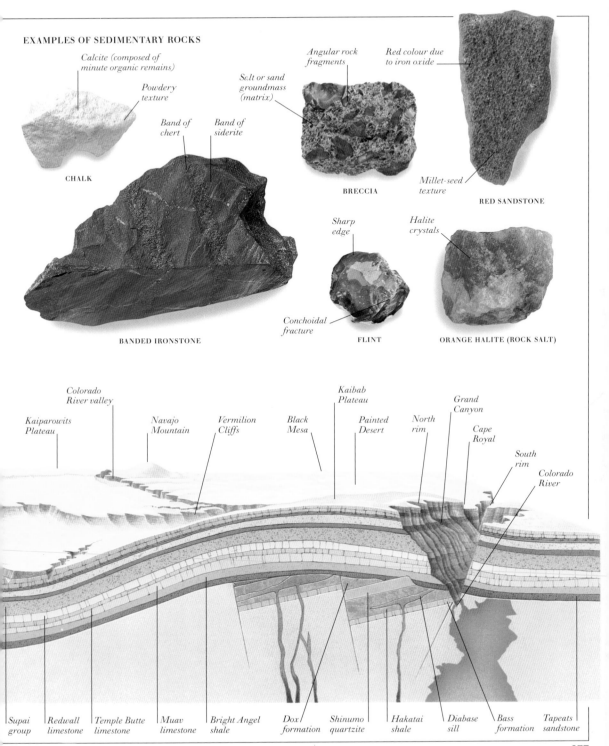

Calcite (composed of minute organic remains)

Powdery texture

CHALK

Band of chert

Band of siderite

BANDED IRONSTONE

Angular rock fragments

Salt or sand groundmass (matrix)

BRECCIA

Red colour due to iron oxide

Millet-seed texture

RED SANDSTONE

Sharp edge

Conchoidal fracture

FLINT

Halite crystals

ORANGE HALITE (ROCK SALT)

Kaiparowits Plateau

Colorado River valley

Navajo Mountain

Vermilion Cliffs

Black Mesa

Kaibab Plateau

Painted Desert

North rim

Grand Canyon

Cape Royal

South rim

Colorado River

Supai group

Redwall limestone

Temple Butte limestone

Muav limestone

Bright Angel shale

Dox formation

Shinumo quartzite

Hakatai shale

Diabase sill

Bass formation

Tapeats sandstone

Fossils

FOSSILS ARE THE REMAINS of plants and animals that have been preserved in rock. A fossil may be the preserved remains of an organism itself, an impression of it in rock, or preserved traces (known as trace fossils) left by an organism while it was alive, such as organic carbon outlines, fossilized footprints, or droppings. Most dead organisms soon rot away or are eaten by scavengers. For fossilization to occur, rapid burial by sediment is necessary. The organism decays, but the harder parts – bones, teeth, and shells, for example – may be preserved and hardened by minerals from the surrounding sediment. Fossilization may also occur even when the hard parts of an organism are dissolved away to leave an impression called a mould. The mould is filled by minerals, thereby creating a cast of the organism. The study of fossils (palaeontology) can not only show how living things have evolved, but can also help to reveal the Earth's geological history – for example, by aiding in the dating of rock strata.

PROCESS OF FOSSILIZATION

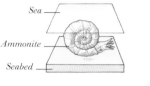

Sea
Ammonite
Seabed

ANIMAL DIES

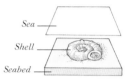

Sea
Shell
Seabed

SOFT PARTS ROT

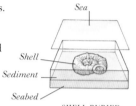

Sea
Shell
Sediment
Seabed

SHELL BURIED

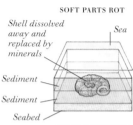

Shell dissolved away and replaced by minerals
Sea
Sediment
Sediment
Seabed

SHELL FOSSILIZED

EXAMPLES OF FOSSILS

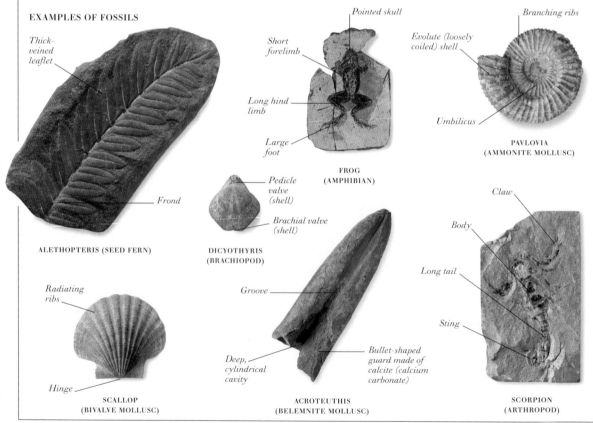

Thick-veined leaflet

Frond

ALETHOPTERIS (SEED FERN)

Radiating ribs

Hinge

**SCALLOP
(BIVALVE MOLLUSC)**

Short forelimb

Long hind limb

Large foot

Pointed skull

**FROG
(AMPHIBIAN)**

Pedicle valve (shell)

Brachial valve (shell)

**DICYOTHYRIS
(BRACHIOPOD)**

Groove

Deep, cylindrical cavity

Bullet-shaped guard made of calcite (calcium carbonate)

**ACROTEUTHIS
(BELEMNITE MOLLUSC)**

Branching ribs

Evolute (loosely coiled) shell

Umbilicus

**PAVLOVIA
(AMMONITE MOLLUSC)**

Claw

Body

Long tail

Sting

**SCORPION
(ARTHROPOD)**

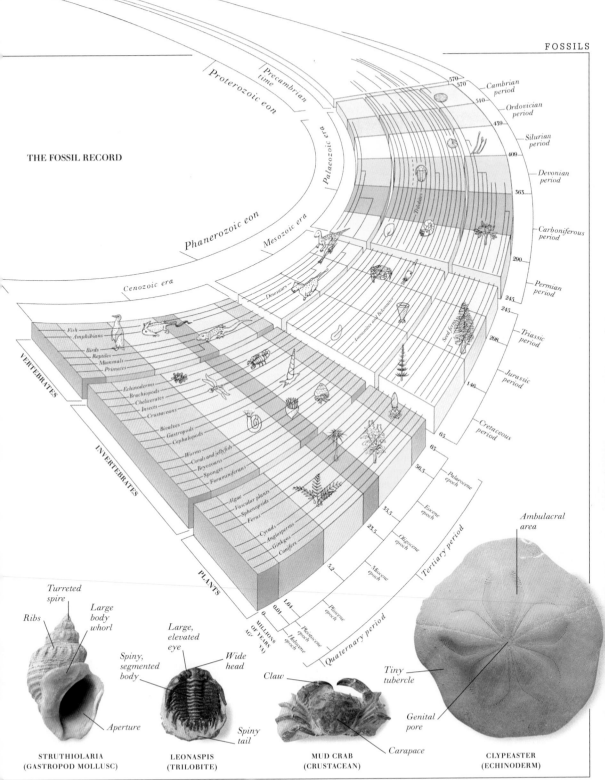

THE FOSSIL RECORD

Precambrian time

Proterozoic eon

Palaeozoic era

Phanerozoic eon

Mesozoic era

Cenozoic era

570
570 — Cambrian period
510 — Ordovician period
439 — Silurian period
409 — Devonian period
363
Carboniferous period
290
245 — Permian period
245
Triassic period
208
Jurassic period
146
Cretaceous period
65
65
56.5 — Palaeocene epoch
35.5 — Eocene epoch
23.5 — Oligocene epoch
Tertiary period
5.2 — Miocene epoch
1.64 — Pliocene epoch
0.01 — Pleistocene epoch
Holocene epoch
Quaternary period

Trilobite

Dinosaurs

Ammonites and Belemnites

Seed ferns

VERTEBRATES

Fish
Amphibians
Birds
Reptiles
Mammals
Primates

INVERTEBRATES

Echinoderms
Brachiopods
Chelicerates
Insects
Crustaceans
Bivalves
Gastropods
Cephalopods
Worms
Corals and jellyfish
Bryozoans
Sponges
Foraminiferans

PLANTS

Algae
Vascular plants
Sphenopsids
Ferns
Cycads
Angiosperms
Ginkgos
Conifers

MILLIONS OF YEARS AGO (MYA)

Turreted spire
Ribs
Large body whorl

Aperture

**STRUTHIOLARIA
(GASTROPOD MOLLUSC)**

Large, elevated eye
Spiny, segmented body
Wide head

Spiny tail

**LEONASPIS
(TRILOBITE)**

Claw

Carapace

**MUD CRAB
(CRUSTACEAN)**

Ambulacral area

Tiny tubercle

Genital pore

**CLYPEASTER
(ECHINODERM)**

279

Mineral resources

Stalk   *Leaf*

PLANT MATTER

MINERAL RESOURCES CAN BE DEFINED AS naturally occurring substances that can be extracted from the Earth and are useful as fuels and raw materials. Coal, oil, and gas – collectively called fossil fuels – are commonly included in this group, but are not strictly minerals, because they are of organic origin. Coal formation begins when vegetation is buried and partly decomposed to form peat. Overlying sediments compress the peat and transform it into lignite (soft brown coal). As the overlying sediments accumulate, increasing pressure and temperature eventually transform the lignite into bituminous and hard anthracite coals. Oil and gas are usually formed from organic matter that was deposited in marine sediments. Under the effects of heat and pressure, the compressed organic matter undergoes complex chemical changes to form oil and gas. The oil and gas percolate upwards through water-saturated, permeable rocks and they may rise to the Earth's surface or accumulate below an impermeable layer of rock that has been folded or faulted to form a trap – an anticline (upfold) trap, for example. Minerals are inorganic substances that may consist of a single chemical element, such as gold, silver, or copper, or combinations of elements (see pp. 268-269). Some minerals are concentrated in mineralization zones in rock associated with crustal movements or volcanic activity. Others may be found in sediments as placer deposits – accumulations of high-density minerals that have been weathered out of rocks, transported, and deposited (on river-beds, for example).

OIL RIG, NORTH SEA

Decayed plant matter

About 60% carbon   PEAT

About 70% carbon

Crumbly texture   LIGNITE (BROWN COAL)   *Powdery texture*

About 80% carbon

Shiny surface   BITUMINOUS COAL   *About 95% carbon*

ANTHRACITE COAL

HOW COAL IS FORMED

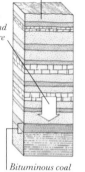

Vegetation

Increasing pressure and temperature

Increasing layers of overlying sediment

Increasing pressure and temperature

Increasing layers of overlying sediment

Increasing pressure and temperature

Peat (about 60% carbon)

PEAT

Lignite (about 70% carbon)

LIGNITE (BROWN COAL)

Bituminous coal (about 80% carbon)

BITUMINOUS COAL

EXAMPLES OF OIL AND GAS TRAPS

Impermeable rock

Oil

Folded impermeable rock

Pinch-out

Water-saturated permeable rock

Fault

Gas

Oil

Water-saturated permeable rock

Fault

FAULT TRAP

PINCH-OUT TRAP

Anticline

Folded impermeable rock

Water-saturated permeable rock

Gas

Oil

Folded impermeable rock

Water-saturated permeable rock

Oil

Impermeable salt dome

ANTICLINE TRAP

SALT-DOME TRAP

MAJOR COAL, OIL, AND GAS DEPOSITS

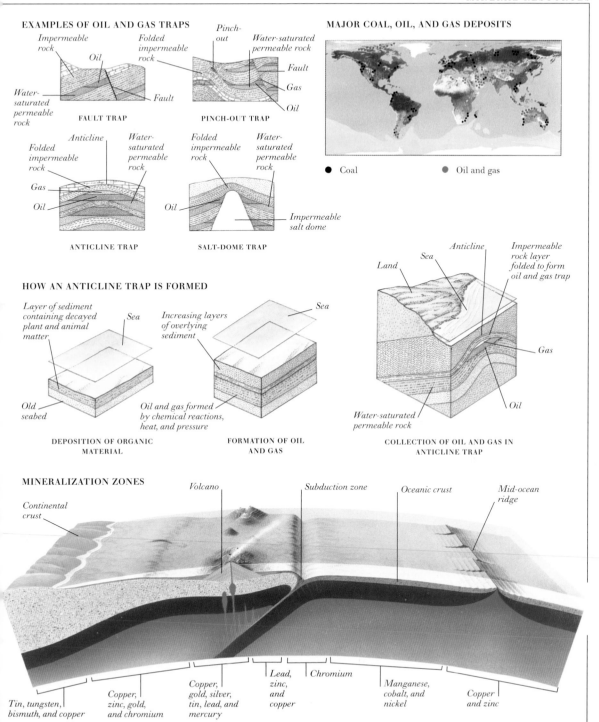

● Coal

● Oil and gas

HOW AN ANTICLINE TRAP IS FORMED

Layer of sediment containing decayed plant and animal matter

Sea

Old seabed

Increasing layers of overlying sediment

Sea

Oil and gas formed by chemical reactions, heat, and pressure

DEPOSITION OF ORGANIC MATERIAL

FORMATION OF OIL AND GAS

Land

Sea

Anticline

Impermeable rock layer folded to form oil and gas trap

Gas

Oil

Water-saturated permeable rock

COLLECTION OF OIL AND GAS IN ANTICLINE TRAP

MINERALIZATION ZONES

Continental crust

Volcano

Subduction zone

Oceanic crust

Mid-ocean ridge

Tin, tungsten, bismuth, and copper

Copper, zinc, gold, and chromium

Copper, gold, silver, tin, lead, and mercury

Lead, zinc, and copper

Chromium

Manganese, cobalt, and nickel

Copper and zinc

Weathering and erosion

WEATHERING IS THE BREAKING DOWN of rocks on the Earth's surface. There are two main types: physical (or mechanical) and chemical. Physical weathering may be caused by temperature changes, such as freezing and thawing, or by abrasion from material carried by winds, rivers, or glaciers. Rocks may also be broken down by the actions of animals and plants, such as the burrowing of animals and the growth of roots. Chemical weathering causes rocks to decompose by changing their chemical composition – for example, rainwater may dissolve certain minerals in a rock. Erosion is the wearing away and removal of land surfaces by water, wind, or ice. It is greatest in areas of little or no surface vegetation, such as deserts, where sand dunes may form.

FORMATION OF A HAMADA (ROCK PAVEMENT)

Wind blows away small particles

Larger particles aggregate

Hamada forms

FIRST STAGE

SECOND STAGE

FINAL STAGE

FEATURES OF WEATHERING AND EROSION

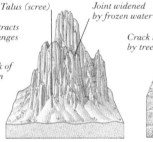

Mesa (flat-topped plateau)

Canyon

Zeugen

Joint

Hard rock

Soft rock

Shelf formed of hard rock

Talus (scree)

Alluvial fan (alluvial cone)

Bahada (gentle slope covered with loose rock)

Bolson (alluvium-filled basin)

FEATURES PRODUCED BY WIND ACTION

Wind-blown sand

Mushroom-shaped rock

Neck

Rock base eroded by wind-blown sand

ROCK PEDESTAL

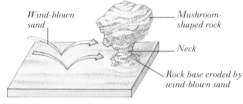

Wind-blown sand

Widened joint

Soft rock

Hard rock

Wind-blown sand

Furrow

Hard rock

Soft rock eroded by wind-blown sand

ZEUGEN

YARDANG

EXAMPLES OF PHYSICAL WEATHERING PROCESSES

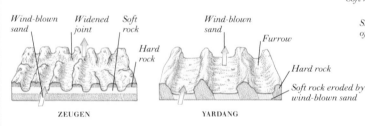

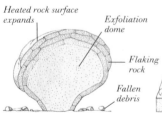

Heated rock surface expands

Exfoliation dome

Flaking rock

Fallen debris

EXFOLIATION (ONION-SKIN WEATHERING)

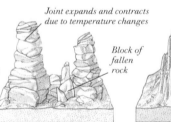

Joint expands and contracts due to temperature changes

Block of fallen rock

BLOCK DISINTEGRATION

Talus (scree)

Joint widened by frozen water

FROST WEDGING

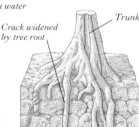

Joint widened by frozen water

Crack widened by tree root

Trunk

TREE ROOT ACTION

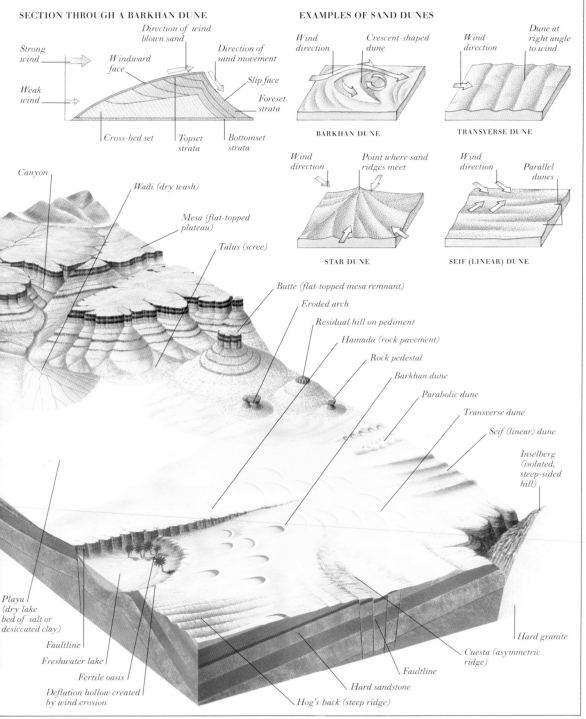

SECTION THROUGH A BARKHAN DUNE

Strong wind

Weak wind

Windward face

Direction of wind-blown sand

Direction of sand movement

Slip face

Foreset strata

Cross-bed set

Topset strata

Bottomset strata

EXAMPLES OF SAND DUNES

Wind direction

Crescent-shaped dune

BARKHAN DUNE

Wind direction

Dune at right angle to wind

TRANSVERSE DUNE

Wind direction

Point where sand ridges meet

STAR DUNE

Wind direction

Parallel dunes

SEIF (LINEAR) DUNE

Canyon

Wadi (dry wash)

Mesa (flat-topped plateau)

Talus (scree)

Butte (flat-topped mesa remnant)

Eroded arch

Residual hill on pediment

Hamada (rock pavement)

Rock pedestal

Barkhan dune

Parabolic dune

Transverse dune

Seif (linear) dune

Inselberg (isolated, steep-sided hill)

Playa (dry lake bed of salt or desiccated clay)

Faultline

Freshwater lake

Fertile oasis

Deflation hollow created by wind erosion

Hog's-back (steep ridge)

Hard sandstone

Faultline

Cuesta (asymmetric ridge)

Hard granite

283

Caves

CAVES COMMONLY FORM in areas of limestone, although on coastlines they also occur in other rocks. Limestone is made of calcite (calcium carbonate), which dissolves in the carbonic acid naturally present in rainwater, and in humic acids from the decay of vegetation. The acidic water trickles down through cracks and joints in the limestone and between rock layers, breaking up the surface terrain into clints (blocks of rock), separated by grikes (deep cracks), and punctuated by sink-holes (also called swallow-holes or potholes) into which surface streams may disappear. Underground, the acidic water dissolves the rock around crevices, opening up a network of passages and caves, which can become large caverns if the roofs collapse. Various features are formed when the dissolved calcite is redeposited; for example, it may be redeposited along an underground stream to form a gour (series of calcite ridges), or in caves and passages to form stalactites and stalagmites. Stalactites develop where calcite is left behind as water drips from the roof; where the drops land, stalagmites build up.

STALACTITE WITH RING MARKS

Ring mark

MERGED STALACTITES

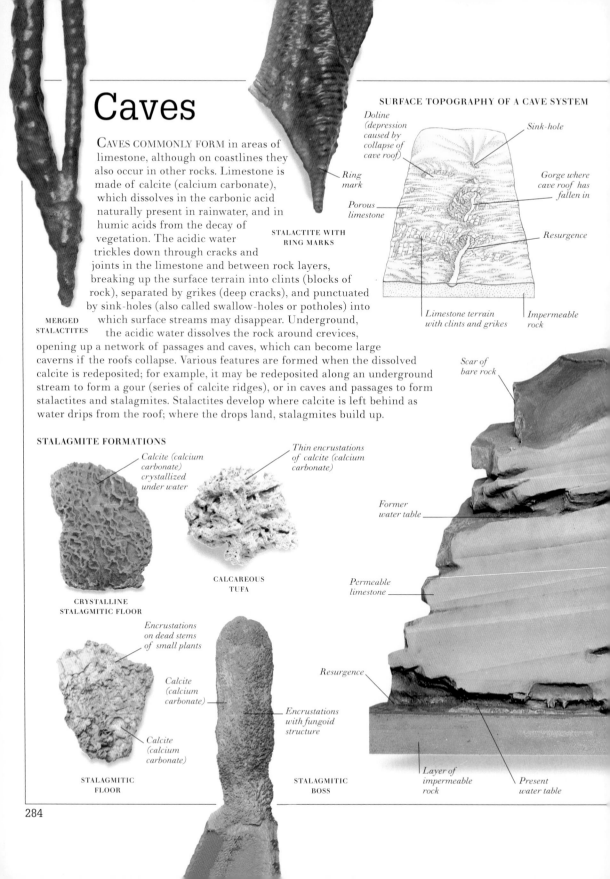

SURFACE TOPOGRAPHY OF A CAVE SYSTEM

Doline (depression caused by collapse of cave roof)

Sink-hole

Porous limestone

Gorge where cave roof has fallen in

Resurgence

Limestone terrain with clints and grikes

Impermeable rock

STALAGMITE FORMATIONS

Calcite (calcium carbonate) crystallized under water

Thin encrustations of calcite (calcium carbonate)

CALCAREOUS TUFA

CRYSTALLINE STALAGMITIC FLOOR

Encrustations on dead stems of small plants

Calcite (calcium carbonate)

Calcite (calcium carbonate)

STALAGMITIC FLOOR

Encrustations with fungoid structure

STALAGMITIC BOSS

Scar of bare rock

Former water table

Permeable limestone

Resurgence

Layer of impermeable rock

Present water table

284

DEVELOPMENT OF A CAVE SYSTEM

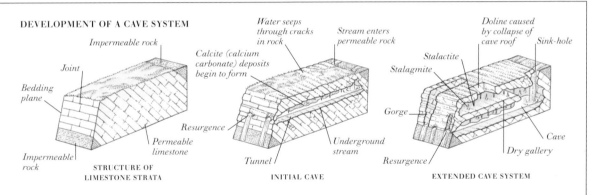

Impermeable rock

Joint

Bedding plane

Impermeable rock

Permeable limestone

Resurgence

STRUCTURE OF LIMESTONE STRATA

Water seeps through cracks in rock

Stream enters permeable rock

Calcite (calcium carbonate) deposits begin to form

Tunnel

Underground stream

INITIAL CAVE

Doline caused by collapse of cave roof

Sink-hole

Stalactite

Stalagmite

Gorge

Resurgence

Cave

Dry gallery

EXTENDED CAVE SYSTEM

INTERCONNECTED CAVE SYSTEM

Stalactite

Pillar (column)

Gorge

Stalactite

Dry gallery (former course of underground stream)

Gour (series of calcite ridges) deposited by running water

Stalagmite

Joint in rock enlarged by water

Bedding plane

Curtain of deposited calcite (calcium carbonate)

Tunnel

Cave

Passage

Cavern

Gour (series of calcite ridges)

Glaciers

GLACIER BAY, ALASKA

A VALLEY GLACIER IS A LARGE MASS OF ICE that forms on land and moves slowly downhill under its own weight. It is formed from snow that collects in cirques (mountain hollows also known as corries) and compresses into ice as more and more snow accumulates. The cirque is deepened by frost wedging and abrasion (see pp. 282-283), and arêtes (sharp ridges) develop between adjacent cirques. Eventually, so much ice builds up that the glacier begins to move downhill. As the glacier moves it collects moraine (debris), which may range in size from particles of dust to large boulders. The rocks at the base of the glacier erode the glacial valley, giving it a U-shaped cross-section. Under the glacier, *roches moutonnées* (eroded outcrops of hard rock) and drumlins (rounded mounds of rock and clay) are left behind on the valley floor. The glacier ends at a terminus (the snout), where the ice melts as fast as it arrives. If the temperature increases, the ice melts faster than it arrives, and the glacier retreats. The retreating glacier leaves behind its moraine and also erratics (isolated single boulders). Glacial streams from the melting glacier deposit eskers and kames (ridges and mounds of sand and gravel), but carry away the finer sediment to form a stratified outwash plain. Lumps of ice carried on to this plain melt, creating holes called kettles.

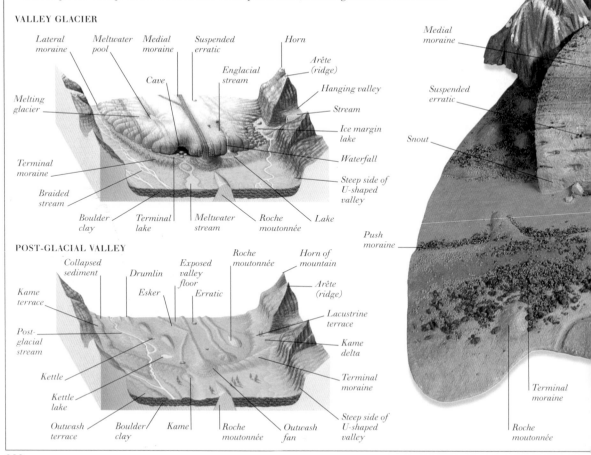

VALLEY GLACIER

- Lateral moraine
- Meltwater pool
- Medial moraine
- Suspended erratic
- Horn
- Medial moraine
- Cave
- Englacial stream
- Arête (ridge)
- Hanging valley
- Melting glacier
- Stream
- Suspended erratic
- Ice margin lake
- Snout
- Terminal moraine
- Waterfall
- Braided stream
- Steep side of U-shaped valley
- Boulder clay
- Terminal lake
- Meltwater stream
- Roche moutonnée
- Lake
- Push moraine

POST-GLACIAL VALLEY

- Collapsed sediment
- Drumlin
- Exposed valley floor
- Roche moutonnée
- Horn of mountain
- Kame terrace
- Esker
- Erratic
- Arête (ridge)
- Post-glacial stream
- Lacustrine terrace
- Kame delta
- Kettle
- Terminal moraine
- Kettle lake
- Terminal moraine
- Outwash terrace
- Boulder clay
- Kame
- Roche moutonnée
- Outwash fan
- Steep side of U-shaped valley
- Roche moutonnée

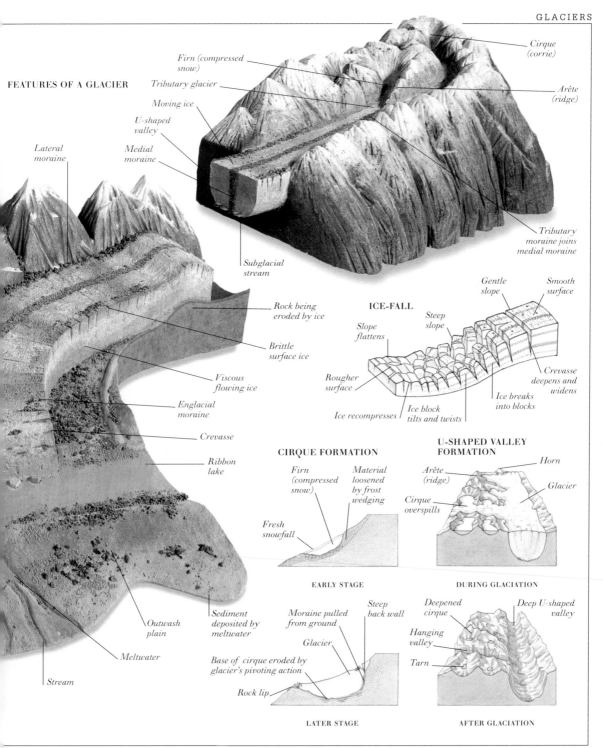

FEATURES OF A GLACIER

Firn (compressed snow)

Tributary glacier

Moving ice

U-shaped valley

Medial moraine

Lateral moraine

Cirque (corrie)

Arête (ridge)

Tributary moraine joins medial moraine

Subglacial stream

Rock being eroded by ice

Brittle surface ice

Viscous flowing ice

Englacial moraine

Crevasse

Ribbon lake

Outwash plain

Meltwater

Stream

Sediment deposited by meltwater

ICE-FALL

Gentle slope

Smooth surface

Steep slope

Slope flattens

Rougher surface

Ice recompresses

Ice block tilts and twists

Ice breaks into blocks

Crevasse deepens and widens

CIRQUE FORMATION

Firn (compressed snow)

Material loosened by frost wedging

Fresh snowfall

EARLY STAGE

Moraine pulled from ground

Steep back wall

Glacier

Base of cirque eroded by glacier's pivoting action

Rock lip

LATER STAGE

U-SHAPED VALLEY FORMATION

Arête (ridge)

Horn

Glacier

Cirque overspills

DURING GLACIATION

Deepened cirque

Deep U-shaped valley

Hanging valley

Tarn

AFTER GLACIATION

Rivers

RIVERS FORM PART of the water cycle – the continuous circulation of water between the land, sea, and atmosphere. The source of a river may be a mountain spring or lake, or a melting glacier. The course that the river subsequently takes depends on the slope of the terrain and on the rock types and formations over which it flows. In its early, upland stages, a river tumbles steeply over rocks and boulders and cuts a steep-sided V-shaped valley. Farther downstream, it flows smoothly over sediments and forms winding meanders, eroding sideways to create broad valleys and plains. On reaching the coast, the river may deposit sediment to form an estuary or delta (see pp. 290-291).

RIVER CAPTURE

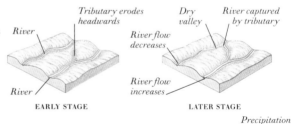

Tributary erodes
headwards

River

River

Dry
valley

River captured
by tributary

River flow
decreases

River flow
increases

EARLY STAGE

LATER STAGE

THE WATER CYCLE

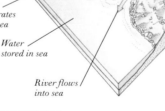

Precipitation
falls on high
ground

Water
carried
downstream
by river

Wind

Water vapour released
into atmosphere by
trees and other plants

Wind

Water vapour
forms clouds

Water
evaporates
from sea

Water
stored in sea

River flows
into sea

Water
evaporates
from lake

Water seeps
underground
and flows to sea

SATELLITE IMAGE OF GANGES RIVER DELTA, BANGLADESH

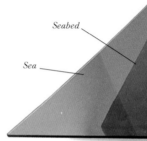

Ganges
River

Ganges
delta

Infertile
swampland

Distributary

Large volume
of sediment

Seabed

Sea

Sediment layers

RIVER DRAINAGE PATTERNS

RADIAL

CENTRIPETAL

PARALLEL

DENDRITIC

DERANGED

TRELLISED

ANNULAR

RECTANGULAR

STAGES IN A RIVER'S DEVELOPMENT

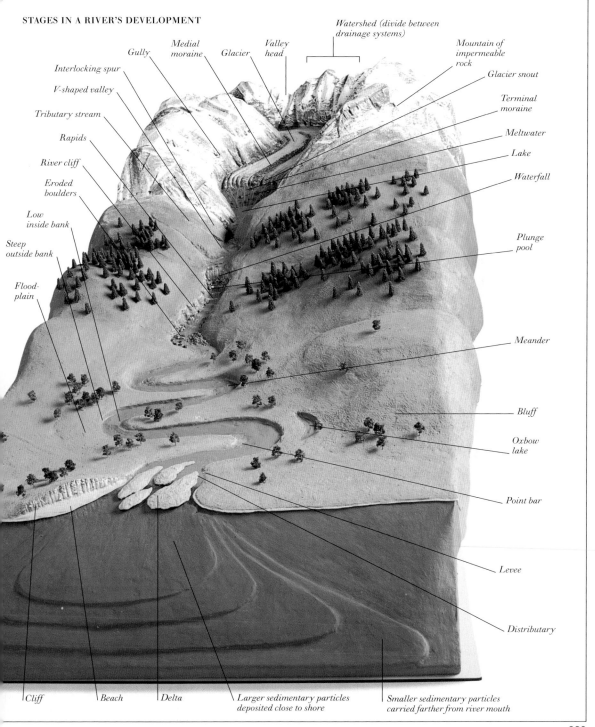

Watershed (divide between drainage systems)

Medial moraine

Gully

Glacier

Valley head

Mountain of impermeable rock

Glacier snout

Interlocking spur

Terminal moraine

V-shaped valley

Meltwater

Tributary stream

Lake

Rapids

Waterfall

River cliff

Eroded boulders

Low inside bank

Plunge pool

Steep outside bank

Flood-plain

Meander

Bluff

Oxbow lake

Point bar

Levee

Distributary

Cliff

Beach

Delta

Larger sedimentary particles deposited close to shore

Smaller sedimentary particles carried farther from river mouth

River features

RIVERS ARE ONE OF THE MAJOR FORCES that shape the landscape. Near its source, a river is steep (see pp. 288-289). It erodes downwards, carving out V-shaped valleys and deep gorges. Waterfalls and rapids are formed where the river flows from hard rock to softer, more easily eroded rock. Farther downstream, meanders may form and there is greater sideways erosion, resulting in a broad river valley. The river sometimes erodes through the neck of a meander to form an oxbow lake. Sediment deposited on the valley floor by meandering rivers and during floods helps to create a flood-plain. Floods may also deposit sediment on the banks of the river to form levees. As a river spills into the sea or a lake, it deposits large amounts of sediment, and may form a delta. A delta is an area of sand-bars, swamps, and lagoons through which the river flows in several channels called distributaries – the Mississippi delta, for example. Often, a rise in sea level may have flooded the river-mouth to form a broad estuary, a tidal section where seawater mixes with fresh water.

HOW WATERFALLS AND RAPIDS ARE FORMED

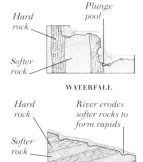

WATERFALL

RAPIDS

A RIVER VALLEY DRAINAGE SYSTEM

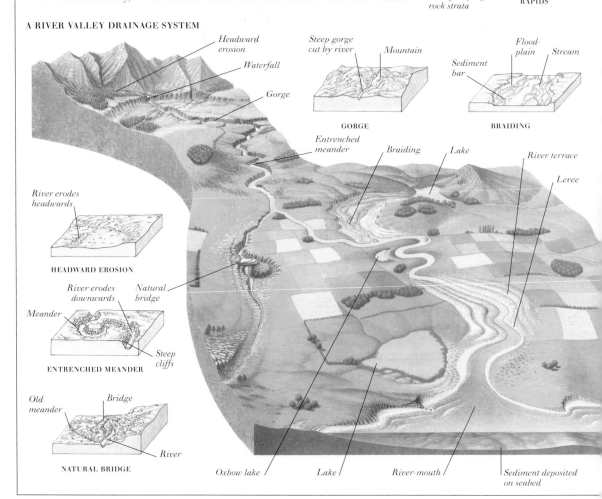

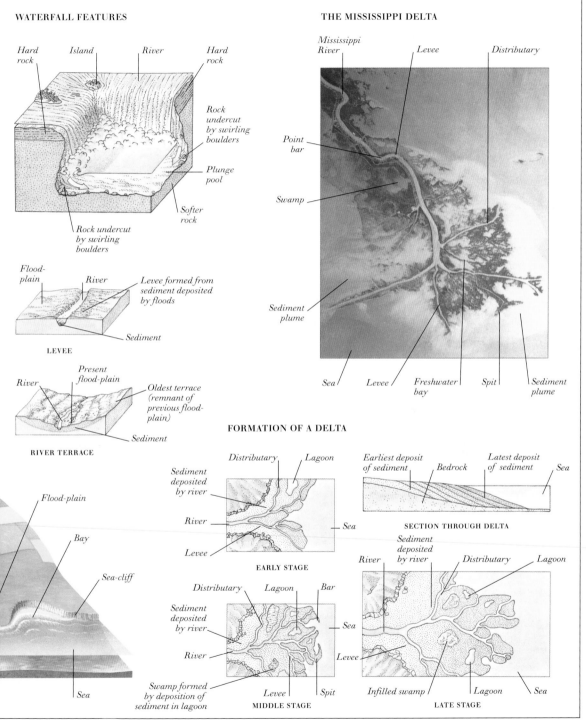

WATERFALL FEATURES

Hard rock
Island
River
Hard rock
Rock undercut by swirling boulders
Plunge pool
Softer rock
Rock undercut by swirling boulders

Flood-plain
River
Levee formed from sediment deposited by floods
Sediment

LEVEE

River
Present flood-plain
Oldest terrace (remnant of previous flood-plain)
Sediment

RIVER TERRACE

Flood-plain
Bay
Sea-cliff
Sea

THE MISSISSIPPI DELTA

Mississippi River
Levee
Distributary
Point bar
Swamp
Sediment plume
Sea
Levee
Freshwater bay
Spit
Sediment plume

FORMATION OF A DELTA

Distributary
Lagoon
Sediment deposited by river
River
Sea
Levee

EARLY STAGE

Earliest deposit of sediment
Bedrock
Latest deposit of sediment
Sea

SECTION THROUGH DELTA

Distributary
Lagoon
Bar
Sediment deposited by river
River
Sea
Swamp formed by deposition of sediment in lagoon
Levee
Spit

MIDDLE STAGE

Sediment deposited by river
River
Distributary
Lagoon
Levee
Infilled swamp
Lagoon
Sea

LATE STAGE

291

Lakes and groundwater

NATURAL LAKE OCCUR WHERE a large quantity of water collects in a hollow in impermeable rock, or is prevented from draining away by a barrier, such as moraine (glacial deposits) or solidified lava. Lakes are often relatively short-lived landscape features, as they tend to become silted up by sediment from the streams and rivers that feed them. Some of the more long-lasting lakes are found in deep rift valleys formed by vertical movements of the Earth's crust (see pp. 58-59) – for example, Lake Baikal in Russia, the world's largest freshwater lake, and the Dead Sea in the Middle East, one of the world's saltiest lakes. Where water is able to drain away, it sinks into the ground until it reaches a layer of impermeable rock, then accumulates in the permeable rock above it; this water-saturated permeable rock is called an aquifer. The saturated zone varies in depth according to seasonal and climatic changes. In wet conditions, the water stored underground builds up, while in dry periods it becomes depleted. Where the upper edge of the saturated zone – the water table – meets the ground surface, water emerges as springs. In an artesian basin, where the aquifer is below an aquiclude (layer of impermeable rock), the water table throughout the basin is determined by its height at the rim. In the centre of such a basin, the water table is above ground level. The water in the basin is thus trapped below the water table and can rise under its own pressure along faultlines or well shafts.

LAKE BAIKAL, RUSSIA

EXAMPLES OF SPRINGS

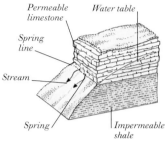

Permeable limestone · Water table · Spring line · Stream · Spring · Impermeable shale

LIMESTONE SPRING

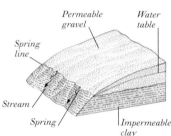

Permeable gravel · Water table · Spring line · Stream · Spring · Impermeable clay

COASTAL (VALLEY) SPRING

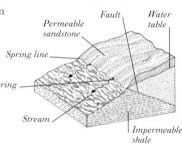

Fault · Water table · Permeable sandstone · Spring line · Spring · Stream · Impermeable shale

FAULT SPRING

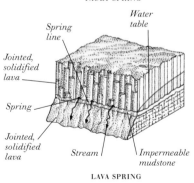

Water table · Spring line · Jointed, solidified lava · Spring · Jointed, solidified lava · Stream · Impermeable mudstone

LAVA SPRING

STRUCTURE OF AN ARTESIAN BASIN

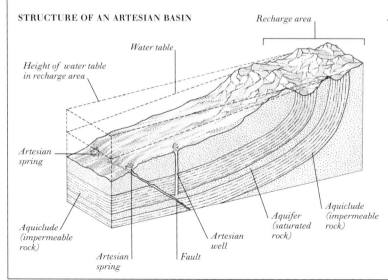

Water table · Recharge area · Height of water table in recharge area · Artesian spring · Aquiclude (impermeable rock) · Artesian spring · Artesian well · Fault · Aquifer (saturated rock) · Aquiclude (impermeable rock)

FEATURES OF A GROUNDWATER SYSTEM

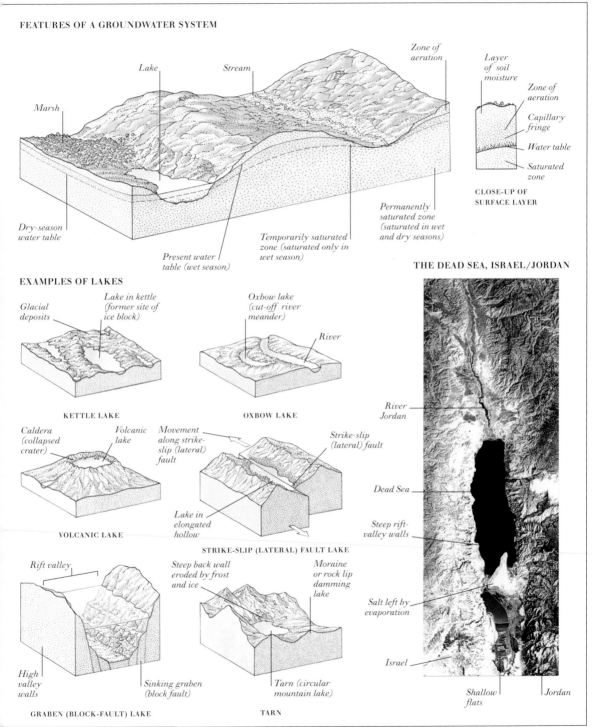

Zone of
aeration

Lake

Stream

Marsh

Layer
of soil
moisture

Zone of
aeration

Capillary
fringe

Water table

Saturated
zone

CLOSE-UP OF
SURFACE LAYER

Dry-season
water table

Present water
table (wet season)

Temporarily saturated
zone (saturated only in
wet season)

Permanently
saturated zone
(saturated in wet
and dry seasons)

EXAMPLES OF LAKES

Glacial
deposits

Lake in kettle
(former site of
ice block)

Oxbow lake
(cut-off river
meander)

River

THE DEAD SEA, ISRAEL/JORDAN

KETTLE LAKE

OXBOW LAKE

Caldera
(collapsed
crater)

Volcanic
lake

Movement
along strike-
slip (lateral)
fault

Strike-slip
(lateral) fault

River
Jordan

Lake in
elongated
hollow

Dead Sea

VOLCANIC LAKE

STRIKE-SLIP (LATERAL) FAULT LAKE

Steep rift-
valley walls

Rift valley

Steep back wall
eroded by frost
and ice

Moraine
or rock lip
damming
lake

Salt left by
evaporation

High
valley
walls

Sinking graben
(block fault)

Tarn (circular
mountain lake)

Israel

GRABEN (BLOCK-FAULT) LAKE

TARN

Shallow
flats

Jordan

293

Coastlines

COASTLINES ARE AMONG THE MOST RAPIDLY changing landscape
features. Some are eroded by waves, wind, and rain, causing
cliffs to be undercut and caves to be hollowed out of solid rock.
Others are built up by waves transporting sand and small rocks in a
process known as longshore drift, and by rivers depositing sediment in
deltas. Additional influences include the activities of living organisms
such as coral, crustal movements, and sea-level variations due to
climatic changes. Rising land or a drop in sea level creates an emergent
coastline, with cliffs and beaches stranded above the new shoreline.
Sinking land or a rise in sea level produces a drowned coastline, typified
by fjords (submerged glacial valleys) or submerged river valleys.

FEATURES OF A SEA-CLIFF

Cliff-top

Cliff-face

High tide
level

Low tide
level

Offshore
deposits

Wave-cut
platform

Undercut
area of cliff

Mature river

Headland

Bedding
plane

Sea-cliff

Remnants of
former headland

Estuary

FEATURES OF WAVES

Wave
height

Crest

Wavelength

Trough

Shorter wavelength
near beach

Circular orbit of water
and suspended particles

Orbit deformed into ellipse
as water gets shallower

LONGSHORE DRIFT

Pebble

Backwash

Movement of
material
along beach

Build-up
of material
against groyne

Beach

Groyne

Swash
zone

Swash

Waves approaching
shore at an
oblique angle

DEPOSITIONAL FEATURES OF COASTLINES

Bay-head
beach

Wave
direction

Headland

Wave
direction

Tombolo

Island

Wave
direction

Cuspate
foreland

Wave
direction

Barrier
beach

Lagoon

BAY HEAD BEACH

TOMBOLO

CUSPATE FORELAND

BARRIER BEACH

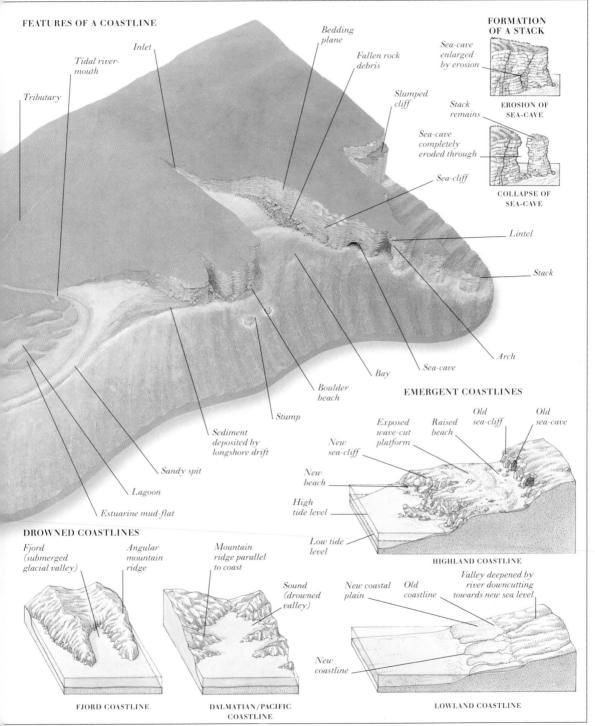

FEATURES OF A COASTLINE

Tributary

Tidal river-mouth

Inlet

Bedding plane

Fallen rock debris

Slumped cliff

Sea-cliff

Lintel

Stack

Arch

Sea-cave

Bay

Boulder beach

Stump

Sediment deposited by longshore drift

Sandy spit

Lagoon

Estuarine mud-flat

FORMATION OF A STACK

Sea-cave enlarged by erosion

EROSION OF SEA-CAVE

Stack remains

Sea-cave completely eroded through

COLLAPSE OF SEA-CAVE

EMERGENT COASTLINES

Exposed wave-cut platform

Raised beach

Old sea-cliff

Old sea-cave

New sea-cliff

New beach

High tide level

Low tide level

HIGHLAND COASTLINE

DROWNED COASTLINES

Fjord (submerged glacial valley)

Angular mountain ridge

Mountain ridge parallel to coast

Sound (drowned valley)

New coastal plain

Old coastline

Valley deepened by river downcutting towards new sea level

New coastline

FJORD COASTLINE

DALMATIAN/PACIFIC COASTLINE

LOWLAND COASTLINE

Oceans and seas

OCEANS AND SEAS COVER ABOUT 70 PER CENT of the Earth's surface and account for about 97 per cent of its total water. These oceans and seas play a crucial role in regulating temperature variations and determining climate. Their waters absorb heat from the Sun, especially in tropical regions, and the surface currents distribute it around the Earth, warming overlying air masses and neighbouring land in winter and cooling them in summer. The oceans are never still. Differences in temperature and salinity drive deep current systems, while surface currents are generated by winds blowing over the oceans. All currents are deflected – to the right in the Northern Hemisphere, to the left in the Southern Hemisphere – as a result of the Earth's rotation. This deflective factor is known as the Coriolis force. A current that begins on the surface is immediately deflected. This current in turn generates a current in the layer of water beneath, which is also deflected. As the movement is transmitted downwards, the deflections form an Ekman spiral. The waters of the oceans and seas are also moved by the constant ebb and flow of tides. These are caused by the gravitational pull of the Moon and Sun. The highest tides (Spring tides) occur at full and new Moon; the lowest tides (neap tides) occur at first and last quarter.

SURFACE CURRENTS

OFFSHORE CURRENTS

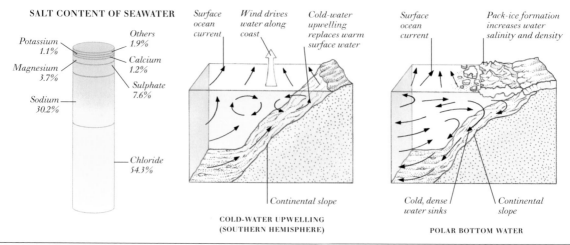

SALT CONTENT OF SEAWATER

Potassium 1.1%
Magnesium 3.7%
Sodium 30.2%
Others 1.9%
Calcium 1.2%
Sulphate 7.6%
Chloride 54.3%

Surface ocean current

Wind drives water along coast

Cold-water upwelling replaces warm surface water

Continental slope

COLD-WATER UPWELLING (SOUTHERN HEMISPHERE)

Surface ocean current

Pack-ice formation increases water salinity and density

Cold, dense water sinks

Continental slope

POLAR BOTTOM WATER

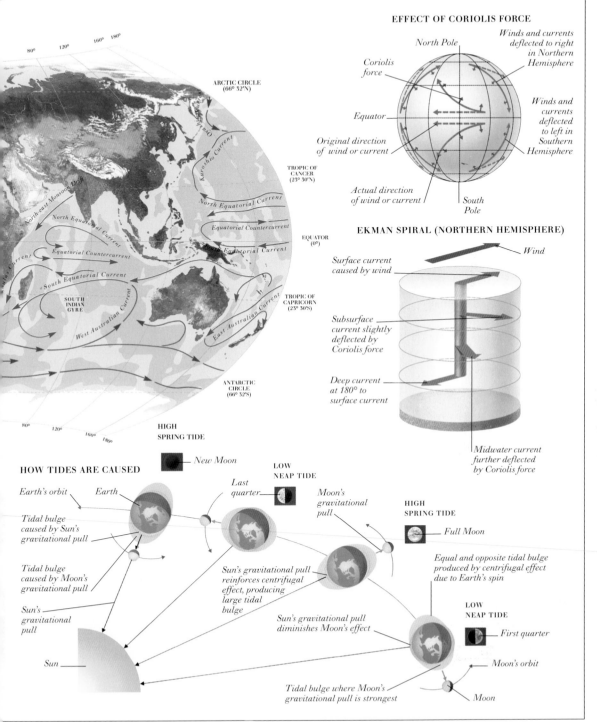

ARCTIC CIRCLE
(66° 32'N)

Oyashio Current

Kuroshio Current

North Equatorial Current

**TROPIC OF
CANCER**
(23° 30'N)

North-east Monsoon Drift

North Equatorial Current

Equatorial Countercurrent

South Equatorial Current

EQUATOR
(0°)

Somali Current

Equatorial Countercurrent

South Equatorial Current

**SOUTH
INDIAN
GYRE**

West Australian Current

East Australian Current

**TROPIC OF
CAPRICORN**
(23° 30'S)

**ANTARCTIC
CIRCLE**
(66° 32'S)

EFFECT OF CORIOLIS FORCE

North Pole

Coriolis
force

Equator

Original direction
of wind or current

Actual direction
of wind or current

South
Pole

Winds and currents
deflected to right
in Northern
Hemisphere

Winds and
currents
deflected
to left in
Southern
Hemisphere

EKMAN SPIRAL (NORTHERN HEMISPHERE)

Surface current
caused by wind

Wind

Subsurface
current slightly
deflected by
Coriolis force

Deep current
at 180° to
surface current

Midwater current
further deflected
by Coriolis force

HOW TIDES ARE CAUSED

**HIGH
SPRING TIDE**

New Moon

Earth's orbit

Earth

**LOW
NEAP TIDE**

Last
quarter

Moon's
gravitational
pull

Tidal bulge
caused by Sun's
gravitational pull

Tidal bulge
caused by Moon's
gravitational pull

Sun's
gravitational
pull

Sun's gravitational pull
reinforces centrifugal
effect, producing
large tidal
bulge

**HIGH
SPRING TIDE**

Full Moon

Equal and opposite tidal bulge
produced by centrifugal effect
due to Earth's spin

Sun's gravitational pull
diminishes Moon's effect

**LOW
NEAP TIDE**

First quarter

Sun

Moon's orbit

Tidal bulge where Moon's
gravitational pull is strongest

Moon

297

The ocean floor

THE OCEAN FLOOR COMPRISES TWO SECTIONS: the continental shelf and slope, and the deep-ocean floor. The continental shelf and slope are part of the continental crust, but may extend far into the ocean. Sloping quite gently to a depth of about 140 metres, the continental shelf is covered in sandy deposits shaped by waves and tidal currents. At the edge of the continental shelf, the seabed slopes down to the abyssal plain, which lies at an average depth of about 3,800 metres. On this deep-ocean floor is a layer of sediment made up of clays, fine oozes formed from the remains of tiny sea creatures, and occasional mineral-rich deposits. Echo-sounding and remote sensing from satellites has revealed that the abyssal plain is divided by a system of mountain ranges, far bigger than any on land – the mid-ocean ridge. Here, magma (molten rock) wells up from the Earth's interior and solidifies, widening the ocean floor (see pp. 58-59). As the ocean floor spreads, volcanoes that have formed over hot spots in the crust move away from their magma source; they become extinct and are increasingly submerged and eroded. Volcanoes eroded below sea level remain as seamounts (underwater mountains). In warm waters, a volcano that projects above the ocean surface often acquires a fringing coral reef, which may develop into an atoll as the volcano becomes submerged.

CONTINENTAL-SHELF FLOOR

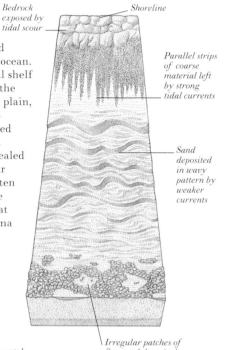

Bedrock exposed by tidal scour

Shoreline

Parallel strips of coarse material left by strong tidal currents

Sand deposited in wavy pattern by weaker currents

FEATURES OF THE OCEAN FLOOR

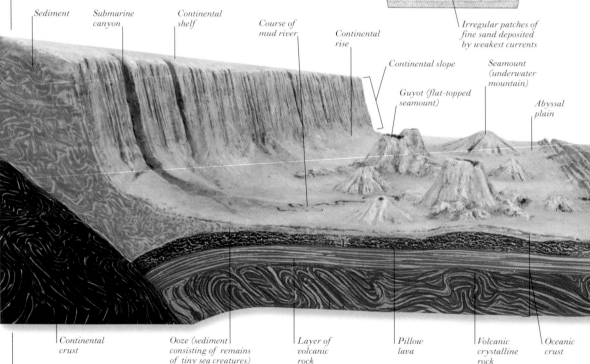

Sediment

Submarine canyon

Continental shelf

Course of mud river

Continental rise

Irregular patches of fine sand deposited by weakest currents

Continental slope

Seamount (underwater mountain)

Guyot (flat-topped seamount)

Abyssal plain

Continental crust

Ooze (sediment consisting of remains of tiny sea creatures)

Layer of volcanic rock

Pillow lava

Volcanic crystalline rock

Oceanic crust

DEEP-OCEAN FLOOR SEDIMENTS

Calcareous ooze

Pelagic clay

Glacial sediments

Siliceous ooze

Terrigenous sediments

Continental margin sediments

Metalliferous muds

Major nodule fields

ECHO-SOUND PROFILE OF OCEAN FLOOR

Sand wave

Event mark indicates synchronization of survey equipment

Minor oscillations caused by ship's movement

Sand wave

Seabed profile

Velocity of sound in water (1,493 m/sec)

Reference code

Mid-ocean ridge

Ocean trench

Magma (molten rock)

Sediment

DEVELOPMENT OF AN ATOLL

Volcanic island

Coral grows on shoreline

Sea level

FRINGING REEF

Eroded volcanic island subsides

Lagoon

Coral continues to grow, forming barrier reef

BARRIER REEF

Coral continues to grow where waves bring food

Lagoon

Dead coral

Volcanic island becomes submerged

ATOLL

Coral submerged too deeply to grow

Volcanic island is submerged further

SUBMERGED ATOLL

299

The atmosphere

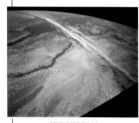

JET STREAM

THE EARTH IS SURROUNDED BY ITS ATMOSPHERE, a blanket of gases that enables life to exist on the planet. This layer has no definite outer edge, gradually becoming thinner until it merges into space, but over 80 per cent of atmospheric gases are held by gravity within about 20 kilometres of the Earth's surface. The atmosphere blocks out much harmful ultraviolet solar radiation, and insulates the Earth against extremes of temperature by limiting both incoming solar radiation and the escape of re-radiated heat into space. This natural balance may be distorted by the greenhouse effect, as gases such as carbon dioxide have built up in the atmosphere, trapping more heat. Close to the Earth's surface, differences in air temperature and pressure cause air to circulate between the equator and poles. This circulation, together with the Coriolis force, gives rise to the prevailing surface winds and the high-level jet streams.

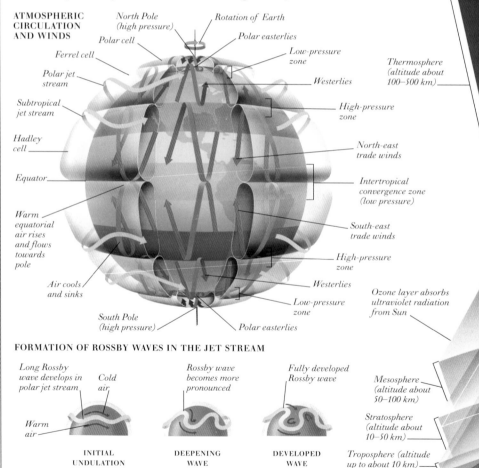

ATMOSPHERIC CIRCULATION AND WINDS

- North Pole (high pressure)
- Rotation of Earth
- Polar cell
- Polar easterlies
- Ferrel cell
- Low-pressure zone
- Polar jet stream
- Westerlies
- Subtropical jet stream
- High-pressure zone
- Hadley cell
- North-east trade winds
- Equator
- Intertropical convergence zone (low pressure)
- Warm equatorial air rises and flows towards pole
- South-east trade winds
- High-pressure zone
- Air cools and sinks
- Westerlies
- South Pole (high pressure)
- Low-pressure zone
- Polar easterlies

Exosphere (altitude above about 500 km)

Corona

Thermosphere (altitude about 100–500 km)

Ozone layer absorbs ultraviolet radiation from Sun

FORMATION OF ROSSBY WAVES IN THE JET STREAM

Long Rossby wave develops in polar jet stream

Cold air

Rossby wave becomes more pronounced

Fully developed Rossby wave

Warm air

| INITIAL UNDULATION | DEEPENING WAVE | DEVELOPED WAVE |

Mesosphere (altitude about 50–100 km)

Stratosphere (altitude about 10–50 km)

Troposphere (altitude up to about 10 km)

STRUCTURE OF THE ATMOSPHERE

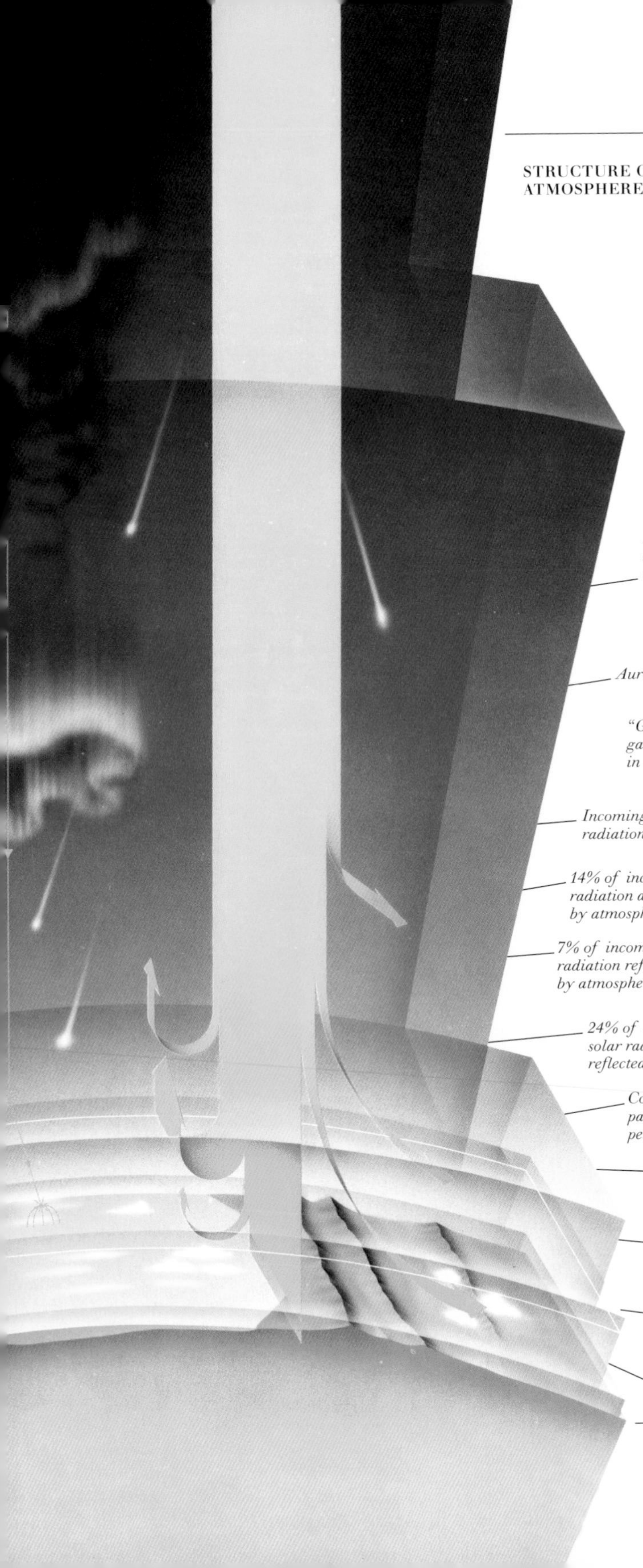

GLOBAL WARMING

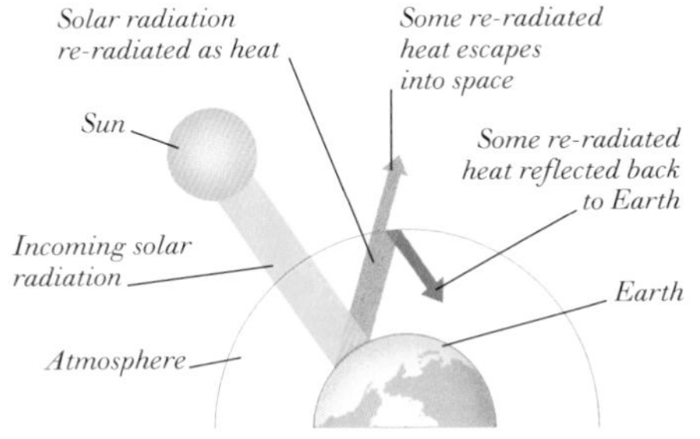

Solar radiation re-radiated as heat

Some re-radiated heat escapes into space

Sun

Some re-radiated heat reflected back to Earth

Incoming solar radiation

Earth

Atmosphere

NATURALLY MODERATED GREENHOUSE EFFECT

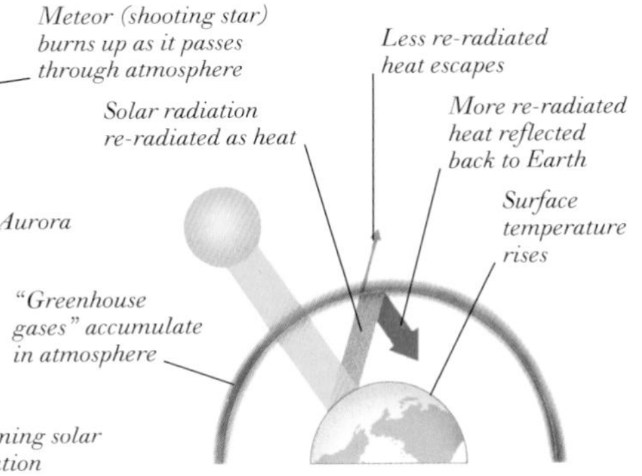

Meteor (shooting star) burns up as it passes through atmosphere

Less re-radiated heat escapes

Solar radiation re-radiated as heat

More re-radiated heat reflected back to Earth

Aurora

Surface temperature rises

"Greenhouse gases" accumulate in atmosphere

Incoming solar radiation

UNBALANCED GREENHOUSE EFFECT

14% of incoming solar radiation absorbed by atmosphere

7% of incoming solar radiation reflected by atmosphere

COMPOSITION OF THE LOWER ATMOSPHERE

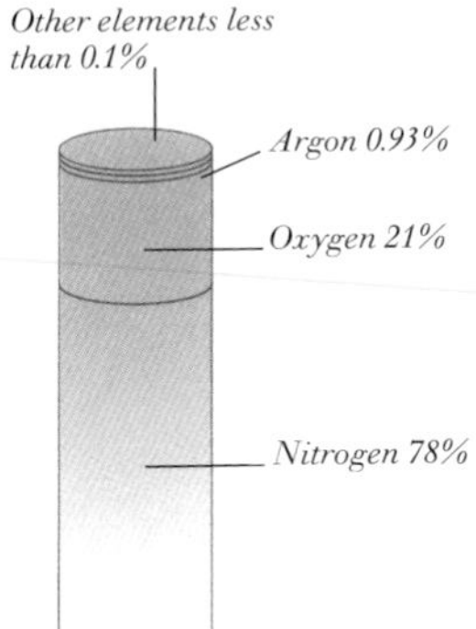

Other elements less than 0.1%

24% of incoming solar radiation reflected by clouds

Argon 0.93%

Cosmic rays (high-energy particles from space) penetrate to stratosphere

Oxygen 21%

Some absorbed heat re-radiated by atmosphere

4% of incoming solar radiation reflected by oceans and land

Nitrogen 78%

51% of incoming solar radiation absorbed by Earth's surface

Some absorbed heat re-radiated by clouds

Weather

WEATHER IS DEFINED AS THE ATMOSPHERIC CONDITIONS at a particular time and place; climate is the average weather conditions for a given region over time. Weather is assessed in terms of temperature, wind, cloud cover, and precipitation, such as rain or snow. Fine weather is associated with high-pressure areas, where air is sinking. Cloudy, wet, changeable weather is common in low-pressure zones with rising, unstable air. Such conditions occur at temperate latitudes, where warm air meets cool air along the polar fronts. Here, spiralling low-pressure cells known as depressions (mid-latitude cyclones) often form. A depression usually contains a sector of warmer air, beginning at a warm front and ending at a cold front. If the two fronts merge, forming an occluded front, the warm air is pushed upwards. An extreme form of low-pressure cell is a hurricane (also called a typhoon or tropical cyclone), which brings torrential rain and exceptionally strong winds.

TYPES OF OCCLUDED FRONT

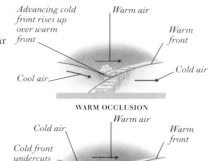

Advancing cold front rises up over warm front

Warm air

Warm front

Cool air

Cold air

WARM OCCLUSION

Cold air

Warm air

Warm front

Cold front undercuts warm front

Cool air

COLD OCCLUSION

FORMS OF PRECIPITATION

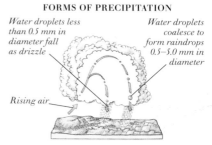

Water droplets less than 0.5 mm in diameter fall as drizzle

Water droplets coalesce to form raindrops 0.5–5.0 mm in diameter

Rising air

RAIN FROM CLOUDS NOT REACHING FREEZING LEVEL

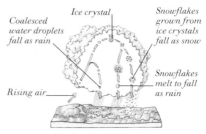

Coalesced water droplets fall as rain

Ice crystal

Snowflakes grown from ice crystals fall as snow

Rising air

Snowflakes melt to fall as rain

RAIN AND SNOW FROM CLOUDS REACHING FREEZING LEVEL

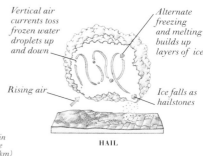

Vertical air currents toss frozen water droplets up and down

Alternate freezing and melting builds up layers of ice

Rising air

Ice falls as hailstones

HAIL

TYPES OF CLOUD

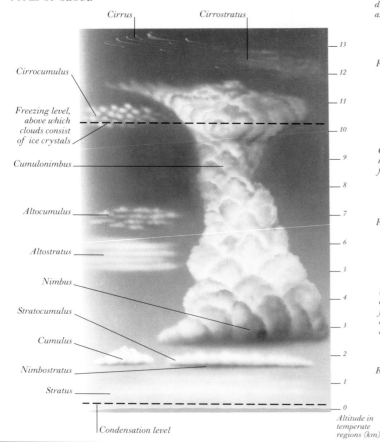

Cirrus

Cirrostratus

Cirrocumulus

Freezing level, above which clouds consist of ice crystals

Cumulonimbus

Altocumulus

Altostratus

Nimbus

Stratocumulus

Cumulus

Nimbostratus

Stratus

Condensation level

13

12

11

10

9

8

7

6

5

4

3

2

1

0

Altitude in temperate regions (km)

STRUCTURE OF A HURRICANE

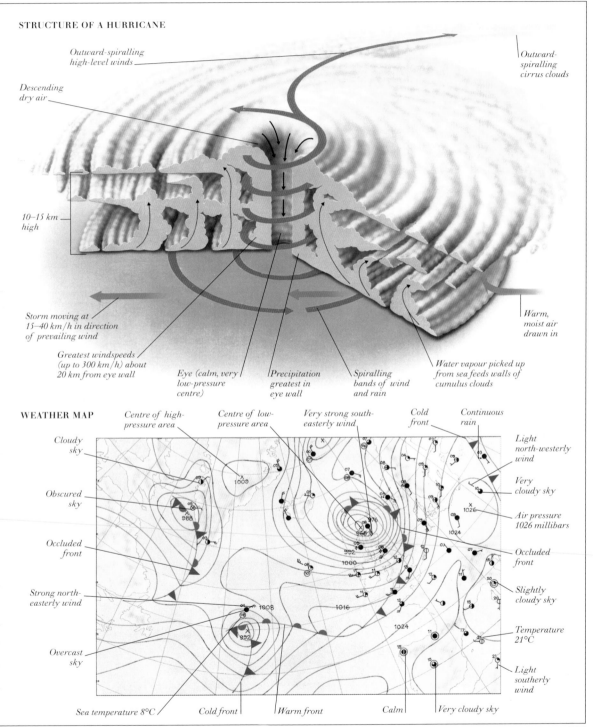

Outward-spiralling
high-level winds

Outward-
spiralling
cirrus clouds

Descending
dry air

10–15 km
high

Storm moving at
15–40 km/h in direction
of prevailing wind

Greatest windspeeds
(up to 300 km/h) about
20 km from eye wall

Eye (calm, very
low-pressure
centre)

Precipitation
greatest in
eye wall

Spiralling
bands of wind
and rain

Water vapour picked up
from sea feeds walls of
cumulus clouds

Warm,
moist air
drawn in

WEATHER MAP

Centre of high-
pressure area

Centre of low-
pressure area

Very strong south-
easterly wind

Cold
front

Continuous
rain

Cloudy
sky

Light
north-westerly
wind

Obscured
sky

Very
cloudy sky

Occluded
front

Air pressure
1026 millibars

Strong north-
easterly wind

Occluded
front

Slightly
cloudy sky

Overcast
sky

Temperature
21°C

Light
southerly
wind

Sea temperature 8°C

Cold front

Warm front

Calm

Very cloudy sky

303

PHYSICS AND CHEMISTRY

The variety of matter

PLANT AND INSECT
(LIVING MATTER)

MATTER IS ANYTHING THAT HAS A MASS. It includes everything from natural substances, such as minerals or living organisms, to synthetic materials. Matter can exist in three distinct states – solid, liquid, and gas. A solid is rigid and retains its shape. A liquid is fluid, has a definite volume, and will take the shape of its container. A gas (also fluid) fills a space, so its volume will be the same as the volume of its container. Most substances can exist as a solid, a liquid, or a gas: the state is determined by temperature. At very high temperatures, matter becomes plasma, often considered to be a fourth state of matter. All matter is composed of microscopic particles, such as atoms and molecules (see pp. 308-309). The arrangement and interactions of these particles give a substance its physical and chemical properties, by which matter can be identified. There is a huge variety of matter because particles can arrange themselves in countless ways, in one substance or by mixing with others. Natural glass, for example, seems to be a solid but is, in fact, a supercool liquid: the atoms are not locked into a pattern and can flow. Pure substances known as elements (see p. 310) combine to form compounds or mixtures. Mixtures called colloids are made up of larger particles of matter suspended in a solid, liquid, or gas, while a solution is one substance dissolved in another.

TYPES OF COLLOID

HAIR GEL (SOLID IN LIQUID)

SHAVING FOAM
(AIR IN LIQUID)

MIST
(LIQUID IN GAS)

EXAMPLES OF MATTER

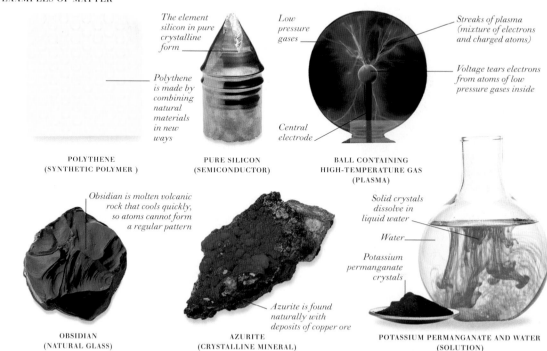

The element silicon in pure crystalline form

Polythene is made by combining natural materials in new ways

Low pressure gases

Streaks of plasma (mixture of electrons and charged atoms)

Voltage tears electrons from atoms of low pressure gases inside

Central electrode

POLYTHENE
(SYNTHETIC POLYMER)

PURE SILICON
(SEMICONDUCTOR)

BALL CONTAINING
HIGH-TEMPERATURE GAS
(PLASMA)

Obsidian is molten volcanic rock that cools quickly, so atoms cannot form a regular pattern

Solid crystals dissolve in liquid water

Water

Potassium permanganate crystals

Azurite is found naturally with deposits of copper ore

OBSIDIAN
(NATURAL GLASS)

AZURITE
(CRYSTALLINE MINERAL)

POTASSIUM PERMANGANATE AND WATER
(SOLUTION)

STATES OF MATTER

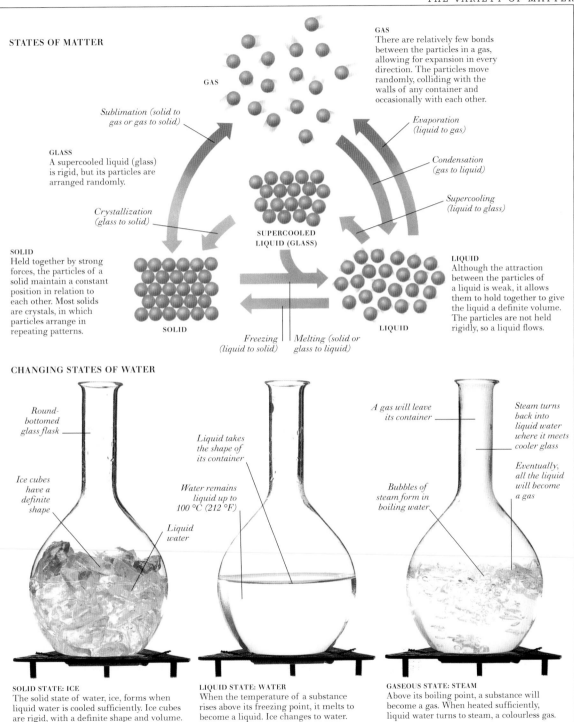

GAS

GAS
There are relatively few bonds between the particles in a gas, allowing for expansion in every direction. The particles move randomly, colliding with the walls of any container and occasionally with each other.

Sublimation (solid to gas or gas to solid)

Evaporation (liquid to gas)

Condensation (gas to liquid)

GLASS
A supercooled liquid (glass) is rigid, but its particles are arranged randomly.

Supercooling (liquid to glass)

Crystallization (glass to solid)

SUPERCOOLED LIQUID (GLASS)

SOLID
Held together by strong forces, the particles of a solid maintain a constant position in relation to each other. Most solids are crystals, in which particles arrange in repeating patterns.

LIQUID
Although the attraction between the particles of a liquid is weak, it allows them to hold together to give the liquid a definite volume. The particles are not held rigidly, so a liquid flows.

SOLID

LIQUID

Freezing (liquid to solid) *Melting (solid or glass to liquid)*

CHANGING STATES OF WATER

Round-bottomed glass flask

Ice cubes have a definite shape

Liquid takes the shape of its container

Water remains liquid up to 100 °C (212 °F)

Liquid water

A gas will leave its container

Steam turns back into liquid water where it meets cooler glass

Bubbles of steam form in boiling water

Eventually, all the liquid will become a gas

SOLID STATE: ICE
The solid state of water, ice, forms when liquid water is cooled sufficiently. Ice cubes are rigid, with a definite shape and volume.

LIQUID STATE: WATER
When the temperature of a substance rises above its freezing point, it melts to become a liquid. Ice changes to water.

GASEOUS STATE: STEAM
Above its boiling point, a substance will become a gas. When heated sufficiently, liquid water turns to steam, a colourless gas.

Atoms and molecules

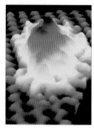

FALSE-COLOUR
IMAGE OF ACTUAL
GOLD ATOMS

ATOMS ARE THE smallest individual parts of an element (see pp. 310-311). They are tiny, with diameters in the order of one ten-thousand-millionth of a metre (10^{-10} m). Two or more atoms join together (bond) to form a molecule of a substance known as a compound. For example, when atoms of the elements hydrogen and fluorine join together, they form a molecule of the compound hydrogen fluoride. So molecules are the smallest individual parts of a compound. Atoms themselves are not indivisible – they possess an internal structure. At their centre is a dense nucleus, consisting of protons, which have a positive electric charge (see p. 316), and neutrons, which are uncharged. Around the nucleus are the negatively charged electrons. It is the electrons that give a substance most of its physical and chemical properties. They do not follow definite paths around the nucleus. Instead, electrons are said to be found within certain regions, called orbitals. These are arranged around the nucleus in "shells", each containing electrons of a particular energy. For example, the first shell (1) can hold up to two electrons, in a so-called s-orbital (1s). The second shell (2) can hold up to eight electrons, in s-orbitals (2s) and p-orbitals (2p). If an atom loses an electron, it becomes a positive ion (cation). If an electron is gained, an atom becomes a negative ion (anion). Ions of opposite charges will attract and join together, in a type of bonding known as ionic bonding. In covalent bonding, the atoms bond by sharing their electrons in what become molecular orbitals.

ATOMIC ORBITALS

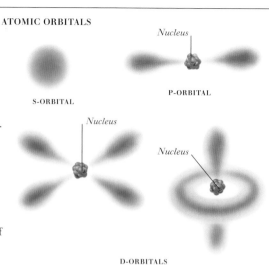

S-ORBITAL

P-ORBITAL

Nucleus

Nucleus

Nucleus

Nucleus

D-ORBITALS

MOLECULAR ORBITALS

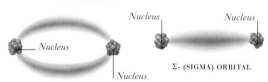

Nucleus

Nucleus

Nucleus

Nucleus

Σ- (SIGMA) ORBITAL

π- (PI) ORBITAL

Nucleus

SP³-HYBRID ORBITAL

EXAMPLE OF IONIC BONDING

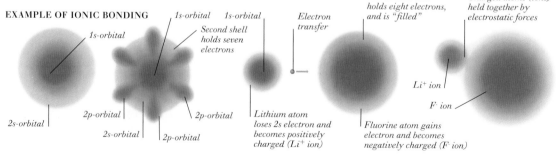

1s-orbital

1s-orbital

Second shell holds seven electrons

1s-orbital

Electron transfer

Second shell now holds eight electrons, and is "filled"

Charged atoms (ions) held together by electrostatic forces

2s-orbital

2p-orbital

2s-orbital

2p-orbital

2p-orbital

Lithium atom loses 2s electron and becomes positively charged (Li^+ ion)

Fluorine atom gains electron and becomes negatively charged (F^- ion)

Li^+ ion

F^- ion

1. NEUTRAL LITHIUM ATOM (Li)

NEUTRAL FLUORINE ATOM (F)

2. ELECTRON TRANSFER

3. IONIC BONDING: LITHIUM FLUORIDE MOLECULE (LiF)

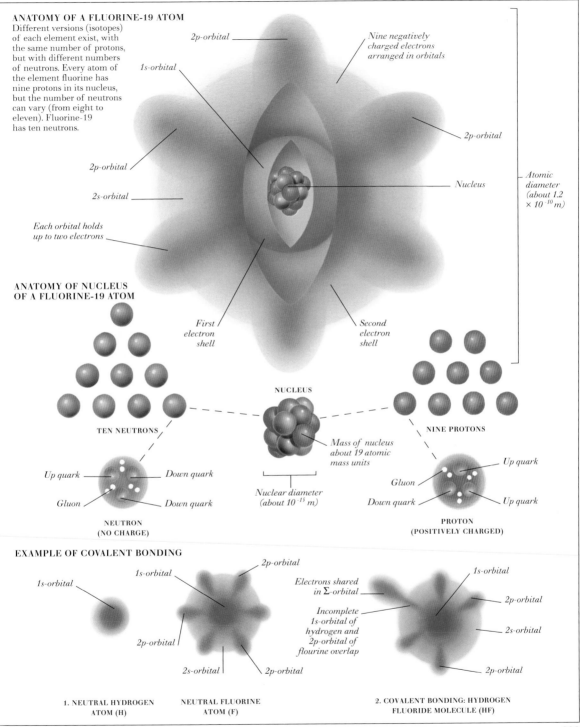

ANATOMY OF A FLUORINE-19 ATOM
Different versions (isotopes) of each element exist, with the same number of protons, but with different numbers of neutrons. Every atom of the element fluorine has nine protons in its nucleus, but the number of neutrons can vary (from eight to eleven). Fluorine-19 has ten neutrons.

2p-orbital

1s-orbital

2p-orbital

2s-orbital

Each orbital holds up to two electrons

Nine negatively charged electrons arranged in orbitals

2p-orbital

Nucleus

Atomic diameter (about 1.2 $\times 10^{-10}$ m)

First electron shell

Second electron shell

ANATOMY OF NUCLEUS OF A FLUORINE-19 ATOM

NUCLEUS

TEN NEUTRONS

NINE PROTONS

Mass of nucleus about 19 atomic mass units

Up quark

Down quark

Gluon

Down quark

Nuclear diameter (about 10^{-15} m)

Gluon

Down quark

Up quark

Up quark

NEUTRON (NO CHARGE)

PROTON (POSITIVELY CHARGED)

EXAMPLE OF COVALENT BONDING

1s-orbital

1s-orbital

2p-orbital

2p-orbital

2s-orbital

2p-orbital

Electrons shared in Σ-orbital

Incomplete 1s-orbital of hydrogen and 2p-orbital of fluorine overlap

1s-orbital

2p-orbital

2s-orbital

2p-orbital

1. NEUTRAL HYDROGEN ATOM (H)

NEUTRAL FLUORINE ATOM (F)

2. COVALENT BONDING: HYDROGEN FLUORIDE MOLECULE (HF)

309

The periodic table

AN ELEMENT is a substance that consists of atoms of one type only. The 92 elements that occur naturally, and the 17 elements created artificially, are often arranged into a chart called the periodic table. Each element is defined by its atomic number – the number of protons in the nucleus of each of its atoms (it is also the number of electrons present). Atomic number increases along each row (period) and down each column (group). The shape of the table is determined by the way in which electrons arrange themselves around the nucleus: the positioning of elements in order of increasing atomic number brings together atoms with a similar pattern of orbiting electrons (orbitals). These appear in blocks. Electrons occupy shells of a certain energy (see pp. 308-309). Periods are ordered according to the filling of successive shells with electrons, while groups reflect the number of electrons in the outer shell (valency electrons). These outer electrons are important – they decide the chemical properties of the atom. Elements that appear in the same group have similar properties because they have the same number of electrons in their outer shell. Elements in Group 0 have "filled shells", where the outer shell holds its maximum number of electrons, and are stable. Atoms of Group I elements have just one electron in their outer shell. This makes them unstable – and ready to react with other substances.

METALS AND NON-METALS

Elements at the left-hand side of each period are metals. Metals easily lose electrons and form positive ions. Non-metals, on the right of a period, tend to become negative ions. Semi-metals, which have properties of both metals and non-metals, are between the two.

TYPES OF ELEMENT KEY:

- Alkali metals
- Alkaline earth metals
- Transition metals
- Lanthanides
- Actinides
- Poor metals
- Semi-metals
- Non-metals
- Noble gases
- Unknown chemical properties

RELATIVE ATOMIC MASS
Atomic mass (formerly atomic weight) is the mass of each atom of an element. It is equal to the number of protons plus the number of neutrons (electrons have negligible mass). The figures given are the averages for all the different versions (isotopes) of each element, measured relative to the mass of carbon-12.

Atomic number
Chemical symbol
Chemical name
Relative atomic mass

1
H
Hydrogen
1.0

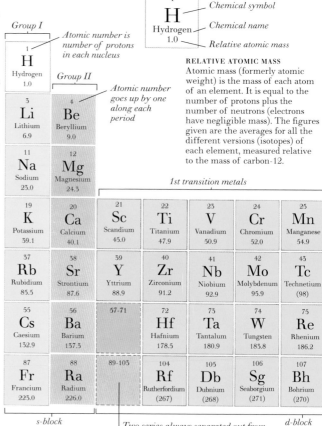

Atomic number is number of protons in each nucleus

Atomic number goes up by one along each period

Group I

1
H
Hydrogen
1.0

Group II

1st transition metals

Group I	Group II					
1 H Hydrogen 1.0						
3 Li Lithium 6.9	4 Be Beryllium 9.0					
11 Na Sodium 23.0	12 Mg Magnesium 24.3					
19 K Potassium 39.1	20 Ca Calcium 40.1	21 Sc Scandium 45.0	22 Ti Titanium 47.9	23 V Vanadium 50.9	24 Cr Chromium 52.0	25 Mn Manganese 54.9
37 Rb Rubidium 85.5	38 Sr Strontium 87.6	39 Y Yttrium 88.9	40 Zr Zirconium 91.2	41 Nb Niobium 92.9	42 Mo Molybdenum 95.9	43 Tc Technetium (98)
55 Cs Caesium 132.9	56 Ba Barium 137.3	57-71	72 Hf Hafnium 178.5	73 Ta Tantalum 180.9	74 W Tungsten 183.8	75 Re Rhenium 186.2
87 Fr Francium 223.0	88 Ra Radium 226.0	89-103	104 Rf Rutherfordium (267)	105 Db Dubnium (268)	106 Sg Seaborgium (271)	107 Bh Bohrium (270)

s-block

d-block

Two series always separated out from the table to give it a coherent shape

Soft, silvery, and highly reactive metal

SODIUM: GROUP 1 METAL

Silvery, reactive metal

MAGNESIUM: GROUP 2 METAL

Hard, silvery metal

CHROMIUM: 1ST TRANSITION METAL

Radioactive metal

PLUTONIUM: ACTINIDE SERIES METAL

57 La Lanthanum 138.9	58 Ce Cerium 140.1	59 Pr Praseodymium 140.9	60 Nd Neodymium 144.2
89 Ac Actinium (227)	90 Th Thorium 232.0	91 Pa Protactinium 231.0	92 U Uranium 238.0

Bright yellow crystal

Purple-black solid turns to gas easily

**IODINE:
GROUP 7
SOLID NON-
METAL**

**SULPHUR:
GROUP 6 SOLID NON-METAL**

DIAMOND

ALLOTROPES OF CARBON
Some elements exist in more than one form — these are known as allotropes. Carbon powder, graphite, and diamond are allotropes of carbon. They all consist of carbon atoms, but have very different physical properties.

GRAPHITE

CARBON POWDER

Group 0

Period

Short period

Long period

	Boron and carbon groups		*Nitrogen and oxygen groups*		*Halogens*	
	Group III	*Group IV*	*Group V*	*Group VI*	*Group VII*	2 **He** Helium 4.0
	5 **B** Boron 10.8	6 **C** Carbon 12.0	7 **N** Nitrogen 14.0	8 **O** Oxygen 16.0	9 **F** Fluorine 19.0	10 **Ne** Neon 20.2
	13 **Al** Aluminium 27.0	14 **Si** Silicon 28.1	15 **P** Phosphorus 31.0	16 **S** Sulphur 32.1	17 **Cl** Chlorine 35.5	18 **Ar** Argon 40.0

2nd transition metals *3rd transition metals*

26 **Fe** Iron 55.8	27 **Co** Cobalt 58.9	28 **Ni** Nickel 58.7	29 **Cu** Copper 63.5	30 **Zn** Zinc 65.4	31 **Ga** Gallium 69.7	32 **Ge** Germanium 72.6	33 **As** Arsenic 74.9	34 **Se** Selenium 79.0	35 **Br** Bromine 79.9	36 **Kr** Krypton 85.8
44 **Ru** Ruthenium 101.1	45 **Rh** Rhodium 102.9	46 **Pd** Palladium 106.4	47 **Ag** Silver 107.9	48 **Cd** Cadmium 112.4	49 **In** Indium 114.8	50 **Sn** Tin 118.7	51 **Sb** Antimony 121.8	52 **Te** Tellurium 127.6	53 **I** Iodine 126.9	54 **Xe** Xenon 131.5
76 **Os** Osmium 190.2	77 **Ir** Iridium 192.2	78 **Pt** Platinum 195.1	79 **Au** Gold 197.0	80 **Hg** Mercury 200.6	81 **Tl** Thallium 204.4	82 **Pb** Lead 207.2	83 **Bi** Bismuth 209.0	84 **Po** Polonium (209)	85 **At** Astatine (210)	86 **Rn** Radon (222)
108 **Hs** Hassium (269)	109 **Mt** Meitnerium (278)	110 **Ds** Darmstadtium (281)	111 **Rg** Roentgenium (281)	112 **Cn** Copernicium (285)	115 **Uut** Ununtrium (286)	114 **Uuq** Ununquadium (289)	115 **Uup** Ununpentium (289)	116 **Uuh** Ununhexium (293)	117 **Uus** Ununseptium (294)	118 **Uuo** Ununoctium (294)

d-block *p-block*

Unreactive, colourless gas glows red in discharge tube

Yellow, unreactive precious metal

Soft, shiny, reactive metal

Shiny semi-metal

NOBLE GASES
Group 0 contains elements that have a filled (complete) outer shell of electrons, which means the atoms do not need to lose or gain electrons by bonding with other atoms. This makes them stable and they do not easily form ions or react with other elements. Noble gases are also called rare or inert gases.

**NEON:
GROUP 0
COLOURLESS
GAS**

**GOLD:
3RD TRANSITION METAL**

**TIN:
GROUP 4 POOR METAL**

**ANTIMONY:
GROUP 5 SEMI-METAL**

61 **Pm** Promethium (145)	62 **Sm** Samarium 150.4	63 **Eu** Europium 152.0	64 **Gd** Gadolinium 157.3	65 **Tb** Terbium 158.9	66 **Dy** Dysprosium 162.5	67 **Ho** Holmium 164.9	68 **Er** Erbium 167.3	69 **Tm** Thulium 168.9	70 **Yb** Ytterbium 173.0	71 **Lu** Lutetium 175.0
93 **Np** Neptunium (237)	94 **Pu** Plutonium (244)	95 **Am** Americium (243)	96 **Cm** Curium (247)	97 **Bk** Berkelium (247)	98 **Cf** Californium (251)	99 **Es** Einsteinium (252)	100 **Fm** Fermium (257)	101 **Md** Mendelevium (258)	102 **No** Nobelium (259)	105 **Lr** Lawrencium (262)

f-block

Chemical reactions

A CHEMICAL REACTION TAKES PLACE whenever bonds between atoms are broken or made. In each case, atoms or groups of atoms rearrange, making new substances (products) from the original ones (reactants). Reactions happen naturally, or can be made to happen; they may take years, or only an instant. Some of the main types are shown here. A reaction usually involves a change in energy (see pp. 314-315). In a burning reaction, for example, the making of new bonds between atoms releases energy as heat and light. This type of reaction, in which heat is given off, is an exothermic reaction. Many reactions, like burning, are irreversible, but some can take place in either direction, and are said to be reversible. Reactions can be used to form solids from solutions: in a double decomposition reaction, two compounds in solution break down and re-form into two new substances, often creating a precipitate (insoluble solid); in displacement, an element (eg. copper) displaces another element (eg. silver) from a solution. The rate (speed) of a reaction is determined by many different factors, such as temperature, and the size and shape of the reactants. To describe and keep track of reactions, internationally recognized chemical symbols and equations are used. Reactions are also used in the laboratory to identify matter. An experiment with candle wax, for example, demonstrates that it contains carbon and hydrogen.

SALT FORMATION (ACID ON METAL)

Glass beaker

Hydrogen gas (H_2) given off

Zinc (Zn) replaces hydrogen in acid (HCl) to form zinc chloride solution ($ZnCl_2$)

Hydrogen in acid driven off when acid meets a reactive metal

Zinc metal chippings (Zn)

Hydrochloric acid (HCl)

Effervescence

Zinc metal chippings (Zn)

THE REACTION
Hydrochloric acid added to zinc produces zinc chloride and hydrogen.
$Zn + 2HCl \rightarrow ZnCl_2 + H_2$

DISPLACEMENT

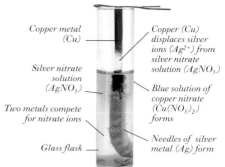

Copper metal (Cu)

Silver nitrate solution ($AgNO_3$)

Two metals compete for nitrate ions

Glass flask

Copper (Cu) displaces silver ions (Ag^{2+}) from silver nitrate solution ($AgNO_3$)

Blue solution of copper nitrate ($Cu(NO_3)_2$) forms

Needles of silver metal (Ag) form

THE REACTION
Copper metal added to silver nitrate solution produces copper nitrate and silver metal.
$Cu + 2AgNO_3 \rightarrow Cu(NO_3)_2 + 2Ag$

BURNING MATTER

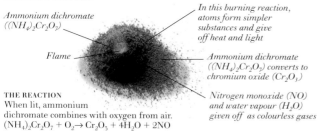

Ammonium dichromate ((NH_4)$_2Cr_2O_7$)

Flame

In this burning reaction, atoms form simpler substances and give off heat and light

Ammonium dichromate ((NH_4)$_2Cr_2O_7$) converts to chromium oxide (Cr_2O_3)

Nitrogen monoxide (NO) and water vapour (H_2O) given off as colourless gases

THE REACTION
When lit, ammonium dichromate combines with oxygen from air.
$(NH_4)_2Cr_2O_7 + O_2 \rightarrow Cr_2O_3 + 4H_2O + 2NO$

A REVERSIBLE REACTION

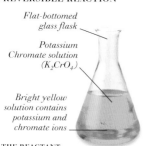

Flat-bottomed glass flask

Potassium Chromate solution (K_2CrO_4)

Bright yellow solution contains potassium and chromate ions

1. THE REACTANT
Potassium chromate dissolves in water to form potassium ions and chromate ions.
$K_2CrO_4 \rightarrow 2K^+ + CrO_4^{2-}$

Pipette

Hydrochloric acid (HCl) added in drops

Acid causes reaction to take place

Chromate ions converted to orange dichromate ions

Potassium dichromate (KCr_2O_7) forms

2. THE REACTION
Addition of hydrochloric acid changes chromate ions into dichromate ions.
$2CrO_4^{2-} \rightarrow Cr_2O_7^{2-}$

Pipette

Sodium hydroxide (NaOH) added in drops

Sodium hydroxide (NaOH) neutralizes the acid

Solution turns to bright orange of potassium dichromate

Solution returns to original bright yellow colour

Potassium dichromate (KCr_2O_7) re-forms to potassium chromate (K_2CrO_4)

3. REVERSING
Addition of sodium hydroxide changes dichromate ions back into chromate ions.
$Cr_2O_7^{2-} \rightarrow 2CrO_4^{2-}$

FERMENTATION

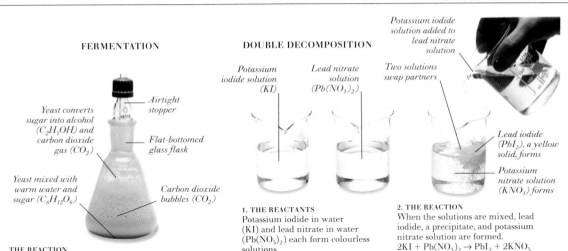

Yeast converts sugar into alcohol (C$_2$H$_5$OH) and carbon dioxide gas (CO$_2$)

Airtight stopper

Flat-bottomed glass flask

Yeast mixed with warm water and sugar (C$_6$H$_{12}$O$_6$)

Carbon dioxide bubbles (CO$_2$)

THE REACTION
Yeast converts sugar and warm water into alcohol and carbon dioxide.
C$_6$H$_{12}$O$_6$ → 2C$_2$H$_5$OH + 2CO$_2$

DOUBLE DECOMPOSITION

Potassium iodide solution (KI)

Lead nitrate solution (Pb(NO$_3$)$_2$)

Two solutions swap partners

Potassium iodide solution added to lead nitrate solution

Lead iodide (PbI$_2$), a yellow solid, forms

Potassium nitrate solution (KNO$_3$) forms

1. THE REACTANTS
Potassium iodide in water (KI) and lead nitrate in water (Pb(NO$_3$)$_2$) each form colourless solutions.

2. THE REACTION
When the solutions are mixed, lead iodide, a precipitate, and potassium nitrate solution are formed.
2KI + Pb(NO$_3$)$_2$ → PbI$_2$ + 2KNO$_3$

TESTING CANDLE WAX, AN ORGANIC COMPOUND

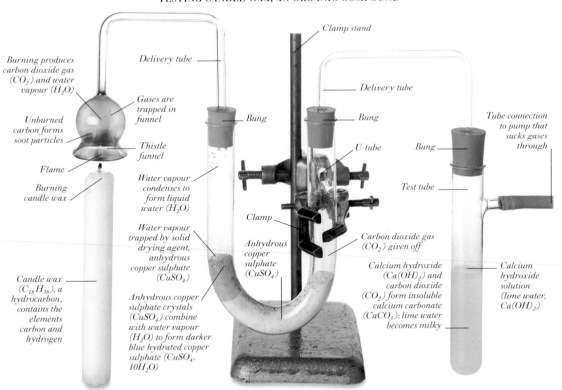

Clamp stand

Burning produces carbon dioxide gas (CO$_2$) and water vapour (H$_2$O)

Delivery tube

Gases are trapped in funnel

Unburned carbon forms soot particles

Thistle funnel

Flame

Burning candle wax

Bung

Delivery tube

Bung

U-tube

Bung

Tube connection to pump that sucks gases through

Test tube

Water vapour condenses to form liquid water (H$_2$O)

Clamp

Carbon dioxide gas (CO$_2$) given off

Calcium hydroxide solution (lime water, Ca(OH)$_2$)

Candle wax (C$_{18}$H$_{38}$), a hydrocarbon, contains the elements carbon and hydrogen

Water vapour trapped by solid drying agent, anhydrous copper sulphate (CuSO$_4$)

Anhydrous copper sulphate (CuSO$_4$)

Anhydrous copper sulphate crystals (CuSO$_4$) combine with water vapour (H$_2$O) to form darker blue hydrated copper sulphate (CuSO$_4$. 10H$_2$O)

Calcium hydroxide (Ca(OH)$_2$) and carbon dioxide (CO$_2$) form insoluble calcium carbonate (CaCO$_3$): lime water becomes milky

Calcium hydroxide solution (lime water, Ca(OH)$_2$)

1. THE BURNING REACTION
Burning wax produces carbon dioxide gas and water vapour.
2C$_{18}$H$_{38}$ + 55O$_2$ → 36CO$_2$ + 38H$_2$O

2. TESTING FOR WATER VAPOUR
A solid drying agent traps water vapour, proving the presence of hydrogen in the candle wax.
CuSO$_4$ + 10H$_2$O → CuSO$_4$. 10H$_2$O

3. TESTING FOR CARBON DIOXIDE
Calcium hydroxide in solution reacts with carbon dioxide, forming a carbonate and turning milky.
Ca(OH)$_2$ + CO$_2$ → CaCO$_3$ + H$_2$O

Energy

Anything that happens – from a pin-drop to an explosion – requires energy. Energy is the capacity for "doing work" (making something happen). Various forms of energy exist, including light, heat, sound, electrical, chemical, nuclear, kinetic, and potential energies. The Law of Conservation of Energy states that the total amount of energy in the Universe is fixed – energy cannot be created or destroyed. It means that energy can only change from one form to another (energy transfer). For example, potential energy is energy that is "stored", and can be used in the future. An object gains potential energy when it is lifted; as the object is released, potential energy changes into the energy of motion (kinetic energy). During transference, some of the energy converts into heat. A combined heat and power station can put some of the otherwise "waste" heat to useful effect in local schools and housing. Most of the Earth's energy is provided by the Sun, in the form of electromagnetic radiation (see pp. 316-317). Some of this energy transfers to plant and animal life, and ultimately to fossil fuels, where it is stored in chemical form. Our bodies obtain energy from the food we eat, while energy needed for other tasks, such as heating and transport, can be obtained by burning fossil fuels – or by harnessing natural forces like wind or moving water – to generate electricity. Another source is nuclear power, where energy is released by reactions in the nucleus of an atom. All energy is measured by the international unit, the joule (J). As a guide, one joule is about equal to the amount of energy needed to lift an apple one metre.

SANKEY DIAGRAM SHOWING ENERGY FLOW IN A COAL-FIRED COMBINED HEAT AND POWER STATION

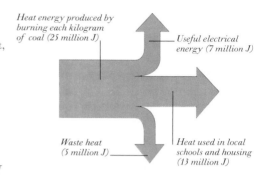

Heat energy produced by burning each kilogram of coal (25 million J)

Useful electrical energy (7 million J)

Waste heat (5 million J)

Heat used in local schools and housing (13 million J)

CROSS-SECTION OF HYDROELECTRIC POWER STATION WITH FRANCIS TURBINE

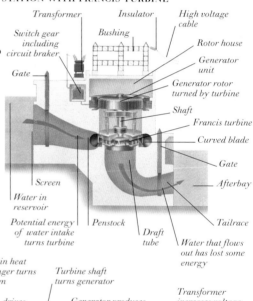

Transformer

Insulator

High voltage cable

Switch gear including circuit braker

Bushing

Rotor house

Generator unit

Gate

Generator rotor turned by turbine

Shaft

Francis turbine

Curved blade

Gate

Afterbay

Screen

Water in reservoir

Potential energy of water intake turns turbine

Penstock

Draft tube

Tailrace

Water that flows out has lost some energy

CROSS-SECTION OF NUCLEAR POWER STATION WITH PRESSURIZED WATER REACTOR

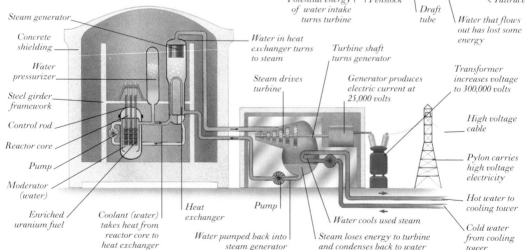

Steam generator

Concrete shielding

Water pressurizer

Steel girder framework

Control rod

Reactor core

Pump

Moderator (water)

Enriched uranium fuel

Coolant (water) takes heat from reactor core to heat exchanger

Heat exchanger

Water pumped back into steam generator

Water in heat exchanger turns to steam

Steam drives turbine

Turbine shaft turns generator

Pump

Water cools used steam

Steam loses energy to turbine and condenses back to water

Generator produces electric current at 25,000 volts

Transformer increases voltage to 300,000 volts

High voltage cable

Pylon carries high voltage electricity

Hot water to cooling tower

Cold water from cooling tower

ENERGY SYSTEMS

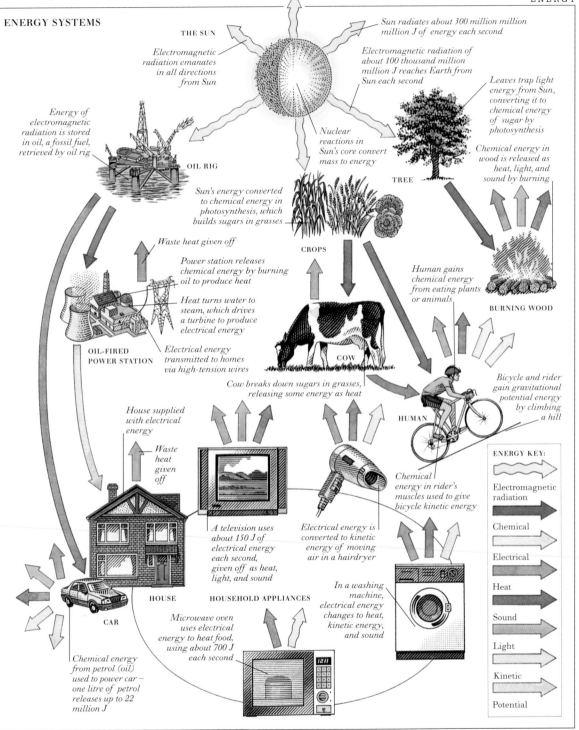

THE SUN

Sun radiates about 300 million million million J of energy each second

Electromagnetic radiation emanates in all directions from Sun

Electromagnetic radiation of about 100 thousand million million J reaches Earth from Sun each second

Leaves trap light energy from Sun, converting it to chemical energy of sugar by photosynthesis

Energy of electromagnetic radiation is stored in oil, a fossil fuel, retrieved by oil rig

Nuclear reactions in Sun's core convert mass to energy

Chemical energy in wood is released as heat, light, and sound by burning

OIL RIG

TREE

Sun's energy converted to chemical energy in photosynthesis, which builds sugars in grasses

CROPS

Waste heat given off

Power station releases chemical energy by burning oil to produce heat

Human gains chemical energy from eating plants or animals

BURNING WOOD

Heat turns water to steam, which drives a turbine to produce electrical energy

OIL-FIRED POWER STATION

Electrical energy transmitted to homes via high-tension wires

Cow breaks down sugars in grasses, releasing some energy as heat

COW

Bicycle and rider gain gravitational potential energy by climbing a hill

HUMAN

House supplied with electrical energy

Waste heat given off

Chemical energy in rider's muscles used to give bicycle kinetic energy

A television uses about 150 J of electrical energy each second, given off as heat, light, and sound

Electrical energy is converted to kinetic energy of moving air in a hairdryer

ENERGY KEY:

Electromagnetic radiation

Chemical

Electrical

In a washing machine, electrical energy changes to heat, kinetic energy, and sound

Heat

HOUSE

HOUSEHOLD APPLIANCES

Sound

CAR

Microwave oven uses electrical energy to heat food, using about 700 J each second

Light

Kinetic

Chemical energy from petrol (oil) used to power car – one litre of petrol releases up to 22 million J

Potential

Electricity and magnetism

ELECTRICAL EFFECTS result from an imbalance of electric charge. There are two types of electric charge, named positive (carried by protons) and negative (carried by electrons). If charges are opposite (unlike), they attract one another, while like charges repel. Forces of attraction and repulsion (electrostatic forces) exist between any two charged particles. Matter is normally uncharged, but if electrons are gained, an object will gain an overall negative charge; if they are removed, it becomes positive. Objects with an overall negative or positive charge are said to have an imbalance of charge, and exert the same forces as individual negative and positive charges. On this larger scale, the forces will always act to regain the balance of charge. This causes static electricity. Lightning, for example, is produced by clouds discharging a huge excess of negative electrons. If charges are "free" – in a wire or material that allows electrons to pass through it – the forces cause a flow of charge called an electric current. Some substances exhibit the strange phenomenon of magnetism – which also produces attractive and repulsive forces. Magnetic substances consist of small regions called domains. Normally unmagnetized, they can be magnetized by being placed in a magnetic field. Magnetism and electricity are inextricably linked, a fact put to use in motors and generators.

LIGHTNING

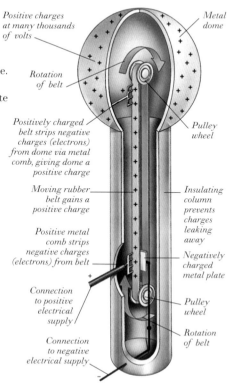

Positive charges at many thousands of volts

Metal dome

Rotation of belt

Positively charged belt strips negative charges (electrons) from dome via metal comb, giving dome a positive charge

Pulley wheel

Moving rubber belt gains a positive charge

Insulating column prevents charges leaking away

Positive metal comb strips negative charges (electrons) from belt

Negatively charged metal plate

Connection to positive electrical supply

Pulley wheel

Rotation of belt

Connection to negative electrical supply

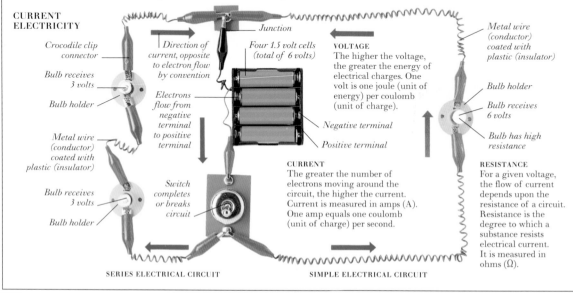

CURRENT ELECTRICITY

Crocodile clip connector

Bulb receives 3 volts

Bulb holder

Metal wire (conductor) coated with plastic (insulator)

Bulb receives 3 volts

Bulb holder

Direction of current, opposite to electron flow by convention

Electrons flow from negative terminal to positive terminal

Switch completes or breaks circuit

Junction

Four 1.5 volt cells (total of 6 volts)

Negative terminal

Positive terminal

VOLTAGE
The higher the voltage, the greater the energy of electrical charges. One volt is one joule (unit of energy) per coulomb (unit of charge).

CURRENT
The greater the number of electrons moving around the circuit, the higher the current. Current is measured in amps (A). One amp equals one coulomb (unit of charge) per second.

Metal wire (conductor) coated with plastic (insulator)

Bulb holder

Bulb receives 6 volts

Bulb has high resistance

RESISTANCE
For a given voltage, the flow of current depends upon the resistance of a circuit. Resistance is the degree to which a substance resists electrical current. It is measured in ohms (Ω).

SERIES ELECTRICAL CIRCUIT

SIMPLE ELECTRICAL CIRCUIT

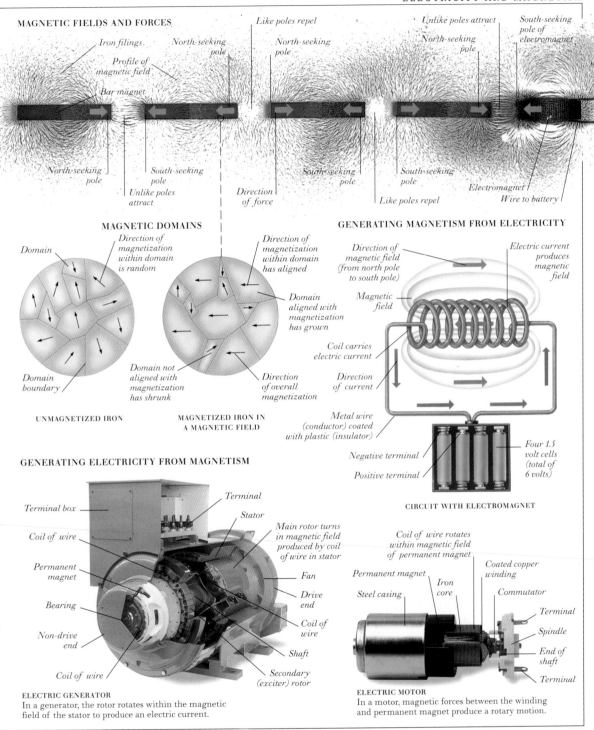

MAGNETIC FIELDS AND FORCES

Iron filings

Profile of magnetic field

Bar magnet

North-seeking pole

North-seeking pole

Like poles repel

North-seeking pole

Unlike poles attract

North-seeking pole

South-seeking pole of electromagnet

North-seeking pole

South-seeking pole

Unlike poles attract

South-seeking pole

Direction of force

South-seeking pole

Like poles repel

South-seeking pole

Like poles repel

Electromagnet

Wire to battery

MAGNETIC DOMAINS

Domain

Direction of magnetization within domain is random

Domain boundary

UNMAGNETIZED IRON

Direction of magnetization within domain has aligned

Domain aligned with magnetization has grown

Domain not aligned with magnetization has shrunk

Direction of overall magnetization

MAGNETIZED IRON IN A MAGNETIC FIELD

GENERATING MAGNETISM FROM ELECTRICITY

Direction of magnetic field (from north pole to south pole)

Electric current produces magnetic field

Magnetic field

Coil carries electric current

Direction of current

Metal wire (conductor) coated with plastic (insulator)

Negative terminal

Positive terminal

Four 1.5 volt cells (total of 6 volts)

CIRCUIT WITH ELECTROMAGNET

GENERATING ELECTRICITY FROM MAGNETISM

Terminal box

Coil of wire

Permanent magnet

Bearing

Non-drive end

Coil of wire

Terminal

Stator

Main rotor turns in magnetic field produced by coil of wire in stator

Fan

Drive end

Coil of wire

Shaft

Secondary (exciter) rotor

ELECTRIC GENERATOR
In a generator, the rotor rotates within the magnetic field of the stator to produce an electric current.

Coil of wire rotates within magnetic field of permanent magnet

Permanent magnet

Steel casing

Iron core

Coated copper winding

Commutator

Terminal

Spindle

End of shaft

Terminal

ELECTRIC MOTOR
In a motor, magnetic forces between the winding and permanent magnet produce a rotary motion.

317

Light

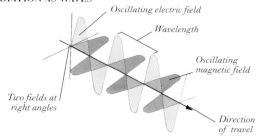

INFRA-RED IMAGE OF A HOUSE

LIGHT IS A FORM OF ENERGY. It is a type of electromagnetic radiation, like X-rays or radio waves. All electromagnetic radiation is produced by electric charges (see pp. 316-317): it is caused by the effects of oscillating electric and magnetic fields as they travel through space. Electromagnetic radiation is considered to have both wave and particle properties. It can be thought of as a wave of electricity and magnetism. In that case, the difference between the various forms of radiation is their wavelength. Radiation can also be said to consist of particles, or packets of energy, called photons. The difference between light and X-rays, for instance, is the amount of energy that each photon carries. The complete range of radiation is referred to as the electromagnetic spectrum, extending from low energy, long wavelength radio waves to high energy, short wavelength gamma rays. Light is the only part of the electromagnetic spectrum that is visible. White light from the Sun is made up of all the visible wavelengths of radiation, which can be seen when it is separated by using a prism. Light, like all forms of electromagnetic radiation, can be reflected (bounced back) and refracted (bent). Different parts of the electromagnetic spectrum are produced in different ways. Sometimes visible light – and infra-red radiation – is generated by the vibrating particles of warm or hot objects. The emission of light in this way is called incandescence. Light can also be produced by fluorescence, a phenomenon in which electrons gain and lose energy within atoms.

MAXWELLIAN DIAGRAM OF ELECTROMAGNETIC RADIATION AS WAVES

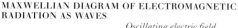

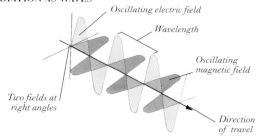

Oscillating electric field

Wavelength

Oscillating magnetic field

Two fields at right angles

Direction of travel

ELECTROMAGNETIC RADIATION AS PARTICLES

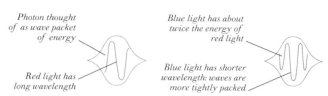

Photon thought of as wave packet of energy

Blue light has about twice the energy of red light

Red light has long wavelength

Blue light has shorter wavelength: waves are more tightly packed

PHOTON OF RED LIGHT

PHOTON OF BLUE LIGHT

SPLITTING WHITE LIGHT INTO THE SPECTRUM

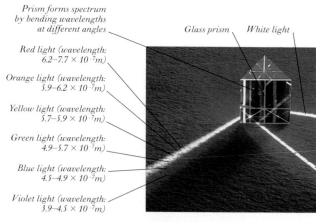

Prism forms spectrum by bending wavelengths at different angles

Glass prism   *White light*

Red light (wavelength: $6.2–7.7 \times 10^{-7}$ m)

Orange light (wavelength: $5.9–6.2 \times 10^{-7}$ m)

Yellow light (wavelength: $5.7–5.9 \times 10^{-7}$ m)

Green light (wavelength: $4.9–5.7 \times 10^{-7}$ m)

Blue light (wavelength: $4.5–4.9 \times 10^{-7}$ m)

Violet light (wavelength: $3.9–4.5 \times 10^{-7}$ m)

THE ELECTROMAGNETIC SPECTRUM

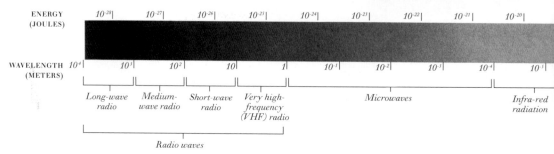

ENERGY (JOULES)	10^{-28}	10^{-27}	10^{-26}	10^{-25}	10^{-24}	10^{-23}	10^{-22}	10^{-21}	10^{-20}

WAVELENGTH (METERS) 10^4 10^3 10^2 10 1 10^{-1} 10^{-2} 10^{-3} 10^{-4} 10^{-5}

Long-wave radio   *Medium-wave radio*   *Short-wave radio*   *Very high-frequency (VHF) radio*   *Microwaves*   *Infra-red radiation*

Radio waves

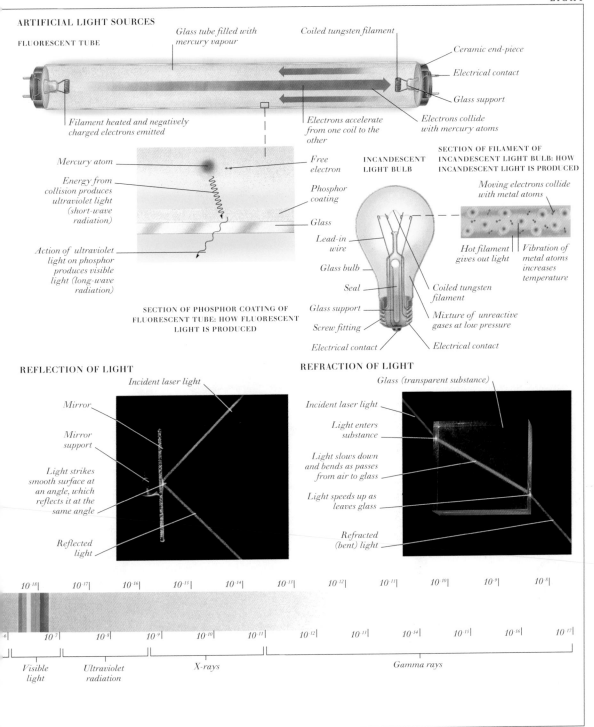

ARTIFICIAL LIGHT SOURCES

FLUORESCENT TUBE

Glass tube filled with mercury vapour

Coiled tungsten filament

Ceramic end-piece

Electrical contact

Glass support

Electrons collide with mercury atoms

Electrons accelerate from one coil to the other

Filament heated and negatively charged electrons emitted

Mercury atom

Energy from collision produces ultraviolet light (short-wave radiation)

Action of ultraviolet light on phosphor produces visible light (long-wave radiation)

Free electron

Phosphor coating

Glass

INCANDESCENT LIGHT BULB

SECTION OF FILAMENT OF INCANDESCENT LIGHT BULB: HOW INCANDESCENT LIGHT IS PRODUCED

Moving electrons collide with metal atoms

Hot filament gives out light

Vibration of metal atoms increases temperature

Lead-in wire

Glass bulb

Seal

Glass support

Screw fitting

Electrical contact

Coiled tungsten filament

Mixture of unreactive gases at low pressure

Electrical contact

SECTION OF PHOSPHOR COATING OF FLUORESCENT TUBE: HOW FLUORESCENT LIGHT IS PRODUCED

REFLECTION OF LIGHT

Incident laser light

Mirror

Mirror support

Light strikes smooth surface at an angle, which reflects it at the same angle

Reflected light

REFRACTION OF LIGHT

Glass (transparent substance)

Incident laser light

Light enters substance

Light slows down and bends as passes from air to glass

Light speeds up as leaves glass

Refracted (bent) light

10^{-18} | 10^{-17} | 10^{-16} | 10^{-15} | 10^{-14} | 10^{-13} | 10^{-12} | 10^{-11} | 10^{-10} | 10^{-9} | 10^{-8} |

10^{-6} | 10^{-7} | 10^{-8} | 10^{-9} | 10^{-10} | 10^{-11} | 10^{-12} | 10^{-13} | 10^{-14} | 10^{-15} | 10^{-16} | 10^{-17} |

Visible light

Ultraviolet radiation

X-rays

Gamma rays

Force and motion

FORCES ARE PUSHES OR PULLS that change the motion of objects. To make a stationary object move, or a moving object stop, a force is needed. A force is also required to change the speed or direction of an object. This change in speed or direction is known as acceleration. Acceleration depends on the size (magnitude) of the force, and on the mass of the object. The effects of forces were first summarized by Isaac Newton in his three laws of motion. The international unit of force, named after him, is the newton (N), which is approximately equal to the weight of one apple. Gravity – the force of attraction between any two masses – can be measured using a newton meter (spring balance). Forces are put to useful effect in machines. A simple machine, such as a wheel and axle, is a device that changes the size or direction of an applied force. It allows an applied force (the effort) to produce another force (the load). A lever uses a bar that turns on a fulcrum to exert force. In all simple machines, there is a relationship between force and distance. A small force (in a compound pulley, for instance) moves through a large distance to lift a heavy object a small distance. This is called the Law of Simple Machines.

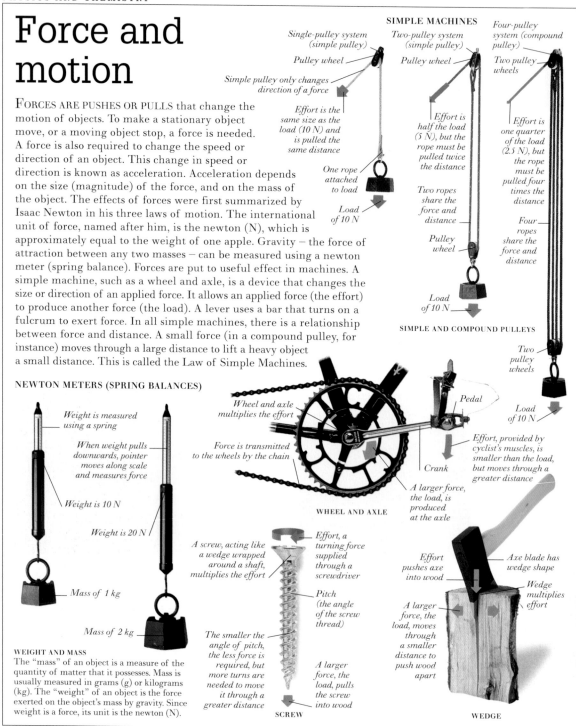

SIMPLE MACHINES

Single-pulley system (simple pulley)

Pulley wheel

Simple pulley only changes direction of a force

Effort is the same size as the load (10 N) and is pulled the same distance

One rope attached to load

Load of 10 N

Two-pulley system (simple pulley)

Pulley wheel

Effort is half the load (5 N), but the rope must be pulled twice the distance

Two ropes share the force and distance

Pulley wheel

Load of 10 N

SIMPLE AND COMPOUND PULLEYS

Four-pulley system (compound pulley)

Two pulley wheels

Effort is one quarter of the load (2.5 N), but the rope must be pulled four times the distance

Four ropes share the force and distance

Two pulley wheels

Load of 10 N

NEWTON METERS (SPRING BALANCES)

Weight is measured using a spring

When weight pulls downwards, pointer moves along scale and measures force

Weight is 10 N

Weight is 20 N

Mass of 1 kg

Mass of 2 kg

WEIGHT AND MASS
The "mass" of an object is a measure of the quantity of matter that it possesses. Mass is usually measured in grams (g) or kilograms (kg). The "weight" of an object is the force exerted on the object's mass by gravity. Since weight is a force, its unit is the newton (N).

Wheel and axle multiplies the effort

Force is transmitted to the wheels by the chain

Pedal

Crank

Effort, provided by cyclist's muscles, is smaller than the load, but moves through a greater distance

A larger force, the load, is produced at the axle

WHEEL AND AXLE

A screw, acting like a wedge wrapped around a shaft, multiplies the effort

Effort, a turning force supplied through a screwdriver

Pitch (the angle of the screw thread)

The smaller the angle of pitch, the less force is required, but more turns are needed to move it through a greater distance

A larger force, the load, pulls the screw into wood

SCREW

Effort pushes axe into wood

A larger force, the load, moves through a smaller distance to push wood apart

Axe blade has wedge shape

Wedge multiplies effort

WEDGE

NEWTON'S THREE LAWS OF MOTION

NEWTON'S FIRST LAW
When no force acts on a body, it will continue in a state of rest or uniform motion.

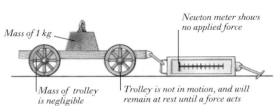

Newton meter shows no applied force

Mass of 1 kg

Mass of trolley is negligible

Trolley is not in motion, and will remain at rest until a force acts

NO FORCE, NO ACCELERATION: STATE OF REST

Constant speed

Mass of 1 kg

Newton meter shows no applied force

Trolley is in motion, and will continue at a constant speed in a straight line until a force acts

NO FORCE, NO ACCELERATION: UNIFORM MOTION

NEWTON'S SECOND LAW
When a force acts on a body, the motion of the body will change. The size of the change will depend upon the mass of the object and the magnitude of the applied force.

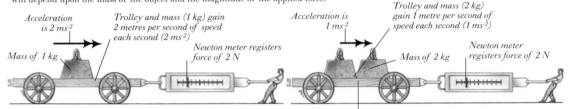

Acceleration is 2 ms^{-2}

Trolley and mass (1 kg) gain 2 metres per second of speed each second (2 ms^{-2})

Mass of 1 kg

Newton meter registers force of 2 N

Acceleration is 1 ms^{-2}

Trolley and mass (2 kg) gain 1 metre per second of speed each second (1 ms^{-2})

Mass of 2 kg

Newton meter registers force of 2 N

With the same applied force, an object with 2 kg mass accelerates at half the rate of object with 1 kg mass

FORCE AND ACCELERATION: SMALL MASS, LARGE ACCELERATION   **FORCE AND ACCELERATION: LARGE MASS, SMALL ACCELERATION**

NEWTON'S THIRD LAW
If one object exerts a force on another, an equal and opposite force, called the reaction force, is applied by the second object on the first.

Newton meters pull on each other with equal and opposite forces

Acceleration: the trolley and mass accelerate at 2 ms^{-2}

Newton meter registers force of 2 N to the left

Newton meter registers force of 2 N to the right

Mass of 1 kg

Person experiences a reaction force

ACTION AND REACTION

THREE CLASSES OF LEVER

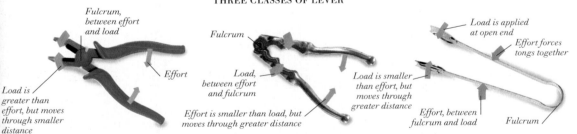

Fulcrum, between effort and load

Effort

Load is greater than effort, but moves through smaller distance

CLASS 1 LEVER
Pliers consist of two class 1 levers.

Fulcrum

Load, between effort and fulcrum

Effort is smaller than load, but moves through greater distance

CLASS 2 LEVER
Nutcrackers consist of two class 2 levers.

Load is applied at open end

Effort forces tongs together

Load is smaller than effort, but moves through greater distance

Effort, between fulcrum and load

Fulcrum

CLASS 3 LEVER
Tongs consist of two class 3 levers.

RAIL AND ROAD

Steam locomotives

Wagons that are pulled along tracks have been used to transport material since the 16th century, but these trains were drawn by men or horses until the invention of the steam locomotive. Steam locomotives enabled the basic railway system to realize its true potential. In 1804, Richard Trevithick built the world's first working steam locomotive in South Wales. It was not entirely successful, but it encouraged others to develop new designs. By 1829, the British engineer Robert Stephenson had built the "Rocket", considered to be the forerunner of the modern locomotive. The "Rocket" was a self-sufficient unit, carrying coal to heat the boiler and a water supply for generating steam. Steam passed from the boiler to force the pistons back and forth, and this movement turned the driving wheels, propelling the train forwards. Used steam was then expelled in characteristic "chuffs". Later steam locomotives, like "Ellerman Lines" and the "Mallard", worked in a similar way, but on a much larger scale. The simple design and reliability of steam locomotives ensured that they changed very little in 120 years of use, before being replaced from the 1950s by more efficient diesel and electric power (see pp. 326-329).

"ROCKET" STEAM LOCOMOTIVE, 1829

Chimney

Smokebox

Leaf spring

"Rocked" nameplate

Pipe takes steam from boiler to cylinder

Regulator (throttle)

Wrought iron boiler

Remains of firebox

Valve chest

Valve setting control

Wooden buffer beam

Wooden driving wheel

Metal tyre

Axle

Ballast

Rail chair

Wrought iron rail

Wooden sleeper

Piston rod

Cylinder

Carrying wheel

Driver's platform

"ELLERMAN LINES", 1949 (CUTAWAY VIEW)

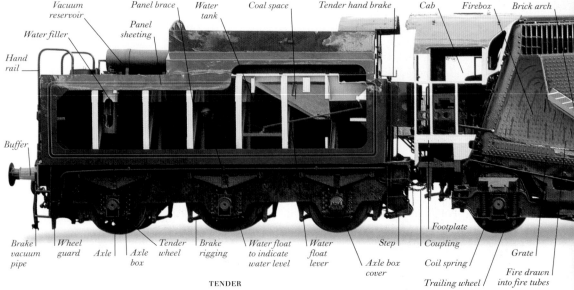

Vacuum reservoir

Panel brace

Water tank

Coal space

Tender hand brake

Cab

Firebox

Brick arch

Stay

Water filler

Panel sheeting

Hand rail

Buffer

Brake vacuum pipe

Wheel guard

Axle

Axle box

Tender wheel

Brake rigging

Water float to indicate water level

Water float lever

Axle box cover

Step

Coupling

Footplate

Coil spring

Trailing wheel

Grate

Fire drawn into fire tubes

TENDER

CAB INTERIOR OF "MALLARD" EXPRESS STEAM LOCOMOTIVE, 1938

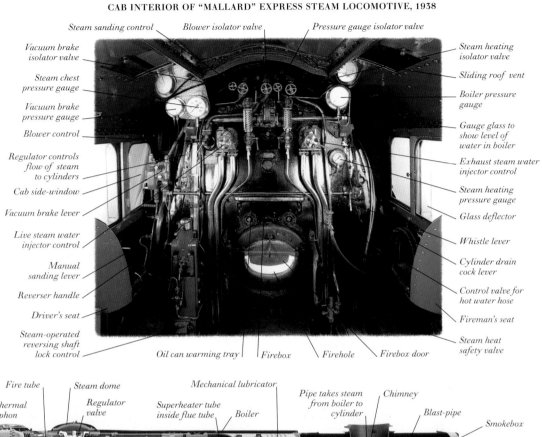

Steam sanding control
Blower isolator valve
Pressure gauge isolator valve

Vacuum brake isolator valve
Steam chest pressure gauge
Vacuum brake pressure gauge
Blower control
Regulator controls flow of steam to cylinders
Cab side-window
Vacuum brake lever
Live steam water injector control
Manual sanding lever
Reverser handle
Driver's seat
Steam-operated reversing shaft lock control

Steam heating isolator valve
Sliding roof vent
Boiler pressure gauge
Gauge glass to show level of water in boiler
Exhaust steam water injector control
Steam heating pressure gauge
Glass deflector
Whistle lever
Cylinder drain cock lever
Control valve for hot water hose
Fireman's seat
Steam heat safety valve

Oil can warming tray
Firebox
Firehole
Firebox door

Fire tube
Steam dome
Mechanical lubricator
Pipe takes steam from boiler to cylinder
Chimney

Thermal siphon
Regulator valve
Superheater tube inside flue tube
Boiler
Blast-pipe
Smokebox
Smokebox door
Lubricating pipe
Piston valve
Buffer

Brake shoe
Brake rigging
Coupling rod
Driving wheel
Crank
Expansion lever
Connecting rod
Combination lever
Slide bar
Piston, linked to connecting rod
Bogie frame
Cylinder
Screw coupling
Leading wheel

STEAM LOCOMOTIVE

Diesel trains

RUDOLF DIESEL FIRST DEMONSTRATED the diesel engine in Germany in 1898, but it was not until the 1940s that diesel locomotives were successfully established on both passenger and freight services, in the US. Early diesel locomotives like the "Union Pacific" were more expensive to build than steam locomotives, but were more efficient and cheaper to operate, especially where oil was plentiful. One feature of diesel engines is that the power output cannot be coupled directly to the wheels. To convert the mechanical energy produced by diesel engines, a transmission system is needed. Almost all diesel locomotives have electric transmissions, and are known as "diesel-electric" locomotives. The diesel engine works by drawing air into the cylinders and compressing it to increase its temperature; a small quantity of diesel fuel is then injected into it. The resulting combustion drives the generator (more recently an alternator) to produce electricity, which is fed to electric motors connected to the wheels. Diesel-electric locomotives are essentially electric locomotives that carry their own power plants, and are used worldwide today. The "Deltic" diesel-electric locomotive, similar to the one shown here, replaced classic express steam locomotives, and ran at speeds up to 160 kph (100 mph).

**FRONT VIEW OF "UNION PACIFIC"
DIESEL-ELECTRIC LOCOMOTIVE, 1950s**

Exhaust vent

Windscreen wiper

Horn

Cab front window

Head-light

Cab door

Name of operating railroad

Illuminated locomotive unit number

Railroad crest

Cab step

Step

Motor-driven bogie axle

Air-brake coupling hose

Centre buck-eye coupler

PROTOTYPE "DELTIC" DIESEL-ELECTRIC LOCOMOTIVE, 1956

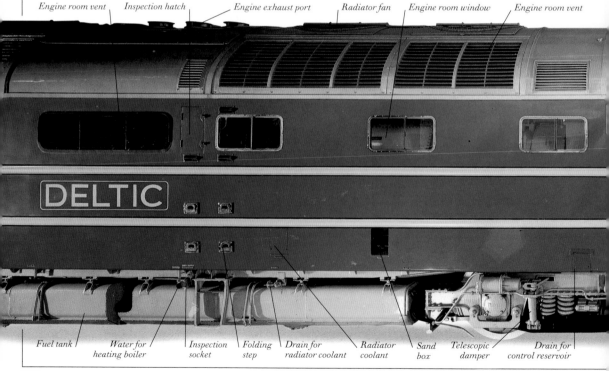

Engine room vent

Inspection hatch

Engine exhaust port

Radiator fan

Engine room window

Engine room vent

Fuel tank

Water for heating boiler

Inspection socket

Folding step

Drain for radiator coolant

Radiator coolant

Sand box

Telescopic damper

Drain for control reservoir

DIESEL ENGINE OF BRITISH RAIL CLASS 20 DIESEL-ELECTRIC LOCOMOTIVE

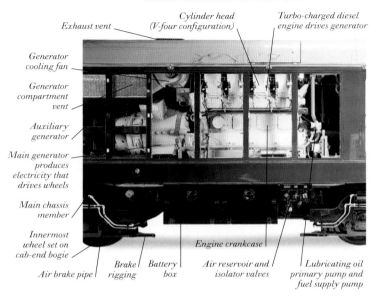

Exhaust vent

Cylinder head
(V-four configuration)

Turbo-charged diesel
engine drives generator

Generator
cooling fan

Generator
compartment
vent

Auxiliary
generator

Main generator
produces
electricity that
drives wheels

Main chassis
member

Innermost
wheel set on
cab-end bogie

Air brake pipe

Brake
rigging

Battery
box

Engine crankcase

Air reservoir and
isolator valves

Lubricating oil
primary pump and
fuel supply pump

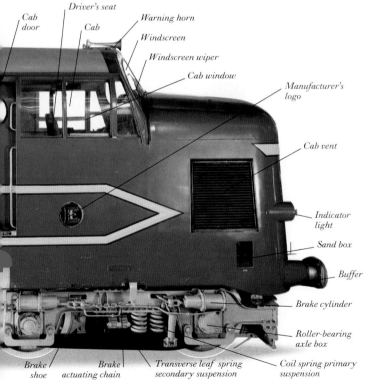

Cab
door

Driver's seat

Cab

Warning horn

Windscreen

Windscreen wiper

Cab window

Manufacturer's
logo

Cab vent

Indicator
light

Sand box

Buffer

Brake cylinder

Roller-bearing
axle box

Brake
shoe

Brake
actuating chain

Transverse leaf spring
secondary suspension

Coil spring primary
suspension

EXAMPLES OF FREIGHT CARS

BOX CAR

HOPPER CAR

REFRIGERATOR CAR

LIVESTOCK CAR

FLAT CAR WITH BULKHEADS

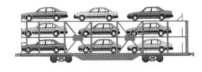

AUTOMOBILE CAR

Electric and high-speed trains

THE FIRST ELECTRIC LOCOMOTIVE ran in 1879 in Berlin, Germany. In Europe, electric trains developed as a more efficient alternative to the steam locomotive and diesel-electric power. Like diesels, electric trains employ electric motors to drive the wheels but, unlike diesels, the electricity is generated externally at a power station. Electric current is picked up either from a catenary (overhead cable) via a pantograph, or from a third rail. Since it does not carry its own power-generating equipment, an electric locomotive has a better power-to-weight ratio and greater acceleration than its diesel-electric equivalent. This makes electric trains suitable for urban routes with many stops. They are also faster, quieter, and less polluting. The latest electric French TGV (Train à Grande Vitesse) reaches 300 kph (186 mph); other trains, like the London to Paris and Brussels "Eurostar", can run at several voltages and operate between different countries. Simpler electric trains perform special duties – the "People Mover" at Gatwick Airport in Britain runs between terminals.

HOW ALTERNATING CURRENT (AC) ELECTRIC TRAINS WORK

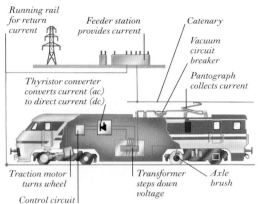

Running rail for return current

Feeder station provides current

Catenary

Vacuum circuit breaker

Pantograph collects current

Thyristor converter converts current (ac) to direct current (dc)

Traction motor turns wheel

Control circuit

Transformer steps down voltage

Axle brush

FRONT VIEW OF PARIS METRO

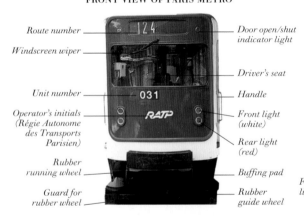

Route number

Windscreen wiper

Unit number

Operator's initials (Régie Autonome des Transports Parisien)

Rubber running wheel

Guard for rubber wheel

Door open/shut indicator light

Driver's seat

Handle

Front light (white)

Rear light (red)

Buffing pad

Rubber guide wheel

FRONT VIEW OF ITALIAN STATE RAILWAYS CLASS 402 ELECTRIC LOCOMOTIVE

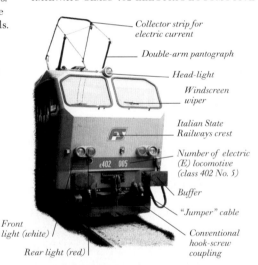

Collector strip for electric current

Double-arm pantograph

Head-light

Windscreen wiper

Italian State Railways crest

Number of electric (E) locomotive (class 402 No. 5)

Buffer

"Jumper" cable

Conventional hook-screw coupling

Front light (white)

Rear light (red)

SIDE VIEW OF SHANGHAI MAGLEV TRAIN

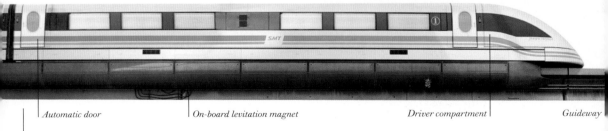

Automatic door

On-board levitation magnet

Driver compartment

Guideway

"EUROSTAR" MULTI-VOLTAGE ELECTRIC TRAIN

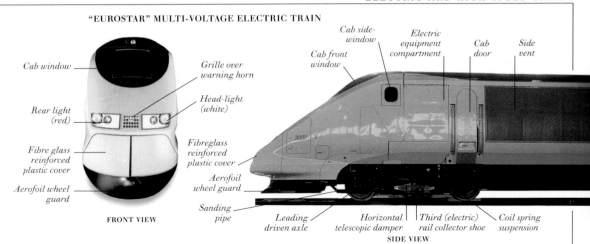

Cab window

Grille over
warning horn

Head-light
(white)

Rear light
(red)

Fibre glass
reinforced
plastic cover

Fibreglass
reinforced
plastic cover

Aerofoil wheel
guard

Aerofoil
wheel guard

FRONT VIEW

Cab side-
window

Electric
equipment
compartment

Cab
door

Side
vent

Cab front
window

Sanding
pipe

Leading
driven axle

Horizontal
telescopic damper

Third (electric)
rail collector shoe

Coil spring
suspension

SIDE VIEW

TGV ELECTRIC HIGH-SPEED TRAIN

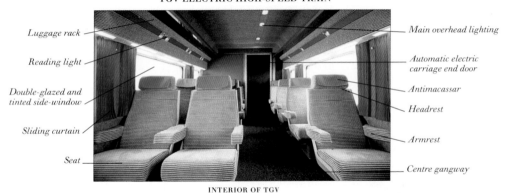

Luggage rack

Reading light

Double-glazed and
tinted side-window

Sliding curtain

Seat

Main overhead lighting

Automatic electric
carriage end door

Antimacassar

Headrest

Armrest

Centre gangway

INTERIOR OF TGV

Cab door

Hand rail

Side vent

Roof vent

Cab side-window

Cab front window

Windscreen
wiper

Emergency
exit door

Access
panel for
servicing

Nose air
deflector dam

306

SNCF

Vertical damper

Horizontal damper

SIDE VIEW OF TGV

Train equipment

MODERN RAILWAY TRACK consists of two parallel steel rails clipped on to a support called a sleeper. Sleepers are usually made of reinforced concrete, although wood and steel are still used. The distance between the inside edges of the rails is the track gauge. It evolved in Britain, which uses a gauge of 1,435 mm (4 ft 8½ in), known as the standard gauge. As engineering grew more sophisticated, narrower gauges were adopted because they cost less to build. The loading gauge, which is equally important, determines the size of the largest loaded vehicle that may pass through tunnels and under bridges with adequate clearance. Safe train operation relies on following a signalling system. At first, signalling was based on a simple time interval between trains, but it now depends on maintaining a safe distance between successive trains travelling in the same direction. Most modern signals are colour lights, but older mechanical semaphore signals are still used. On the latest high-speed lines, train drivers receive control instructions by electronic means. Signalling depends on reliable control of the train by effective braking. For fast, modern trains, which have considerable momentum, it is essential that each vehicle in the train can be braked by the driver or by a train control system, such as Automatic Train Protection (ATP). Braking is achieved by the brake shoe acting on the wheel rim (rim brakes), by disc brakes, or, increasingly, by electrical braking.

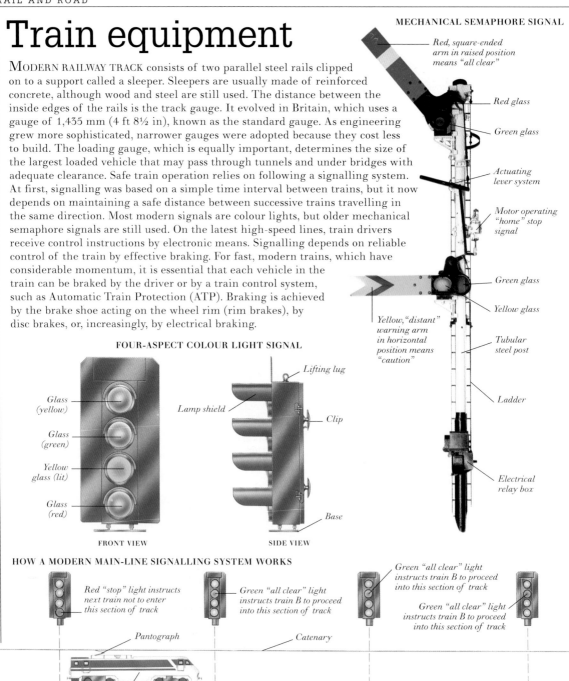

MECHANICAL SEMAPHORE SIGNAL

- Red, square-ended arm in raised position means "all clear"
- Red glass
- Green glass
- Actuating lever system
- Motor operating "home" stop signal
- Green glass
- Yellow glass
- Yellow, "distant" warning arm in horizontal position means "caution"
- Tubular steel post
- Ladder
- Electrical relay box

FOUR-ASPECT COLOUR LIGHT SIGNAL

- Glass (yellow)
- Glass (green)
- Yellow glass (lit)
- Glass (red)
- Lifting lug
- Lamp shield
- Clip
- Base

FRONT VIEW   SIDE VIEW

HOW A MODERN MAIN-LINE SIGNALLING SYSTEM WORKS

- Red "stop" light instructs next train not to enter this section of track
- Green "all clear" light instructs train B to proceed into this section of track
- Green "all clear" light instructs train B to proceed into this section of track
- Green "all clear" light instructs train B to proceed into this section of track
- Pantograph
- Catenary
- Train B
- Track

EXAMPLES OF INTERNATIONAL TRACK GAUGES

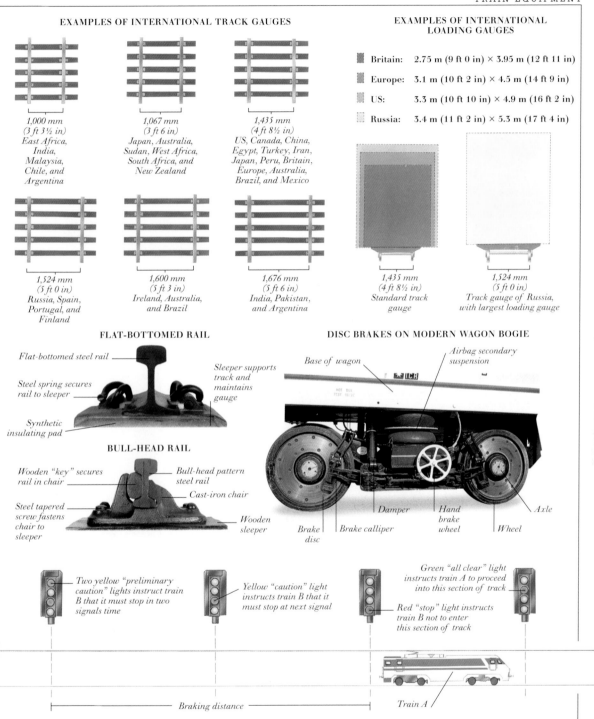

1,000 mm
(3 ft 3½ in)
East Africa,
India,
Malaysia,
Chile, and
Argentina

1,067 mm
(3 ft 6 in)
Japan, Australia,
Sudan, West Africa,
South Africa, and
New Zealand

1,435 mm
(4 ft 8½ in)
US, Canada, China,
Egypt, Turkey, Iran,
Japan, Peru, Britain,
Europe, Australia,
Brazil, and Mexico

1,524 mm
(5 ft 0 in)
Russia, Spain,
Portugal, and
Finland

1,600 mm
(5 ft 3 in)
Ireland, Australia,
and Brazil

1,676 mm
(5 ft 6 in)
India, Pakistan,
and Argentina

EXAMPLES OF INTERNATIONAL LOADING GAUGES

Britain: 2.75 m (9 ft 0 in) × 3.95 m (12 ft 11 in)

Europe: 3.1 m (10 ft 2 in) × 4.5 m (14 ft 9 in)

US: 3.3 m (10 ft 10 in) × 4.9 m (16 ft 2 in)

Russia: 3.4 m (11 ft 2 in) × 5.3 m (17 ft 4 in)

1,435 mm
(4 ft 8½ in)
Standard track
gauge

1,524 mm
(5 ft 0 in)
Track gauge of Russia,
with largest loading gauge

FLAT-BOTTOMED RAIL

Flat-bottomed steel rail

Steel spring secures rail to sleeper

Synthetic insulating pad

Sleeper supports track and maintains gauge

BULL-HEAD RAIL

Wooden "key" secures rail in chair

Steel tapered screw fastens chair to sleeper

Bull-head pattern steel rail

Cast-iron chair

Wooden sleeper

DISC BRAKES ON MODERN WAGON BOGIE

Base of wagon

Airbag secondary suspension

Brake disc

Brake calliper

Damper

Hand brake wheel

Axle

Wheel

Two yellow "preliminary caution" lights instruct train B that it must stop in two signals time

Yellow "caution" light instructs train B that it must stop at next signal

Green "all clear" light instructs train A to proceed into this section of track

Red "stop" light instructs train B not to enter this section of track

Braking distance

Train A

Trams and buses

METROLINK TRAM, MANCHESTER, BRITAIN

AS CITY POPULATIONS exploded in the 1800s, there was an urgent need for mass transportation. Trams were an early solution. The first trams, like buses, were horse-drawn, but in 1881, electric street tramways appeared in Berlin, Germany. Electric trams soon became widespread throughout Europe and North America. Trams run on rails along a fixed route, using electric motors that receive power from overhead cables. As road networks developed, motorized buses offered a flexible alternative to trams. By the 1930s, they had replaced tram systems in many cities. City buses typically have doors at both front and rear to make loading and unloading easier. Double-decker designs are popular, occupying the same amount of street space as single-decker buses but able to transport twice the number of people. Buses are also commonly used for inter-city travel and touring. Tour buses have reclining seats, large windows, luggage space, and toilets. Recently, as city traffic has become increasingly congested, many city planners have designed new tram routes to run alongside bus routes as part of an integrated transport system.

EARLY TRAM, c.1900

Trolley boom

Trolley head

Trolley base

Drop window

Upper deck

Quarter light

Brake

Stair

Lower deck

Platform

Controller

Truck

Lifeguard

MCW METROBUS, LONDON, BRITAIN

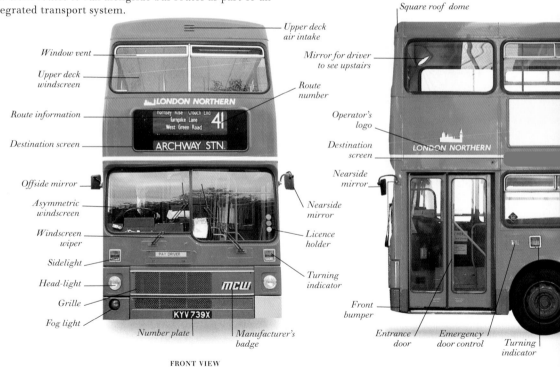

Square roof dome

Upper deck air intake

Window vent

Mirror for driver to see upstairs

Upper deck windscreen

Route number

Route information

Operator's logo

Destination screen

Destination screen

Offside mirror

Nearside mirror

Asymmetric windscreen

Nearside mirror

Windscreen wiper

Licence holder

Sidelight

Head-light

Turning indicator

Grille

Fog light

Front bumper

Number plate

Manufacturer's badge

Entrance door

Emergency door control

Turning indicator

LONDON NORTHERN

Hornsey Rise Crouch End
Turnpike Lane
West Green Road

41

ARCHWAY STN.

PAY DRIVER

mcw

KYV 739X

LONDON NORTHERN

FRONT VIEW

SINGLE-DECKER BUS, NEW YORK, US

Wheelchair access

Sliding window

Sloped roof dome

Tinted glass

Air intake

Tyre

Axle

Exit door

Access panel

Sidelight

Entrance door

Bumper

SIDE VIEW

Marker light

Repeater indicator

Entrance door

Side mirror

Route number

Head-light

Turning indicator

Number plate

Bumper

FRONT VIEW

DOUBLE-DECKER TOUR BUS, PARIS, FRANCE

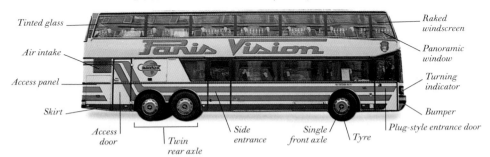

Tinted glass

Air intake

Access panel

Skirt

Access door

Twin rear axle

Side entrance

Single front axle

Tyre

Raked windscreen

Panoramic window

Turning indicator

Bumper

Plug-style entrance door

Sliding window vent

Upper saloon window

Advertising panel

Air intake

Lower saloon window

Fleet number

Engine access panel

Rear bumper

Emergency door control

Two-leaf style exit door

Legal lettering

London Buses logo

Tyre

Skirt

Axle

SIDE VIEW

The first cars

THE EARLIEST ROAD VEHICLE powered by an engine, the Cugnot steam traction engine, was built in 1770. More practical steam carriages, such as the Bordino, were available in the early 19th century, but they were heavy and cumbersome. Restrictive laws and the introduction of railways, faster and able to carry more passengers, saw the decline of "cars" powered by steam. It was not until 1860 that the first practical power unit for road vehicles was developed, with the invention of the internal combustion engine by the Belgian Etienne Lenoir. By around 1890, Karl Benz and Gottlieb Daimler in Germany, and Albert de Dion and Armand Peugeot in France were building cars for sale to the public. These early cars, despite being primitive, expensive, and produced in limited numbers, heralded the age of the motor car.

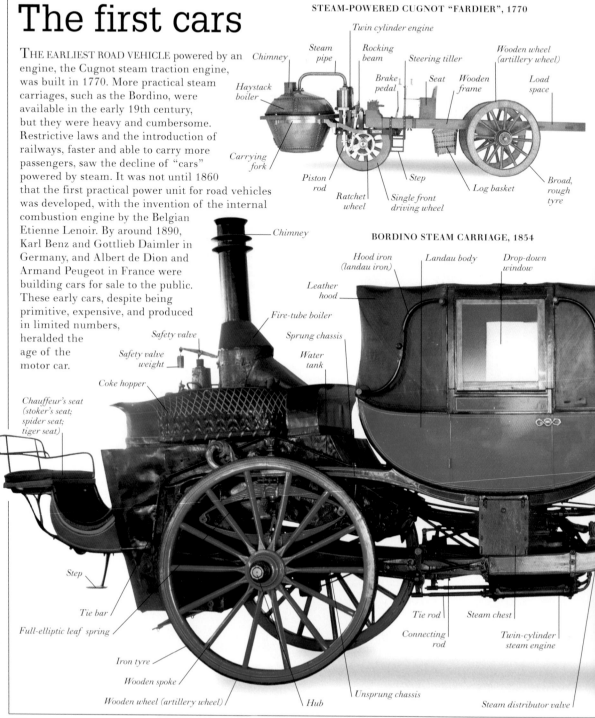

STEAM-POWERED CUGNOT "FARDIER", 1770

Twin cylinder engine

Chimney

Steam pipe

Rocking beam

Steering tiller

Wooden wheel (artillery wheel)

Brake pedal

Seat

Wooden frame

Load space

Haystack boiler

Carrying fork

Piston rod

Ratchet wheel

Step

Single front driving wheel

Log basket

Broad, rough tyre

BORDINO STEAM CARRIAGE, 1854

Chimney

Hood iron (landau iron)

Landau body

Drop-down window

Leather hood

Fire-tube boiler

Sprung chassis

Safety valve

Water tank

Safety valve weight

Coke hopper

Chauffeur's seat (stoker's seat; spider seat; tiger seat)

Step

Tie bar

Full-elliptic leaf spring

Iron tyre

Wooden spoke

Wooden wheel (artillery wheel)

Hub

Unsprung chassis

Tie rod

Connecting rod

Steam chest

Twin-cylinder steam engine

Steam distributor valve

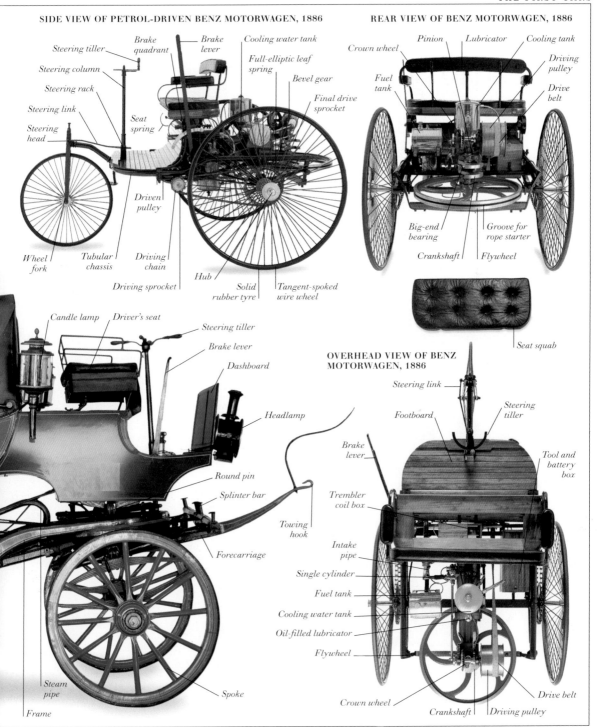

SIDE VIEW OF PETROL-DRIVEN BENZ MOTORWAGEN, 1886

Brake quadrant
Brake lever
Cooling water tank
Steering tiller
Full-elliptic leaf spring
Steering column
Bevel gear
Steering rack
Final drive sprocket
Steering link
Steering head
Seat spring
Driven pulley
Wheel fork
Tubular chassis
Driving chain
Driving sprocket
Hub
Solid rubber tyre
Tangent-spoked wire wheel

REAR VIEW OF BENZ MOTORWAGEN, 1886

Crown wheel
Pinion
Lubricator
Cooling tank
Driving pulley
Fuel tank
Drive belt
Big-end bearing
Groove for rope starter
Crankshaft
Flywheel
Seat squab

Candle lamp
Driver's seat
Steering tiller
Brake lever
Dashboard
Headlamp

OVERHEAD VIEW OF BENZ MOTORWAGEN, 1886

Steering link
Footboard
Steering tiller
Brake lever
Tool and battery box
Round pin
Splinter bar
Trembler coil box
Towing hook
Intake pipe
Forecarriage
Single cylinder
Fuel tank
Cooling water tank
Oil-filled lubricator
Flywheel
Steam pipe
Spoke
Frame
Crown wheel
Crankshaft
Driving pulley
Drive belt

335

Elegance and utility

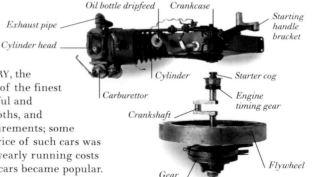

Oil bottle dripfeed

Crankcase

Starting handle bracket

Exhaust pipe

Cylinder head

Cylinder

Starter cog

Carburettor

Engine timing gear

Crankshaft

Gear band

Flywheel

DURING THE FIRST DECADE OF THE 20TH CENTURY, the motorist who could afford it had a choice of some of the finest cars ever made. These handbuilt cars were powerful and luxurious, using the finest woods, leathers, and cloths, and bodywork made to the customer's individual requirements; some had six-cylinder engines as big as 15 litres. The price of such cars was several times that of an average house, and their yearly running costs were also very high. As a result, basic, utilitarian cars became popular. Costing perhaps one-tenth of the price of a luxury car, these cars had very little trim and often had only single-cylinder engines.

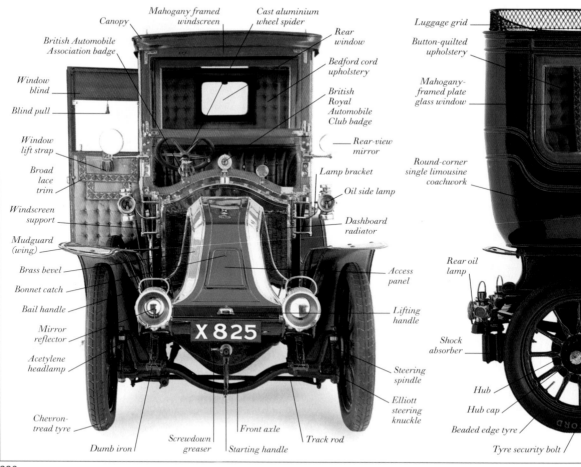

FRONT VIEW OF 1906 RENAULT

Canopy

Mahogany framed windscreen

Cast aluminium wheel spider

Rear window

British Automobile Association badge

Bedford cord upholstery

Window blind

British Royal Automobile Club badge

Blind pull

Window lift strap

Rear-view mirror

Broad lace trim

Lamp bracket

Oil side lamp

Windscreen support

Dashboard radiator

Mudguard (wing)

Brass bevel

Access panel

Bonnet catch

Bail handle

Lifting handle

Mirror reflector

Acetylene headlamp

Steering spindle

Elliott steering knuckle

Chevron-tread tyre

X 825

Dumb iron

Screwdown greaser

Front axle

Starting handle

Track rod

SIDE VIEW OF 1906 RENAULT

Luggage grid

Button-quilted upholstery

Mahogany-framed plate glass window

Round-corner single limousine coachwork

Rear oil lamp

Shock absorber

Hub

Hub cap

Beaded edge tyre

Tyre security bolt

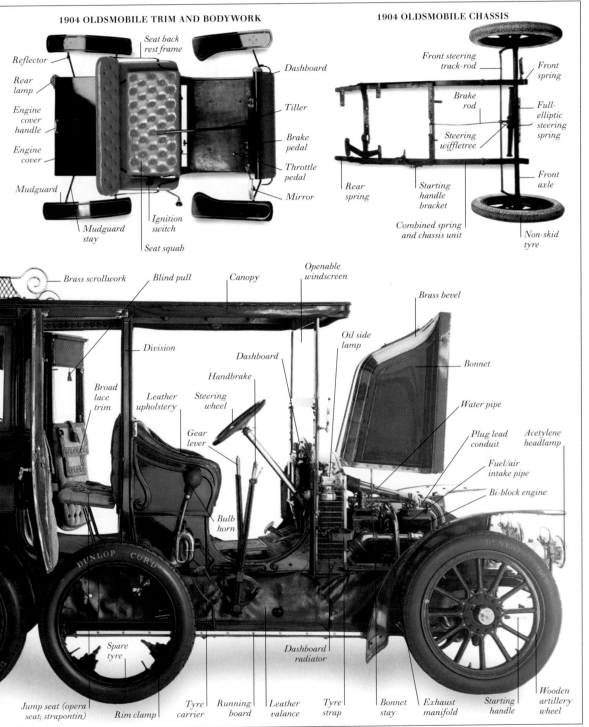

1904 OLDSMOBILE TRIM AND BODYWORK

Reflector

Rear lamp

Engine cover handle

Engine cover

Mudguard

Mudguard stay

Seat back rest frame

Ignition switch

Seat squab

Dashboard

Tiller

Brake pedal

Throttle pedal

Mirror

1904 OLDSMOBILE CHASSIS

Front steering track-rod

Front spring

Brake rod

Full-elliptic steering spring

Steering wiffletree

Rear spring

Starting handle bracket

Combined spring and chassis unit

Front axle

Non-skid tyre

Brass scrollwork

Blind pull

Canopy

Openable windscreen

Brass bevel

Division

Dashboard

Oil side lamp

Bonnet

Broad lace trim

Leather upholstery

Handbrake

Steering wheel

Water pipe

Plug lead conduit

Acetylene headlamp

Gear lever

Fuel/air intake pipe

Bulb horn

Bi-block engine

Spare tyre

Dashboard radiator

Jump seat (opera seat; strapontin)

Rim clamp

Tyre carrier

Running board

Leather valance

Tyre strap

Bonnet stay

Exhaust manifold

Starting handle

Wooden artillery wheel

Mass-production

THE FIRST CARS WERE HAND-ASSEMBLED from individually built parts, a time-consuming procedure that required skilled mechanics and made cars very expensive. This problem was solved, in America, by a Detroit car manufacturer named Henry Ford; he introduced mass-production by using standardized parts, and later combined these with a moving production line. The work was brought to the workers, each of whom performed one simple task in the construction process as the chassis moved along the line. The first mass-produced car, the Ford Model T, was launched in 1908 and was available in a limited range of body styles and colours. However, when the production line was introduced in 1914, the colour range was cut back; the Model T became available, as Henry Ford said, in "any colour you like, so long as it's black". Ford cut the production time for a car from several days to about 12 hours, and eventually to minutes, making cars much cheaper than before. As a result, by 1920 half the cars in the world were Model T Fords.

Throttle lever
Openable windscreen
Steering wheel
Ignition lever
Windscreen stay
Dashboard
Side lamp
Bulb horn
Spring shock absorber
Mudguard (wing)
Headlamp
Radiator
Front transverse leaf spring
Front axle
Number plate
Starting handle
Steering knuckle
Steering spindle connecting-rod

STAGES OF FORD MODEL T PRODUCTION

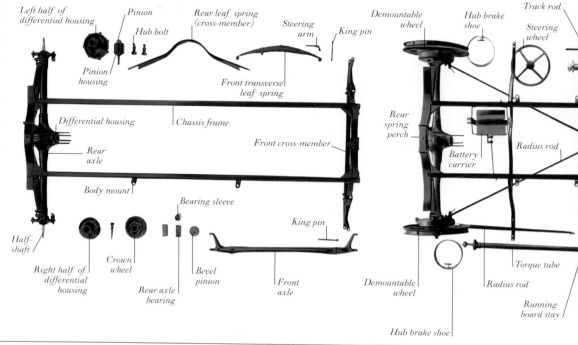

Left half of differential housing
Pinion
Rear leaf spring (cross-member)
Steering arm
King pin
Demountable wheel
Hub brake shoe
Track rod
Steering wheel
Hub bolt
Pinion housing
Front transverse leaf spring
Differential housing
Chassis frame
Front cross-member
Rear spring perch
Radius rod
Rear axle
Body mount
Bearing sleeve
Battery carrier
Half-shaft
King pin
Right half of differential housing
Crown wheel
Bevel pinion
Front axle
Rear axle bearing
Demountable wheel
Radius rod
Torque tube
Running-board stay
Hub brake shoe

SIDE VIEW OF 1913 FORD MODEL T

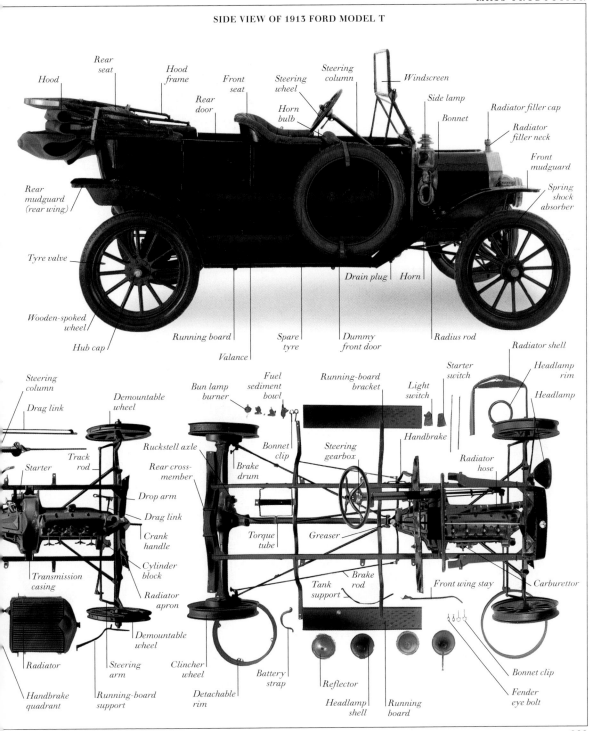

Hood

Rear seat

Hood frame

Front seat

Steering wheel

Steering column

Windscreen

Side lamp

Bonnet

Radiator filler cap

Horn bulb

Radiator filler neck

Front mudguard

Spring shock absorber

Rear mudguard (rear wing)

Rear door

Tyre valve

Drain plug

Horn

Wooden-spoked wheel

Running board

Spare tyre

Dummy front door

Radius rod

Hub cap

Valance

Radiator shell

Steering column

Demountable wheel

Bun lamp burner

Fuel sediment bowl

Running-board bracket

Light switch

Starter switch

Headlamp rim

Headlamp

Drag link

Ruckstell axle

Bonnet clip

Steering gearbox

Handbrake

Track rod

Rear cross-member

Brake drum

Radiator hose

Starter

Drop arm

Drag link

Crank handle

Cylinder block

Transmission casing

Radiator apron

Torque tube

Greaser

Brake rod

Front wing stay

Carburettor

Tank support

Radiator

Demountable wheel

Steering arm

Clincher wheel

Battery strap

Bonnet clip

Handbrake quadrant

Running-board support

Detachable rim

Reflector

Headlamp shell

Running board

Fender eye bolt

The "people's car"

THE MOST POPULAR CAR in the history of car manufacture is the Volkswagen Beetle, originally called the KdF Wagen. The car was developed in Germany in the 1930s by Dr. Ferdinand Porsche. At that time, Germany had only half the number of cars of Britain or France, and Adolf Hitler took a personal interest in the development of the Volkswagen ("people's car"). The intention was to provide a new industry, new jobs, and a car so cheap that anyone in work could afford it. Dr. Porsche designed a car that was cheap to build and run; its rear-mounted, air-cooled engine cut down the number of parts needed and also reduced weight. However, few civilians managed to obtain the Beetle before the outbreak of the Second World War in 1939. After the war, the Beetle proved so popular that eventually more than 20 million were sold.

WORKING PARTS OF VOLKSWAGEN BEETLE

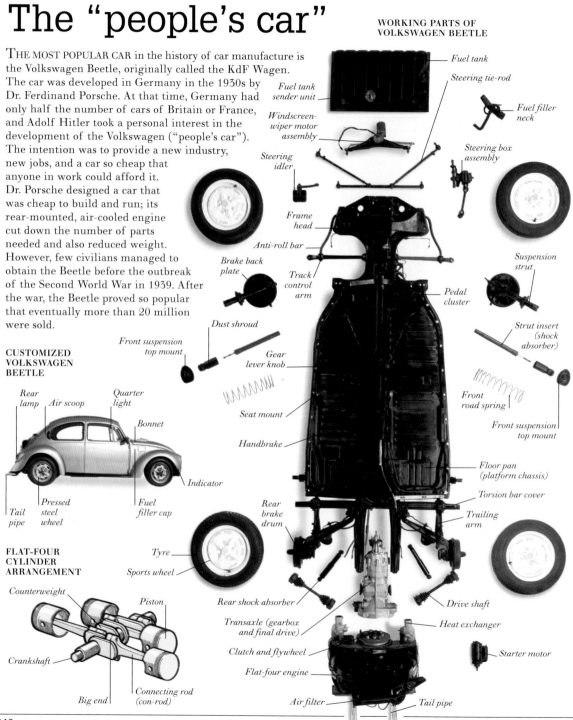

Fuel tank

Steering tie-rod

Fuel tank sender unit

Fuel filler neck

Windscreen-wiper motor assembly

Steering idler

Steering box assembly

Frame head

Anti-roll bar

Suspension strut

Brake back plate

Track control arm

Pedal cluster

Dust shroud

Strut insert (shock absorber)

Front suspension top mount

Gear lever knob

Front road spring

Seat mount

Front suspension top mount

Handbrake

Floor pan (platform chassis)

Torsion bar cover

Rear brake drum

Trailing arm

Rear shock absorber

Drive shaft

Transaxle (gearbox and final drive)

Heat exchanger

Clutch and flywheel

Starter motor

Flat-four engine

Air filter

Tail pipe

CUSTOMIZED VOLKSWAGEN BEETLE

Rear lamp

Air scoop

Quarter light

Bonnet

Indicator

Tail pipe

Pressed steel wheel

Fuel filler cap

FLAT-FOUR CYLINDER ARRANGEMENT

Tyre

Sports wheel

Counterweight

Piston

Crankshaft

Big end

Connecting rod (con-rod)

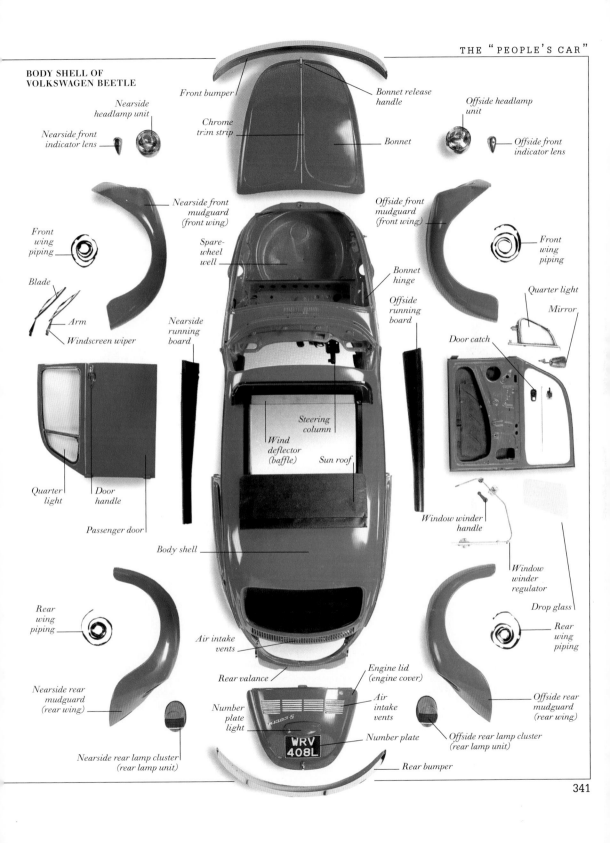

**BODY SHELL OF
VOLKSWAGEN BEETLE**

Front bumper

Bonnet release
handle

Nearside
headlamp unit

Offside headlamp
unit

Nearside front
indicator lens

Chrome
trim strip

Bonnet

Offside front
indicator lens

Nearside front
mudguard
(front wing)

Offside front
mudguard
(front wing)

Front
wing
piping

Spare-
wheel
well

Bonnet
hinge

Front
wing
piping

Blade

Offside
running
board

Quarter light

Mirror

Arm

Nearside
running
board

Door catch

Windscreen wiper

Steering
column

Window winder
handle

Wind
deflector
(baffle)

Sun roof

Quarter
light

Door
handle

Window
winder
regulator

Passenger door

Body shell

Drop glass

Rear
wing
piping

Rear
wing
piping

Air intake
vents

Engine lid
(engine cover)

Nearside rear
mudguard
(rear wing)

Rear valance

Air
intake
vents

Offside rear
mudguard
(rear wing)

Number
plate
light

WRV
408L

Number plate

Offside rear lamp cluster
(rear lamp unit)

Nearside rear lamp cluster
(rear lamp unit)

Rear bumper

Early engines

STEAM AND ELECTRICITY were used to power cars until early this century, but neither power source was ideal. Electric cars had to stop frequently to recharge their heavy batteries, and steam cars gave smooth power delivery but were too complicated for the average motorist to use. A rival power source, the internal combustion engine, was invented in 1860 by Etienne Lenoir (see pp. 334-335). This engine converted the force of a controlled explosion into rotary motion, to turn the wheels of a vehicle. Early variations on this basic model included sleeve valves, separately cast cylinders, and the two-stroke combustion cycle. Today, many internal combustion engines, including the Wankel rotary and diesels (see pp. 346-347), use the four-stroke cycle, first demonstrated by Nikolaus Otto in 1876. The Otto cycle, often described as "suck, squeeze, bang, blow", has proved the best method of ensuring that the engine turns over smoothly and that exhaust emissions are controllable.

BERSEY ELECTRIC CAB, 1896

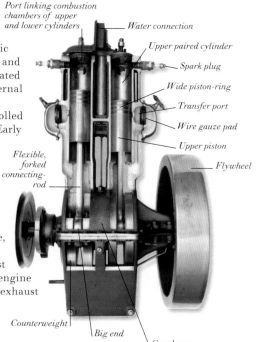

Port linking combustion chambers of upper and lower cylinders

Water connection

Upper paired cylinder

Spark plug

Wide piston-ring

Transfer port

Wire gauze pad

Upper piston

Flywheel

Flexible, forked connecting-rod

Counterweight

Big end

Crankcase

Mounting for tray of 40 batteries

Housing for electric motors

SECTIONED WHITE STEAM CAR, 1903

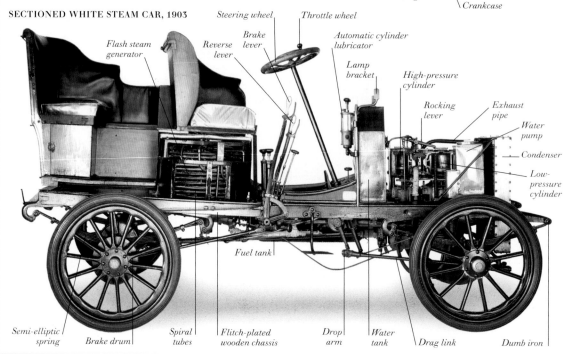

Steering wheel

Throttle wheel

Brake lever

Automatic cylinder lubricator

Reverse lever

Flash steam generator

Lamp bracket

High-pressure cylinder

Rocking lever

Exhaust pipe

Water pump

Condenser

Low-pressure cylinder

Fuel tank

Semi-elliptic spring

Brake drum

Spiral tubes

Flitch-plated wooden chassis

Drop arm

Water tank

Drag link

Dumb iron

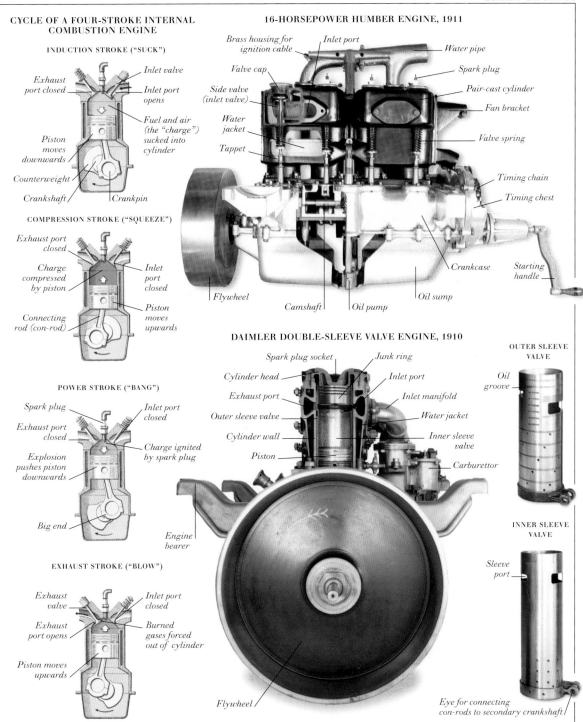

CYCLE OF A FOUR-STROKE INTERNAL COMBUSTION ENGINE

INDUCTION STROKE ("SUCK")

Exhaust port closed

Inlet valve

Inlet port opens

Fuel and air (the "charge") sucked into cylinder

Piston moves downwards

Counterweight

Crankshaft

Crankpin

COMPRESSION STROKE ("SQUEEZE")

Exhaust port closed

Charge compressed by piston

Inlet port closed

Piston moves upwards

Connecting rod (con-rod)

POWER STROKE ("BANG")

Spark plug

Inlet port closed

Exhaust port closed

Explosion pushes piston downwards

Charge ignited by spark plug

Big end

EXHAUST STROKE ("BLOW")

Exhaust valve

Inlet port closed

Exhaust port opens

Burned gases forced out of cylinder

Piston moves upwards

16-HORSEPOWER HUMBER ENGINE, 1911

Brass housing for ignition cable

Inlet port

Water pipe

Valve cap

Spark plug

Side valve (inlet valve)

Pair-cast cylinder

Water jacket

Fan bracket

Tappet

Valve spring

Timing chain

Timing chest

Flywheel

Camshaft

Oil pump

Oil sump

Crankcase

Starting handle

DAIMLER DOUBLE-SLEEVE VALVE ENGINE, 1910

Spark plug socket

Junk ring

Cylinder head

Inlet port

Exhaust port

Inlet manifold

Outer sleeve valve

Water jacket

Cylinder wall

Inner sleeve valve

Piston

Carburettor

Engine bearer

Flywheel

OUTER SLEEVE VALVE

Oil groove

INNER SLEEVE VALVE

Sleeve port

Eye for connecting con-rods to secondary crankshaft

343

Modern engines

TODAY'S PETROL ENGINE WORKS on the same basic principles as the first car engines of a century ago, although it has been greatly refined. Modern engines, often made from special metal alloys, are much lighter than earlier engines. Computerized ignition systems, fuel injectors, and multi-valve cylinder heads achieve a more efficient combustion of the fuel/air mixture (the charge) so that less fuel is wasted. As a result of this greater efficiency, the power and performance of a modern engine are increased, and the level of pollution in the exhaust gases is reduced. Exhaust pollution levels today are also lowered by the increasing use of special filters called catalytic converters, which absorb many exhaust pollutants. The need to produce ever more efficient engines means that it can take up to seven years to develop a new engine for a family car, at a cost of many millions of pounds.

FRONT VIEW OF A FORD COSWORTH V6 12-VALVE

Idle control valve
Plenum chamber
Valve rocker
Power steering pump reservoir
Steering pump pulley
Cogged drive belt
Alternator
Viscous coupling
Oil dipstick
High-tension ignition lead (spark plug lead)
Fan
Crankshaft pulley
Oil sump

FRONT VIEW OF A FORD COSWORTH V6 24-VALVE

Idle control valve
Exhaust gas recirculation valve
Steering pump drive pulley
Belt tensioner
Alternator cooling fan
Oil sump
Plenum chamber
Camshaft timing gear
Camshaft chain
Air conditioning pump
Drive belt
Crankshaft pulley

SECTIONED VIEW OF A JAGUAR STRAIGHT 6

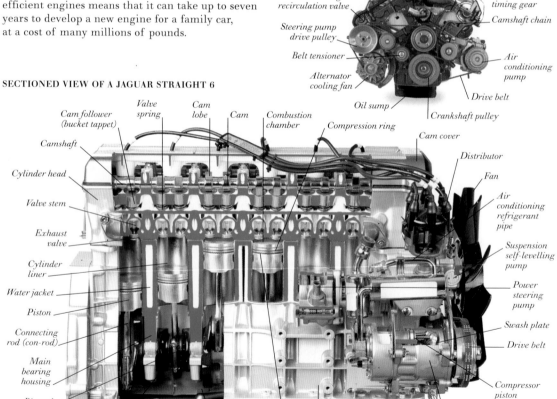

Cam follower (bucket tappet)
Valve spring
Cam lobe
Cam
Combustion chamber
Compression ring
Cam cover
Camshaft
Distributor
Cylinder head
Fan
Valve stem
Air conditioning refrigerant pipe
Exhaust valve
Suspension self-levelling pump
Cylinder liner
Power steering pump
Water jacket
Swash plate
Piston
Drive belt
Connecting rod (con-rod)
Main bearing housing
Compressor piston
Big end
Transmission adaptor plate
Air conditioning compressor
Crankshaft counterweight
Oil sump
Oil pick-up pipe
Anti-surge baffle
Crankcase
Oil-control ring (scraper ring)

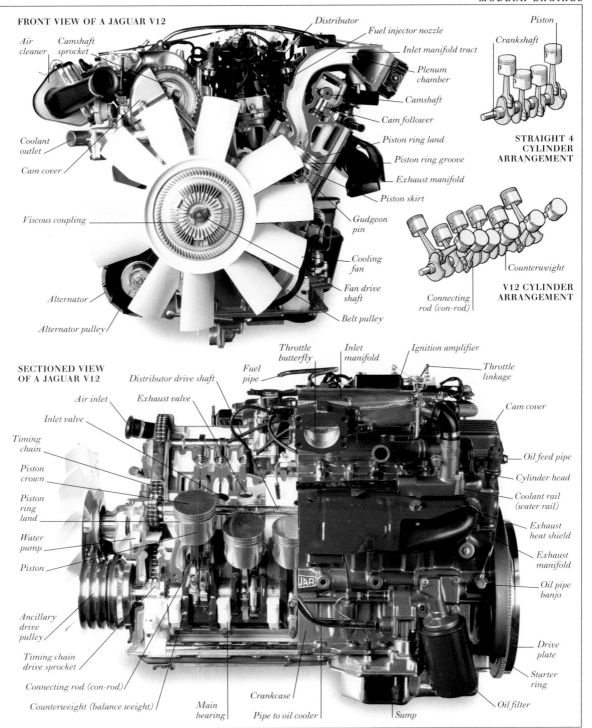

FRONT VIEW OF A JAGUAR V12

Air cleaner

Camshaft sprocket

Distributor

Fuel injector nozzle

Inlet manifold tract

Plenum chamber

Camshaft

Cam follower

Coolant outlet

Cam cover

Piston ring land

Piston ring groove

Exhaust manifold

Piston skirt

Viscous coupling

Gudgeon pin

Cooling fan

Alternator

Fan drive shaft

Alternator pulley

Belt pulley

Piston

Crankshaft

STRAIGHT 4 CYLINDER ARRANGEMENT

Counterweight

Connecting rod (con-rod)

V12 CYLINDER ARRANGEMENT

SECTIONED VIEW OF A JAGUAR V12

Throttle butterfly

Inlet manifold

Ignition amplifier

Throttle linkage

Fuel pipe

Distributor drive shaft

Air inlet

Exhaust valve

Cam cover

Inlet valve

Timing chain

Piston crown

Piston ring land

Water pump

Piston

Oil feed pipe

Cylinder head

Coolant rail (water rail)

Exhaust heat shield

Exhaust manifold

Oil pipe banjo

Ancillary drive pulley

Timing chain drive sprocket

Connecting rod (con-rod)

Counterweight (balance weight)

Main bearing

Pipe to oil cooler

Crankcase

Sump

Drive plate

Starter ring

Oil filter

Alternative engines

THE MOST COMMON TYPE OF ALTERNATIVE ENGINE is the diesel engine, which, instead of igniting the compressed fuel/air mixture with a spark, uses compression alone, heating the mixture to the point where it explodes. A diesel engine's fuel consumption is low in comparison with similarly sized piston engines, despite its heavier, reinforced moving parts and cylinder block. Another type of engine is the rotary-combustion, first successfully developed by Felix Wankel in the 1950s. Its two trilobate (three-sided) rotors revolve in housings shaped in a fat figure-of-eight. The four sequences of the four-stroke cycle, which occur consecutively in a piston engine, occur simultaneously in a rotary engine, producing power in a continuous stream.

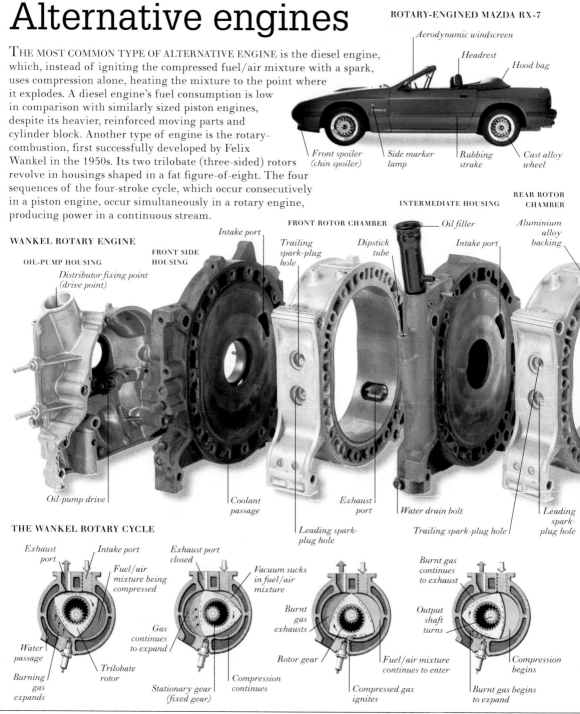

ROTARY-ENGINED MAZDA RX-7

- Aerodynamic windscreen
- Headrest
- Hood bag
- Front spoiler (chin spoiler)
- Side marker lamp
- Rubbing strake
- Cast alloy wheel

WANKEL ROTARY ENGINE

- OIL-PUMP HOUSING
- Distributor fixing point (drive point)
- FRONT SIDE HOUSING
- Intake port
- FRONT ROTOR CHAMBER
- Trailing spark-plug hole
- Dipstick tube
- Oil filler
- INTERMEDIATE HOUSING
- Intake port
- REAR ROTOR CHAMBER
- Aluminium alloy backing
- Oil-pump drive
- Coolant passage
- Exhaust port
- Leading spark-plug hole
- Water drain bolt
- Trailing spark-plug hole
- Leading spark-plug hole

THE WANKEL ROTARY CYCLE

- Exhaust port
- Intake port
- Fuel/air mixture being compressed
- Water passage
- Burning gas expands
- Gas continues to expand
- Trilobate rotor
- Stationary gear (fixed gear)
- Compression continues
- Exhaust port closed
- Vacuum sucks in fuel/air mixture
- Burnt gas exhausts
- Rotor gear
- Compressed gas ignites
- Fuel/air mixture continues to enter
- Burnt gas continues to exhaust
- Output shaft turns
- Compression begins
- Burnt gas begins to expand

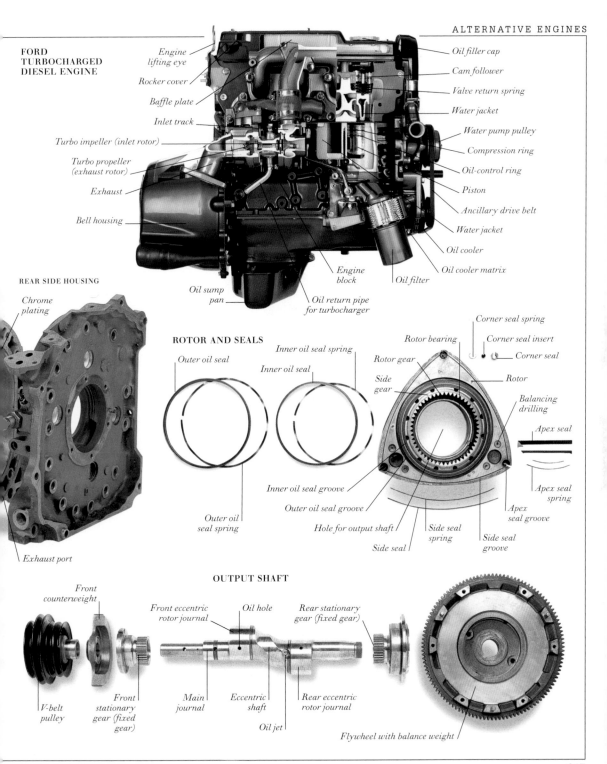

**FORD
TURBOCHARGED
DIESEL ENGINE**

Engine
lifting eye

Rocker cover

Baffle plate

Inlet track

Turbo impeller (inlet rotor)

Turbo propeller
(exhaust rotor)

Exhaust

Bell housing

Oil filler cap

Cam follower

Valve return spring

Water jacket

Water pump pulley

Compression ring

Oil-control ring

Piston

Ancillary drive belt

Water jacket

Oil cooler

Oil cooler matrix

Oil filter

Engine
block

Oil sump
pan

Oil return pipe
for turbocharger

REAR SIDE HOUSING

Chrome
plating

Exhaust port

ROTOR AND SEALS

Outer oil seal

Inner oil seal spring

Inner oil seal

Rotor bearing

Rotor gear

Side
gear

Corner seal spring

Corner seal insert

Corner seal

Rotor

Balancing
drilling

Apex seal

Inner oil seal groove

Outer oil seal groove

Outer oil
seal spring

Hole for output shaft

Side seal

Side seal
spring

Apex seal
spring

Apex
seal groove

Side seal
groove

OUTPUT SHAFT

Front
counterweight

Front eccentric
rotor journal

Oil hole

Rear stationary
gear (fixed gear)

V-belt
pulley

Front
stationary
gear (fixed
gear)

Main
journal

Eccentric
shaft

Oil jet

Rear eccentric
rotor journal

Flywheel with balance weight

Bodywork

RENAULT LOGO

THE BODY OF A MODERN mass-produced car is built on the monocoque (single-shell) principle, in which the roof, side panels, and floor are welded into a single integral unit. This bodyshell protects and supports the car's internal parts. Steel and glass are used to construct the bodyshell, creating a unit that is both light and strong. Its lightness helps to conserve energy, while its strength protects the occupants. Modern bodywork is designed with the aid of computers, which are used to predict factors such as aerodynamic efficiency and impact-resistance. High-technology is also employed on the production line, where robots are used to assemble, weld, and paint the body.

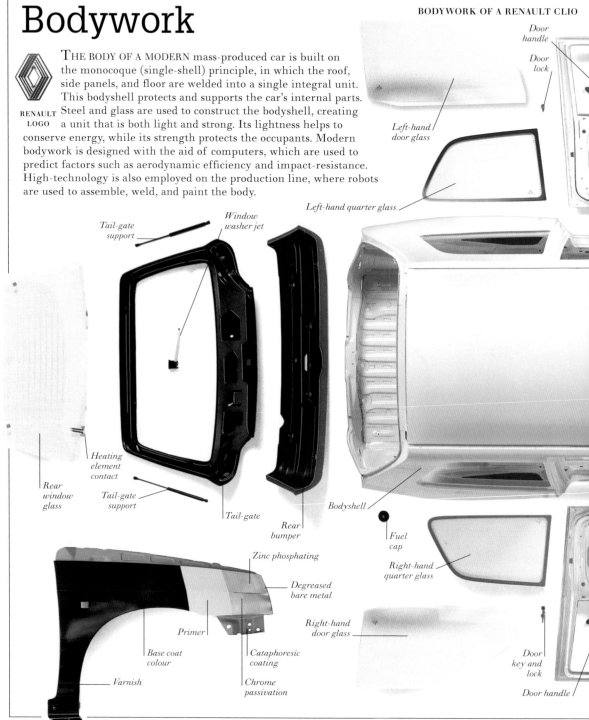

Door handle

Door lock

Left-hand door glass

Left-hand quarter glass

Tail-gate support

Window washer jet

Heating element contact

Rear window glass

Tail-gate support

Tail-gate

Rear bumper

Bodyshell

Fuel cap

Zinc phosphating

Right-hand quarter glass

Degreased bare metal

Primer

Base coat colour

Cataphoresic coating

Right-hand door glass

Chrome passivation

Varnish

Door key and lock

Door handle

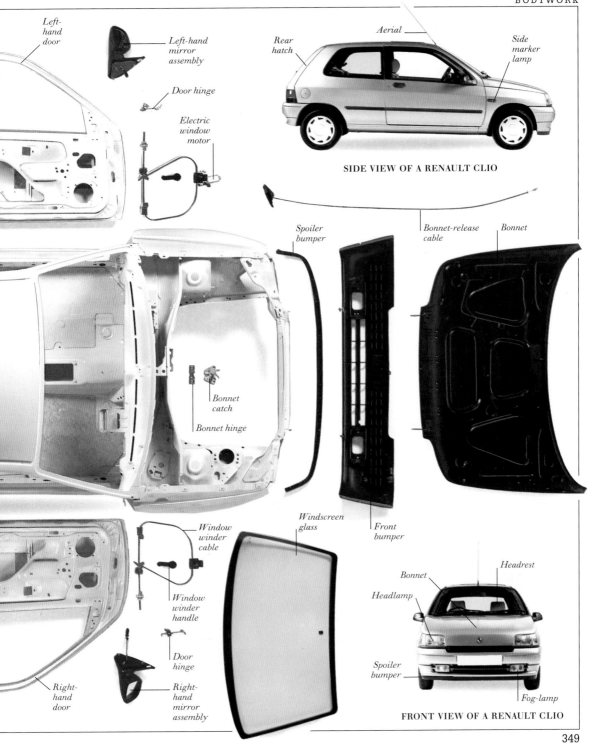

Left-hand door

Left-hand mirror assembly

Door hinge

Electric window motor

Rear hatch

Aerial

Side marker lamp

SIDE VIEW OF A RENAULT CLIO

Spoiler bumper

Bonnet-release cable

Bonnet

Bonnet catch

Bonnet hinge

Window winder cable

Window winder handle

Door hinge

Windscreen glass

Front bumper

Right-hand door

Right-hand mirror assembly

Headrest

Bonnet

Headlamp

Spoiler bumper

Fog-lamp

FRONT VIEW OF A RENAULT CLIO

349

Mechanical components

A TYPICAL MODERN CAR has several thousand individual mechanical components. These are assembled to form the car's various mechanical systems: engine and exhaust, transmission, steering, suspension, and brakes. To ensure that each system functions properly, components are manufactured to extremely fine tolerances – to within a five-hundredth of a millimetre (about one ten-thousandth of an inch) in some cases.

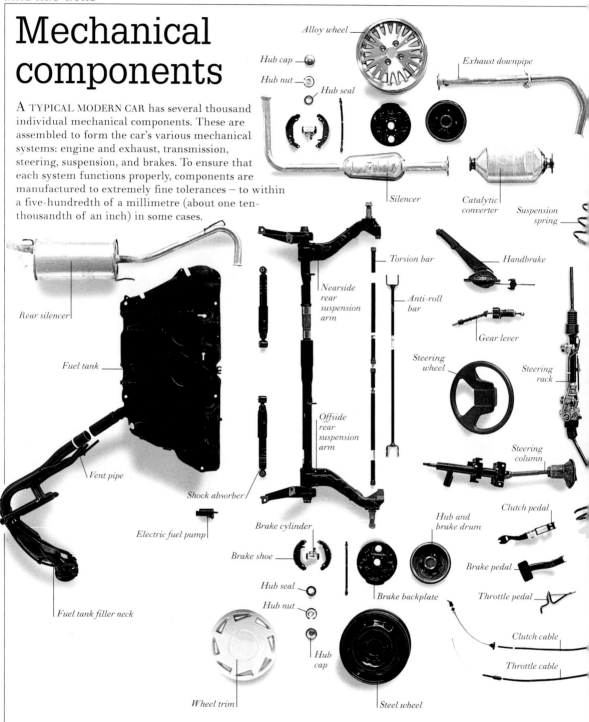

Alloy wheel

Hub cap

Hub nut

Hub seal

Exhaust downpipe

Silencer

Catalytic converter

Suspension spring

Rear silencer

Fuel tank

Vent pipe

Electric fuel pump

Fuel tank filler neck

Shock absorber

Brake cylinder

Brake shoe

Hub seal

Hub nut

Hub cap

Wheel trim

Steel wheel

Torsion bar

Nearside rear suspension arm

Anti-roll bar

Offside rear suspension arm

Handbrake

Gear lever

Steering wheel

Steering rack

Steering column

Clutch pedal

Hub and brake drum

Brake pedal

Brake backplate

Throttle pedal

Clutch cable

Throttle cable

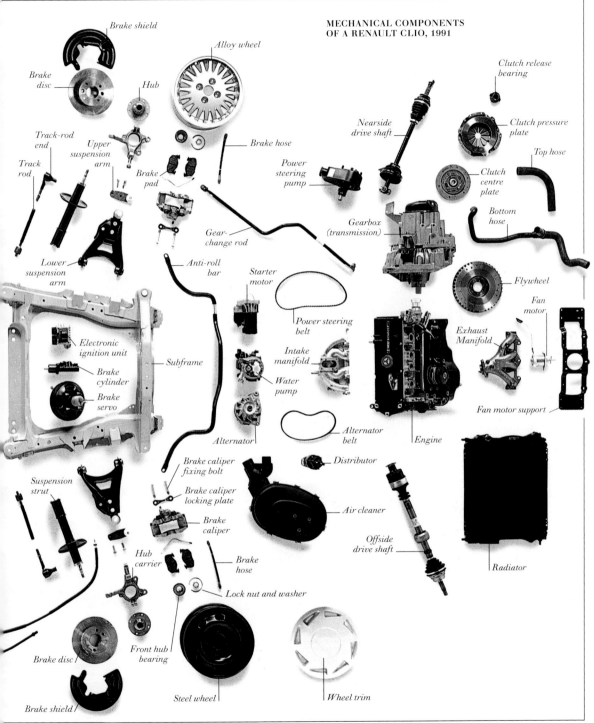

MECHANICAL COMPONENTS
OF A RENAULT CLIO, 1991

Brake shield

Alloy wheel

Clutch release
bearing

Brake
disc

Hub

Clutch pressure
plate

Nearside
drive shaft

Brake hose

Top hose

Track-rod
end

Upper
suspension
arm

Power
steering
pump

Clutch
centre
plate

Track
rod

Brake
pad

Bottom
hose

Gear-
change rod

Gearbox
(transmission)

Lower
suspension
arm

Anti-roll
bar

Starter
motor

Flywheel

Fan
motor

Electronic
ignition unit

Subframe

Power steering
belt

Intake
manifold

Exhaust
Manifold

Brake
cylinder

Brake
servo

Water
pump

Fan motor support

Alternator
belt

Alternator

Engine

Brake caliper
fixing bolt

Distributor

Suspension
strut

Brake caliper
locking plate

Brake
caliper

Air cleaner

Hub
carrier

Brake
hose

Offside
drive shaft

Brake disc

Front hub
bearing

Lock nut and washer

Radiator

Brake shield

Steel wheel

Wheel trim

351

Car trim

A MODERN CAR HAS TWO TYPES OF TRIM, according to the materials used: hard (chrome and plastics) and soft (upholstery materials). Safety and comfort are priorities in the trim's design: seats help the occupants to maintain a comfortable posture, rubber seals keep out dirt and moisture, and headlamps light the way. Older cars had interior or leather panelling cut and fitted by craftsmen; modern cars use precisely moulded plastics and seat fabrics cut by robot-controlled lasers to reduce costs and production time. Doors are now trimmed off the production line so that complex wiring can be built in.

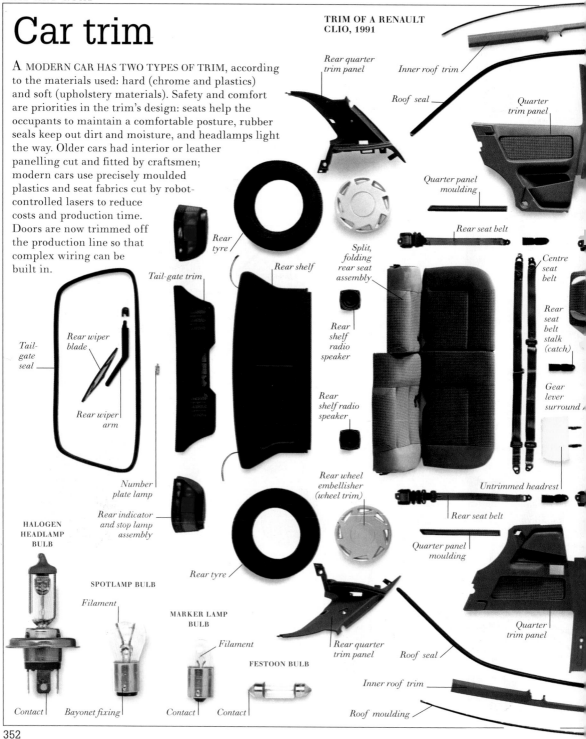

TRIM OF A RENAULT CLIO, 1991

Rear quarter trim panel

Inner roof trim

Roof seal

Quarter trim panel

Quarter panel moulding

Rear seat belt

Split, folding rear seat assembly

Centre seat belt

Rear shelf

Rear tyre

Rear shelf radio speaker

Rear seat belt stalk (catch)

Gear lever surround

Tail-gate trim

Rear wiper blade

Tail-gate seal

Rear wiper arm

Number plate lamp

Rear indicator and stop lamp assembly

Rear shelf radio speaker

Rear wheel embellisher (wheel trim)

Untrimmed headrest

Rear seat belt

Quarter panel moulding

HALOGEN HEADLAMP BULB

Rear tyre

SPOTLAMP BULB

Filament

MARKER LAMP BULB

Filament

FESTOON BULB

Quarter trim panel

Rear quarter trim panel

Roof seal

Inner roof trim

Roof moulding

Contact

Bayonet fixing

Contact

Contact

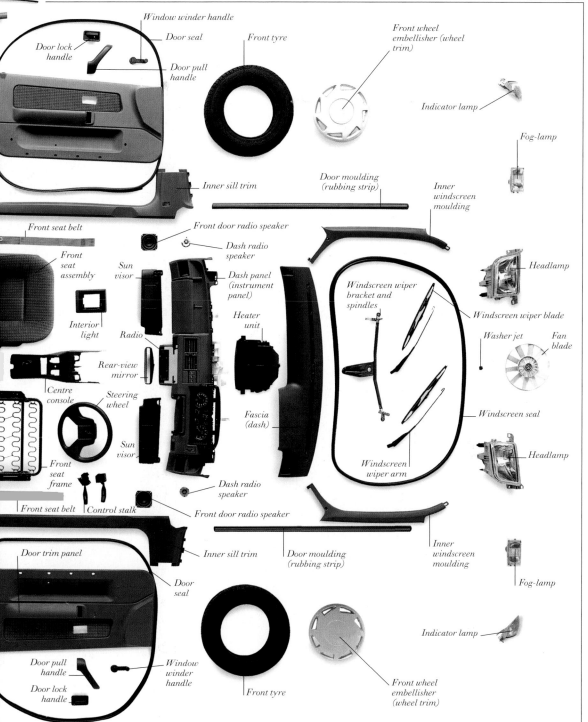

Window winder handle

Door seal

Front tyre

Front wheel embellisher (wheel trim)

Door lock handle

Door pull handle

Indicator lamp

Fog-lamp

Inner sill trim

Door moulding (rubbing strip)

Inner windscreen moulding

Front seat belt

Front door radio speaker

Dash radio speaker

Headlamp

Front seat assembly

Sun visor

Dash panel (instrument panel)

Windscreen wiper bracket and spindles

Windscreen wiper blade

Interior light

Heater unit

Washer jet

Fan blade

Radio

Rear-view mirror

Centre console

Steering wheel

Fascia (dash)

Windscreen seal

Sun visor

Headlamp

Front seat frame

Windscreen wiper arm

Front seat belt

Control stalk

Dash radio speaker

Front door radio speaker

Inner windscreen moulding

Door trim panel

Inner sill trim

Door moulding (rubbing strip)

Fog-lamp

Door seal

Door pull handle

Window winder handle

Indicator lamp

Door lock handle

Front tyre

Front wheel embellisher (wheel trim)

Hybrid car

THERE HAVE BEEN SEVERAL proposed alternatives to conventional petrol- or diesel-powered cars, including cars that use solar or battery power. The object is to lower harmful emissions and conserve natural resources. One of the alternatives already in production is the hybrid car. A hybrid vehicle uses two or more fuels. Examples include diesel-electric trains and mopeds. The latter combine the power of a petrol engine with pedal power. In a hybrid car, petrol consumption is reduced by the provision of additional power by an electric motor during acceleration. The motor is driven by power from on-board batteries that are recharged by an engine-driven generator when the car is decelerating or cruising. Some hybrid cars transfer energy from the wheels to a flywheel during braking. The flywheel drives the generator, which recharges the batteries.

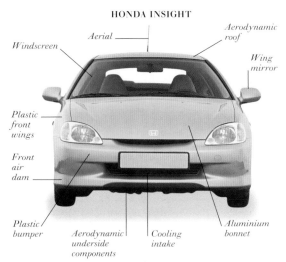

HONDA INSIGHT

Aerial

Aerodynamic roof

Windscreen

Wing mirror

Plastic front wings

Front air dam

Plastic bumper

Aerodynamic underside components

Cooling intake

Aluminium bonnet

SIDE VIEW OF 1-LITRE VTEC ENGINE

Motor power cables

Air-intake duct

Ignition coils

Coolant pipe

Electric motor housing

Lightweight plastic intake manifold

Lightweight magnesium alloy oil sump pan

Oil filter

Air conditioning compressor

FRONT VIEW OF 1-LITRE VTEC ENGINE

Rocker cover

Ignition coils

Dipstick

Water pump

Belt tensioner

Engine drive belt

Air conditioning compressor

Crankshaft pulley

Drive belt

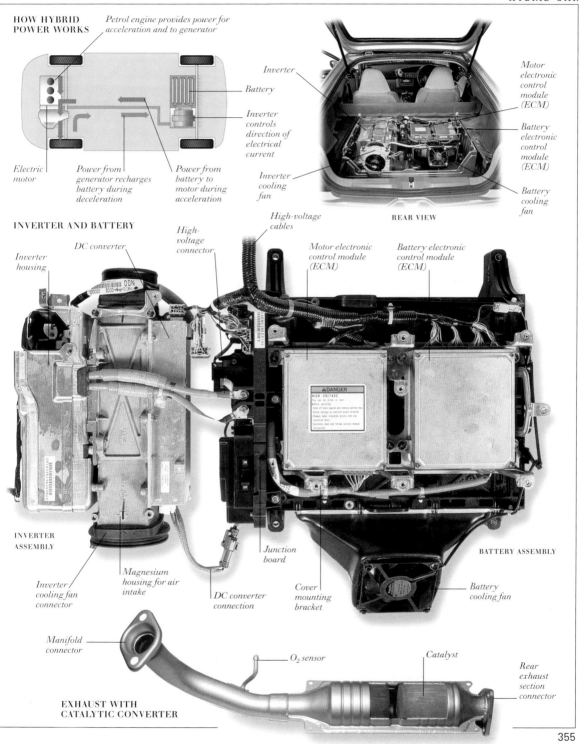

HOW HYBRID POWER WORKS

Petrol engine provides power for acceleration and to generator

Battery

Inverter controls direction of electrical current

Electric motor

Power from generator recharges battery during deceleration

Power from battery to motor during acceleration

Inverter

Motor electronic control module (ECM)

Battery electronic control module (ECM)

Inverter cooling fan

Battery cooling fan

REAR VIEW

INVERTER AND BATTERY

High-voltage cables

High-voltage connector

Inverter housing

DC converter

Motor electronic control module (ECM)

Battery electronic control module (ECM)

DANGER
HIGH VOLTAGE

INVERTER ASSEMBLY

BATTERY ASSEMBLY

Junction board

Inverter cooling fan connector

Magnesium housing for air intake

DC converter connection

Cover mounting bracket

Battery cooling fan

Manifold connector

O₂ sensor

Catalyst

Rear exhaust section connector

EXHAUST WITH CATALYTIC CONVERTER

Racing cars

SINCE MOTORING BEGAN, racing cars have been a major focus of innovation in car design. Features that are now commonplace, such as disc brakes, turbochargers, and even safety belts, were used first on competition cars. Research into racing cars has contributed to a new understanding of engine performance, aerodynamics, and tyre adhesion, and has led to the development of ultra-light materials such as carbon-fibre for car bodies. A modern McLaren Formula One car has a low, streamlined body and an open cockpit but, unlike its forerunner, it also has front and rear wings that push the wheels firmly on to the track, huge tyres for extra grip, and electronic sensors that continually relay information to the pits about the car's performance.

72° V10 ENGINE

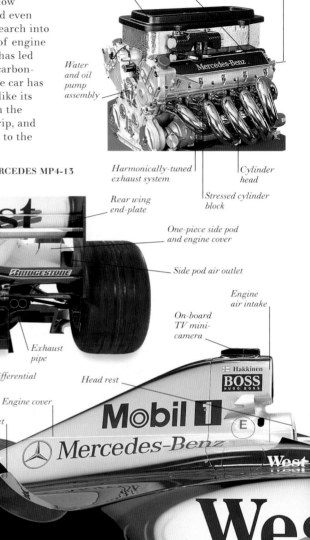

Fuel injection trumpet guard

Cam cover

Gearbox fixing stud

Water and oil pump assembly

Harmonically-tuned exhaust system

Cylinder head

Stressed cylinder block

BACK VIEW OF MCLAREN MERCEDES MP4-13

Upper flap

Grooved racing tyre

Warning light

Half-shaft

Diffuser

Exhaust pipe

Differential

Rear wing end-plate

One-piece side pod and engine cover

Side pod air outlet

Engine air intake

On-board TV mini-camera

Head rest

SIDE VIEW OF MCLAREN MERCEDES MP4-13

Engine cover

Winglet

Rear wing end-plate

Alloy wheel

Wheel nut

Side pod

OVERHEAD VIEW OF MCLAREN MERCEDES MP4-13

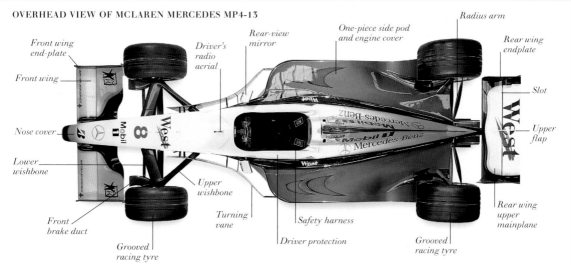

Front wing
end-plate

Front wing

Nose cover

Lower
wishbone

Front
brake duct

Grooved
racing tyre

Upper
wishbone

Turning
vane

Driver's
radio
aerial

Rear-view
mirror

One-piece side pod
and engine cover

Radius arm

Rear wing
endplate

Slot

Upper
flap

West

Rear wing
upper
mainplane

Grooved
racing tyre

Driver protection

Safety harness

FRONT VIEW OF MCLAREN MERCEDES MP4-13

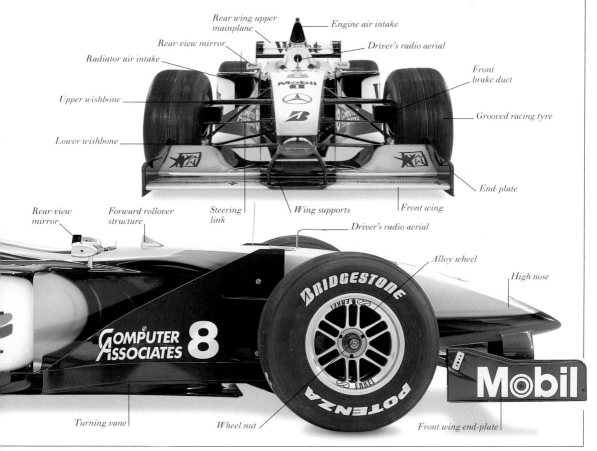

Rear wing upper
mainplane

Engine air intake

Rear-view mirror

Driver's radio aerial

Radiator air intake

Front
brake duct

Upper wishbone

Grooved racing tyre

Lower wishbone

End-plate

Rear-view
mirror

Forward rollover
structure

Steering
link

Wing supports

Front wing

Driver's radio aerial

Alloy wheel

High nose

Turning vane

Wheel nut

Front wing end-plate

357

Bicycle anatomy

THE BICYCLE IS A TWO-WHEELED, light-weight machine, which is propelled by human power. It is efficient, cheap, easily manufactured, and one of the world's most popular forms of transport. The first pedal-driven bicycle was built in Scotland in 1839. Since then the basic design – of a frame, wheels, brakes, handlebars, and saddle – has been gradually improved, with the addition of a chain, gear system, and pneumatic tyres (tyres inflated with air). The recent invention of the mountain bike (all-terrain bike) has been an important development. With its strong, rugged frame, wide tyres, and 21 gears, a mountain bike enables riders to reach rough and hilly areas that were previously inaccessible to cyclists.

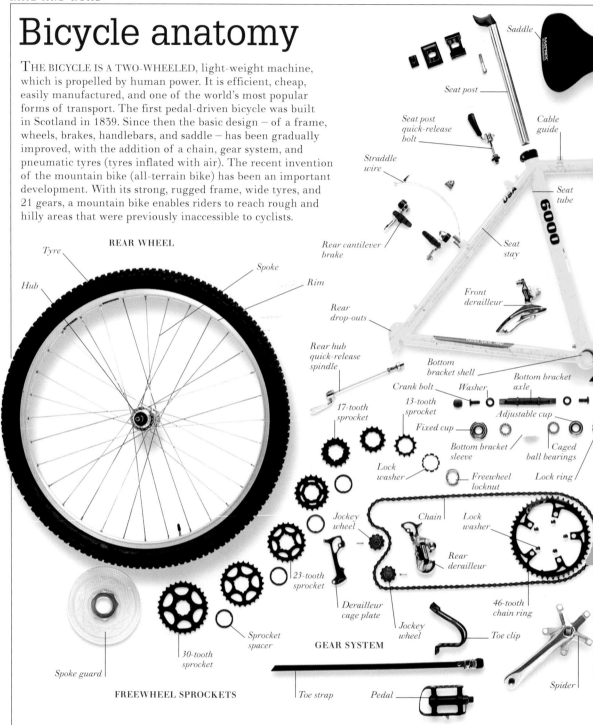

Saddle

Seat post

Seat post
quick-release
bolt

Cable
guide

Straddle
wire

Seat
tube

Rear cantilever
brake

6000

Seat
stay

Front
derailleur

REAR WHEEL

Tyre

Spoke

Hub

Rim

Rear
drop-outs

Rear hub
quick-release
spindle

Bottom
bracket shell

Bottom bracket
axle

Crank bolt

Washer

17-tooth
sprocket

13-tooth
sprocket

Adjustable cup

Fixed cup

Caged
ball bearings

Bottom bracket
sleeve

Lock
washer

Freewheel
locknut

Lock ring

Jockey
wheel

Chain

Lock
washer

Rear
derailleur

23-tooth
sprocket

Derailleur
cage plate

46-tooth
chain ring

Jockey
wheel

Toe clip

Sprocket
spacer

GEAR SYSTEM

30-tooth
sprocket

Spoke guard

Spider

FREEWHEEL SPROCKETS

Toe strap

Pedal

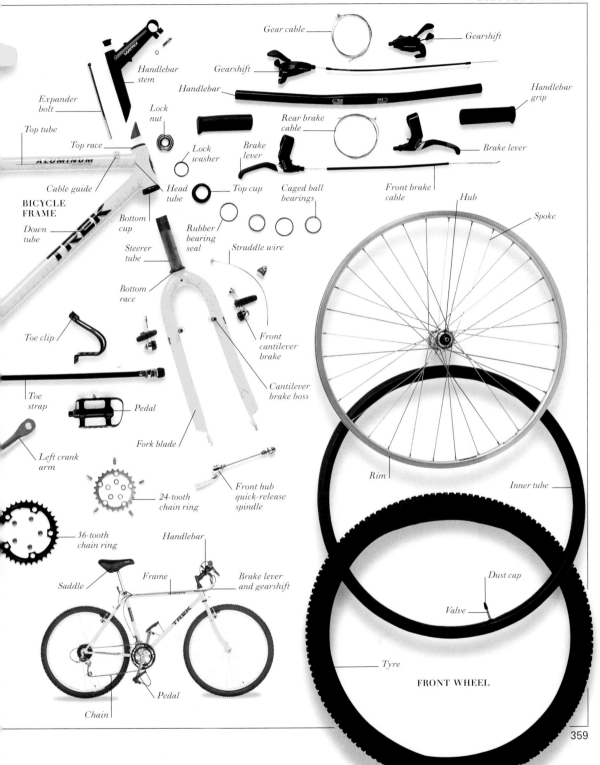

Gear cable

Gearshift

Gearshift

Handlebar stem

Handlebar

Handlebar grip

Expander bolt

Lock nut

Rear brake cable

Top tube

Top race

Lock washer

Brake lever

Brake lever

Cable guide

Head tube

Top cup

Caged ball bearings

Front brake cable

Hub

Spoke

BICYCLE FRAME

Down tube

Bottom cup

Rubber bearing seal

Straddle wire

Steerer tube

Bottom race

Front cantilever brake

Toe clip

Cantilever brake boss

Rim

Inner tube

Toe strap

Pedal

Fork blade

Left crank arm

24-tooth chain ring

Front hub quick-release spindle

36-tooth chain ring

Handlebar

Dust cap

Saddle

Frame

Brake lever and gearshift

Valve

Pedal

Tyre

FRONT WHEEL

Chain

359

Bicycles

ALTHOUGH ALL BICYCLES are made up of the same basic components, they can vary greatly in design. A racing bike, such as the Eddy Merckx model, with its light frame and steep head- and seat-angles, is built for speed. Its design forces the rider to adopt the "aerotuck", a crouched, aerodynamic position. While a touring bike resembles the racing bike in many respects, it is designed for comfort and stability on long-distance journeys. Touring bikes are characterized by more relaxed frame angles, heavy chain stays that support the rear panniers, and a long wheelbase (the distance between the wheel axles) for reliable handling. All-round bicycles, known as "hybrids", combine the light weight and speed of sports bikes with the rugged durability of mountain bikes (see pp. 358-359). Bicycles that are not designed for conventional road use include time-trial bikes, which have a short head tube, sloping top tube, "aero" handlebars, and aerodynamic tubing. Most Human Powered Vehicles (HPVs) are recumbents – the rider has a recumbent position – which maximize power output and minimize drag (resistance). Essential to the safety of all riders are helmets, and both front and rear lights; locks protect against theft.

FRONT AND REAR LIGHTS

White front light

Red rear light

HELMET

Hard outer shell

Air vent

Polystyrene padding

Quick-release strap

EDDY MERCKX RACING BICYCLE

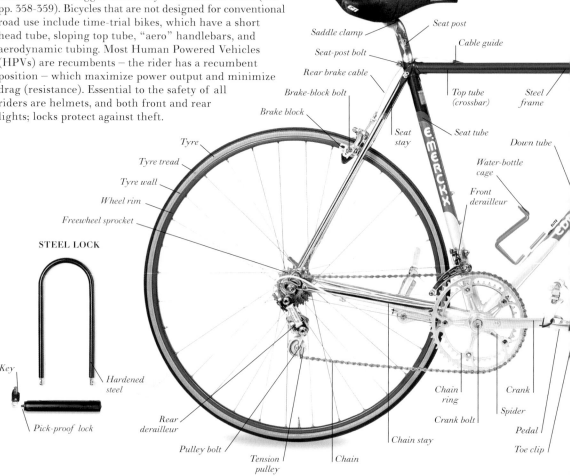

Saddle

Saddle clamp

Seat post

Cable guide

Seat-post bolt

Rear brake cable

Brake-block bolt

Top tube (crossbar)

Steel frame

Brake block

Seat stay

Seat tube

Down tube

Tyre

Water-bottle cage

Tyre tread

Front derailleur

Tyre wall

Wheel rim

Freewheel sprocket

STEEL LOCK

Key

Hardened steel

Pick-proof lock

Rear derailleur

Pulley bolt

Tension pulley

Chain

Chain ring

Crank bolt

Chain stay

Crank

Spider

Pedal

Toe clip

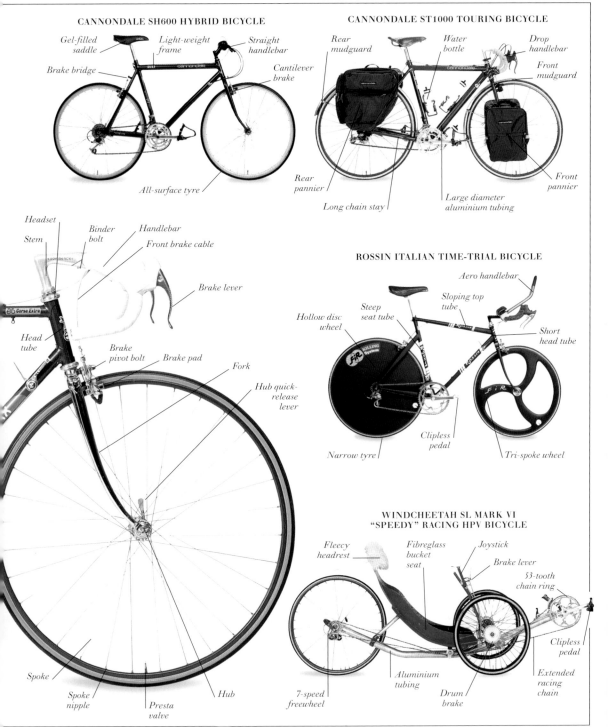

CANNONDALE SH600 HYBRID BICYCLE

Gel-filled saddle

Light-weight frame

Straight handlebar

Brake bridge

Cantilever brake

All-surface tyre

CANNONDALE ST1000 TOURING BICYCLE

Rear mudguard

Water bottle

Drop handlebar

Front mudguard

Rear pannier

Long chain stay

Large diameter aluminium tubing

Front pannier

Headset

Stem

Binder bolt

Handlebar

Front brake cable

Brake lever

Head tube

Brake pivot bolt

Brake pad

Fork

Hub quick-release lever

ROSSIN ITALIAN TIME-TRIAL BICYCLE

Aero handlebar

Steep seat tube

Sloping top tube

Hollow disc wheel

Short head tube

Narrow tyre

Clipless pedal

Tri-spoke wheel

WINDCHEETAH SL MARK VI "SPEEDY" RACING HPV BICYCLE

Fleecy headrest

Fibreglass bucket seat

Joystick

Brake lever

53-tooth chain ring

Clipless pedal

Aluminium tubing

Drum brake

Extended racing chain

7-speed freewheel

Spoke

Spoke nipple

Presta valve

Hub

The motorcycle

THE MOTORCYCLE HAS EVOLVED from a motorized cycle – a basic bicycle with an engine – into a sophisticated, high-performance machine. In 1901, the Werner brothers established the most viable location for the engine by positioning it low in the centre of the chassis (see pp. 364-365): the new Werner became the basis for the modern motorcycle. Motorcycles are used for many purposes – for commuting, delivering messages, touring, and racing – and different machines have been developed according to the demands of different types of riders. The Vespa scooter, for instance, which is small-wheeled, economical, and easy-to-ride, was designed to meet the needs of the commuter. Sidecars provided transport for the family until the arrival of cheap cars caused their popularity to decline. Enthusiast riders generally favour larger capacity machines that are capable of greater performance and offer more comfort. Four-cylinder machines have been common since the Honda CB750 appeared in 1969. Despite advances in motorcycle technology, many riders are attracted to the traditional looks of motorcycles like the twin-cylinder Harley-Davidson. The Harley-Davidson Glides exploit the style of the classic American V-twin engine, where the cylinders are placed in a V-formation.

1901 WERNER MOTORCYCLE

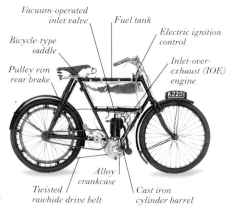

Vacuum-operated inlet valve
Fuel tank
Electric ignition control
Bicycle-type saddle
Pulley rim rear brake
Inlet-over-exhaust (IOE) engine
Alloy crankcase
Twisted rawhide drive belt
Cast iron cylinder barrel

1988 HARLEY-DAVIDSON FLHS ELECTRA GLIDE

1965 BMW R/60 WITH 1952 STEIB CHAIR

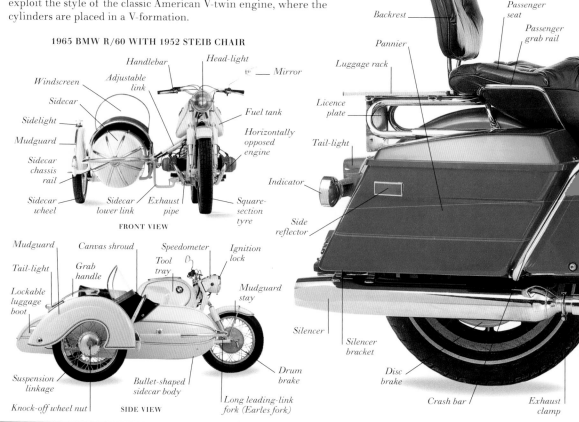

Backrest
Passenger seat
Passenger grab rail
Pannier
Luggage rack
Licence plate
Tail-light
Indicator
Side reflector
Silencer
Silencer bracket
Disc brake
Crash bar
Exhaust clamp

Handlebar
Head-light
Mirror
Windscreen
Adjustable link
Sidecar
Fuel tank
Sidelight
Horizontally opposed engine
Mudguard
Sidecar chassis rail
Sidecar wheel
Sidecar lower link
Exhaust pipe
Square-section tyre

FRONT VIEW

Mudguard
Canvas shroud
Speedometer
Ignition lock
Tail-light
Grab handle
Tool tray
Lockable luggage boot
Mudguard stay
Suspension linkage
Bullet-shaped sidecar body
Drum brake
Knock-off wheel nut
Long leading-link fork (Earles fork)

SIDE VIEW

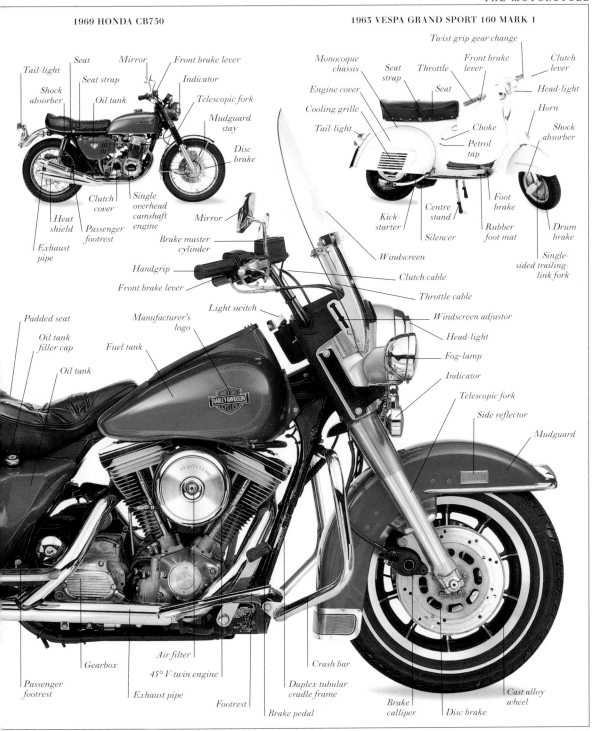

1969 HONDA CB750

Tail-light
Seat
Mirror
Front brake lever
Indicator
Seat strap
Shock absorber
Oil tank
Telescopic fork
Mudguard stay
Disc brake
Clutch cover
Single overhead camshaft engine
Mirror
Heat shield
Passenger footrest
Exhaust pipe

1963 VESPA GRAND SPORT 160 MARK 1

Twist grip gear change
Monocoque chassis
Seat strap
Throttle
Front brake lever
Clutch lever
Engine cover
Seat
Head-light
Cooling grille
Horn
Tail-light
Choke
Shock absorber
Petrol tap
Kick-starter
Centre stand
Foot brake
Drum brake
Silencer
Rubber foot mat
Single-sided trailing-link fork
Windscreen

Brake master cylinder
Handgrip
Clutch cable
Front brake lever
Throttle cable
Light switch
Windscreen adjustor
Head-light
Padded seat
Manufacturer's logo
Fog-lamp
Oil tank filler cap
Fuel tank
Indicator
Oil tank
Telescopic fork
Side reflector
Mudguard

HARLEY-DAVIDSON

EIGHTY CUBIC

Passenger footrest
Gearbox
Air filter
45° V-twin engine
Crash bar
Duplex tubular cradle frame
Brake calliper
Cast alloy wheel
Exhaust pipe
Footrest
Brake pedal
Disc brake

The motorcycle chassis

THE MOTORCYCLE CHASSIS is the main "body" of the motorcycle, to which the engine is attached. Consisting of the frame, wheels, suspension, and brakes, the chassis performs various functions. The frame, which is built from steel or alloy, keeps the wheels in line to maintain the handling of the motorcycle, and serves as a structure for mounting other components. The engine and gearbox unit is bolted into place, while items such as the seat, the mudguards, and the fairing are more easily removable. Suspension cushions the rider from irregularities in the road surface. In most suspension systems, coil springs controlled by an oil damper separate the main mass of the motorcycle from the wheels. At the front, the spring and damper are usually incorporated in a telescopic fork; the rear employs a pivoted swingarm. The suspension also helps to retain maximum contact between the tyres and the road, necessary to effective braking and steering. Drum brakes were common until the 1970s, but modern motorcycles use disc brakes, which are more powerful.

1985 HONDA VF750 WITH BODYWORK

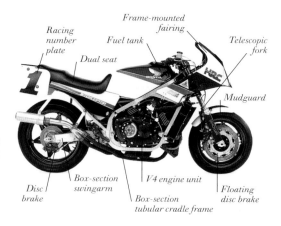

Racing number plate
Frame-mounted fairing
Fuel tank
Dual seat
Telescopic fork
Mudguard
Disc brake
Box-section swingarm
V4 engine unit
Box-section tubular cradle frame
Floating disc brake

1985 HONDA VF750 WITH BODYWORK REMOVED

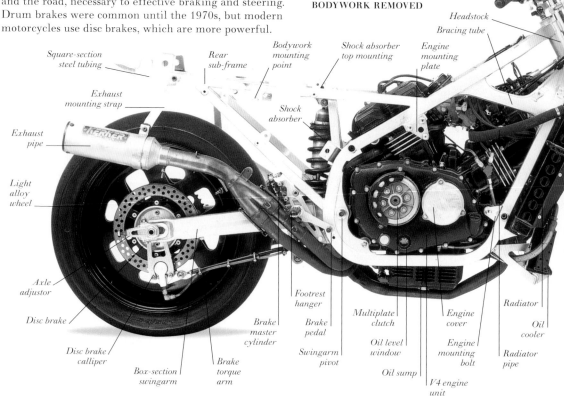

Brake master cylinder
Headstock
Bracing tube
Engine mounting plate
Shock absorber top mounting
Bodywork mounting point
Square-section steel tubing
Rear sub-frame
Shock absorber
Exhaust mounting strap
Exhaust pipe
Light alloy wheel
Axle adjustor
Disc brake
Disc brake calliper
Box-section swingarm
Brake torque arm
Brake master cylinder
Brake pedal
Footrest hanger
Swingarm pivot
Multiplate clutch
Oil level window
Oil sump
Engine cover
Engine mounting bolt
V4 engine unit
Radiator
Oil cooler
Radiator pipe

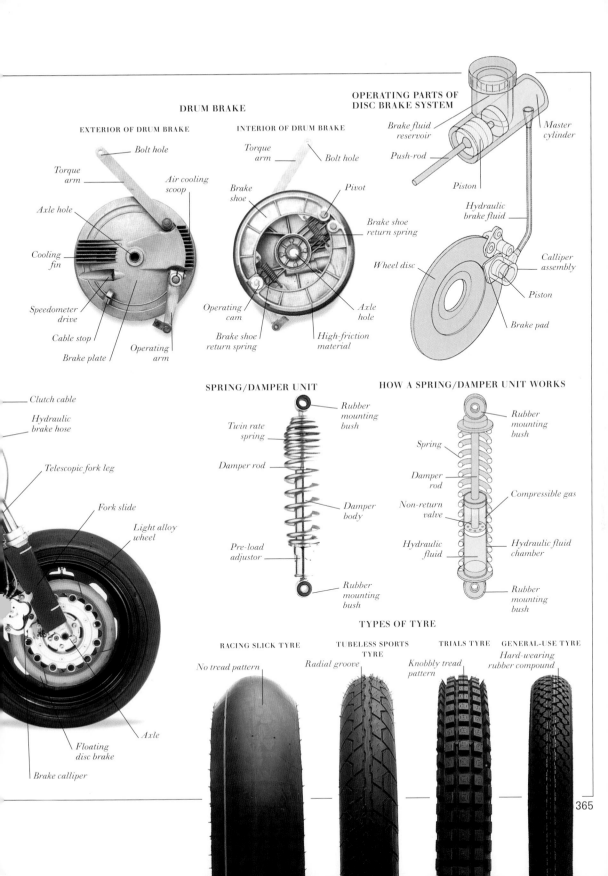

DRUM BRAKE

EXTERIOR OF DRUM BRAKE

Bolt hole

Torque arm

Air cooling scoop

Axle hole

Cooling fin

Speedometer drive

Cable stop

Brake plate

Operating arm

INTERIOR OF DRUM BRAKE

Torque arm

Bolt hole

Brake shoe

Pivot

Brake shoe return spring

Wheel disc

Operating cam

Brake shoe return spring

Axle hole

High-friction material

OPERATING PARTS OF DISC BRAKE SYSTEM

Brake fluid reservoir

Master cylinder

Push-rod

Piston

Hydraulic brake fluid

Calliper assembly

Piston

Brake pad

Clutch cable

Hydraulic brake hose

Telescopic fork leg

Fork slide

Light alloy wheel

Axle

Floating disc brake

Brake calliper

SPRING/DAMPER UNIT

Twin rate spring

Damper rod

Pre-load adjustor

Rubber mounting bush

Damper body

Rubber mounting bush

HOW A SPRING/DAMPER UNIT WORKS

Spring

Damper rod

Non-return valve

Hydraulic fluid

Rubber mounting bush

Compressible gas

Hydraulic fluid chamber

Rubber mounting bush

TYPES OF TYRE

RACING SLICK TYRE

No tread pattern

TUBELESS SPORTS TYRE

Radial groove

TRIALS TYRE

Knobbly tread pattern

GENERAL-USE TYRE

Hard-wearing rubber compound

Motorcycle engines

MOTORCYCLE ENGINES must be light-weight and compact, and have a good power output. They have between one and six cylinders, can be cooled by air or water, and the capacity of the combustion chamber varies from 49cc (cubic centimetres) to 1500cc. Two types of internal combustion engine are common: the four-stroke, which is used in cars (see pp. 342-343), and the two-stroke. A basic two-stroke engine has only three moving parts – the crankshaft, the connecting rod, and the piston – but the power output is high. The engine fires every two strokes (rather than every four), giving a "power stroke" every revolution (see p. 343). Power is conveyed from the engine to the rear wheel by the transmission system. This usually consists of a clutch, a gearbox, and a final drive system. Clutches are multiplate devices, which run in oil. Gearboxes have five or six speeds and are operated by foot pedal. Shaft and belt drive systems are used in some cases, but chain drive to the rear wheel is most common.

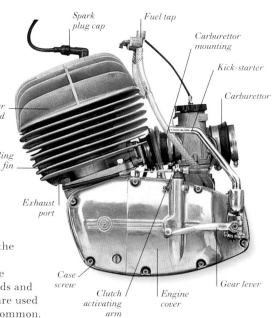

Spark plug cap

Fuel tap

Carburettor mounting

Kick-starter

Carburettor

Cylinder head

Cooling fin

Exhaust port

Case screw

Clutch activating arm

Engine cover

Gear lever

TRANSMISSION SYSTEM

GEARBOX

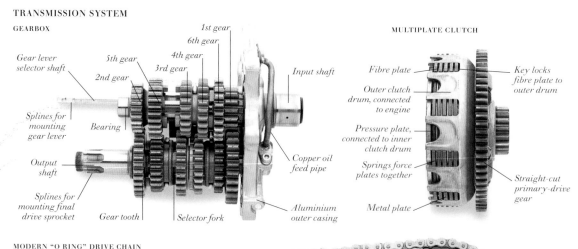

Gear lever selector shaft

5th gear

2nd gear

4th gear

3rd gear

6th gear

1st gear

Input shaft

Splines for mounting gear lever

Bearing

Output shaft

Splines for mounting final drive sprocket

Gear tooth

Selector fork

Copper oil feed pipe

Aluminium outer casing

MULTIPLATE CLUTCH

Fibre plate

Outer clutch drum, connected to engine

Pressure plate, connected to inner clutch drum

Springs force plates together

Metal plate

Key locks fibre plate to outer drum

Straight-cut primary-drive gear

MODERN "O RING" DRIVE CHAIN

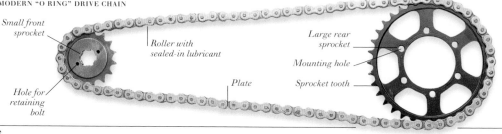

Small front sprocket

Roller with sealed-in lubricant

Large rear sprocket

Mounting hole

Sprocket tooth

Hole for retaining bolt

Plate

**VELOCETTE OVERHEAD
VALVE (OHV) ENGINE**

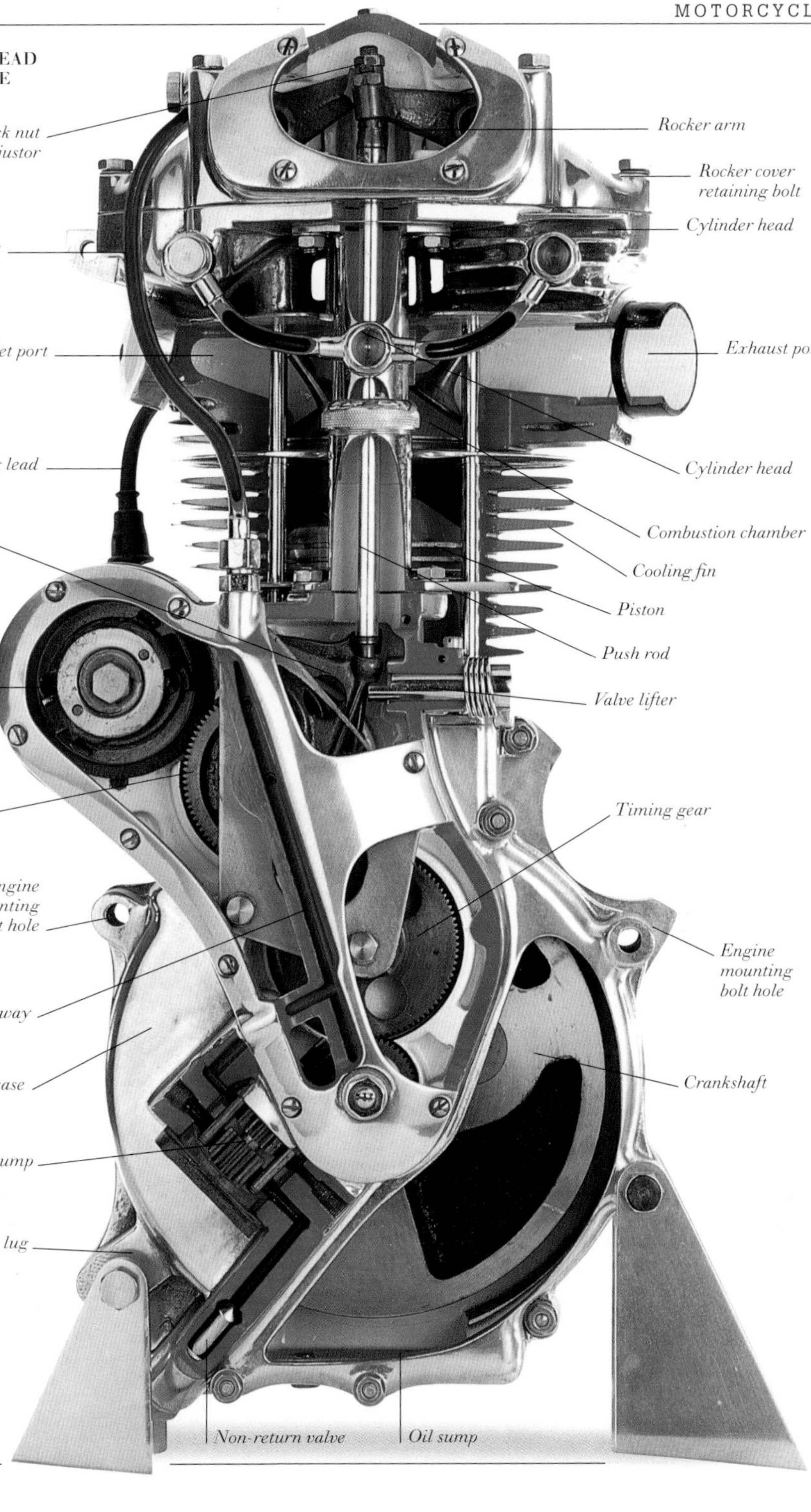

Screw and lock nut
tappet adjustor

Oil feed pipe

Inlet port

Spark plug lead

Cam follower

Magneto drive

Camshaft gear

Engine
mounting
bolt hole

Oil passageway

Crankcase

Oil pump

Mounting lug

Rocker arm

Rocker cover
retaining bolt

Cylinder head

Exhaust port

Cylinder head

Combustion chamber

Cooling fin

Piston

Push rod

Valve lifter

Timing gear

Engine
mounting
bolt hole

Crankshaft

Non-return valve

Oil sump

367

Competition motorcycles

THERE ARE MANY TYPES of motorcycle sport and in each, a specialist machine has evolved to perform to specific requirements. Races take place on roads or tracks or "off-road", in fields, dirt tracks, and even the desert. "Grand Prix" world championships in road-racing are contested by three classes: 125cc, 250cc two-strokes; the top class of 500cc two-strokes; and 900cc four-stroke machines. The latest racing sidecars have more in common with racing cars than motorcycles. The rider and passenger operate within an all-enclosing, aerodynamic fairing. The Suzuki RGV500 shown here, like other Grand Prix machines, carries advertising, which helps to cover the cost of developing motorcycle technology. In Speedway, which originated in the US in 1902, motorcycles operate without brakes or a gearbox. Off-road competition motorcycles have less emphasis on high power output. In Motocross, for example, which is held on rough terrain, they must have high ground clearance, flexible long-travel suspension, and tyres with a chunky tread pattern.

1992 HUSQVARNA MOTOCROSS TC610

Throttle cable
Hand protector
Flexible plastic mudguard
Telescopic fork
Plastic guard
Axle
Knobbly tyre
Disc brake
Brake calliper
Handlebar brace
Radiator air vent
Overhead camshaft engine
Gear lever
Shock absorber
Alloy swingarm
Long seat
Racing number
Light-weight exhaust system
Disc brake
Shock absorber linkage

1992 SUZUKI RGV500
SIDE VIEW

Exhaust pipe
Racing number
Air vent
One-piece seat and tail unit
Minimal seat padding
Shock absorber
Arched alloy swingarm

Exhaust pipe
Vent
Handlebar
Footrest
Rear brake pedal
Drive chain
Wide, slick tyre

Exhaust pipe
Silencer
Shock absorber mounting
Three-spoke alloy wheel
Exhaust pipe
Axle adjustor
Disc brake
Rear brake calliper
Slick racing tyre
Drive chain
Footrest
Brake pedal
Disc brake master cylinder
Light-weight alloy frame

REAR VIEW

1981 WESLAKE SPEEDWAY

1968 KIRBY BSA RACING SIDECAR

FRONT VIEW

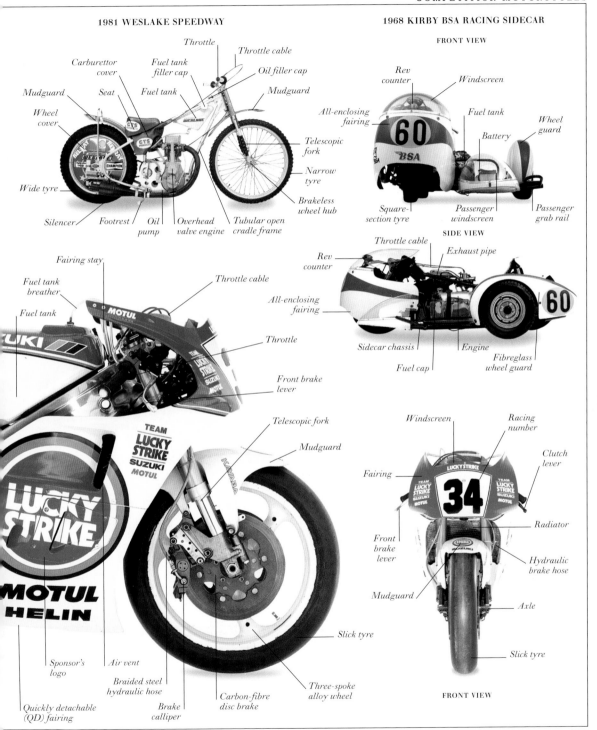

Throttle

Throttle cable

Carburettor cover

Fuel tank filler cap

Oil filler cap

Fuel tank

Mudguard

Mudguard

Seat

Wheel cover

Telescopic fork

Narrow tyre

Brakeless wheel hub

Wide tyre

Silencer

Footrest

Oil pump

Overhead valve engine

Tubular open cradle frame

Rev counter

Windscreen

All-enclosing fairing

Fuel tank

Battery

Wheel guard

Square-section tyre

Passenger windscreen

Passenger grab rail

SIDE VIEW

Throttle cable

Exhaust pipe

Rev counter

All-enclosing fairing

Sidecar chassis

Fuel cap

Engine

Fibreglass wheel guard

Fairing stay

Throttle cable

Fuel tank breather

Fuel tank

Throttle

Front brake lever

Telescopic fork

Mudguard

Windscreen

Racing number

Fairing

Clutch lever

Front brake lever

Radiator

Mudguard

Hydraulic brake hose

Axle

Sponsor's logo

Air vent

Braided steel hydraulic hose

Brake calliper

Carbon-fibre disc brake

Three-spoke alloy wheel

Slick tyre

Quickly detachable (QD) fairing

Slick tyre

FRONT VIEW

369

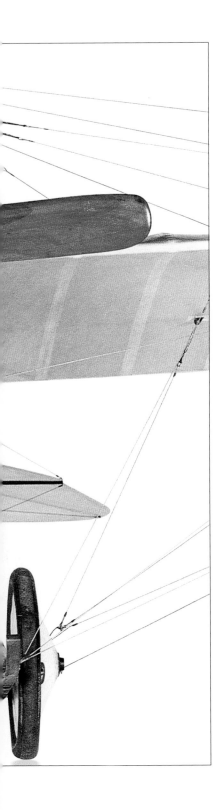

SEA AND AIR

Ships of Greece and Rome

ROMAN ANCHOR

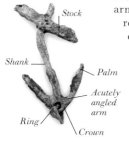

Stock

Shank

Palm

Acutely angled arm

Ring

Crown

IN THE EXPANSIVE EMPIRES OF GREECE AND ROME, powerful fleets were needed for battle, trade, and communication. Greek galleys were powered by a sail and many oars. A new armament, the embolos (ram), was fitted on to the galley bow. As ramming duels required fast and manoeuvrable boats, extra rows of oarsmen were added, culminating in the trireme. During the fifth and fourth centuries B.C., the trireme dominated the Mediterranean. It was powered by 170 oarsmen, rowing with one oar each. The oarsmen were ranged on three levels, as the model opposite shows. The trireme also carried archers and soldiers for boarding. Galleys were pulled out of the water when not in use, and were kept in dockyard ship-sheds. The merchant ships of the Greeks and Romans were mighty vessels too. The full-bodied Roman corbita, for example, could hold up to 400 tons and carried a cargo of spices, gems, silk, and animals. The construction of these boats was based on a stout hull with planking secured by mortice and tenon. Some of these ships embarked on long voyages, sailing even as far as India. To make them easier to steer, corbitas set a fore sail called an "artemon". It flew from a forward-leaning mast that was a forerunner of the long bowsprits carried by the great clipper ships of the 19th century.

ROMAN CORBITA

Roband (rope band)

Ceruchi (lift)

Double halyard

Bullseye

Fore mast

Buntline

Heraldic device

Ring

Antenna (yard)

Brace

Ruden (brail line)

Fore stay

Artemon (fore sail)

Oculus (eye)

Anchor

Tabling

Sheet

Bolt rope

Prow

Windlass

Scala (ladder)

Catena (riding bitt)

Ancorale (anchor rope; anchor rode)

Hatch board

Deck beam

Zosteres (rubbing strake)

Cargo hold

ATTIC VASE SHOWING A GALLEY

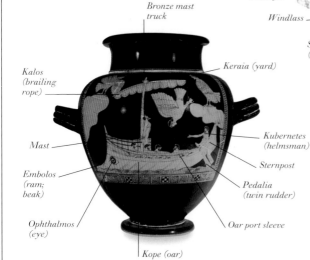

Bronze mast truck

Keraia (yard)

Kalos (brailing rope)

Mast

Kubernetes (helmsman)

Embolos (ram; beak)

Sternpost

Pedalia (twin rudder)

Ophthalmos (eye)

Oar port sleeve

Kope (oar)

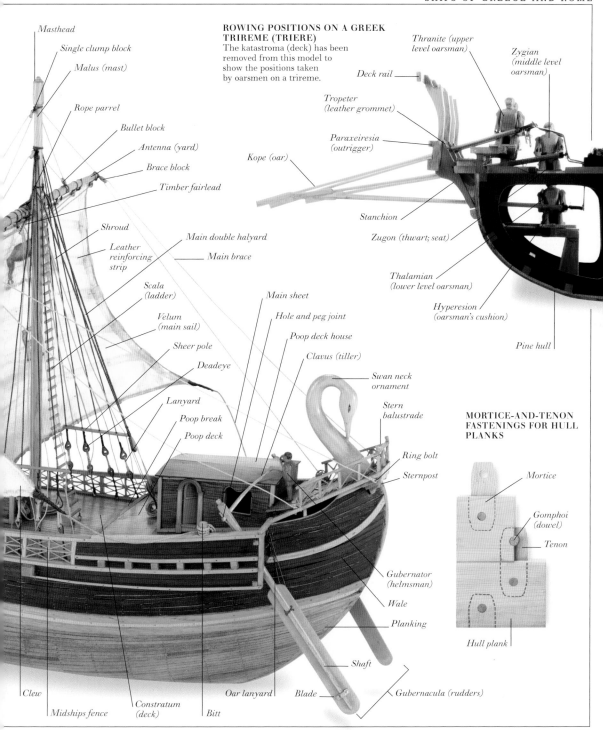

Masthead

Single clump block

Malus (mast)

Rope parrel

Bullet block

Antenna (yard)

Brace block

Timber fairlead

Shroud

Leather reinforcing strip

Scala (ladder)

Velum (main sail)

Sheer pole

Deadeye

Lanyard

Poop break

Poop deck

Clew

Midships fence

Constratum (deck)

Bitt

ROWING POSITIONS ON A GREEK TRIREME (TRIERE)
The katastroma (deck) has been removed from this model to show the positions taken by oarsmen on a trireme.

Deck rail

Tropeter (leather grommet)

Paraxeiresia (outrigger)

Kope (oar)

Stanchion

Zugon (thwart; seat)

Main double halyard

Main brace

Main sheet

Hole and peg joint

Poop deck house

Clavus (tiller)

Swan neck ornament

Stern balustrade

Ring bolt

Sternpost

Gubernator (helmsman)

Wale

Planking

Shaft

Blade

Oar lanyard

Gubernacula (rudders)

Thranite (upper level oarsman)

Zygian (middle level oarsman)

Thalamian (lower level oarsman)

Hyperesion (oarsman's cushion)

Pine hull

MORTICE-AND-TENON FASTENINGS FOR HULL PLANKS

Mortice

Gomphoi (dowel)

Tenon

Hull plank

Viking ships

IN THE DARK AGES and early medieval times, the longships of Scandinavia were one of the most feared sights for people of northern Europe. The Vikings launched raids from Scandinavia every summer in longships equipped with a single steering oar on the right, or "steerboard", side (hence "starboard"). A longship had one row of oars on each side and a single sail. The hull had clinker (overlapping) planks. Prowheads adorned fighting ships during campaigns of war. The sailing longship was also used for local coastal travel. The karv below was probably built as transport for an important family, while the smaller faering (top right) was a rowing boat only. The fleet of William of Normandy that invaded England in 1066 owed much to the Viking boatbuilding tradition, and has been depicted in the Bayeux Tapestry (above). Seals used by port towns and royal courts through the ages provide an excellent record of contemporary ship design. The seal opposite shows how ships changed from the Viking period to the end of the Middle Ages. The introduction of the fighting platform – the castle – and the addition of extra masts and sails changed the character of the medieval ship. Note also that the steering oar has been replaced by a centred rudder.

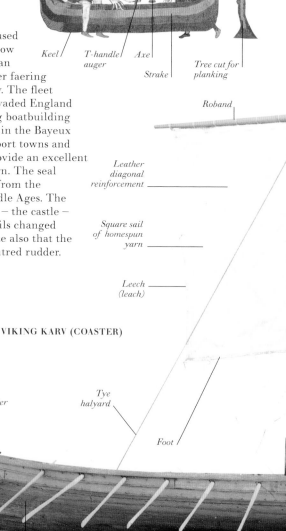

Shave

Broad axe

Breast auger

Sheer

Master shipwright

Stempost

Hood end

Keel

T-handle auger

Axe

Strake

Tree cut for planking

Roband

Leather diagonal reinforcement

Square sail of homespun yarn

Leech (leach)

Zoomorphic head

Eye

Tooth

Braiding

Serpentine neck

Lozenge-shaped recess

Rectangular cross-band

Snake-tail ornament

VIKING KARV (COASTER)

Tye halyard

Tiller

Sternpost

Boss (rudder pivot)

Foot

DRAGON PROWHEAD

Steering oar (side rudder)

Oar

Starboard (steerboard) side

Keel

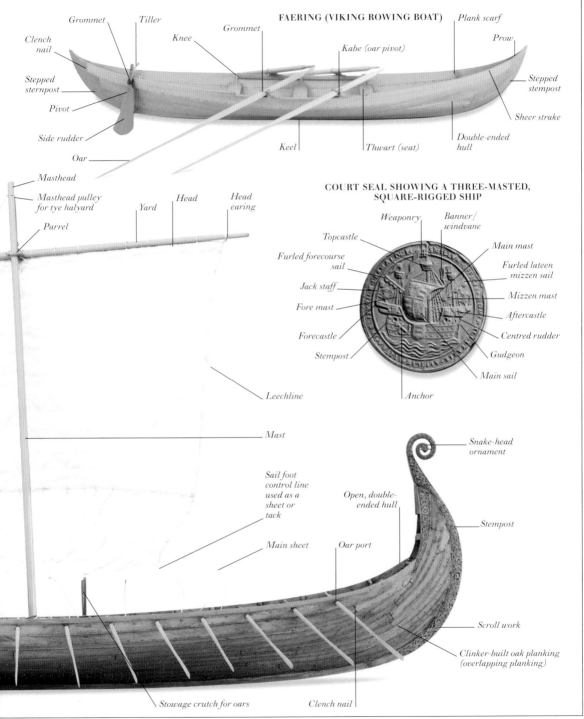

FAERING (VIKING ROWING BOAT)

Grommet

Tiller

Clench nail

Knee

Grommet

Plank scarf

Prow

Kabe (oar pivot)

Stepped sternpost

Pivot

Stepped stempost

Side rudder

Sheer strake

Oar

Keel

Thwart (seat)

Double-ended hull

Masthead

Masthead pulley for tye halyard

Yard

Head

Head earing

COURT SEAL SHOWING A THREE-MASTED, SQUARE-RIGGED SHIP

Parrel

Weaponry

Banner/ windvane

Topcastle

Main mast

Furled forecourse sail

Furled lateen mizzen sail

Jack staff

Mizzen mast

Fore mast

Aftercastle

Forecastle

Centred rudder

Stempost

Gudgeon

Leechline

Main sail

Anchor

Mast

Snake-head ornament

Sail foot control line used as a sheet or tack

Open, double-ended hull

Stempost

Main sheet

Oar port

Scroll work

Clinker-built oak planking (overlapping planking)

Stowage crutch for oars

Clench nail

Medieval warships and traders

FROM THE 16TH CENTURY, SHIPS WERE BUILT WITH A NEW FORM OF HULL, constructed from carvel (edge-to-edge) planking. Warships of the time, like King Henry VIII of England's Mary Rose, boasted awesome fire power. This ship carried both long-range cannon in bronze, and short-range, anti-personnel guns in iron. Elsewhere, ships took on a multiformity of shapes. Dhows transported slaves from East Africa to Arabia, their fore-and-aft rigged lateen sails allowing them to sail close to the wind around the lands of the Indian Ocean. The Chinese sailed to East Africa and Arabia in junks, trading goods that were carried in watertight compartments. New astronomical tools helped medieval sailors to find their way. Cross-staves and astrolabes were used to measure the altitude of the sun or stars. One of a choice of four cross-pieces was slid up or down the staff of the cross-stave – which was graduated in degrees of altitude – until its top aligned with the celestial body and its base with the horizon. The sighting rule of the astrolabe was simply lined up with a known body, and its altitude read from marks on the metal disc. With sundials, the sailor could use the shadow of the sun to show the time of day.

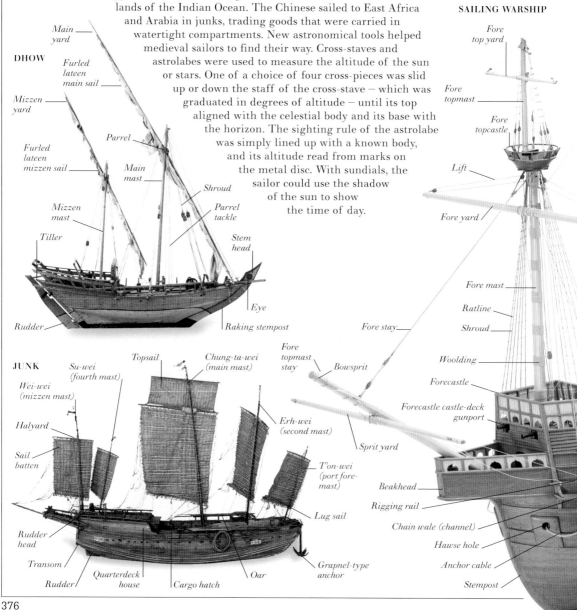

DHOW

Main yard
Furled lateen main sail
Mizzen yard
Furled lateen mizzen sail
Parrel
Main mast
Mizzen mast
Tiller
Shroud
Parrel tackle
Stem head
Rudder
Eye
Raking stempost

JUNK

Su-wei (fourth mast)
Wei-wei (mizzen mast)
Topsail
Chung-ta-wei (main mast)
Fore topmast stay
Bowsprit
Halyard
Sail batten
Erh-wei (second mast)
Sprit yard
T'on-wei (port fore-mast)
Rudder head
Transom
Rudder
Quarterdeck house
Cargo hatch
Oar
Lug sail
Grapnel-type anchor
Fore stay

SAILING WARSHIP

Fore top yard
Fore topmast
Fore topcastle
Lift
Fore yard
Fore mast
Ratline
Shroud
Woolding
Forecastle
Forecastle castle-deck gunport
Beakhead
Rigging rail
Chain wale (channel)
Hawse hole
Anchor cable
Stempost

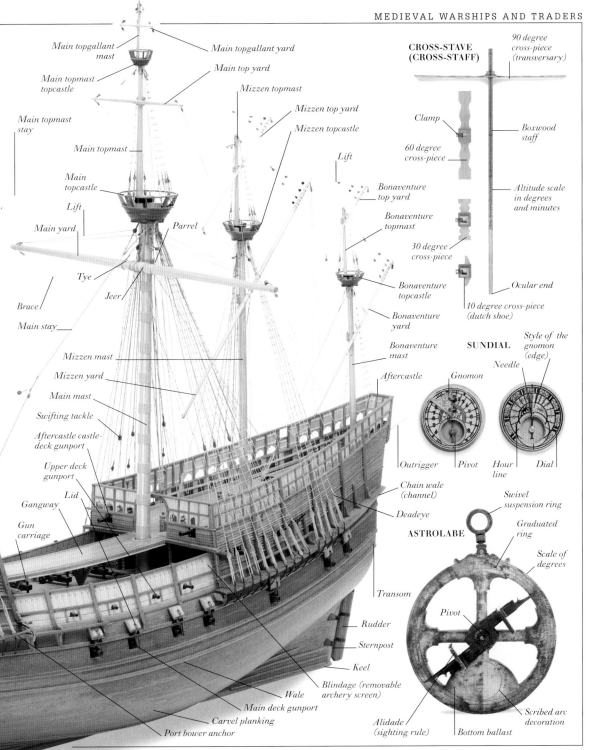

Main topgallant mast

Main topgallant yard

Main topmast topcastle

Main top yard

Mizzen topmast

Main topmast stay

Mizzen top yard

Mizzen topcastle

Main topmast

Lift

Main topcastle

Bonaventure top yard

Lift

Bonaventure topmast

Main yard

Parrel

Brace

Tye

Jeer

Bonaventure topcastle

Main stay

Bonaventure yard

Bonaventure mast

Mizzen mast

Aftercastle

Mizzen yard

Main mast

Swifting tackle

Aftercastle castle-deck gunport

Upper deck gunport

Lid

Chain wale (channel)

Gangway

Deadeye

Gun carriage

Outrigger

Pivot

Hour line

Dial

Transom

Rudder

Sternpost

Keel

Blindage (removable archery screen)

Wale

Main deck gunport

Carvel planking

Port bower anchor

CROSS-STAVE (CROSS-STAFF)

90 degree cross-piece (transversary)

Clamp

Boxwood staff

60 degree cross-piece

Altitude scale in degrees and minutes

30 degree cross-piece

Ocular end

10 degree cross-piece (dutch shoe)

SUNDIAL

Style of the gnomon (edge)

Needle

Gnomon

Swivel suspension ring

ASTROLABE

Graduated ring

Scale of degrees

Pivot

Alidade (sighting rule)

Scribed arc decoration

Bottom ballast

The expansion of sail

BY THE 18TH CENTURY, SAILING SHIPS had become fast and effective floating fortresses. The navies of the north European powers competed with each other by building heavily-armed fighting ships called "men-of-war". The distinctive round stern of the ship below, with its open gallery, balcony, and elaborate wood carving is typical of the period. Hulls around this time were semicircular in cross section, although many boat designers were soon to return to the V-shaped hulls used by the Vikings. Ships of the period carried more sail than ever before. A labyrinth of rigging supported the masts and yards from which the profusion of square sails were set. Ships grew higher, as extra masts were fitted above the lower mast, and the bowsprit became longer to allow the ship to carry staysails, spritsails, and jibsails. Ships went into battle in single file, so that broadsides from the multiple decks of guns would have maximum effect. Ships were classified by rates, the rating of a vessel depending on how many guns it had. A first rate ship had more than 100 guns. The guns fired solid round shot, usually made of iron.

WOODEN SAILING SHIP

BOW

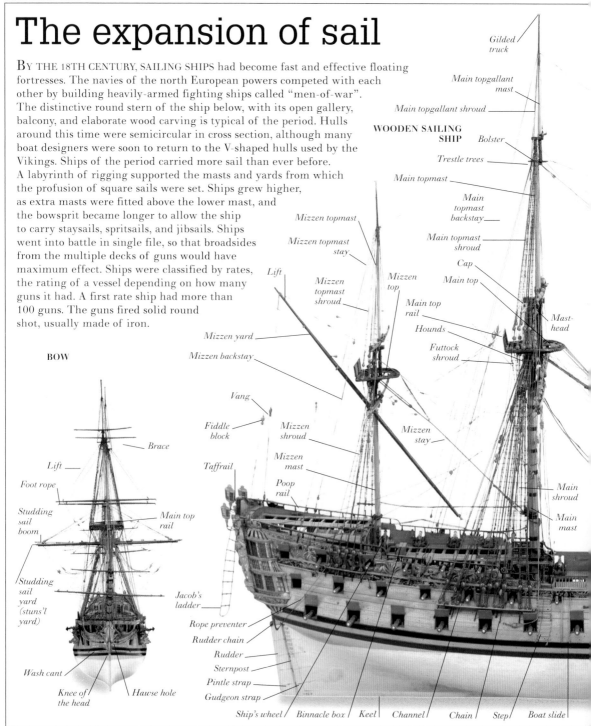

Gilded truck

Main topgallant mast

Main topgallant shroud

Bolster

Trestle trees

Main topmast

Main topmast backstay

Main topmast shroud

Cap

Main top

Masthead

Main top rail

Hounds

Futtock shroud

Mizzen topmast

Mizzen topmast stay

Mizzen top

Main top rail

Lift

Mizzen topmast shroud

Mizzen yard

Mizzen backstay

Vang

Fiddle block

Mizzen shroud

Mizzen stay

Mizzen mast

Mizzen stay

Main shroud

Main mast

Taffrail

Poop rail

Brace

Lift

Foot rope

Studding sail boom

Main top rail

Studding sail yard (stuns'l yard)

Jacob's ladder

Rope preventer

Rudder chain

Rudder

Sternpost

Pintle strap

Gudgeon strap

Wash cant

Knee of the head

Hawse hole

Ship's wheel

Binnacle box

Keel

Channel

Chain

Step

Boat slide

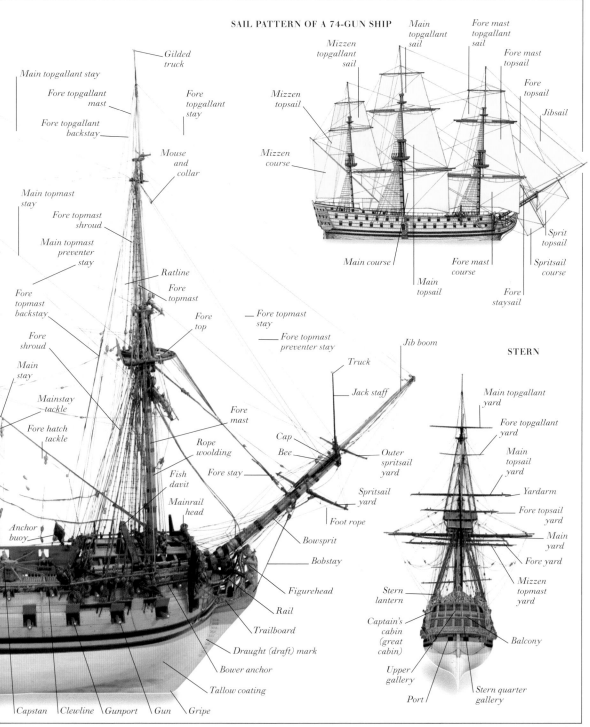

SAIL PATTERN OF A 74-GUN SHIP

Mizzen topgallant sail

Main topgallant sail

Fore mast topgallant sail

Fore mast topsail

Fore topsail

Mizzen topsail

Jibsail

Mizzen course

Main course

Main topsail

Fore mast course

Sprit topsail

Fore staysail

Fore mast topgallant sail

Spritsail course

Gilded truck

Main topgallant stay

Fore topgallant mast

Fore topgallant stay

Fore topgallant backstay

Mouse and collar

Main topmast stay

Fore topmast shroud

Main topmast preventer stay

Ratline

Fore topmast

Fore topmast backstay

Fore top

Fore shroud

Main stay

Mainstay tackle

Fore hatch tackle

Anchor buoy

Fore topmast stay

Fore topmast preventer stay

Fore mast

Rope woolding

Fish davit

Mainrail head

Jib boom

STERN

Truck

Jack staff

Cap

Bee

Fore stay

Outer spritsail yard

Spritsail yard

Foot rope

Bowsprit

Bobstay

Figurehead

Rail

Trailboard

Draught (draft) mark

Bower anchor

Tallow coating

Capstan Clewline Gunport Gun Gripe

Main topgallant yard

Fore topgallant yard

Main topsail yard

Yardarm

Fore topsail yard

Main yard

Fore yard

Mizzen topmast yard

Stern lantern

Captain's cabin (great cabin)

Balcony

Upper gallery

Stern quarter gallery

Port

A ship of the line

THE 74-GUN WOODEN SHIP WAS A MAINSTAY of British and French battlefleets in the late 18th and early 19th centuries. This "ship of the line" was heavy enough to fight with the most potent of rivals, yet nimble too. The length of such a ship was determined by the number of guns required for each deck, allowing enough room for crews to man them. The gun deck was about 52 m (170 ft) long. The decks had to be very strong to carry the weight of the guns. The deck planks have been removed on the vessel pictured below, to show just how close together the beams had to be to make the hull strong enough. Only timber with a perfect grain was used. The upper deck was open at the waist, but afore and abaft were officers' cabins. The forecastle and quarterdeck carried light guns and acted as platforms for working rigging and for reconnaissance. The ship's longboats (launches) were carried on booms between the gangways.

LONGBOAT

UPPER DECK OF A 74-GUN SHIP

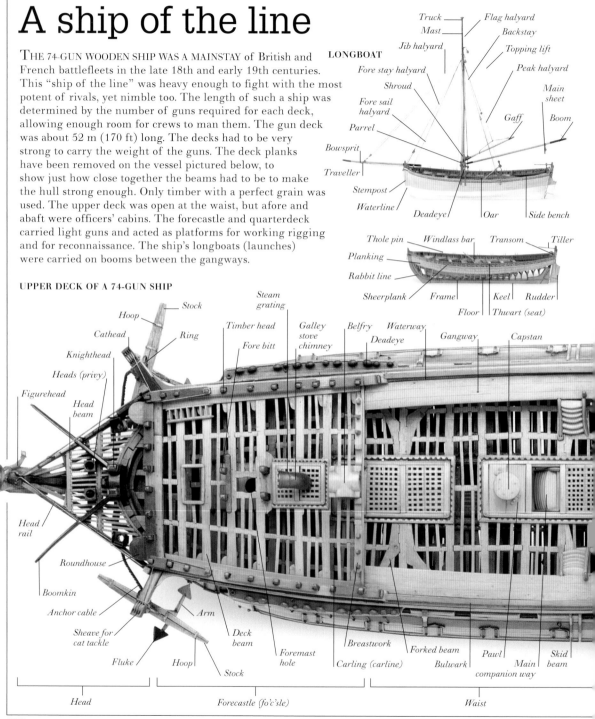

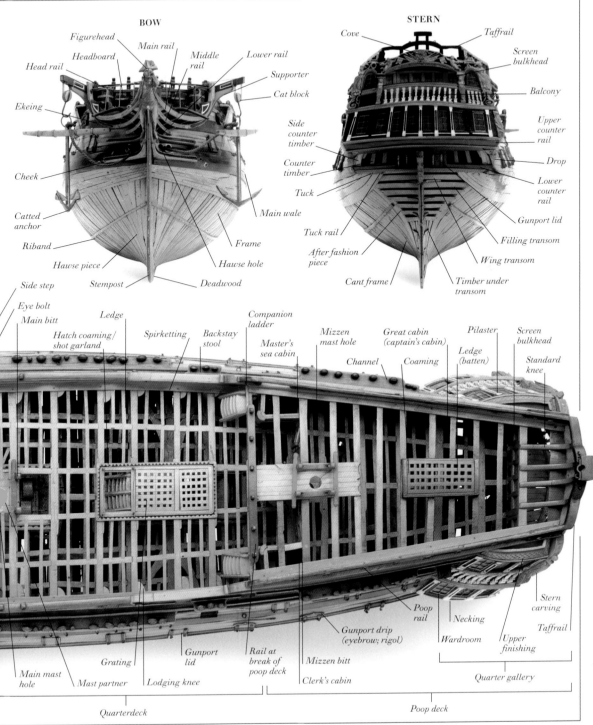

BOW

Figurehead
Main rail
Headboard
Middle rail
Lower rail
Head rail
Supporter
Cat block
Ekeing
Cheek
Catted anchor
Riband
Main wale
Frame
Hawse piece
Hawse hole
Side step
Stempost
Deadwood

STERN

Cove
Taffrail
Screen bulkhead
Balcony
Upper counter rail
Side counter timber
Drop
Counter timber
Lower counter rail
Tuck
Gunport lid
Tuck rail
Filling transom
After fashion piece
Wing transom
Cant frame
Timber under transom

Eye bolt
Main bitt
Ledge
Companion ladder
Mizzen mast hole
Great cabin (captain's cabin)
Pilaster
Screen bulkhead
Hatch coaming/ shot garland
Spirketting
Backstay stool
Master's sea cabin
Channel
Coaming
Ledge (batten)
Standard knee
Poop rail
Necking
Stern carving
Taffrail
Gunport drip (eyebrow; rigol)
Wardroom
Upper finishing
Main mast hole
Grating
Gunport lid
Rail at break of poop deck
Mizzen bitt
Clerk's cabin
Quarter gallery
Mast partner
Lodging knee
Quarterdeck
Poop deck

Rigging

MOST SAILING SHIPS HAVE TWO TYPES OF RIGGING. Standing rigging – kept taut by rigging screws or old-fashioned lanyards and deadeyes – refers to the ropes, wires, and chains that support the masts and yards (horizontal spars). Running rigging, which includes types of block and tackle, halyards, and sheets, is used to hoist, lower, or trim sails.

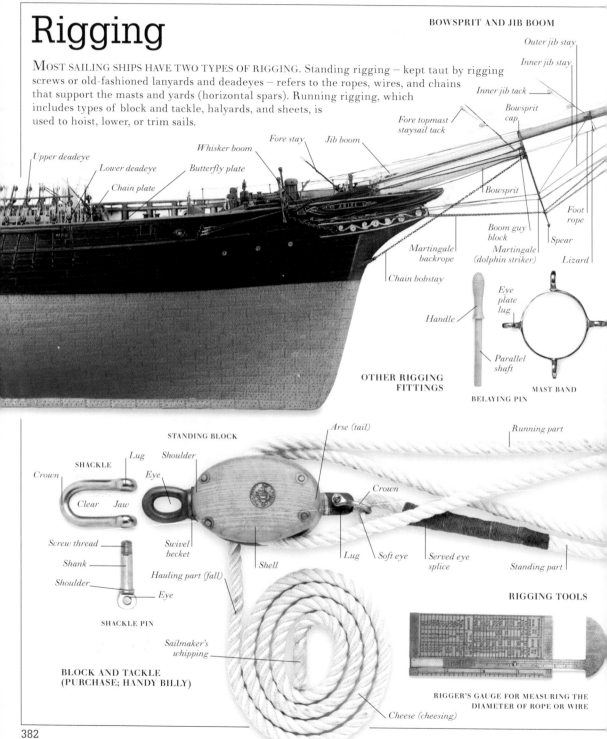

BOWSPRIT AND JIB BOOM

Outer jib stay
Inner jib stay
Inner jib tack
Bowsprit cap
Fore topmast staysail tack
Fore stay
Jib boom
Whisker boom
Butterfly plate
Upper deadeye
Lower deadeye
Chain plate
Bowsprit
Boom guy block
Martingale backrope
Martingale (dolphin striker)
Spear
Lizard
Foot rope
Chain bobstay

OTHER RIGGING FITTINGS

Handle
Eye plate lug
Parallel shaft
BELAYING PIN
MAST BAND

STANDING BLOCK
Arse (tail)
Running part
Shoulder
SHACKLE
Lug
Eye
Crown
Crown
Clear
Jaw
Swivel becket
Shell
Lug
Soft eye
Served eye splice
Standing part
Screw thread
Shank
Shoulder
Eye
Hauling part (fall)
SHACKLE PIN

RIGGING TOOLS

Sailmaker's whipping

BLOCK AND TACKLE (PURCHASE; HANDY BILLY)

RIGGER'S GAUGE FOR MEASURING THE DIAMETER OF ROPE OR WIRE

Cheese (cheesing)

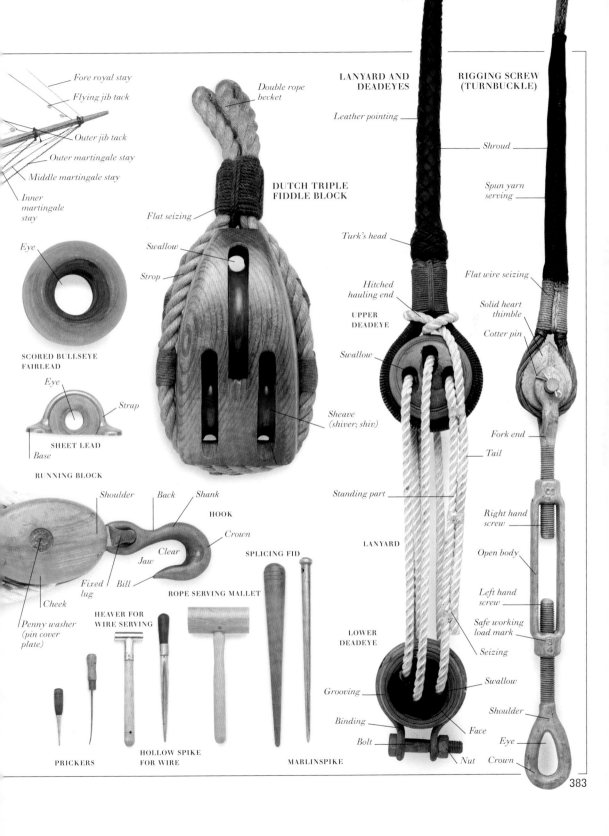

Fore royal stay

Flying jib tack

Outer jib tack

Outer martingale stay

Middle martingale stay

Inner martingale stay

Eye

SCORED BULLSEYE FAIRLEAD

Eye

Strap

Base

SHEET LEAD

RUNNING BLOCK

Shoulder

Back

Shank

HOOK

Crown

Clear

Jaw

Bill

Fixed lug

Cheek

Penny washer (pin cover plate)

HEAVER FOR WIRE SERVING

PRICKERS

HOLLOW SPIKE FOR WIRE

Double rope becket

DUTCH TRIPLE FIDDLE BLOCK

Flat seizing

Swallow

Strop

Sheave (shiver; shiv)

SPLICING FID

ROPE SERVING MALLET

MARLINSPIKE

LANYARD AND DEADEYES

Leather pointing

Turk's head

UPPER DEADEYE

Hitched hauling end

Swallow

Standing part

LANYARD

LOWER DEADEYE

Grooving

Binding

Bolt

Tail

Face

Nut

RIGGING SCREW (TURNBUCKLE)

Shroud

Spun yarn serving

Flat wire seizing

Solid heart thimble

Cotter pin

Fork end

Right hand screw

Open body

Left hand screw

Safe working load mark

Seizing

Swallow

Shoulder

Eye

Crown

383

Sails

THERE ARE TWO MAIN TYPES OF SAIL, often used in combination. Square sails are driving sails. They are usually attached by parrels to yards, square to the mast to catch the following wind. On fore-and-aft sails, such as lateen and lug sails, the luff (leading edge) usually abuts a mast or a stay. The head of the sail may abut a gaff, and the foot a boom. Around the world, a great range of rigs (sail patterns), such as the ketch, lugger, and schooner, have evolved to suit local needs. Sails are made from strips of cloth, cut to give the sail a belly and strong enough to resist the most violent of winds. Cotton and flax are the traditional sail materials, but synthetic fabrics are now commonly used.

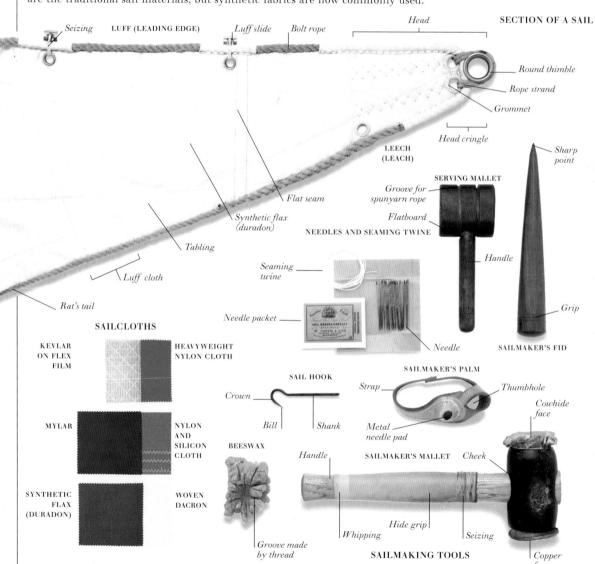

Seizing
LUFF (LEADING EDGE)
Luff slide
Bolt rope
Head
SECTION OF A SAIL
Round thimble
Rope strand
Grommet
Head cringle
LEECH (LEACH)
Sharp point
SERVING MALLET
Groove for spunyarn rope
Flatboard
NEEDLES AND SEAMING TWINE
Flat seam
Synthetic flax (duradon)
Handle
Tabling
Seaming twine
Luff cloth
Grip
Rat's tail
Needle packet
Needle
SAILMAKER'S FID

SAILCLOTHS

KEVLAR ON FLEX FILM
HEAVYWEIGHT NYLON CLOTH

MYLAR
NYLON AND SILICON CLOTH

SYNTHETIC FLAX (DURADON)
WOVEN DACRON

SAIL HOOK
Crown
Bill
Shank

SAILMAKER'S PALM
Strap
Thumbhole
Metal needle pad
Cowhide face

BEESWAX
Handle
SAILMAKER'S MALLET
Cheek

Whipping
Hide grip
Seizing
Groove made by thread
SAILMAKING TOOLS
Copper face

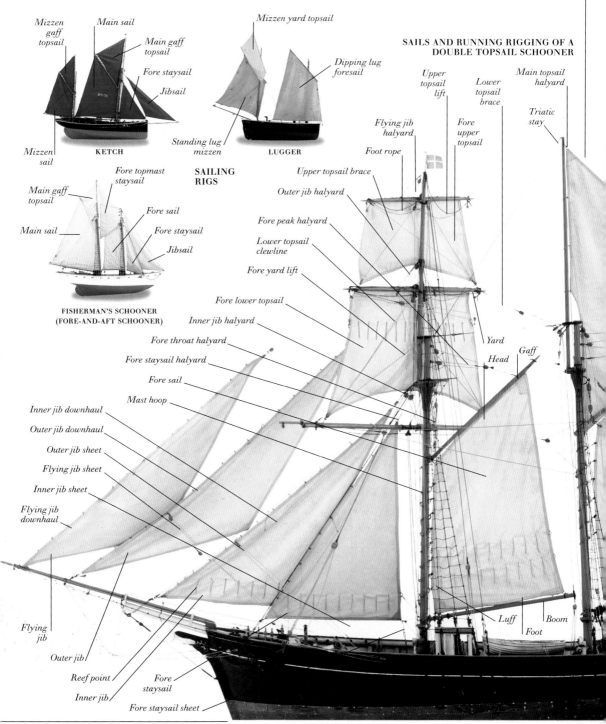

Mizzen gaff topsail

Main sail

Main gaff topsail

Fore staysail

Jibsail

Mizzen sail

KETCH

Mizzen yard topsail

Dipping lug foresail

Standing lug mizzen

LUGGER

Fore topmast staysail

Main gaff topsail

Fore sail

Main sail

Fore staysail

Jibsail

SAILING RIGS

**FISHERMAN'S SCHOONER
(FORE-AND-AFT SCHOONER)**

**SAILS AND RUNNING RIGGING OF A
DOUBLE TOPSAIL SCHOONER**

Upper topsail lift

Lower topsail brace

Main topsail halyard

Fore upper topsail

Triatic stay

Flying jib halyard

Foot rope

Upper topsail brace

Outer jib halyard

Fore peak halyard

Lower topsail clewline

Fore yard lift

Fore lower topsail

Inner jib halyard

Fore throat halyard

Fore staysail halyard

Fore sail

Mast hoop

Inner jib downhaul

Outer jib downhaul

Outer jib sheet

Flying jib sheet

Inner jib sheet

Flying jib downhaul

Yard

Head

Gaff

Luff

Boom

Foot

Flying jib

Outer jib

Reef point

Inner jib

Fore staysail

Fore staysail sheet

385

Mooring and anchoring

FOR LARGE VESSELS IN OPEN WATER, ANCHORAGE IS ESSENTIAL. By holding a ship securely to the seabed, an anchor prevents the vessel from being at the mercy of wave, tide, and current. The earliest anchors were nothing more than stones. In later years, many anchors had a standard design, much like the Admiralty pattern anchor shown on this page. The Danforth anchor is somewhat different. It has particularly deep flukes to give it great holding power. On large sailing ships, anchors were worked by teams of sailors. They turned the drum of a capstan by pushing on bars slotted into the revolving cylinder. This, in turn, lifted or lowered the anchor chain. In calm harbours and estuaries, ships can moor (make fast) without using anchors. Berthing ropes can be attached to bollards both inboard and on the quayside. Berthing ropes are joined to each other by bends, like those opposite.

**STONE ANCHOR
(KILLICK)**

Rope hole

**TYPES
OF ANCHOR**

CLOSE-
STOWING
ANCHOR

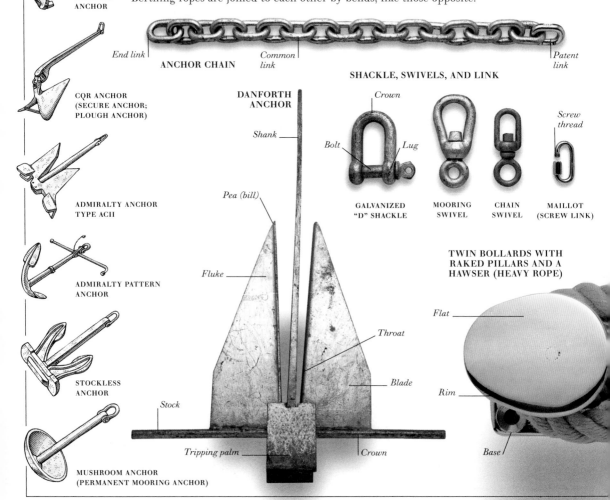

End link

ANCHOR CHAIN

Common
link

Patent
link

CQR ANCHOR
(SECURE ANCHOR;
PLOUGH ANCHOR)

**DANFORTH
ANCHOR**

Shank

Pea (bill)

Fluke

SHACKLE, SWIVELS, AND LINK

Crown

Bolt

Lug

Screw
thread

**GALVANIZED
"D" SHACKLE**

**MOORING
SWIVEL**

**CHAIN
SWIVEL**

**MAILLOT
(SCREW LINK)**

ADMIRALTY ANCHOR
TYPE ACII

ADMIRALTY PATTERN
ANCHOR

STOCKLESS
ANCHOR

MUSHROOM ANCHOR
(PERMANENT MOORING ANCHOR)

Stock

Tripping palm

Crown

Throat

Blade

**TWIN BOLLARDS WITH
RAKED PILLARS AND A
HAWSER (HEAVY ROPE)**

Flat

Rim

Base

BERTHING ROPES (HAWSERS)

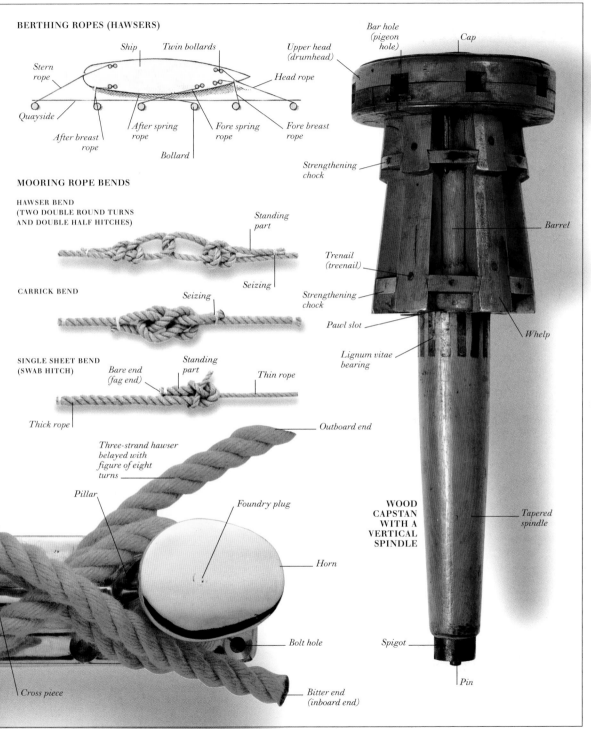

Stern rope · Ship · Twin bollards · Upper head (drumhead) · Bar hole (pigeon hole) · Cap · Head rope · Quayside · After breast rope · After spring rope · Bollard · Fore spring rope · Fore breast rope · Strengthening chock · Barrel

MOORING ROPE BENDS

HAWSER BEND (TWO DOUBLE ROUND TURNS AND DOUBLE HALF HITCHES)

Standing part · Seizing

CARRICK BEND

Seizing

SINGLE SHEET BEND (SWAB HITCH)

Bare end (fag end) · Standing part · Thin rope · Thick rope

Three-strand hawser belayed with figure of eight turns · Outboard end · Pillar · Foundry plug · Horn · Bolt hole · Cross piece · Bitter end (inboard end)

Trenail (treenail) · Strengthening chock · Pawl slot · Lignum vitae bearing · Whelp

WOOD CAPSTAN WITH A VERTICAL SPINDLE

Tapered spindle · Spigot · Pin

387

Ropes and knots

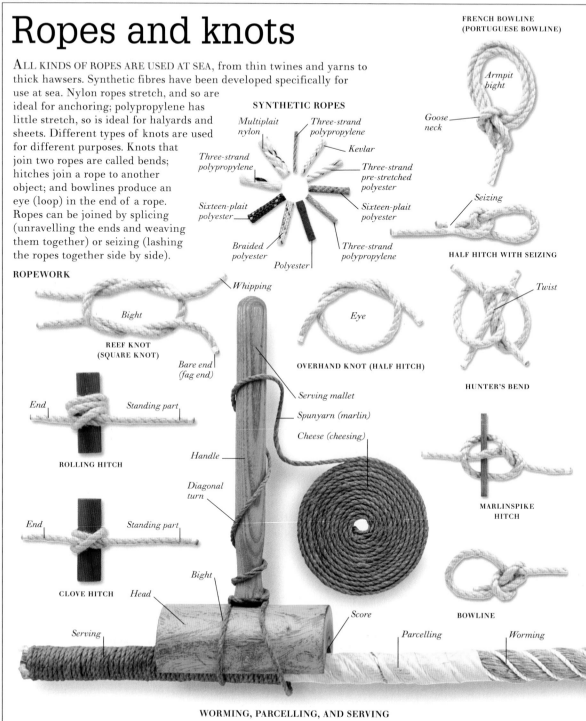

ALL KINDS OF ROPES ARE USED AT SEA, from thin twines and yarns to thick hawsers. Synthetic fibres have been developed specifically for use at sea. Nylon ropes stretch, and so are ideal for anchoring; polypropylene has little stretch, so is ideal for halyards and sheets. Different types of knots are used for different purposes. Knots that join two ropes are called bends; hitches join a rope to another object; and bowlines produce an eye (loop) in the end of a rope. Ropes can be joined by splicing (unravelling the ends and weaving them together) or seizing (lashing the ropes together side by side).

FRENCH BOWLINE (PORTUGUESE BOWLINE)

Armpit bight

Goose neck

Seizing

HALF HITCH WITH SEIZING

SYNTHETIC ROPES

Multiplait nylon

Three-strand polypropylene

Kevlar

Three-strand polypropylene

Three-strand pre-stretched polyester

Sixteen-plait polyester

Sixteen-plait polyester

Braided polyester

Polyester

Three-strand polypropylene

ROPEWORK

Whipping

Bight

REEF KNOT (SQUARE KNOT)

Bare end (fag end)

Eye

OVERHAND KNOT (HALF HITCH)

Twist

HUNTER'S BEND

End

Standing part

ROLLING HITCH

Serving mallet

Spunyarn (marlin)

Cheese (cheesing)

Handle

MARLINSPIKE HITCH

Diagonal turn

End

Standing part

CLOVE HITCH

Head

Bight

BOWLINE

Score

Serving

Parcelling

Worming

WORMING, PARCELLING, AND SERVING

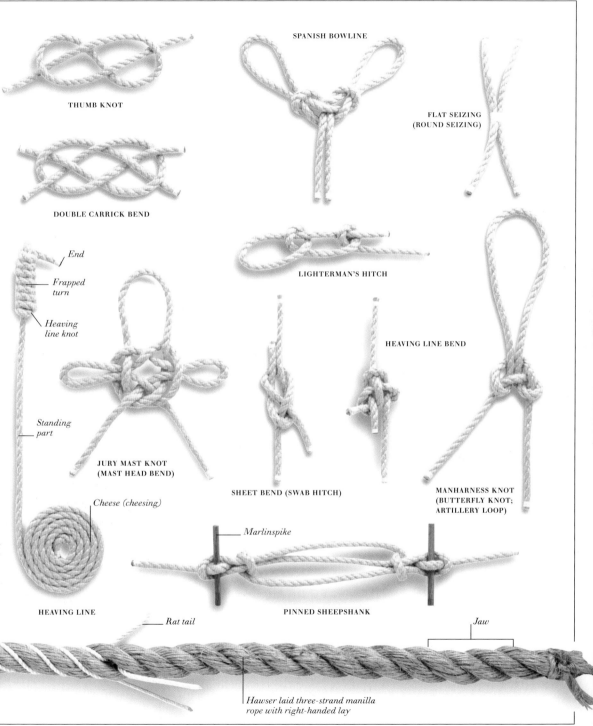

THUMB KNOT

SPANISH BOWLINE

**FLAT SEIZING
(ROUND SEIZING)**

DOUBLE CARRICK BEND

LIGHTERMAN'S HITCH

End

Frapped turn

Heaving line knot

HEAVING LINE BEND

Standing part

**JURY MAST KNOT
(MAST HEAD BEND)**

SHEET BEND (SWAB HITCH)

**MANHARNESS KNOT
(BUTTERFLY KNOT;
ARTILLERY LOOP)**

Cheese (cheesing)

Marlinspike

HEAVING LINE

Rat tail

PINNED SHEEPSHANK

Jaw

*Hawser laid three-strand manilla
rope with right-handed lay*

Paddle wheels and propellers

THE INVENTION OF THE STEAM ENGINE IN THE 18TH CENTURY made mechanically driven ships fitted with paddle wheels or propellers a viable alternative to sails. Paddle wheels have fixed or feathered floats, and the model shown below features both types. Feathered floats give more propulsive power than fixed floats because they are almost upright at all times in the water. Paddle wheels were superseded by the propeller on ocean-going vessels in the mid-19th century. Propellers are more efficient, work better in rough water, and are less vulnerable in collisions. The first propellers were two-bladed but later three- and four-bladed versions are more powerful; the shape and pitch of blades have also been refined over the years. At the beginning of the 18th century, tillers were superseded on many larger ships by the ship's wheel as a means of steering.

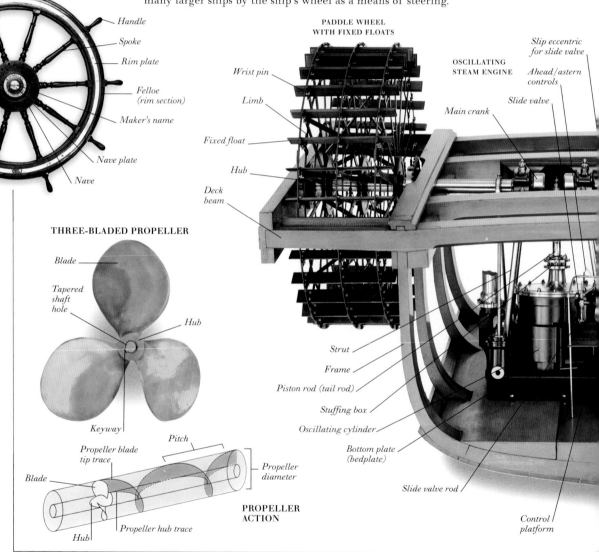

SHIP'S WHEEL

King spoke handle

Handle

Spoke

Rim plate

Felloe (rim section)

Maker's name

Nave plate

Nave

PADDLE WHEEL WITH FIXED FLOATS

Wrist pin

Limb

Fixed float

Hub

Deck beam

OSCILLATING STEAM ENGINE

Slip eccentric for slide valve

Ahead/astern controls

Main crank

Slide valve

THREE-BLADED PROPELLER

Blade

Tapered shaft hole

Hub

Keyway

Propeller blade tip trace

Pitch

Blade

Propeller diameter

Hub

Propeller hub trace

PROPELLER ACTION

Strut

Frame

Piston rod (tail rod)

Stuffing box

Oscillating cylinder

Bottom plate (bedplate)

Slide valve rod

Control platform

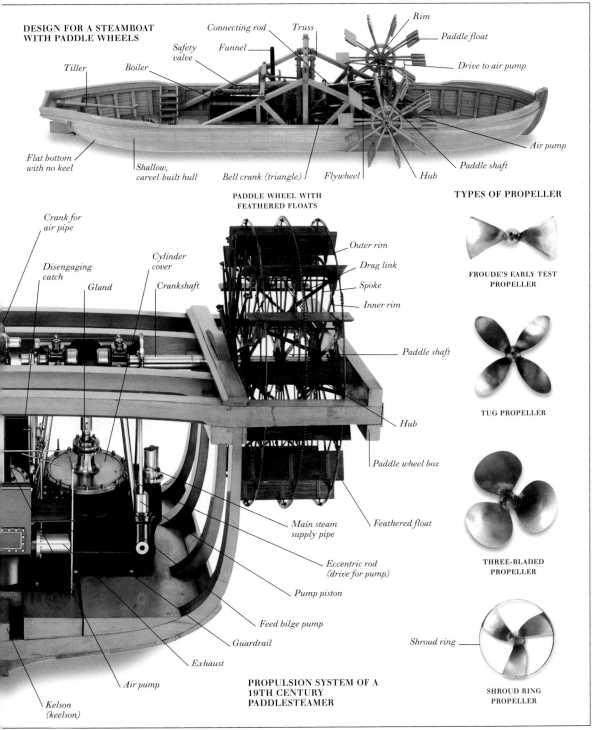

DESIGN FOR A STEAMBOAT WITH PADDLE WHEELS

Connecting rod

Truss

Rim

Paddle float

Safety valve

Funnel

Drive to air pump

Tiller

Boiler

Flat bottom with no keel

Shallow, carvel-built hull

Bell crank (triangle)

Flywheel

Hub

Air pump

Paddle shaft

PADDLE WHEEL WITH FEATHERED FLOATS

TYPES OF PROPELLER

Crank for air pipe

Disengaging catch

Cylinder cover

Gland

Crankshaft

Outer rim

Drag link

Spoke

Inner rim

Paddle shaft

Hub

Paddle wheel box

Feathered float

Main steam supply pipe

Eccentric rod (drive for pump)

Pump piston

Feed bilge pump

Guardrail

Exhaust

Air pump

Kelson (keelson)

PROPULSION SYSTEM OF A 19TH CENTURY PADDLESTEAMER

FROUDE'S EARLY TEST PROPELLER

TUG PROPELLER

THREE-BLADED PROPELLER

Shroud ring

SHROUD RING PROPELLER

Anatomy of an iron ship

IRON PARTS WERE USED IN THE HULLS OF WOODEN SHIPS AS EARLY AS 1675, often in the same form as the wooden parts that they replaced. Eventually, as on the tea clipper Cutty Sark (below), iron rigging was found to be stronger than the traditional rope. The first "ironclads" were warships whose wooden hulls were protected by iron armour plates. Later ironclads actually had iron hulls. The model opposite is based on the British warship HMS Warrior, launched in 1860, the first battleship built entirely of iron. The plan of the iron paddlesteamer (bottom), built somewhat later, shows that this vessel was a sailing ship; but it also boasted a steam propulsion plant amidships that turned two side paddlewheels. Early iron hulls were made from plates that were painstakingly rivetted together (as below), but by the 20th century vessels began to be welded together, whole sections at a time. The Second World War "liberty ship" was one of the first of these "production-line vessels".

Steel yard   Iron wire stay

Steel lower mast

Steel bowsprit

TEA CLIPPER

Wooden planking with copper sheathing

Forged iron anchor

RIVETTED PLATES

Pan head rivet

Plate

Button head rivet (snap head)

Seam

LIBERTY SHIP

Gun section

Accommodation section

Cargo derrick

Weld line

Stern section   Midships section   Cargo hold   Bow section

PLAN OF AN IRON PADDLESTEAMER

Steering position

Steering gear

Stern

Vertical frame ladder

Mast step

Rudder

Rudder post

Heel of rudder post

Mizzen mast

Poop deck

Lounge

Guardrail

Deck lantern

Binnacle

State room

Main mast

After funnel

Steam whistle

Skylight

Crankshaft

Guardrail

Eccentric

Paddle wheel

Connecting rod

Bar keel

Afterpeak

Cabin

Tank

Main mast step

Stern framing

Donkey boiler

Box boiler

Foundation

Reversing wheel

Bottom plate

Side lever

Cylinder

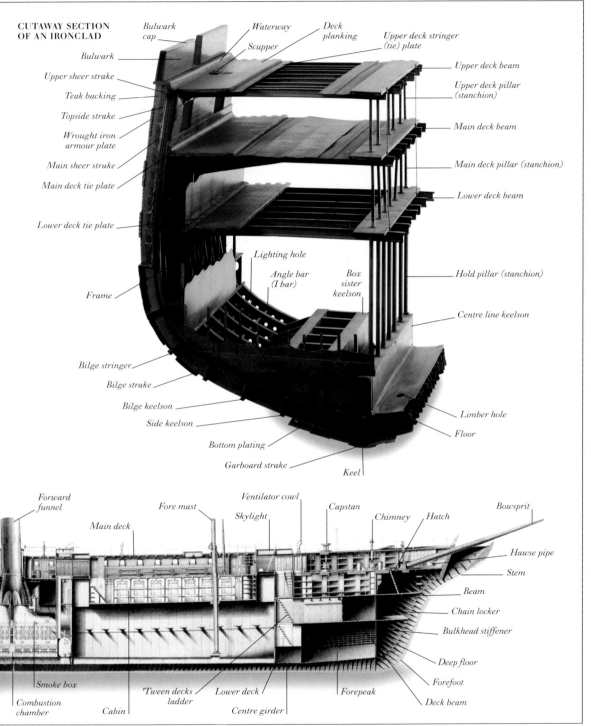

CUTAWAY SECTION
OF AN IRONCLAD

Bulwark
cap

Waterway

Deck
planking

Upper deck stringer
(tie) plate

Scupper

Bulwark

Upper deck beam

Upper sheer strake

Teak backing

Upper deck pillar
(stanchion)

Topside strake

Wrought iron
armour plate

Main deck beam

Main sheer strake

Main deck tie plate

Main deck pillar (stanchion)

Lower deck beam

Lower deck tie plate

Lighting hole

Angle bar
(I bar)

Box
sister
keelson

Hold pillar (stanchion)

Frame

Centre line keelson

Bilge stringer

Bilge strake

Bilge keelson

Side keelson

Limber hole

Bottom plating

Floor

Garboard strake

Keel

Forward
funnel

Ventilator cowl

Main deck

Capstan

Fore mast

Skylight

Chimney

Hatch

Bowsprit

Hawse pipe

Stem

Beam

Chain locker

Bulkhead stiffener

Deep floor

Smoke box

Forefoot

'Tween decks
ladder

Lower deck

Forepeak

Deck beam

Combustion
chamber

Cabin

Centre girder

The battleship

IN THE EARLY YEARS OF THE 20TH CENTURY, sea warfare – attacking enemy vessels or defending a ship – was revolutionized by the introduction of Dreadnought-type battleships like the Brazilian vessel below. These new ships combined the latest advances in steam propulsion, gunnery, and armour plating. The gun turret was designed to fire shells over huge distances. It was protected by armour 30 cm (12 in) thick. The measurements given for the guns of this ship refer to the bore diameter. Where "weight" is quoted, this is the weight of the shell that the gun fires. Torpedoes – as portrayed on the upper cigarette card (right) – were self-propelled underwater missiles, often steered by gyro-control. Depth charges were designed in the First World War for use against submerged U-boats. They are canisters filled with explosives that are detonated by depth-sensitive pistols. The lower cigarette card shows depth charges being fired by a "thrower", fired from a torpedo tube, and rolled from the stern. Ship's shields were fitted to warships from the late 19th century onwards. The shield shown opposite depicts a traditional ship's cannon.

20TH CENTURY WEAPONRY

PROPELLED WEAPONS
TORPEDO
DEPTH CHARGES
Torpedo tube
Warhead
Sight
TORPEDOES
DEPTH CHARGES
Side-thrown canister
Stern-rolled canister
Torpedo-fired canister

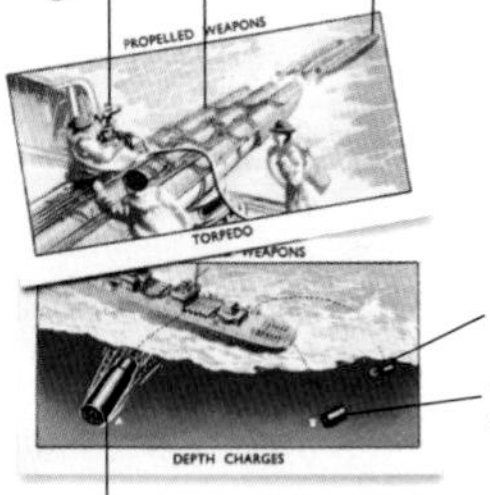

BRAZILIAN BATTLESHIP

Boat handling derrick
Gunnery spotting top
Rangefinder
Forward funnel
Purchase wire
Light screen
Lifeboat
Searchlight
Compass
Searchlight platform
Compass and rangefinder platform
Ship's wheel
Leading block
Tripod mast
Navigating bridge
Boat winch
Conning tower
Captain's shelter/ chart house
Arms of Brazil
Weather shutter for gun
"F" turret
Jack staff
30 cm (12 in) gun
Skylight
Porthole
Stem (false ram bow)
Belt armour
Forward accommodation ladder
Sighting hood
"A" turret
Turret barbette
Open gun mounting
12 cm (4.7 in) gun
Steam launch
Guest boat boom

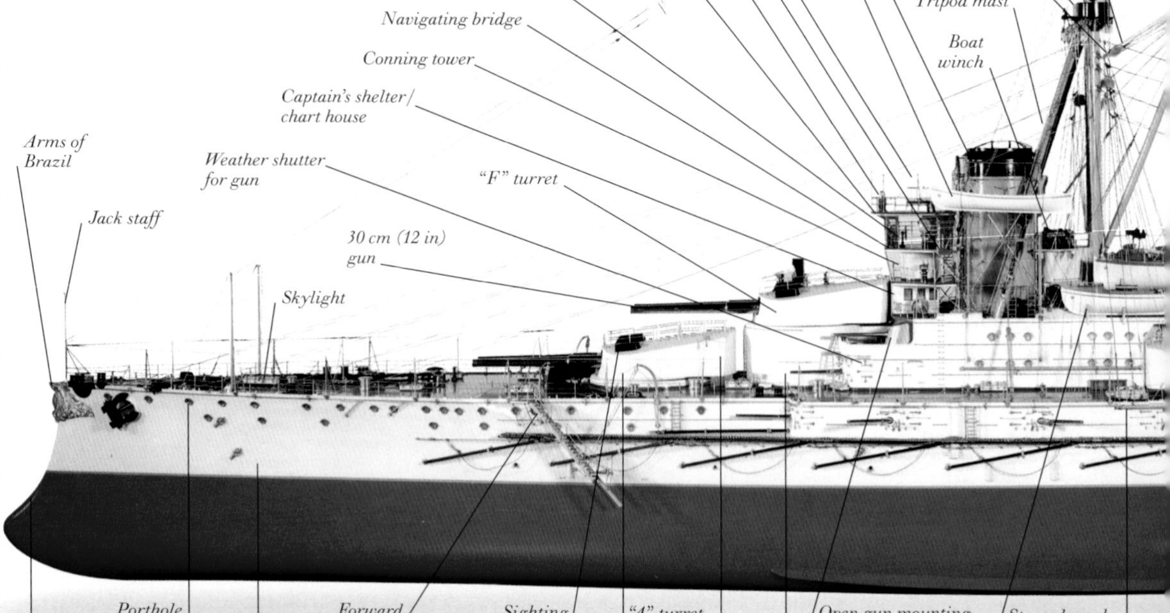

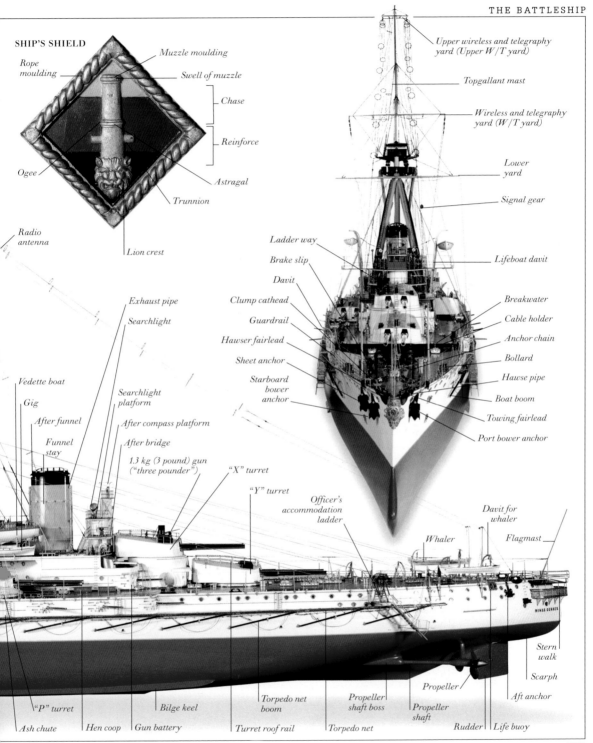

SHIP'S SHIELD

Rope moulding

Muzzle moulding

Swell of muzzle

Chase

Reinforce

Ogee

Astragal

Trunnion

Lion crest

Radio antenna

Upper wireless and telegraphy yard (Upper W/T yard)

Topgallant mast

Wireless and telegraphy yard (W/T yard)

Lower yard

Signal gear

Ladder way

Brake slip

Davit

Clump cathead

Guardrail

Hawser fairlead

Sheet anchor

Starboard bower anchor

Lifeboat davit

Breakwater

Cable holder

Anchor chain

Bollard

Hawse pipe

Boat boom

Towing fairlead

Port bower anchor

Exhaust pipe

Searchlight

Vedette boat

Gig

After funnel

Funnel stay

Searchlight platform

After compass platform

After bridge

1.3 kg (3 pound) gun ("three pounder")

"X" turret

"Y" turret

Officer's accommodation ladder

Davit for whaler

Whaler

Flagmast

Stern walk

Scarph

Aft anchor

Propeller

"P" turret

Ash chute

Hen coop

Gun battery

Bilge keel

Torpedo net boom

Turret roof rail

Torpedo net

Propeller shaft boss

Propeller shaft

Rudder

Life buoy

Frigates and submarines

FROM THE MID-19TH CENTURY, ARMOURED SHIPS provided a new challenge to enemy craft. In response, huge revolving gun turrets were developed. These could fire in any direction, could be loaded from the breech very rapidly, and, instead of cannonballs, they discharged exploding shells. Modern fighting ships, like the frigate, combine heavy ship-borne armament with light helicopter weaponry. Submarines function below the surface of the sea. Their speed and ability to fire missiles from under water are their major assets. The nuclear submarine can stay under water for several years without refuelling.

Stabilizer fin

Aft hydroplane

Propeller

Lower rudder

Rangefinder

Look out periscope

Local control cabinet

Breech wheel

Breech block

Loading arm

Slide locking lever

Slide

Sighting hood

Recoil cylinder

Elevating wheel

Guide for gun loading cage

Blast bag (breeches)

Rammer lever

Gun loading cage

Training rack gearing

Floor of gun house

Turret roller

Roller path

Working chamber

Training gear

Rammer

Waiting position

Roller path support

Floor

"Walking pipe" (water supply)

GUN TURRET
In this turret for two 37 cm (15 in) guns, shells are carried in a hoisting cage. The shell is rammed into the gun, followed by the propellant (charge). Once the breech is closed, the gun is ready for firing. The whole operation requires around 70 sailors.

Barbette (armour)

Main hoisting cage

Turret trunk

Cordite handling room

Cordite supply shuttle

Cordite case

FRIGATE

Ensign staff

Lynx helicopter

SONAR torpedo decoy

Rudder

Variable pitch propeller

Practice projectile

High-explosive projectile

Shell bogie

Shell room

Hydraulic grab

Shell-handling gear

Ladder way

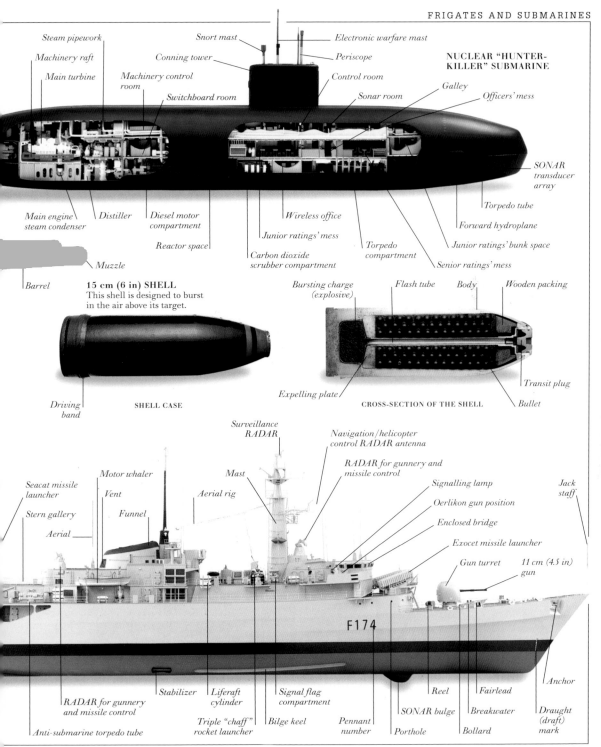

Steam pipework

Machinery raft

Main turbine

Machinery control room

Switchboard room

Snort mast

Conning tower

Periscope

Electronic warfare mast

Control room

Sonar room

Galley

Officers' mess

NUCLEAR "HUNTER-KILLER" SUBMARINE

SONAR transducer array

Main engine steam condenser

Distiller

Diesel motor compartment

Reactor space

Wireless office

Junior ratings' mess

Carbon dioxide scrubber compartment

Torpedo compartment

Senior ratings' mess

Junior ratings' bunk space

Forward hydroplane

Torpedo tube

Barrel

Muzzle

15 cm (6 in) SHELL
This shell is designed to burst in the air above its target.

Bursting charge (explosive)

Flash tube

Body

Wooden packing

Expelling plate

Transit plug

Bullet

Driving band

SHELL CASE

CROSS-SECTION OF THE SHELL

Surveillance RADAR

Navigation/helicopter control RADAR antenna

Mast

RADAR for gunnery and missile control

Seacat missile launcher

Motor whaler

Vent

Aerial rig

Signalling lamp

Oerlikon gun position

Jack staff

Stern gallery

Funnel

Enclosed bridge

Aerial

Exocet missile launcher

Gun turret

11 cm (4.5 in) gun

F174

RADAR for gunnery and missile control

Stabilizer

Liferaft cylinder

Signal flag compartment

Reel

Fairlead

Anchor

Triple "chaff" rocket launcher

Bilge keel

SONAR bulge

Breakwater

Anti-submarine torpedo tube

Pennant number

Porthole

Bollard

Draught (draft) mark

Pioneers of flight

FLIGHT HAS FASCINATED MANKIND for centuries, and countless unsuccessful flying machines have been designed. The first successful flight was made by the French Montgolfier brothers in 1783, when they flew a balloon over Paris. The next major advance was the development of gliders, notably by the Englishman Sir George Cayley, who in 1845 designed the first glider to make a sustained flight, and by the German Otto Lilienthal, who became known as the world's first pilot because he managed to achieve controlled flights. However, powered flight did not become a practical possibility until the invention of lightweight, petrol-driven internal combustion engines at the end of the 19th century. Then, in 1903, the American brothers Orville and Wilbur Wright made the first powered flight in their Wright Flyer biplane, which used a four-cylinder, petrol-driven engine. Aircraft design advanced rapidly, and in 1909 the Frenchman Louis Blériot made his pioneering flight across the English Channel (see pp. 400-401). The American Glenn Curtiss also achieved several "firsts" in his Model-D Pusher and its variants, most notably winning the world's first competition for airspeed at Reims in 1909.

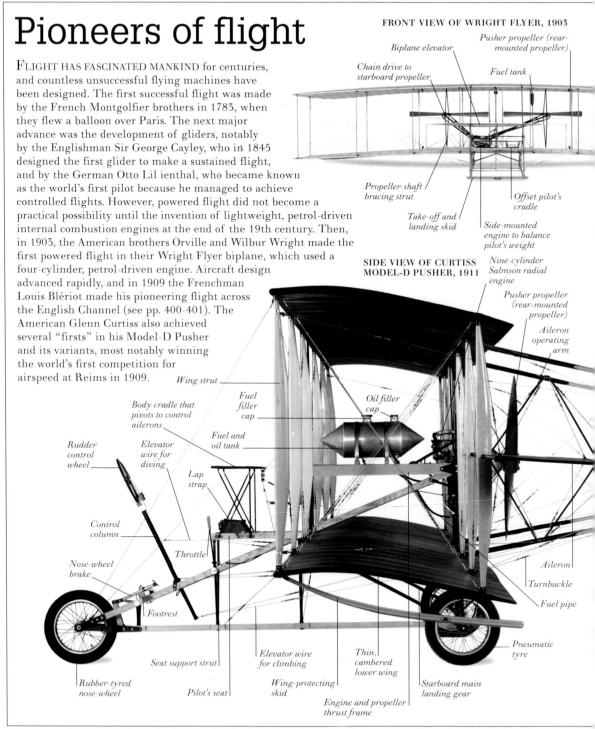

Pusher propeller (rear-mounted propeller)

Biplane elevator

Chain drive to starboard propeller

Fuel tank

Propeller-shaft bracing strut

Offset pilot's cradle

Take-off and landing skid

Side-mounted engine to balance pilot's weight

SIDE VIEW OF CURTISS MODEL-D PUSHER, 1911

Nine-cylinder Salmson radial engine

Pusher propeller (rear-mounted propeller)

Aileron operating arm

Wing strut

Fuel filler cap

Oil filler cap

Body cradle that pivots to control ailerons

Fuel and oil tank

Rudder control wheel

Elevator wire for diving

Lap strap

Control column

Throttle

Nose-wheel brake

Aileron

Turnbuckle

Fuel pipe

Footrest

Pneumatic tyre

Rubber-tyred nose-wheel

Seat support strut

Elevator wire for climbing

Thin, cambered lower wing

Starboard main landing gear

Pilot's seat

Wing-protecting skid

Engine and propeller thrust frame

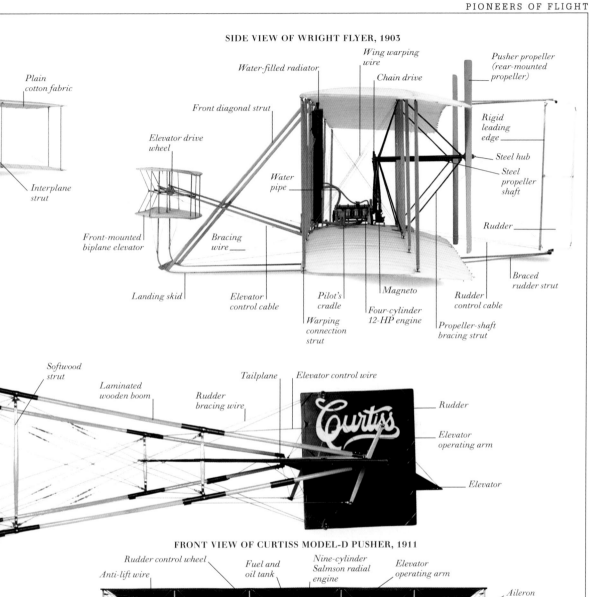

SIDE VIEW OF WRIGHT FLYER, 1903

Plain cotton fabric

Interplane strut

Elevator drive wheel

Front diagonal strut

Water-filled radiator

Wing warping wire

Chain drive

Pusher propeller (rear-mounted propeller)

Rigid leading edge

Steel hub

Steel propeller shaft

Water pipe

Rudder

Front-mounted biplane elevator

Bracing wire

Braced rudder strut

Landing skid

Elevator control cable

Pilot's cradle

Magneto

Rudder control cable

Warping connection strut

Four-cylinder 12-HP engine

Propeller-shaft bracing strut

Softwood strut

Laminated wooden boom

Tailplane

Elevator control wire

Rudder bracing wire

Rudder

Elevator operating arm

Elevator

FRONT VIEW OF CURTISS MODEL-D PUSHER, 1911

Rudder control wheel

Fuel and oil tank

Nine-cylinder Salmson radial engine

Elevator operating arm

Anti-lift wire

Aileron operating arm

Starboard aileron

Port aileron

Carved interplane strut

Wing-protecting skid

Wing-protecting skid

Lift wire

Control column

Tubular steel leg

Interplane strut pin-jointed to front spar

Seat beam

Main landing gear lateral brace

Footrest

Axle

Early monoplanes

MONOPLANES HAVE ONE WING on each side of the fuselage. The principal disadvantage of this arrangement in early, wooden-framed aircraft was that single wings were weak and required strong wires to brace them to king-posts above and below the fuselage. However, single wings also had advantages: they experienced less drag than multiple wings, allowing greater speed; they also made aircraft more manoeuvrable because single wings were easier to warp (twist) than double wings, and warping the wings was how pilots controlled the roll of early aircraft. By 1912, the French pilot Louis Blériot had used a monoplane to make the first flight across the English Channel, and the Briton Robert Blackburn and the Frenchman Armand Deperdussin had proved the greater speed of monoplanes. However, a spate of crashes caused by broken wings discouraged monoplane production, except in Germany, where all-metal monoplanes were developed in 1917. The wings of all-metal monoplanes did not need strengthening by struts or bracing wires, but despite this, such planes were not widely adopted until the 1930s.

FRONT VIEW OF BLACKBURN MONOPLANE, 1912

Taut fabric

Carved wooden propeller

King-post

Hub bolted to propeller

Nose-ring

Pilot's viewing aperture

Exhaust valve push-rod

Gnome seven-cylinder rotary engine

Elevator hinge

Elevator

Landing gear rear cross-member

Wheel fairing

Rubber-sprung wheel

Tailskid

Landing gear front strut

Axle

Landing skid

Landing gear rear strut

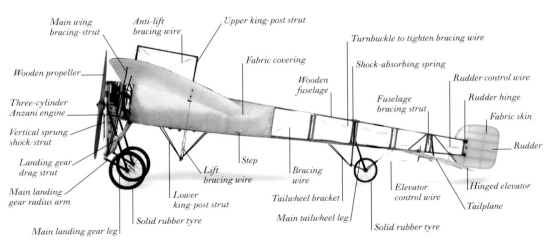

Main wing
bracing-strut

Anti-lift
bracing wire

Upper king-post strut

Fabric covering

Turnbuckle to tighten bracing wire

Wooden propeller

Shock-absorbing spring

Wooden
fuselage

Rudder control wire

Three-cylinder
Anzani engine

Fuselage
bracing strut

Rudder hinge

Fabric skin

Vertical sprung
shock-strut

Rudder

Landing gear
drag strut

Step

Lift
bracing wire

Bracing
wire

Elevator
control wire

Hinged elevator

Main landing
gear radius arm

Lower
king-post strut

Tailplane

Solid rubber tyre

Tailwheel bracket

Main tailwheel leg

Solid rubber tyre

Main landing gear leg

SIDE VIEW OF BLÉRIOT XI, 1909

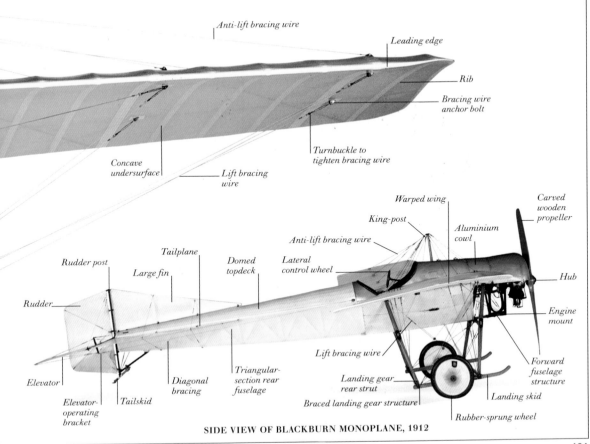

Anti-lift bracing wire

Leading edge

Rib

Bracing wire
anchor bolt

Turnbuckle to
tighten bracing wire

Concave
undersurface

Lift bracing
wire

Warped wing

Carved
wooden
propeller

King-post

Aluminium
cowl

Anti-lift bracing wire

Lateral
control wheel

Rudder post

Tailplane

Domed
topdeck

Hub

Large fin

Engine
mount

Rudder

Elevator

Lift bracing wire

Forward
fuselage
structure

Triangular-
section rear
fuselage

Landing gear
rear strut

Landing skid

Diagonal
bracing

Rubber-sprung wheel

Elevator-
operating
bracket

Tailskid

Braced landing gear structure

SIDE VIEW OF BLACKBURN MONOPLANE, 1912

Biplanes and triplanes

BIPLANES DOMINATED AIRCRAFT DESIGN until the 1930s, largely because some early monoplanes (see pp. 400-401) were too fragile to withstand the stresses of flight. The struts between biplanes' wings made the wings strong compared with those of early monoplanes, although the greater surface area of biplanes' wings increased drag and reduced speed. Many aircraft designers also developed triplanes, which had a particular advantage over biplanes: more wings meant a shorter wingspan to achieve the same lifting power, and a shorter wingspan gave greater manoeuvrability. Triplanes were most successful as fighters during World War I, the German Fokker triplane being a notable example. However, the greater manoeuvrability of triplanes was no advantage for normal flying and so most manufacturers continued to make biplanes. Many other aircraft designs were attempted. Some were quadruplanes, with four pairs of wings. Some had tandem wings (two pairs of monoplane wings, one behind the other). One of the most bizarre designs was by the Englishman Horatio Phillips: it had 20 sets of narrow wings and looked rather like a Venetian blind.

LAMINATED PROPELLER

SIDE VIEW OF AVRO TRIPLANE IV, 1910

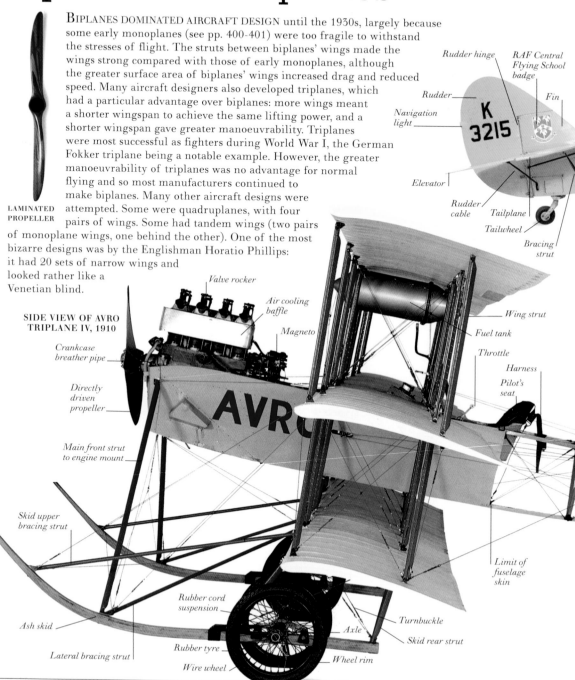

Rudder hinge

RAF Central Flying School badge

Rudder

Fin

Navigation light

Elevator

Rudder cable

Tailplane

Tailwheel

Bracing strut

Valve rocker

Air cooling baffle

Magneto

Wing strut

Fuel tank

Throttle

Harness

Pilot's seat

Crankcase breather pipe

Directly driven propeller

Main front strut to engine mount

Skid upper bracing strut

Limit of fuselage skin

Rubber cord suspension

Turnbuckle

Ash skid

Axle

Skid rear strut

Lateral bracing strut

Rubber tyre

Wheel rim

Wire wheel

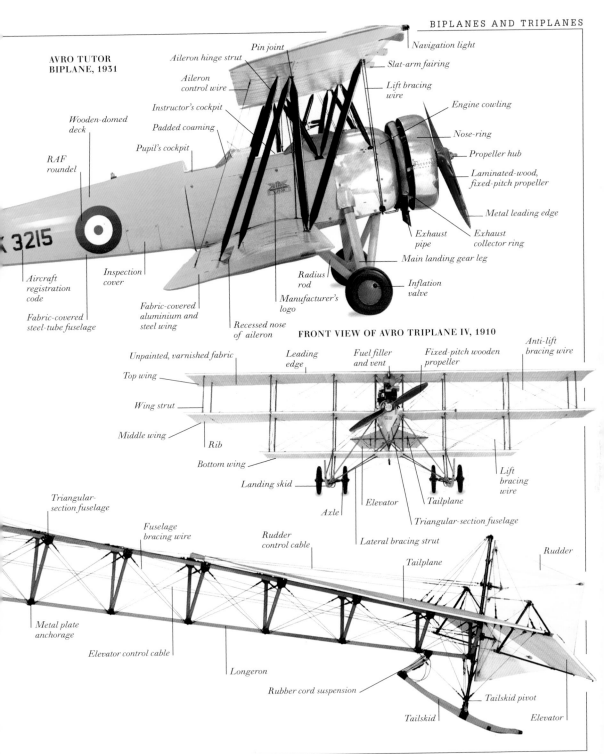

AVRO TUTOR BIPLANE, 1931

Pin joint

Aileron hinge strut

Aileron control wire

Instructor's cockpit

Padded coaming

Pupil's cockpit

Wooden-domed deck

RAF roundel

Navigation light

Slat-arm fairing

Lift bracing wire

Engine cowling

Nose-ring

Propeller hub

Laminated-wood, fixed-pitch propeller

Metal leading edge

Exhaust pipe

Exhaust collector ring

Main landing gear leg

Inflation valve

Radius rod

Manufacturer's logo

Recessed nose of aileron

Aircraft registration code

Inspection cover

Fabric-covered steel-tube fuselage

Fabric-covered aluminium and steel wing

K 3215

FRONT VIEW OF AVRO TRIPLANE IV, 1910

Unpainted, varnished fabric

Leading edge

Fuel filler and vent

Fixed-pitch wooden propeller

Anti-lift bracing wire

Top wing

Wing strut

Middle wing

Rib

Bottom wing

Landing skid

Axle

Elevator

Tailplane

Triangular-section fuselage

Lift bracing wire

Triangular-section fuselage

Fuselage bracing wire

Rudder control cable

Lateral bracing strut

Tailplane

Rudder

Metal plate anchorage

Elevator control cable

Longeron

Rubber cord suspension

Tailskid

Tailskid pivot

Elevator

World War I aircraft

WHEN WORLD WAR I STARTED in 1914, the main purpose of military aircraft was reconnaissance. The British-built BE 2, of which the BE 2B was a variant, was well-suited to this duty; it was very stable in flight, allowing the occupants to study the terrain, take photographs, and make notes. The BE 2 was also one of the first aircraft to drop bombs.

FLYING HELMET

One of the biggest problems for aircraft designers during the war was mounting machine-guns. On aircraft that had front-mounted propellers, the field of fire was restricted by the propeller and other parts of the aircraft. The problem was solved in 1915 by the Dutchman Anthony Fokker, who designed an interrupter gear that prevented a machine-gun from firing when a propeller blade passed in front of the barrel. The German LVG CVI had a forward-firing gun to the right of the engine, as well as a rear-cockpit gun, and a bombing capability. It was one of the most versatile aircraft of the war.

Interplane-strut attachment

Intermediate leading-edge rib

Airspeed-indicator tube

Leading edge

Wingtip

Airspeed-indicator tube

Main rib

Root

Airspeed pilot tube

Interplane strut

Trailing edge

Interplane-strut attachment

Upper side of lower wing

Attachment lug

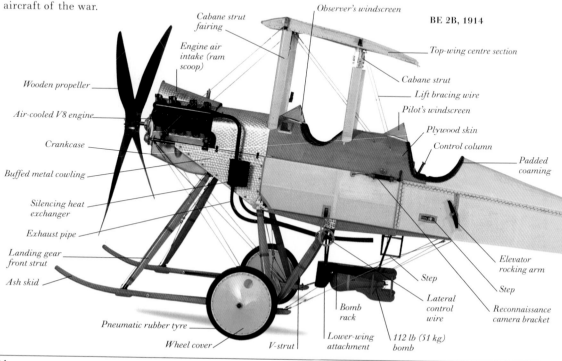

BE 2B, 1914

Cabane strut fairing

Observer's windscreen

Engine air intake (ram scoop)

Top-wing centre section

Wooden propeller

Cabane strut

Lift bracing wire

Air-cooled V8 engine

Pilot's windscreen

Crankcase

Plywood skin

Buffed metal cowling

Control column

Padded coaming

Silencing heat exchanger

Exhaust pipe

Landing gear front strut

Elevator rocking arm

Ash skid

Step

Step

Lateral control wire

Reconnaissance camera bracket

Pneumatic rubber tyre

Bomb rack

112 lb (51 kg) bomb

Wheel cover

V-strut

Lower-wing attachment

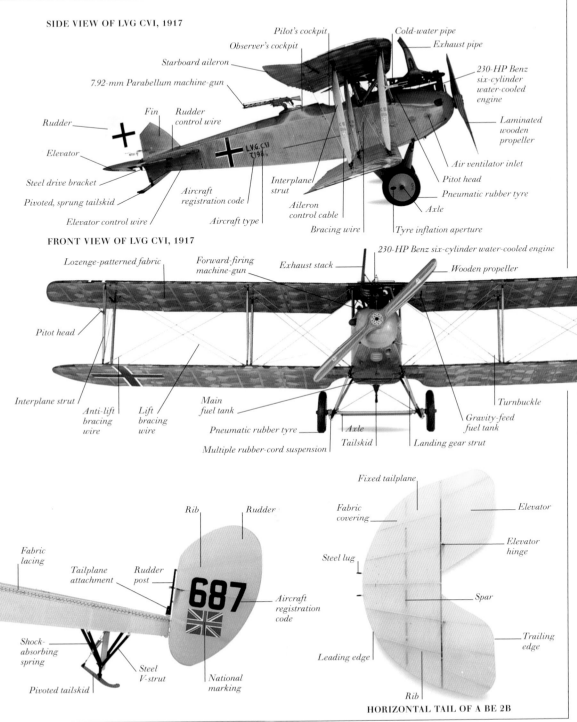

SIDE VIEW OF LVG CVI, 1917

Pilot's cockpit

Observer's cockpit

Starboard aileron

7.92-mm Parabellum machine-gun

Cold-water pipe

Exhaust pipe

230-HP Benz six-cylinder water-cooled engine

Fin

Rudder control wire

Rudder

Elevator

Steel drive bracket

Pivoted, sprung tailskid

Elevator control wire

Aircraft registration code

Aircraft type

Interplane strut

Aileron control cable

Bracing wire

Laminated wooden propeller

Air ventilator inlet

Pitot head

Pneumatic rubber tyre

Axle

Tyre inflation aperture

FRONT VIEW OF LVG CVI, 1917

Lozenge-patterned fabric

Forward-firing machine-gun

Exhaust stack

230-HP Benz six-cylinder water-cooled engine

Wooden propeller

Pitot head

Interplane strut

Anti-lift bracing wire

Lift bracing wire

Main fuel tank

Pneumatic rubber tyre

Multiple rubber-cord suspension

Axle

Tailskid

Landing gear strut

Turnbuckle

Gravity-feed fuel tank

Fabric lacing

Tailplane attachment

Rudder post

Rib

Rudder

687

Aircraft registration code

Shock-absorbing spring

Steel V-strut

Pivoted tailskid

National marking

Fixed tailplane

Fabric covering

Steel lug

Leading edge

Rib

Elevator

Elevator hinge

Spar

Trailing edge

HORIZONTAL TAIL OF A BE 2B

405

Early passenger aircraft

FRONT VIEW OF LOCKHEED ELECTRA, 1934

UNTIL THE 1930s, most passenger aircraft were biplanes, with two pairs of wings and a wooden or metal framework covered with fabric or, sometimes, plywood. Such aircraft were restricted to low speeds and low altitudes because of the drag on their wings. Many had an open cockpit, situated behind or in front of an enclosed – but unpressurized – cabin that carried a maximum of ten people. The passengers usually sat in wicker chairs that were not bolted to the floor, and the journey could be bumpy when flying through turbulence. Warm clothing, and ear plugs to reduce the effects of prolonged noise, were often required. During the 1930s, powerful, streamlined, all-metal monoplanes, such as the Lockheed Electra shown here, became widespread. By 1939, the advent of pressurized cabins allowed fast flights at high altitudes, where there is less turbulence.

Flying boats were still necessary on many routes until 1945 because of inadequate runways and the frequency of emergency sea-landings. World War II, however, resulted in enough good runways being built for land-planes to become standard on all major airline routes.

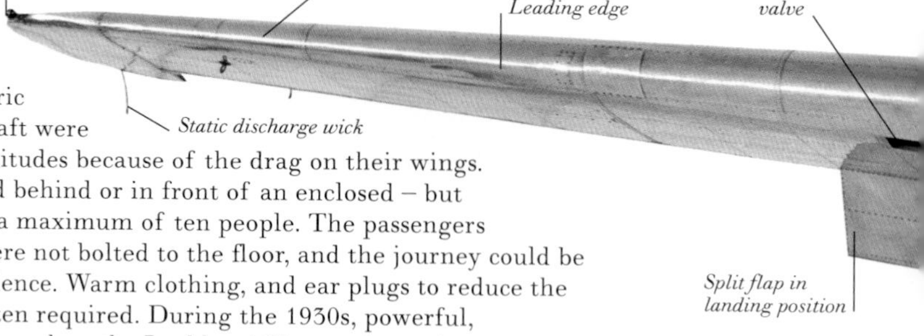

Green starboard navigation light
Flush-riveted metal-skinned wing
Leading edge
Fuel-jettison valve
Static discharge wick
Split flap in landing position

PASSENGER CABIN TRIM

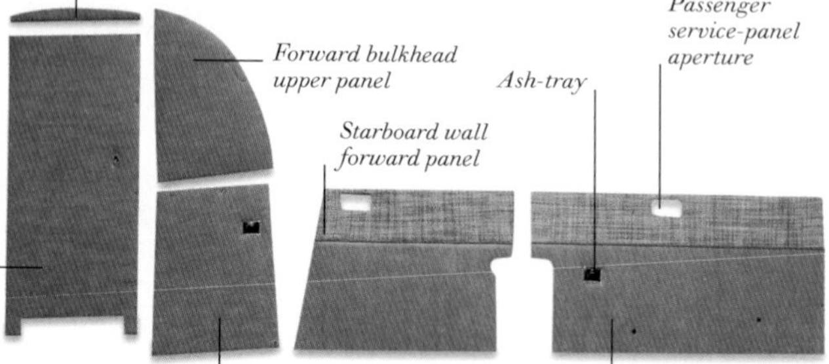

Roof trim panel
Forward bulkhead upper panel
Passenger service-panel aperture
Ash-tray
Starboard wall forward panel
Cockpit door panel
Forward bulkhead lower panel
Starboard wall mid-forward panel

SIDE VIEW OF LOCKHEED ELECTRA, 1934

Cockpit windscreen
Sliding window
Emergency escape hatch
Steel firewall
Passenger window
Air intake
Oil tank
Ventilator exit
Nose
Propeller pitch-change cylinder
Blade counterweight
Spinner mounting disc
Variable-pitch propeller
Exhaust collector ring
Pratt & Whitney nine-cylinder radial engine
Red port navigation light
Landing gear door
Exhaust pipe
Electrically driven split flap
Passenger door
Main landing gear
Brake pipe
Static discharge wick
Aileron
Aluminium wheel
Mudguard
Metal-skinned wing

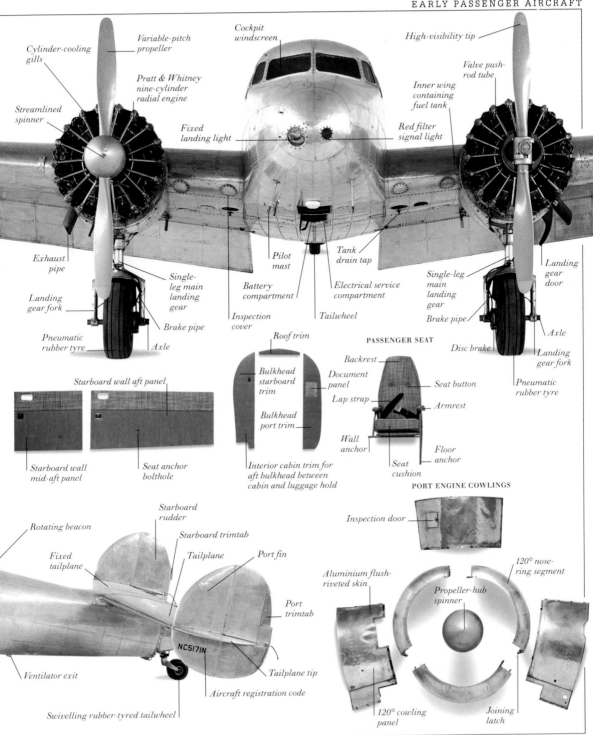

Cockpit windscreen

High-visibility tip

Variable-pitch propeller

Cylinder-cooling gills

Pratt & Whitney nine-cylinder radial engine

Valve push-rod tube

Inner wing containing fuel tank

Streamlined spinner

Fixed landing light

Red filter signal light

Exhaust pipe

Single-leg main landing gear

Pilot mast

Tank drain tap

Single-leg main landing gear

Landing gear door

Landing gear fork

Battery compartment

Electrical service compartment

Brake pipe

Axle

Pneumatic rubber tyre

Brake pipe

Axle

Inspection cover

Tailwheel

Landing gear fork

Disc brake

Pneumatic rubber tyre

Starboard wall aft panel

Roof trim

PASSENGER SEAT

Bulkhead starboard trim

Backrest

Document panel

Seat button

Lap strap

Armrest

Bulkhead port trim

Wall anchor

Floor anchor

Starboard wall mid-aft panel

Seat anchor bolthole

Interior cabin trim for aft bulkhead between cabin and luggage hold

Seat cushion

PORT ENGINE COWLINGS

Inspection door

Rotating beacon

Starboard rudder

Starboard trimtab

Aluminium flush-riveted skin

120° nose-ring segment

Fixed tailplane

Tailplane

Port fin

Propeller-hub spinner

Port trimtab

Ventilator exit

NC517IN

Tailplane tip

Aircraft registration code

Swivelling rubber-tyred tailwheel

120° cowling panel

Joining latch

World War II aircraft

WHEN WORLD WAR II began in 1939, air forces had already replaced most of their fabric-skinned biplanes with all-metal, stressed-skin monoplanes. Aircraft played a far greater role in military operations during World War II than ever before. The wide range of aircraft duties, and the introduction of radar tracking and guidance systems, put pressure on designers to improve aircraft performance. The main areas of improvement were speed, range, and engine power. Bombers became larger and more powerful – converting from two to four engines – in order to carry a heavier bomb load; the US B-17 Flying Fortress could carry up to 6.2 tonnes (6.1 tons) of bombs over a distance of about 3,200 km (2,000 miles). Some aircraft increased their range by using drop tanks (fuel tanks that were jettisoned when empty to reduce drag). Fighters needed speed and manoeuvrability: the Hawker Tempest shown here had a maximum speed of 700 kph (435 mph), and was one of the few Allied aircraft capable of catching the German jet-powered V1 "flying bomb". By 1944, Britain had introduced its first turbojet-powered aircraft, the Gloster Meteor fighter, and Germany had introduced the fastest fighter in the world, the turbojet-powered Me 262, which had a maximum speed of 868 kph (540 mph).

PROPELLER

High-visibility yellow tip

Light-alloy propeller spinner

Variable-pitch aluminium-alloy blade

COMPONENTS OF A HAWKER TEMPEST MARK V, C.1943

STARBOARD ENGINE COWLINGS

Radiator-access cowling

Lower side-cowling

Upper side-cowling

Cowling fastener

Cartridge starter

2,400-HP Napier Sabre 24-cylinder engine

Propeller governor

Radiator header tank

Propeller drive shaft

Distributor

Ejector exhaust

Magneto

Starter motor

Engine top cowling

Cowling fastener

Upper side-cowling

Lower side-cowling

Radiator-access cowling

PORT ENGINE COWLINGS

SECTIONED B-17G FLYING FORTRESS BOMBER, C.1943

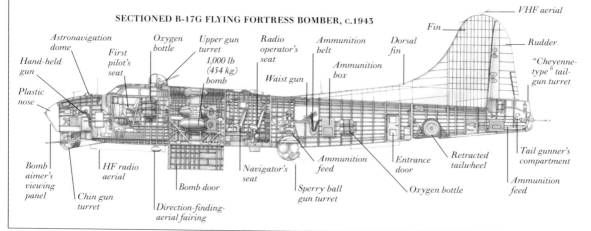

VHF aerial

Fin

Rudder

"Cheyenne-type" tail-gun turret

Astronavigation dome

First pilot's seat

Oxygen bottle

Upper gun turret

1,000 lb (454 kg) bomb

Radio operator's seat

Ammunition belt

Dorsal fin

Ammunition box

Hand-held gun

Waist gun

Plastic nose

Bomb aimer's viewing panel

Chin gun turret

HF radio aerial

Bomb door

Direction-finding-aerial fairing

Navigator's seat

Ammunition feed

Sperry ball gun turret

Entrance door

Oxygen bottle

Retracted tailwheel

Tail gunner's compartment

Ammunition feed

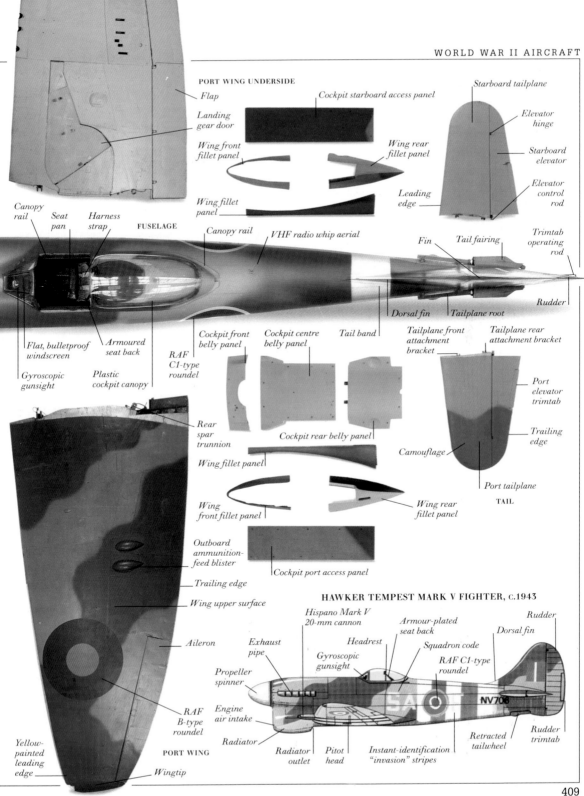

PORT WING UNDERSIDE

Flap

Landing
gear door

Wing front
fillet panel

Cockpit starboard access panel

Wing rear
fillet panel

Starboard tailplane

Elevator
hinge

Starboard
elevator

Elevator
control
rod

Wing fillet
panel

Leading
edge

Canopy
rail

Seat
pan

Harness
strap

FUSELAGE

Canopy rail

VHF radio whip aerial

Fin

Tail fairing

Trimtab
operating
rod

Dorsal fin

Tailplane root

Rudder

Flat, bulletproof
windscreen

Armoured
seat back

Cockpit front
belly panel

Cockpit centre
belly panel

Tail band

Tailplane front
attachment
bracket

Tailplane rear
attachment bracket

RAF
C1-type
roundel

Gyroscopic
gunsight

Plastic
cockpit canopy

Cockpit rear belly panel

Port
elevator
trimtab

Trailing
edge

Rear
spar
trunnion

Wing fillet panel

Camouflage

Port tailplane

TAIL

Wing
front fillet panel

Wing rear
fillet panel

Outboard
ammunition-
feed blister

Cockpit port access panel

Trailing edge

Wing upper surface

HAWKER TEMPEST MARK V FIGHTER, c.1943

Aileron

RAF
B-type
roundel

Yellow-
painted
leading
edge

PORT WING

Wingtip

Hispano Mark V
20-mm cannon

Exhaust
pipe

Gyroscopic
gunsight

Propeller
spinner

Engine
air intake

Radiator

Radiator
outlet

Pitot
head

Headrest

Armour-plated
seat back

Squadron code

RAF C1-type
roundel

Rudder

Dorsal fin

SA

NV708

Instant-identification
"invasion" stripes

Retracted
tailwheel

Rudder
trimtab

409

Modern piston aero-engines

MID WEST TWO-STROKE, THREE-CYLINDER ENGINE

PISTON ENGINES today are used mainly to power the vast numbers of light aircraft and microlights, as well as crop-sprayers and crop-dusters, small helicopters, and fire-bombers (which dump water on large fires). Virtually all heavier aircraft are now powered by jet engines. Modern piston aero-engines work on the same basic principles as the engine used by the Wright brothers in the first powered flight in 1903. However, today's engines are more sophisticated than earlier engines. For example, modern aero-engines may use a two-stroke or a four-stroke combustion cycle; they may have from one to nine air- or water-cooled cylinders, which may be arranged horizontally, in-line, in V formation, or radially; and they may drive the aircraft's propeller either directly or through a reduction gearbox. One of the more unconventional types of modern aero-engine is the rotary engine shown here, which has a trilobate (three-sided) rotor spinning in a chamber shaped like a fat figure-of-eight.

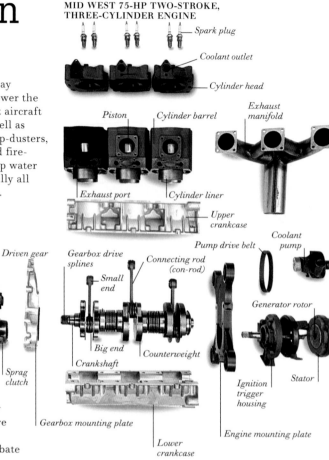

MID WEST 75-HP TWO-STROKE, THREE-CYLINDER ENGINE

- Spark plug
- Coolant outlet
- Cylinder head
- Exhaust manifold
- Piston
- Cylinder barrel
- Exhaust port
- Cylinder liner
- Upper crankcase
- Coolant pump
- Pump drive belt
- Generator rotor
- Stator
- Reduction gearbox
- Driven gear
- Propeller drive flange
- Gearbox drive splines
- Small end
- Connecting rod (con-rod)
- Big end
- Counterweight
- Crankshaft
- Torsional vibration damper
- Sprag clutch
- Gearbox mounting plate
- Lower crankcase
- Ignition trigger housing
- Engine mounting plate

ROTOR AND HOUSINGS OF A MID WEST SINGLE-ROTOR ENGINE

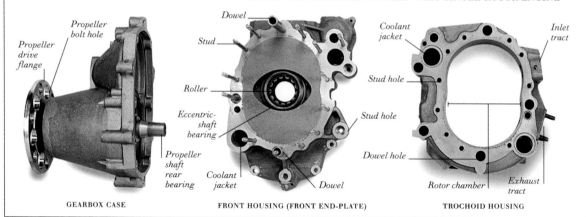

- Propeller bolt hole
- Propeller drive flange
- Dowel
- Stud
- Roller
- Eccentric-shaft bearing
- Coolant jacket
- Inlet tract
- Stud hole
- Stud hole
- Dowel hole
- Propeller shaft rear bearing
- Coolant jacket
- Dowel
- Rotor chamber
- Exhaust tract

GEARBOX CASE

FRONT HOUSING (FRONT END-PLATE)

TROCHOID HOUSING

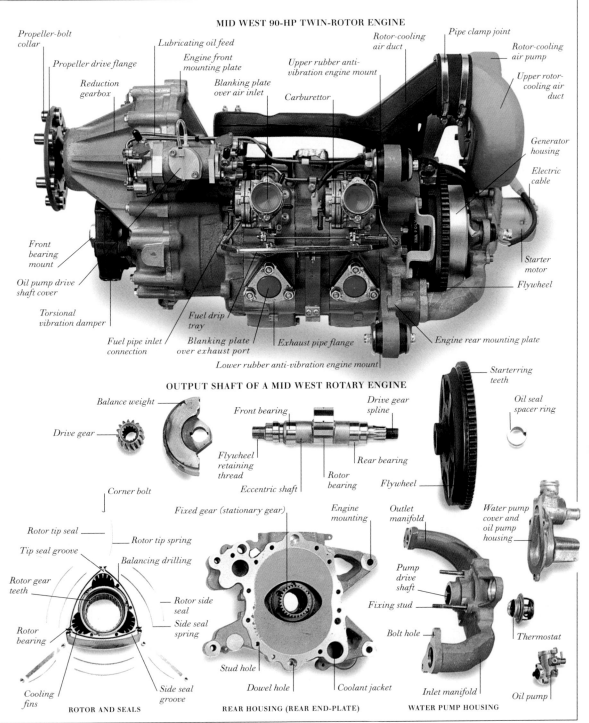

MID WEST 90-HP TWIN-ROTOR ENGINE

Propeller-bolt collar

Propeller drive flange

Reduction gearbox

Lubricating oil feed

Engine front mounting plate

Blanking plate over air inlet

Carburettor

Rotor-cooling air duct

Upper rubber anti-vibration engine mount

Pipe clamp joint

Rotor-cooling air pump

Upper rotor-cooling air duct

Generator housing

Electric cable

Front bearing mount

Oil pump drive shaft cover

Torsional vibration damper

Fuel pipe inlet connection

Fuel drip tray

Blanking plate over exhaust port

Exhaust pipe flange

Lower rubber anti-vibration engine mount

Engine rear mounting plate

Starter motor

Flywheel

OUTPUT SHAFT OF A MID WEST ROTARY ENGINE

Balance weight

Drive gear

Corner bolt

Front bearing

Drive gear spline

Flywheel retaining thread

Rotor bearing

Eccentric shaft

Rear bearing

Flywheel

Starterring teeth

Oil seal spacer ring

Rotor tip seal

Tip seal groove

Rotor gear teeth

Rotor bearing

Cooling fins

ROTOR AND SEALS

Rotor tip spring

Balancing drilling

Rotor side seal

Side seal spring

Side seal groove

Fixed gear (stationary gear)

Engine mounting

Stud hole

Dowel hole

Coolant jacket

REAR HOUSING (REAR END-PLATE)

Outlet manifold

Pump drive shaft

Fixing stud

Bolt hole

Inlet manifold

Water pump cover and oil pump housing

Thermostat

Oil pump

WATER PUMP HOUSING

411

Modern jetliners 1

BAE-146 JETLINER

MODERN JETLINERS HAVE ENABLED ordinary people to travel to places where once only the wealthy could afford to go. Compared with the first jetliners (which were introduced in the 1940s), modern ones are much quieter, burn fuel more efficiently, and produce less air pollution. These advances are largely due to the replacement of turbojet engines with turbofan engines (see pp. 418-419). The greater power of turbofan engines at low speeds enables modern jetliners to carry more fuel and passengers than turbojet aircraft; a modern Boeing 747-400 (popularly known as a "jumbo jet") can fly 400 people for 13,700 km (8,500 miles) without needing to refuel. Jetliners fly at high altitudes, typically cruising at 8,000-11,000 m (26,000-36,000 ft), where they can use fuel efficiently and usually avoid bad weather. The pilot always controls the aircraft during take-off and landing, but at other times the aircraft is usually controlled by an autopilot. Autopilots are complex on-board mechanisms that detect deviations from an aircraft's route and make appropriate adjustments to the flight controls. Flight decks are also equipped with radars that warn pilots of approaching hazards, such as mountain ranges, bad weather, and other aircraft.

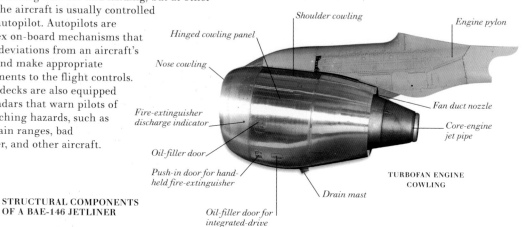

Shoulder cowling

Engine pylon

Hinged cowling panel

Nose cowling

Fire-extinguisher discharge indicator

Fan duct nozzle

Core-engine jet pipe

Oil-filler door

Push-in door for hand-held fire-extinguisher

Drain mast

TURBOFAN ENGINE COWLING

STRUCTURAL COMPONENTS OF A BAE-146 JETLINER

Oil-filler door for integrated-drive generator

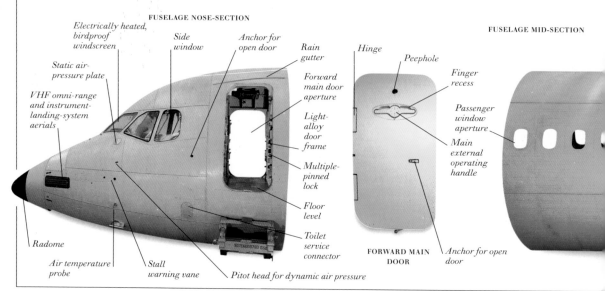

FUSELAGE NOSE-SECTION

FUSELAGE MID-SECTION

Electrically heated, birdproof windscreen

Side window

Anchor for open door

Rain gutter

Hinge

Peephole

Finger recess

Static air-pressure plate

Forward main door aperture

Passenger window aperture

VHF omni-range and instrument-landing-system aerials

Light-alloy door frame

Main external operating handle

Multiple-pinned lock

Floor level

Radome

Toilet service connector

Air temperature probe

Stall warning vane

Pitot head for dynamic air pressure

FORWARD MAIN DOOR

Anchor for open door

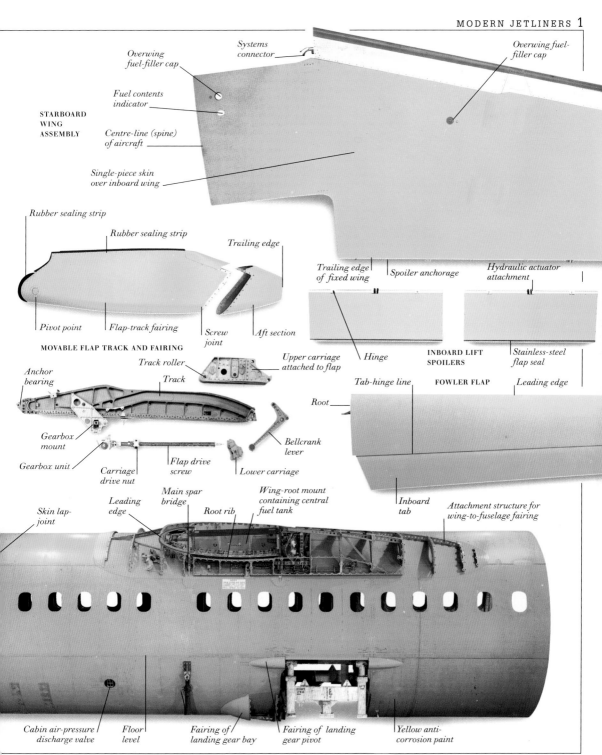

STARBOARD
WING
ASSEMBLY

Overwing
fuel-filler cap

Systems
connector

Overwing fuel-
filler cap

Fuel contents
indicator

Centre-line (spine)
of aircraft

Single-piece skin
over inboard wing

Rubber sealing strip

Rubber sealing strip

Trailing edge

Trailing edge
of fixed wing

Spoiler anchorage

Hydraulic actuator
attachment

Pivot point

Flap-track fairing

Screw
joint

Aft section

Hinge

MOVABLE FLAP TRACK AND FAIRING

**INBOARD LIFT
SPOILERS**

Stainless-steel
flap seal

Track roller

Upper carriage
attached to flap

Tab-hinge line

FOWLER FLAP

Leading edge

Anchor
bearing

Track

Root

Gearbox
mount

Bellcrank
lever

Gearbox unit

Carriage
drive nut

Flap drive
screw

Lower carriage

Skin lap-
joint

Leading
edge

Main spar
bridge

Root rib

Wing-root mount
containing central
fuel tank

Inboard
tab

Attachment structure for
wing-to-fuselage fairing

Cabin air-pressure
discharge valve

Floor
level

Fairing of
landing gear bay

Fairing of landing
gear pivot

Yellow anti-
corrosion paint

Modern jetliners 2

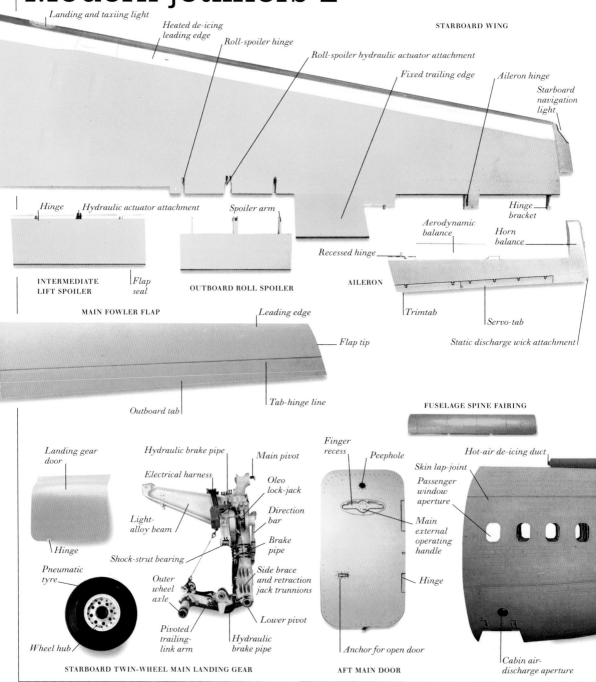

Landing and taxiing light

Heated de-icing leading edge

Roll-spoiler hinge

Roll-spoiler hydraulic actuator attachment

STARBOARD WING

Fixed trailing edge

Aileron hinge

Starboard navigation light

Hinge

Hydraulic actuator attachment

Spoiler arm

Aerodynamic balance

Horn balance

Hinge bracket

Recessed hinge

INTERMEDIATE LIFT SPOILER

Flap seal

OUTBOARD ROLL SPOILER

AILERON

Trimtab

Servo-tab

MAIN FOWLER FLAP

Leading edge

Static discharge wick attachment

Flap tip

Outboard tab

Tab-hinge line

FUSELAGE SPINE FAIRING

Landing gear door

Hydraulic brake pipe

Main pivot

Finger recess

Peephole

Hot-air de-icing duct

Electrical harness

Oleo lock-jack

Skin lap-joint

Passenger window aperture

Light-alloy beam

Direction bar

Hinge

Brake pipe

Shock-strut bearing

Pneumatic tyre

Outer wheel axle

Side brace and retraction jack trunnions

Main external operating handle

Hinge

Lower pivot

Pivoted trailing-link arm

Hydraulic brake pipe

Wheel hub

Anchor for open door

Cabin air-discharge aperture

STARBOARD TWIN-WHEEL MAIN LANDING GEAR

AFT MAIN DOOR

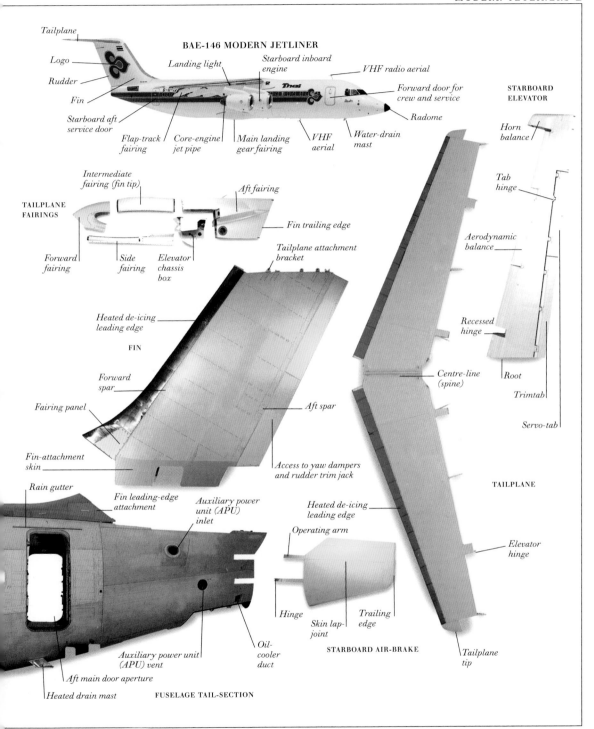

BAE-146 MODERN JETLINER

Tailplane

Logo

Rudder

Fin

Landing light

Starboard inboard engine

VHF radio aerial

Forward door for crew and service

STARBOARD ELEVATOR

Horn balance

Starboard aft service door

Flap-track fairing

Core-engine jet pipe

Main landing gear fairing

VHF aerial

Water-drain mast

Radome

Tab hinge

Aerodynamic balance

Intermediate fairing (fin tip)

Aft fairing

Fin trailing edge

TAILPLANE FAIRINGS

Forward fairing

Side fairing

Elevator chassis box

Tailplane attachment bracket

Recessed hinge

Root

Trimtab

Servo-tab

Heated de-icing leading edge

FIN

Centre-line (spine)

Forward spar

Fairing panel

Aft spar

Fin-attachment skin

Access to yaw dampers and rudder trim jack

TAILPLANE

Rain gutter

Fin leading-edge attachment

Auxiliary power unit (APU) inlet

Heated de-icing leading edge

Operating arm

Elevator hinge

Hinge

Trailing edge

Auxiliary power unit (APU) vent

Oil-cooler duct

Skin lap-joint

STARBOARD AIR-BRAKE

Tailplane tip

Aft main door aperture

Heated drain mast

FUSELAGE TAIL-SECTION

Supersonic jetliners

SUPERSONIC AIRCRAFT FLY FASTER than the speed of sound (Mach 1). There are many supersonic military aircraft, but only two supersonic passenger-carrying aircraft (also called SSTs, or supersonic transports) have been produced: the Russian Tu-144, and Concorde, produced jointly by Britain and France. The Tu-144 was withdrawn in 1978, after only seven months in service. The concorde remained in service from 1976 until 2003, with a break for modifications from July 2000 until October 2001. Its features included a droop nose, which lowered during take-off and landing to aid visibility from the cockpit; the pumping of fuel between forward and aft trim tanks helped stabilize the aircraft. The concorde had a narrow fuselage and shortspan wings to reduce drag during supersonic flight. Its noisy turbojet engines with afterburners enabled it to carry 100 passengers at a cruising speed of Mach 2 at 15,000-18,000 m (50,000-60,000 ft). Once an aircraft is flying faster than Mach 1, it produces a continuous air-pressure wave, which is heard as a "sonic boom".

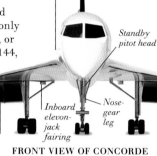

FRONT VIEW OF CONCORDE

Strake

Fin

Standby
pitot head

Starboard
outboard
engine air-intake

Inboard
elevon-
jack
fairing

Nose-
gear
leg

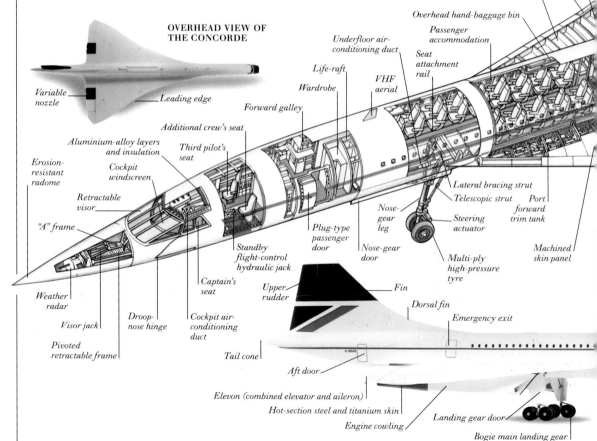

Toilets

Electrothermal
de-icing panel

Starboard
forward trim tank

Overhead hand-baggage bin

Passenger
accommodation

**OVERHEAD VIEW OF
THE CONCORDE**

Underfloor air-
conditioning duct

Seat
attachment
rail

Life-raft

VHF
aerial

Wardrobe

Variable
nozzle

Leading edge

Forward galley

Additional crew's seat

Aluminium-alloy layers
and insulation

Third pilot's
seat

Erosion-
resistant
radome

Cockpit
windscreen

Lateral bracing strut

Telescopic strut

Port
forward
trim tank

Retractable
visor

Nose-
gear
leg

Steering
actuator

"A" frame

Standby
flight-control
hydraulic jack

Plug-type
passenger
door

Nose-gear
door

Multi-ply
high-pressure
tyre

Machined
skin panel

Weather
radar

Captain's
seat

Upper
rudder

Fin

Dorsal fin

Emergency exit

Visor jack

Droop-
nose hinge

Cockpit air-
conditioning
duct

Pivoted
retractable frame

Tail cone

Aft door

Elevon (combined elevator and aileron)

Hot-section steel and titanium skin

Engine cowling

Landing gear door

Bogie main landing gear

SECTIONED VIEW OF THE CONCORDE

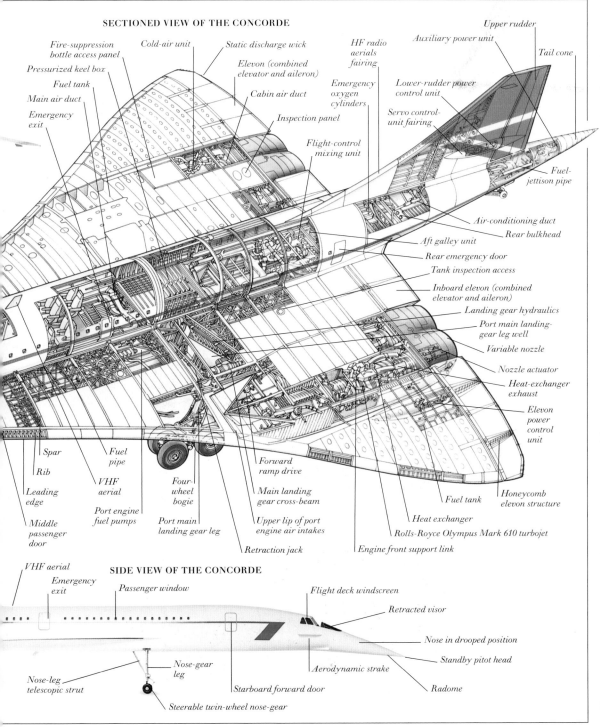

Fire-suppression
bottle access panel

Cold-air unit

Static discharge wick

Upper rudder

Auxiliary power unit

Tail cone

Pressurized keel box

Elevon (combined
elevator and aileron)

HF radio
aerials
fairing

Lower-rudder power
control unit

Fuel tank

Cabin air duct

Emergency
oxygen
cylinders

Servo control-
unit fairing

Main air duct

Inspection panel

Emergency
exit

Flight-control
mixing unit

Fuel-
jettison pipe

Air-conditioning duct

Rear bulkhead

Aft galley unit

Rear emergency door

Tank inspection access

Inboard elevon (combined
elevator and aileron)

Landing gear hydraulics

Port main landing-
gear leg well

Variable nozzle

Nozzle actuator

Heat-exchanger
exhaust

Elevon
power
control
unit

Spar

Fuel
pipe

Rib

VHF
aerial

Four-
wheel
bogie

Forward
ramp drive

Leading
edge

Main landing
gear cross-beam

Fuel tank

Honeycomb
elevon structure

Middle
passenger
door

Port engine
fuel pumps

Port main
landing gear leg

Upper lip of port
engine air intakes

Heat exchanger

Rolls-Royce Olympus Mark 610 turbojet

Retraction jack

Engine front support link

SIDE VIEW OF THE CONCORDE

VHF aerial

Emergency
exit

Passenger window

Flight deck windscreen

Retracted visor

Nose in drooped position

Standby pitot head

Nose-gear
leg

Aerodynamic strake

Nose-leg
telescopic strut

Starboard forward door

Radome

Steerable twin-wheel nose-gear

Jet engines

JET ENGINES ARE USED BY MOST MILITARY and heavy aircraft, and by many helicopters. The simplest type of jet engine, or gas turbine, is the turbojet. It works by continuously burning a mixture of fuel and air in a combustion chamber to produce a jet of hot exhaust gas that is expelled through a nozzle to produce thrust. The hot gas also spins turbine blades, which, in turn, spin the blades of an air compressor; the compressor forces air into the combustion chamber. Many of the fastest aircraft use turbojets, with additional booster units called afterburners, but their use is restricted by their high noise emission. Most jetliners use turbofan jet engines, which are quieter. An enormous fan, driven by a low-pressure turbine, feeds some air into the compressor but feeds most of it through bypass ducts to join the exhaust jetstream in the tail cone. The bypass stream produces most of the thrust. Many smaller, propeller-driven aircraft use turboprop jet engines, in which the engine powers a propeller.

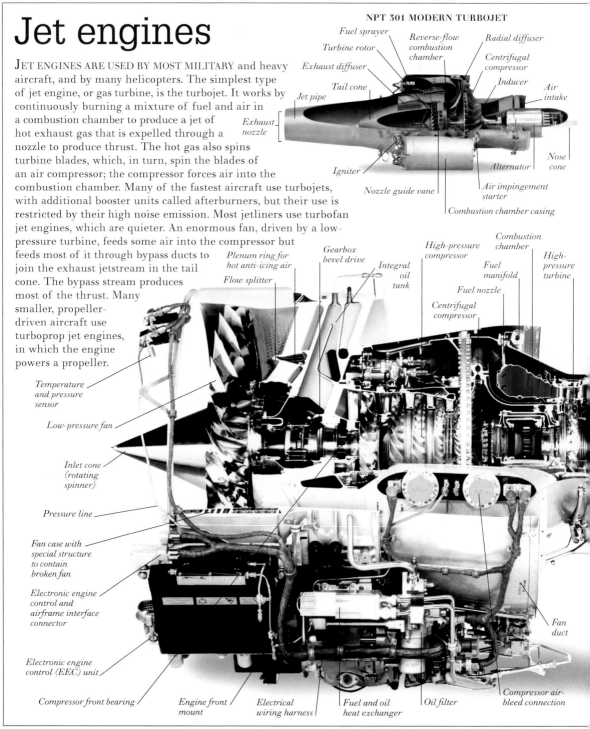

NPT 301 MODERN TURBOJET

Fuel sprayer
Turbine rotor
Reverse-flow combustion chamber
Radial diffuser
Centrifugal compressor
Exhaust diffuser
Inducer
Tail cone
Air intake
Jet pipe
Exhaust nozzle
Jet pipe
Nose cone
Igniter
Alternator
Nozzle guide vane
Air impingement starter
Combustion chamber casing

Temperature and pressure sensor
Low-pressure fan
Inlet cone (rotating spinner)
Pressure line
Fan case with special structure to contain broken fan
Electronic engine control and airframe interface connector
Electronic engine control (EEC) unit
Compressor front bearing
Engine front mount
Electrical wiring harness
Fuel and oil heat exchanger
Oil filter
Compressor air-bleed connection
Fan duct

Plenum ring for hot anti-icing air
Flow splitter
Gearbox bevel drive
Integral oil tank
High-pressure compressor
Combustion chamber
Fuel manifold
High-pressure turbine
Fuel nozzle
Centrifugal compressor

PRATT & WHITNEY CANADA PW120 SERIES MODERN TURBOPROP

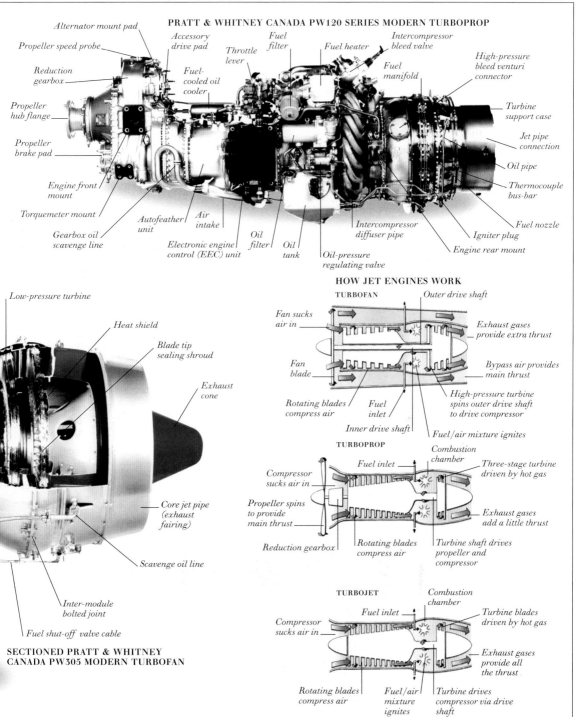

Alternator mount pad

Accessory drive pad

Propeller speed probe

Fuel filter

Fuel heater

Intercompressor bleed valve

Reduction gearbox

Throttle lever

Fuel manifold

High-pressure bleed venturi connector

Fuel-cooled oil cooler

Turbine support case

Propeller hub flange

Jet pipe connection

Propeller brake pad

Oil pipe

Thermocouple bus-bar

Engine front mount

Fuel nozzle

Torquemeter mount

Intercompressor diffuser pipe

Igniter plug

Gearbox oil scavenge line

Autofeather unit

Air intake

Engine rear mount

Electronic engine control (EEC) unit

Oil filter

Oil tank

Oil-pressure regulating valve

SECTIONED PRATT & WHITNEY CANADA PW305 MODERN TURBOFAN

Low-pressure turbine

Heat shield

Blade tip sealing shroud

Exhaust cone

Core jet pipe (exhaust fairing)

Scavenge oil line

Inter-module bolted joint

Fuel shut-off valve cable

HOW JET ENGINES WORK

TURBOFAN

Fan sucks air in

Outer drive shaft

Exhaust gases provide extra thrust

Fan blade

Bypass air provides main thrust

Rotating blades compress air

Fuel inlet

High-pressure turbine spins outer drive shaft to drive compressor

Inner drive shaft

Fuel/air mixture ignites

TURBOPROP

Fuel inlet

Combustion chamber

Compressor sucks air in

Three-stage turbine driven by hot gas

Propeller spins to provide main thrust

Exhaust gases add a little thrust

Reduction gearbox

Rotating blades compress air

Turbine shaft drives propeller and compressor

TURBOJET

Fuel inlet

Combustion chamber

Compressor sucks air in

Turbine blades driven by hot gas

Exhaust gases provide all the thrust

Rotating blades compress air

Fuel/air mixture ignites

Turbine drives compressor via drive shaft

419

Modern military aircraft

MODERN MILITARY AIRCRAFT ARE AMONG THE MOST SOPHISTICATED and expensive products of the 21st century. Fighters need computer-operated controls for manoeuvrability, powerful engines, and effective air-to-air weapons. Most modern fighters also have guided missiles, radar, and passive, infra-red sensors. These developments enable today's fighters to engage in combat with adversaries that are outside visual range. Bombers carry a large weapon load and enough fuel for long-range flights. A few military aircraft, such as the Tornado and the F-14 Tomcat, have variable-sweep ("swing") wings. During take-off and landing their wings are fully extended, but for high-speed flight and low-level attacks the wings are pivoted fully back. A recent development is the "stealth" bomber, which is designed to absorb or deflect enemy radar in order to remain undetected. Earlier bombers, such as the Tornado, use terrain-following radars to fly so close to the ground that they avoid enemy radar detection.

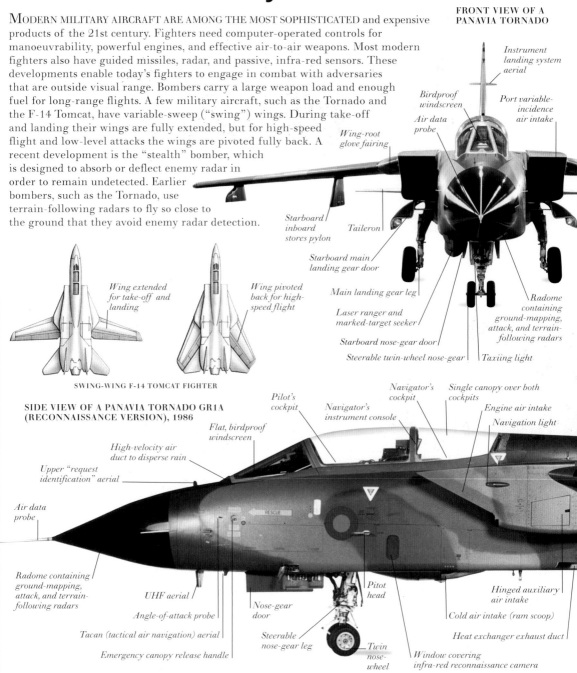

FRONT VIEW OF A PANAVIA TORNADO

Instrument landing system aerial

Birdproof windscreen

Air data probe

Port variable-incidence air intake

Wing-root glove fairing

Starboard inboard stores pylon

Taileron

Starboard main landing gear door

Main landing gear leg

Laser ranger and marked-target seeker

Starboard nose-gear door

Steerable twin-wheel nose-gear

Radome containing ground-mapping, attack, and terrain-following radars

Taxiing light

Wing extended for take-off and landing

Wing pivoted back for high-speed flight

SWING-WING F-14 TOMCAT FIGHTER

SIDE VIEW OF A PANAVIA TORNADO GR1A (RECONNAISSANCE VERSION), 1986

Pilot's cockpit

Navigator's instrument console

Navigator's cockpit

Single canopy over both cockpits

Engine air intake

Navigation light

Flat, birdproof windscreen

High-velocity air duct to disperse rain

Upper "request identification" aerial

Air data probe

Radome containing ground-mapping, attack, and terrain-following radars

UHF aerial

Angle-of-attack probe

Tacan (tactical air navigation) aerial

Emergency canopy release handle

Nose-gear door

Steerable nose-gear leg

Twin nose-wheel

Pitot head

Window covering infra-red reconnaissance camera

Heat exchanger exhaust duct

Cold air intake (ram scoop)

Hinged auxiliary air intake

NORTHROP B-2 ("STEALTH" BOMBER), 1989

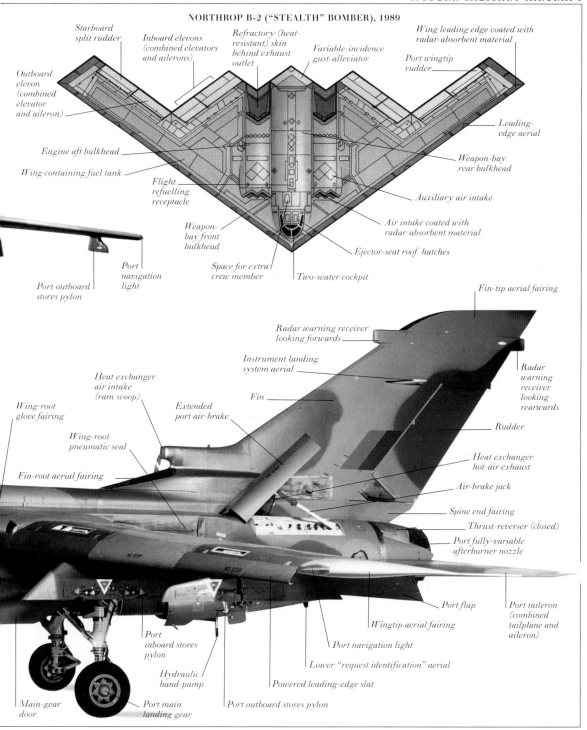

Starboard split rudder

Inboard elevons (combined elevators and ailerons)

Refractory (heat-resistant) skin behind exhaust outlet

Variable-incidence gust-alleviator

Wing leading edge coated with radar-absorbent material

Port wingtip rudder

Outboard elevon (combined elevator and aileron)

Leading-edge aerial

Engine aft bulkhead

Wing containing fuel tank

Flight refuelling receptacle

Weapon-bay rear bulkhead

Weapon-bay front bulkhead

Auxiliary air intake

Air intake coated with radar-absorbent material

Ejector-seat roof hatches

Port outboard stores pylon

Port navigation light

Space for extra crew member

Two-seater cockpit

Fin-tip aerial fairing

Radar warning receiver looking forwards

Instrument landing system aerial

Fin

Radar warning receiver looking rearwards

Heat exchanger air intake (ram scoop)

Extended port air-brake

Rudder

Wing-root glove fairing

Heat exchanger hot-air exhaust

Wing-root pneumatic seal

Air-brake jack

Fin-root aerial fairing

Spine end fairing

Thrust-reverser (closed)

Port fully-variable afterburner nozzle

Port flap

Port taileron (combined tailplane and aileron)

Wingtip aerial fairing

Port inboard stores pylon

Port navigation light

Hydraulic hand-pump

Lower "request identification" aerial

Port outboard stores pylon

Powered leading-edge slat

Main-gear door

Port main landing gear

Helicopters

HELICOPTERS USE ROTATING BLADES for lift, propulsion, and steering. The first machine to achieve sustained, controlled flight using rotating blades was the autogiro built in the 1920s by the Spaniard Juan de la Cierva. His machine had unpowered blades above the fuselage that relied on the flow of air to rotate them and provide lift as the autogiro was driven forwards by a conventional propeller. Then, in 1939, the Russian-born American Igor Sikorsky produced his VS-300, the forerunner of modern helicopters. Its engine-driven blades provided lift, propulsion, and steering. It could take off vertically, hover, and fly in any direction, and had a tail rotor to prevent the helicopter body from spinning. The introduction of gas turbine jet engines to helicopters in 1955 produced quieter, safer, and more powerful machines. Because of their versatility in flight, helicopters are today used for many purposes, including crop-spraying, traffic surveillance, and transporting crews to deep-sea oil rigs, as well as acting as gunships, air ambulances, and air taxis.

BELL 47G-3B1

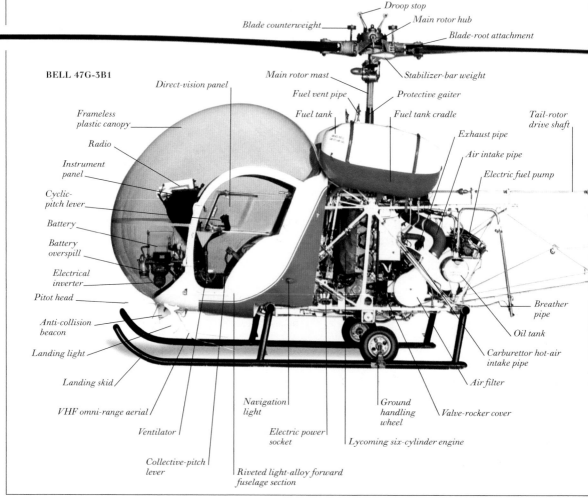

BELL 47G-3B1

Droop stop
Blade counterweight
Main rotor hub
Blade-root attachment
Main rotor mast
Stabilizer-bar weight
Direct-vision panel
Fuel vent pipe
Protective gaiter
Frameless plastic canopy
Fuel tank
Fuel tank cradle
Tail-rotor drive shaft
Exhaust pipe
Radio
Air intake pipe
Instrument panel
Electric fuel pump
Cyclic-pitch lever
Battery
Battery overspill
Electrical inverter
Pitot head
Breather pipe
Anti-collision beacon
Oil tank
Landing light
Carburettor hot-air intake pipe
Landing skid
Air filter
VHF omni-range aerial
Navigation light
Ground handling wheel
Valve-rocker cover
Ventilator
Electric power socket
Lycoming six-cylinder engine
Collective-pitch lever
Riveted light-alloy forward fuselage section

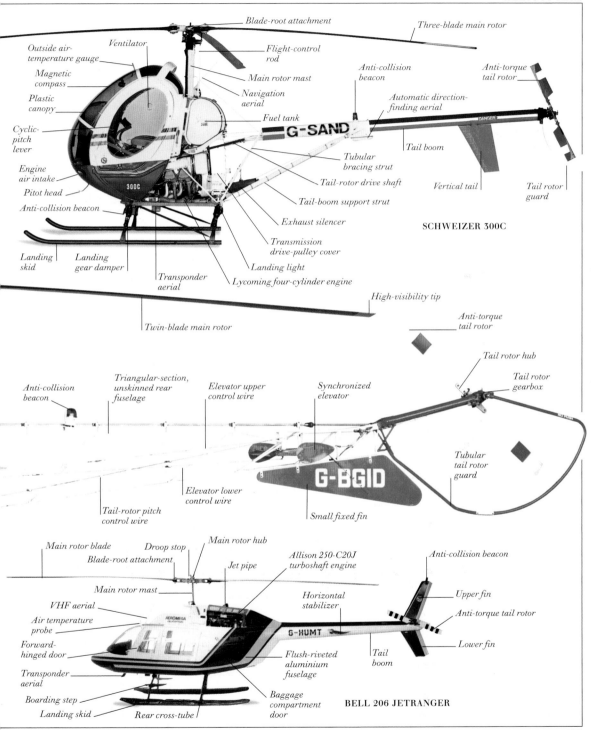

SCHWEIZER 300C

Blade-root attachment

Three-blade main rotor

Outside air-temperature gauge

Ventilator

Flight-control rod

Anti-collision beacon

Anti-torque tail rotor

Magnetic compass

Main rotor mast

Automatic direction-finding aerial

Plastic canopy

Navigation aerial

Cyclic-pitch lever

Fuel tank

DANGER

Engine air intake

Tubular bracing strut

Tail boom

Pitot head

Tail-rotor drive shaft

Vertical tail

Tail rotor guard

Anti-collision beacon

Tail-boom support strut

Exhaust silencer

Landing skid

Landing gear damper

Transmission drive-pulley cover

Transponder aerial

Landing light

Lycoming four-cylinder engine

High-visibility tip

Twin-blade main rotor

Anti-torque tail rotor

Tail rotor hub

Anti-collision beacon

Triangular-section, unskinned rear fuselage

Elevator upper control wire

Synchronized elevator

Tail rotor gearbox

G-BGID

Tubular tail rotor guard

Elevator lower control wire

Tail-rotor pitch control wire

Small fixed fin

Main rotor blade

Droop stop

Main rotor hub

Anti-collision beacon

Blade-root attachment

Jet pipe

Allison 250-C20J turboshaft engine

Main rotor mast

Horizontal stabilizer

Upper fin

VHF aerial

Anti-torque tail rotor

Air temperature probe

G-HUMT

Forward-hinged door

Lower fin

Transponder aerial

Flush-riveted aluminium fuselage

Tail boom

Boarding step

Baggage compartment door

BELL 206 JETRANGER

Landing skid

Rear cross-tube

423

Light aircraft

LIGHT AIRCRAFT, SUCH AS THE ARV SUPER 2 shown here, are small, lightweight, and of simple construction. More than a million have been built since World War I, mainly for recreational use by private owners. Virtually all light aircraft have piston engines, most of which are air-cooled, although some are liquid-cooled. Open cockpits, almost universal in the 1920s, have today been replaced by enclosed cabins. The cabins of high-wing aircraft have one or two doors, whereas those of low-wing aircraft usually have a sliding or hinged canopy. Most modern light aircraft are made of aluminium alloy, although some are made of wood or of fibre-reinforced materials. Light aircraft today also usually have navigational instruments, an electrical system, cabin heating, wheel brakes, and a two-way radio.

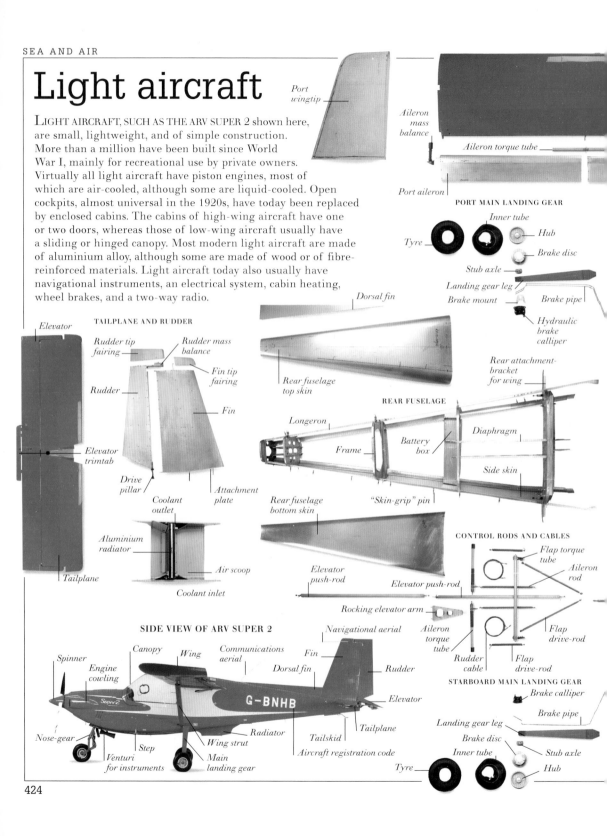

Port wingtip

Aileron mass balance

Aileron torque tube

Port aileron

PORT MAIN LANDING GEAR

Inner tube

Tyre

Hub

Brake disc

Stub axle

Landing gear leg

Brake mount

Brake pipe

Hydraulic brake calliper

Dorsal fin

Rear attachment-bracket for wing

TAILPLANE AND RUDDER

Elevator

Rudder tip fairing

Rudder mass balance

Fin tip fairing

Rudder

Fin

Elevator trimtab

Drive pillar

Coolant outlet

Attachment plate

Aluminium radiator

Air scoop

Tailplane

Coolant inlet

Rear fuselage top skin

REAR FUSELAGE

Longeron

Frame

Battery box

Diaphragm

Side skin

Rear fuselage bottom skin

"Skin-grip" pin

Elevator push-rod

Elevator push-rod

Rocking elevator arm

CONTROL RODS AND CABLES

Flap torque tube

Aileron rod

Aileron torque tube

Rudder cable

Flap drive-rod

Flap drive-rod

STARBOARD MAIN LANDING GEAR

Brake calliper

Brake pipe

Landing gear leg

Brake disc

Inner tube

Stub axle

Hub

Tyre

SIDE VIEW OF ARV SUPER 2

Spinner

Canopy

Wing

Communications aerial

Navigational aerial

Fin

Dorsal fin

Rudder

Engine cowling

Elevator

Tailplane

Radiator

Tailskid

Nose-gear

Wing strut

Aircraft registration code

Venturi for instruments

Step

Main landing gear

G-BNHB

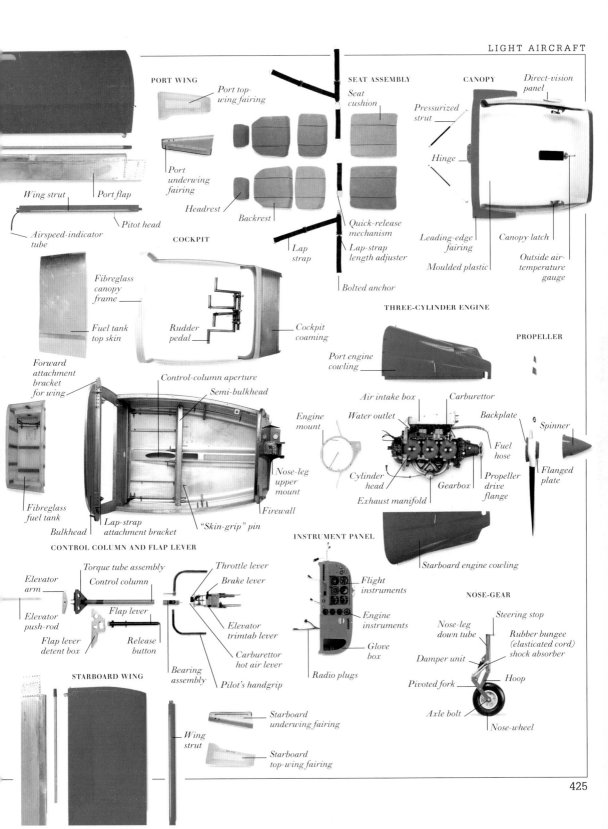

PORT WING

Port top-wing fairing

Port underwing fairing

Headrest

Backrest

Wing strut

Port flap

Pitot head

Airspeed-indicator tube

SEAT ASSEMBLY

Seat cushion

Quick-release mechanism

Lap-strap length adjuster

Lap strap

Bolted anchor

CANOPY

Direct-vision panel

Pressurized strut

Hinge

Leading-edge fairing

Moulded plastic

Canopy latch

Outside air-temperature gauge

COCKPIT

Fibreglass canopy frame

Fuel tank top skin

Rudder pedal

Cockpit coaming

THREE-CYLINDER ENGINE

Port engine cowling

PROPELLER

Air intake box

Carburettor

Backplate

Spinner

Forward attachment bracket for wing

Control-column aperture

Semi-bulkhead

Engine mount

Water outlet

Fuel hose

Flanged plate

Cylinder head

Gearbox

Propeller drive flange

Nose-leg upper mount

Exhaust manifold

Fibreglass fuel tank

Bulkhead

Lap-strap attachment bracket

"Skin-grip" pin

Firewall

INSTRUMENT PANEL

Starboard engine cowling

CONTROL COLUMN AND FLAP LEVER

Torque tube assembly

Throttle lever

Brake lever

Elevator arm

Control column

Flight instruments

Elevator push-rod

Flap lever

Elevator trimtab lever

Engine instruments

NOSE-GEAR

Steering stop

Nose-leg down tube

Flap lever detent box

Release button

Carburettor hot air lever

Glove box

Rubber bungee (elasticated cord) shock absorber

Damper unit

Bearing assembly

Pilot's handgrip

Radio plugs

Pivoted fork

Hoop

STARBOARD WING

Axle bolt

Nose-wheel

Wing strut

Starboard underwing fairing

Starboard top-wing fairing

Gliders, hang-gliders, and microlights

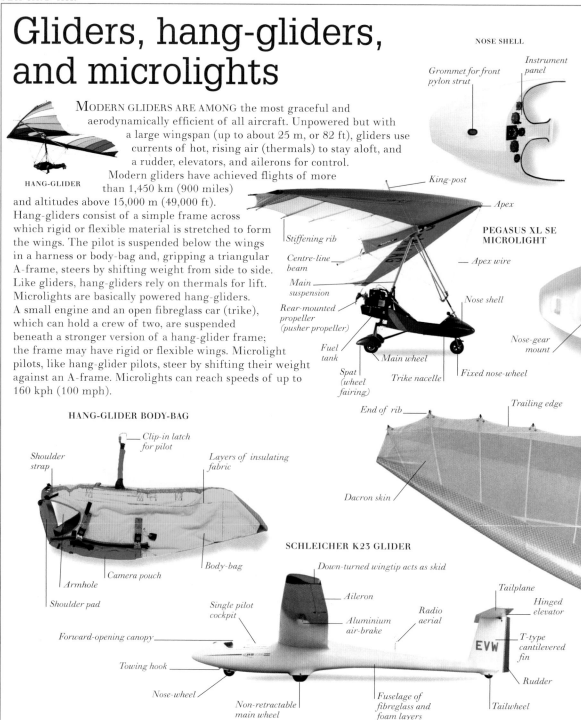

HANG-GLIDER

MODERN GLIDERS ARE AMONG the most graceful and aerodynamically efficient of all aircraft. Unpowered but with a large wingspan (up to about 25 m, or 82 ft), gliders use currents of hot, rising air (thermals) to stay aloft, and a rudder, elevators, and ailerons for control. Modern gliders have achieved flights of more than 1,450 km (900 miles) and altitudes above 15,000 m (49,000 ft). Hang-gliders consist of a simple frame across which rigid or flexible material is stretched to form the wings. The pilot is suspended below the wings in a harness or body-bag and, gripping a triangular A-frame, steers by shifting weight from side to side. Like gliders, hang-gliders rely on thermals for lift. Microlights are basically powered hang-gliders. A small engine and an open fibreglass car (trike), which can hold a crew of two, are suspended beneath a stronger version of a hang-glider frame; the frame may have rigid or flexible wings. Microlight pilots, like hang-glider pilots, steer by shifting their weight against an A-frame. Microlights can reach speeds of up to 160 kph (100 mph).

NOSE SHELL

Grommet for front pylon strut

Instrument panel

King-post

Apex

PEGASUS XL SE MICROLIGHT

Stiffening rib

Centre-line beam

Main suspension

Rear-mounted propeller (pusher propeller)

Fuel tank

Spat (wheel fairing)

Main wheel

Trike nacelle

Apex wire

Nose shell

Nose-gear mount

Fixed nose-wheel

End of rib

Trailing edge

Dacron skin

HANG-GLIDER BODY-BAG

Clip-in latch for pilot

Shoulder strap

Layers of insulating fabric

Armhole

Camera pouch

Body-bag

Shoulder pad

SCHLEICHER K23 GLIDER

Down-turned wingtip acts as skid

Single pilot cockpit

Aileron

Aluminium air-brake

Radio aerial

Tailplane

Hinged elevator

Forward-opening canopy

T-type cantilevered fin

Towing hook

EVW

Rudder

Nose-wheel

Non-retractable main wheel

Fuselage of fibreglass and foam layers

Tailwheel

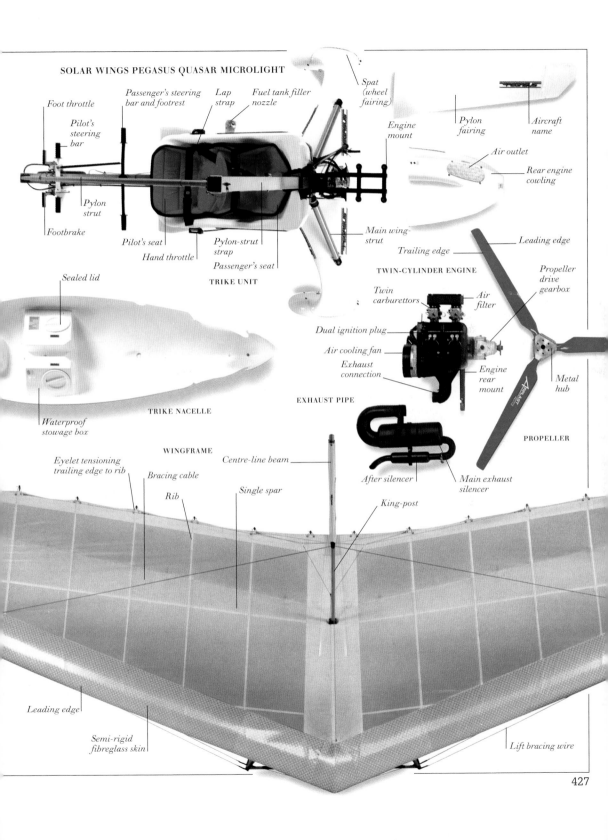

SOLAR WINGS PEGASUS QUASAR MICROLIGHT

Foot throttle

Passenger's steering bar and footrest

Lap strap

Fuel tank filler nozzle

Spat (wheel fairing)

Engine mount

Pilot's steering bar

Pylon fairing

Aircraft name

Air outlet

Rear engine cowling

Pylon strut

Footbrake

Pilot's seat

Hand throttle

Pylon-strut strap

Passenger's seat

Main wing-strut

TRIKE UNIT

TWIN-CYLINDER ENGINE

Trailing edge

Leading edge

Propeller drive gearbox

Sealed lid

Twin carburettors

Air filter

Dual ignition plug

Air cooling fan

Exhaust connection

Engine rear mount

Metal hub

TRIKE NACELLE

EXHAUST PIPE

Waterproof stowage box

PROPELLER

WINGFRAME

Centre-line beam

Eyelet tensioning trailing edge to rib

Bracing cable

Single spar

King-post

Rib

After silencer

Main exhaust silencer

Leading edge

Semi-rigid fibreglass skin

Lift bracing wire

427

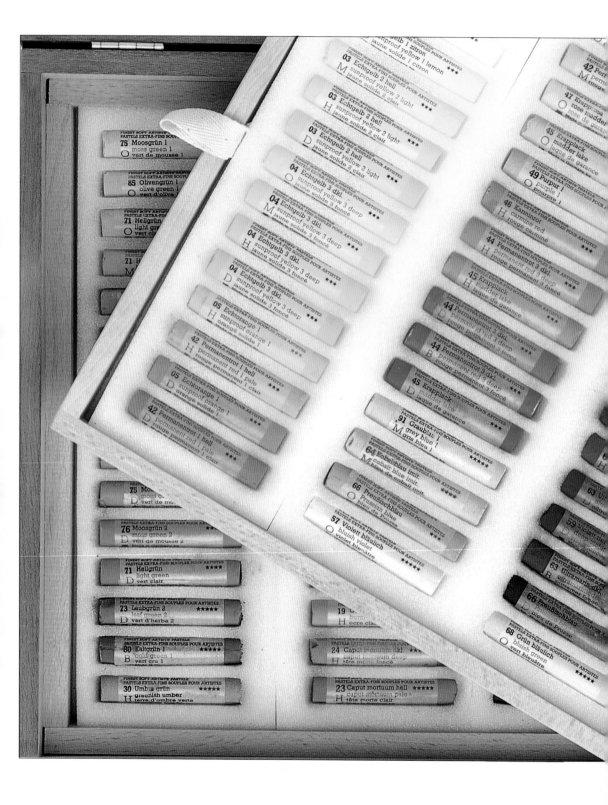

EXAMPLE OF A FRESCO
The Expulsion of the Merchants from the Temple, Giotto, c.1306
Fresco, 200 × 185 cm (78 × 72 in)

*One of a series
of frescoes in the
Arena Chapel,
Padua, Italy*

*Temple acts as
a backdrop for
the action*

*Bianco di San
Giovanni often
used for fresco
whites*

*Patches of azurite
blue have turned
green due to
reaction with
carbon dioxide*

*Gold leaf applied
to apostle's halo*

*Hairline junction
between giornate
is visible*

*Green earth
pigment applied
to robe*

*Child painted
on top of
apostle's robe*

*Red earth
pigment applied
in buon fresco
has retained
rich hue*

*Azurite blue applied in fresco secco has
flaked off to reveal the plaster beneath*

*Dry, matt surface characteristic
of buon fresco*

*Paint applied
in buon fresco
to child's face*

*Artist has to finish giornata
before plaster dries*

Junction between giornate

*A fresco was
generally
worked in
zones from
the top down*

*Area with little
detail can be
painted quickly,
allowing a
larger giornata
to be completed*

*White dove
represents
the Holy Ghost*

*Highly detailed
area takes a
longer time to
paint, restricting
the size of the
giornata*

*Paint applied
in fresco secco
to child's body
has flaked off*

*Sinopia (design)
sketched in
red earth*

**DETAIL FROM "THE
EXPULSION"**

GIORNATE (DAILY SECTIONS) IN "THE EXPULSION"

Oils

OIL PAINTS ARE MADE BY MIXING and grinding pigment with a drying vegetable oil such as linseed oil. The paint can be applied to many different surfaces and textures – the most common being canvas. Before painting, the canvas is stretched on a wooden frame and its surface is prepared with layers of size (glue) and primer. The two main types of brushes used in oil painting are stiff hog hair bristle brushes – generally used for covering large areas; and soft hair brushes made from sable or synthetic material – generally used for fine detail. Other tools, including painting knives, can also be used to achieve different effects. Oil paint can be applied thickly (a technique known as impasto), or can be thinned down using a solvent – such as turpentine or white spirit. Varnishes are sometimes applied to finished paintings to protect their surface and to give them a matt or gloss finish.

KIDNEY-
SHAPED
PALETTE

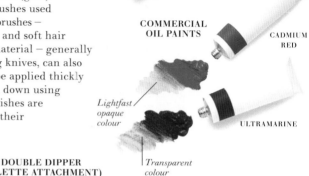

DAMMAR RESIN
VARNISH

Crystals are dissolved and applied to painting to protect its surface

COMMERCIAL
OIL PAINTS

CADMIUM
RED

Lightfast opaque colour

ULTRAMARINE

Transparent colour

LINSEED OIL

Oil derived from seeds of flax plant

EXAMPLES
OF PIGMENTS

CADMIUM
RED

CERULEAN
BLUE

DOUBLE DIPPER
(PALETTE ATTACHMENT)

Screw-top lid

Container for storing solvent or drying oil

HOG HAIR
BRISTLE BRUSHES

Flat hog hair brush

Filbert hog hair brush

Flat hog hair brush

Filbert hog hair brush

SYNTHETIC
BRUSH

Round hog hair brush

EXAMPLES
OF BRUSHES

SABLE
BRUSH

EQUIPMENT FOR
MAKING OIL PAINT

Airtight jar for storing paint

Palette knife for mixing drying oil and pigment

PAINTING KNIVES

TROWEL-
SHAPED
PAINTING
KNIFE

DIAMOND-
SHAPED
PAINTING
KNIFE

Blade

Blade

Glass muller for grinding drying oil and pigment

Glass slab with abrasive surface

Cranked, steel shank

Cranked, steel shank

Long, wooden handle

Protective, plastic case

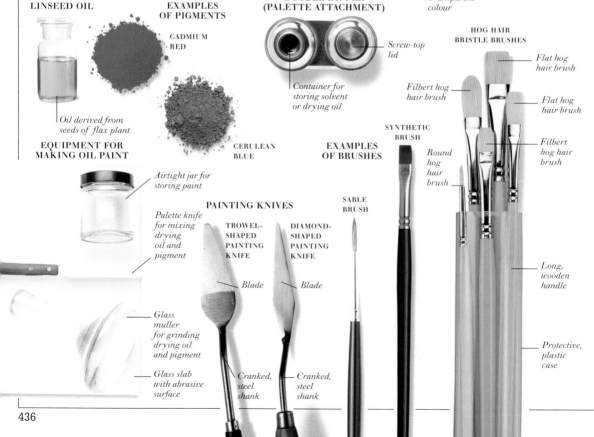

EXAMPLE OF AN OIL PAINTING
Fritillarias, Vincent van Gogh, 1886
Oil on canvas, 73.5 × 60.5 cm (29 × 24 in)

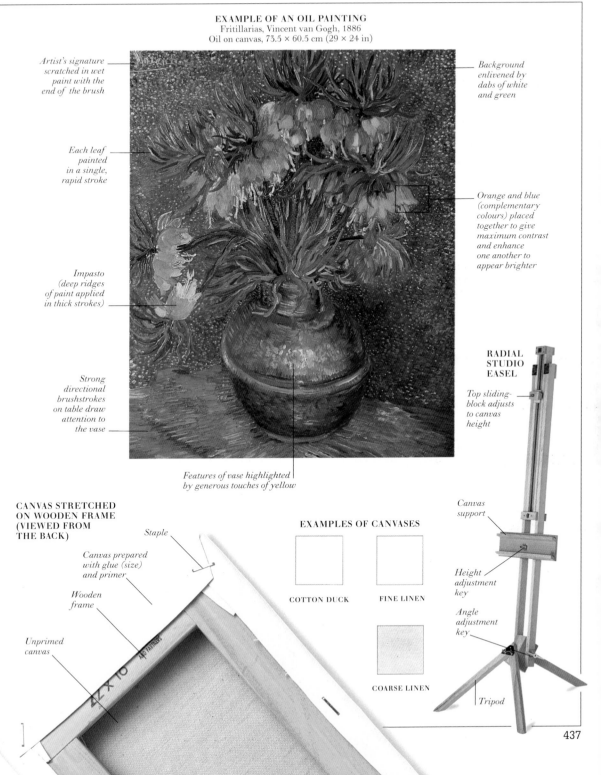

Artist's signature scratched in wet paint with the end of the brush

Background enlivened by dabs of white and green

Each leaf painted in a single, rapid stroke

Orange and blue (complementary colours) placed together to give maximum contrast and enhance one another to appear brighter

Impasto (deep ridges of paint applied in thick strokes)

Strong directional brushstrokes on table draw attention to the vase

Features of vase highlighted by generous touches of yellow

RADIAL STUDIO EASEL

Top sliding-block adjusts to canvas height

Canvas support

Height adjustment key

Angle adjustment key

Tripod

CANVAS STRETCHED ON WOODEN FRAME (VIEWED FROM THE BACK)

Staple

Canvas prepared with glue (size) and primer

Wooden frame

Unprimed canvas

EXAMPLES OF CANVASES

COTTON DUCK

FINE LINEN

COARSE LINEN

437

Watercolour

WATERCOLOUR PAINT IS MADE OF GROUND PIGMENT mixed with a water-soluble binding medium, usually gum arabic. It is usually applied to paper using soft hair brushes such as sable, goat hair, squirrel, and synthetic brushes. Watercolours are often diluted and applied as overlaying washes (thin, transparent layers) to build up depth of colour. Washes can be laid in a variety of ways to create a range of different effects. For example, a wet-in-wet wash can be achieved by laying a wash on top of another wet wash. The two washes blend together to give a fused effect. Sponges are used to modify washes by soaking up paint so that areas of pigment are lightened or removed from the paper. Watercolours can also be applied undiluted – a technique known as dry brush – to create a broken-colour effect. Watercolours are generally transparent and allow light to reflect from the surface of the paper through the layers of paint to give a luminous effect. They can be thickened and made opaque by adding body colour (Chinese white).

GUM ARABIC

Natural sap from acacia tree

NATURAL SPONGE

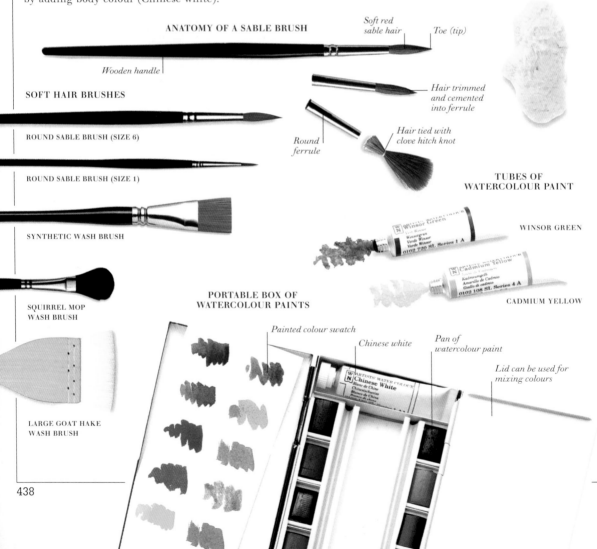

ANATOMY OF A SABLE BRUSH

Soft red sable hair

Toe (tip)

Wooden handle

Hair trimmed and cemented into ferrule

SOFT HAIR BRUSHES

ROUND SABLE BRUSH (SIZE 6)

Round ferrule

Hair tied with clove hitch knot

ROUND SABLE BRUSH (SIZE 1)

SYNTHETIC WASH BRUSH

TUBES OF WATERCOLOUR PAINT

WINSOR GREEN

SQUIRREL MOP WASH BRUSH

PORTABLE BOX OF WATERCOLOUR PAINTS

CADMIUM YELLOW

Painted colour swatch

Chinese white

Pan of watercolour paint

Lid can be used for mixing colours

LARGE GOAT HAKE WASH BRUSH

EXAMPLE OF A WATERCOLOUR
Burning of the Houses of Parliament, Turner, 1834
Watercolour on paper, 29.2 × 44.5 cm (11½ × 17½ in)

Transparent washes laid on top of each other to create tonal depth

Highlight scratched out with a scalpel

Crowd painted with thin strokes laid over a pale wash

Transparent washes allow light to reflect off the surface of the paper to give a luminous effect

Paper shows through thin wash to give flames added highlight

Undiluted paint applied, then partly washed out, to create the impression of water

EXAMPLES OF WASHES

WASH OVER DRY BRUSH
Wash laid over paint applied with dry brush gives two-tone effect

GRADED WASH
Strong wash applied to tilted paper gives graded effect

DRY BRUSH
Undiluted paint dragged across surface of paper gives broken effect

WET-IN-WET
Two diluted washes left to run together to give fused effect

**EXAMPLES OF
WATERCOLOUR PAPERS**

SMOOTH-
TEXTURED
PAPER

MEDIUM-
TEXTURED
PAPER

ROUGH-
TEXTURED
PAPER

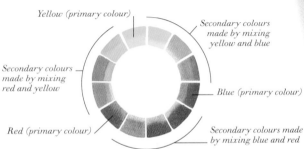

COLOUR WHEEL OF WATERCOLOUR PAINTS

Yellow (primary colour)

Secondary colours made by mixing yellow and blue

Secondary colours made by mixing red and yellow

Blue (primary colour)

Red (primary colour)

Secondary colours made by mixing blue and red

Pastels

PASTELS ARE STICKS OF PIGMENT made by mixing ground pigment with chalk and a binding medium, such as gum arabic. They vary in hardness depending on the proportion of the binding medium to the chalk. Soft pastel – the most common form of pastel – contains just enough binding medium to hold the pigment in stick form. Pastels can be applied directly to any support (surface) with sufficient tooth (texture). When a pastel is drawn over a textured surface, the pigment crumbles and lodges in the fibres of the support. Pastel marks have a particular soft, matt quality and are suitable for techniques such as blending, scumbling, and feathering. Blending is a technique of rubbing and fusing two or more colours on the support using fingers or various tools such as tortillons (paper stumps), soft hair brushes, putty erasers, and soft bread. Scumbling is a technique of building up layers of pastel colours. The side or blunted tip of a soft pastel is lightly drawn over an underpainted area so that patches of the colour beneath show through. Feathering is a technique of applying parallel strokes of colour with the point of a pastel, usually over an existing layer of pastel colour. A thin spray of fixative can be applied – using a mouth diffuser (see pp. 430-431) or aerosol spray fixative – to a finished pastel painting, or in between layers of colour, to prevent smudging.

EQUIPMENT FOR MAKING PASTELS

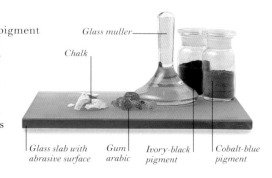

Glass muller

Chalk

Glass slab with abrasive surface

Gum arabic

Ivory-black pigment

Cobalt-blue pigment

EXAMPLES OF SOFT PASTELS

COBALT-BLUE HALF PASTEL

VERMILION HALF PASTEL

OLIVE-GREEN FULL PASTEL

MAUVE FULL PASTEL

EQUIPMENT USED WITH PASTELS

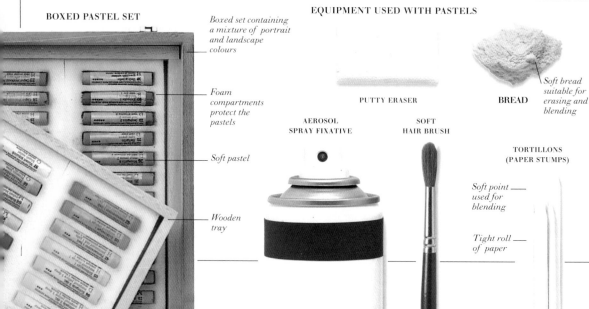

BOXED PASTEL SET

Boxed set containing a mixture of portrait and landscape colours

Foam compartments protect the pastels

Soft pastel

Wooden tray

PUTTY ERASER

BREAD

Soft bread suitable for erasing and blending

AEROSOL SPRAY FIXATIVE

SOFT HAIR BRUSH

TORTILLONS (PAPER STUMPS)

Soft point used for blending

Tight roll of paper

EXAMPLE OF A PASTEL PAINTING
Woman Drying her Neck, Edgar Degas, c.1898
Pastel on cardboard, 62.5 x 65.5 cm (24½ x 25½in)

Pastels applied directly to support

Rich colour of fabric created by overlaying yellows and oranges

Broken colours, characteristic of scumbling technique

Colours are blended together using fingers or tools such as tortillons

Built up layers of pastel

Toned colour of paper visible beneath thinly applied pastels

Pure bright colours laid side by side produce strong contrasts

DETAIL FROM "WOMAN DRYING HER NECK"

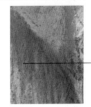

Feathering technique used to produce skin tones

EXAMPLES OF TEXTURED PAPERS AND PASTEL BOARDS

WATERCOLOUR PAPER(ROUGH TEXTURE)

GLASS PAPER

WATERCOLOUR PAPER (MEDIUM TEXTURE)

INGRES PAPER

FLOCKED PASTEL BOARD

CANSON PAPER

EXAMPLES OF COLOURED AND TINTED PAPERS

Acrylics

ACRYLIC PAINT IS MADE BY MIXING PIGMENT with a synthetic resin. It can be thinned with water but dries to become water insoluble. Acrylics are applied to many surfaces, such as paper and acrylic-primed board and canvas. A variety of brushes, painting knives, rollers, air-brushes, plastic scrapers, and other tools are used in acrylic painting. The versatility of acrylics makes them suitable for a wide range of techniques. They can be used opaquely or – by adding water – in a transparent, watercolour style. Acrylic mediums can be added to the paint to adjust its consistency for special effects such as glazing and impasto (ridges of paint applied in thick strokes) or to make it more matt or glossy. Acrylics are quick-drying, which allows layers of paint to be applied on top of each other almost immediately.

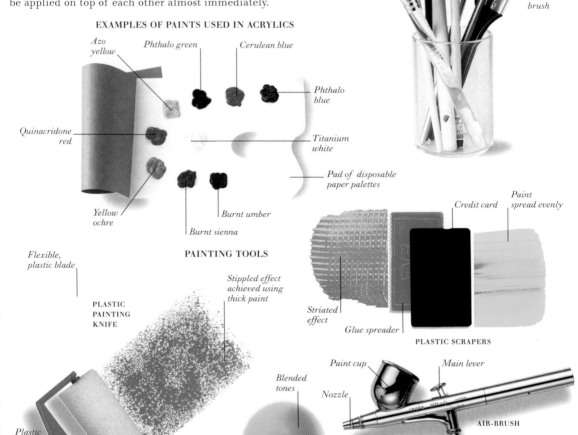

EXAMPLES OF BRUSHES

Sable brush

Hog hair sash brush

Synthetic hog hair brush

Synthetic sable brush

Hog hair brush

Goat hair brush

Synthetic wash brush

Ox hair brush

EXAMPLES OF PAINTS USED IN ACRYLICS

Azo yellow

Phthalo green

Cerulean blue

Phthalo blue

Quinacridone red

Titanium white

Pad of disposable paper palettes

Yellow ochre

Burnt umber

Burnt sienna

PAINTING TOOLS

Flexible, plastic blade

Stippled effect achieved using thick paint

PLASTIC PAINTING KNIFE

Striated effect

Glue spreader

Credit card

Paint spread evenly

PLASTIC SCRAPERS

Plastic handle

Blended tones

Paint cup

Main lever

Nozzle

AIR-BRUSH

SPONGE ROLLER

Uniform tone

Air hose

EXAMPLE OF AN ACRYLIC PAINTING
A Bigger Splash, David Hockney, 1967
Acrylic on canvas, 242.5 x 243.8 cm (95½ x 96 in)

Paint applied evenly using a roller

Cotton duck canvas support (surface)

Flatness of rollered areas enhanced by adding gel medium to the paint

Masking tape stuck on to canvas to define main shapes, and paint applied within these areas using a roller

Thin strip of pool edge left unpainted

Splash painted using thicker paint and small brush

Imprecise edge on end of spring board where paint has seeped under masking tape

EXAMPLES OF ACRYLIC PAINTS AND TECHNIQUES

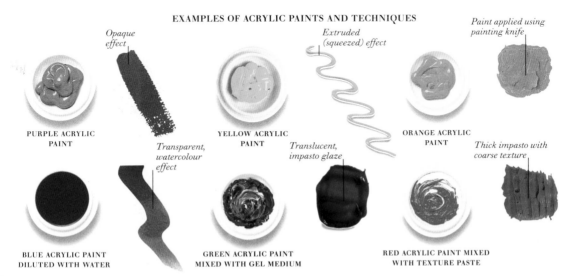

Opaque effect

Extruded (squeezed) effect

Paint applied using painting knife

PURPLE ACRYLIC PAINT

Transparent, watercolour effect

YELLOW ACRYLIC PAINT

Translucent, impasto glaze

ORANGE ACRYLIC PAINT

Thick impasto with coarse texture

BLUE ACRYLIC PAINT DILUTED WITH WATER

GREEN ACRYLIC PAINT MIXED WITH GEL MEDIUM

RED ACRYLIC PAINT MIXED WITH TEXTURE PASTE

Calligraphy

CALLIGRAPHY IS BEAUTIFULLY FORMED LETTERING. The term applies to written text and illumination (the decoration of manuscripts using gold leaf and colour). The essential materials needed to practise calligraphy are a writing tool, ink, and a writing surface. Quills are among the oldest writing tools. They are usually made from goose or turkey feathers, and are noted for their flexibility and ability to produce fine lines. A quill point, however, is not very durable and constant recutting and trimming is required. The most commonly used writing instrument in western calligraphy is a detachable, metal nib held in a penholder. The metal nib is very durable, and there are a wide range of different types. Particular types of nibs – such as copperplate, speedball, and roundhand nibs – are used for specific styles of lettering. Some nibs have integral ink reservoirs and others have reservoirs that are detachable. Brushes are also used for writing, and for filling in outlined letters and painting decoration. Other writing tools used in calligraphy are fountain pens, felt-tip pens, rotring pens, and reed pens. Calligraphy inks may come in liquid form, or as a solid ink stick. Ink sticks are ground down in distilled water to form a liquid ink. The most common writing surfaces for calligraphy are good quality, smooth -surfaced papers. To achieve the best writing position, the calligrapher places the paper on a drawing board set at an angle.

EQUIPMENT USED IN BRUSH LETTERING

Brush rest

Wolf hair brush

Goat hair brush

BRUSHES AND BRUSH REST

Liquid ink made by grinding down ink stick in distilled water

Solid carbon ink stick

Ink stone

INK STICK AND STONE

PENS, NIBS, AND BRUSHES USED IN CALLIGRAPHY

PENHOLDER

COPPERPLATE NIB

SPEEDBALL NIB

Feather

FELT-TIP PEN

ROUNDHAND NIB AND DETACHABLE INK RESERVOIR

AUTOMATIC PEN

Feather stripped for better handling

REED PEN

Barrel

SQUARE SABLE BRUSH

POINTED SABLE BRUSH

Hand-cut point

GOOSE-FEATHER QUILL

GOAT HAIR BRUSH

WOLF HAIR BRUSH

FOUNTAIN PEN AND INK

Bottle of permanent black ink

Barrel

Clip

Nib

Cuter cap

EXAMPLES OF LETTERING STYLES

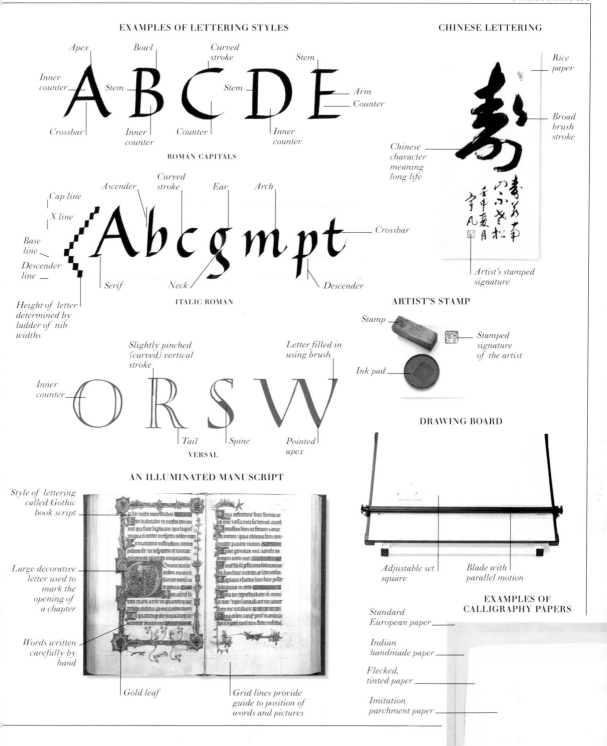

Apex *Bowl* *Curved stroke* *Stem*

Inner counter *Stem* *Stem* *Arm* *Counter*

Crossbar *Inner counter* *Counter* *Inner counter*

ROMAN CAPITALS

Cap line
X line

Ascender *Curved stroke* *Ear* *Arch*

Base line
Descender line

Crossbar

Serif *Neck* *Descender*

Height of letter determined by ladder of nib widths

ITALIC ROMAN

Slightly pinched (curved) vertical stroke *Letter filled in using brush*

Inner counter

Tail *Spine* *Pointed apex*

VERSAL

CHINESE LETTERING

Rice paper

Broad brush stroke

Chinese character meaning long life

Artist's stamped signature

ARTIST'S STAMP

Stamp

Stamped signature of the artist

Ink pad

DRAWING BOARD

Adjustable set square *Blade with parallel motion*

AN ILLUMINATED MANUSCRIPT

Style of lettering called Gothic book script

Large decorative letter used to mark the opening of a chapter

Words written carefully by hand

Gold leaf *Grid lines provide guide to position of words and pictures*

EXAMPLES OF CALLIGRAPHY PAPERS

Standard European paper

Indian handmade paper

Flecked, tinted paper

Imitation parchment paper

Printmaking 1

PRINTS ARE MADE BY FOUR BASIC printing processes – intaglio, lithographic, relief, and screen. In intaglio printing, lines are engraved or etched into the surface of a metal plate. Lines are engraved by hand using sharp metal tools. They are etched by corroding the metal plate with acid, using acid-resistant ground to protect the areas not to be etched. The plate is then inked and wiped, leaving the grooves filled with ink and the surface clean. Dampened paper is laid over the plate, and both paper and plate are passed through the rollers of an etching press. The pressure of the rollers forces the paper into the grooves, so that it takes up the ink, leaving an impression on the paper. Lithographic printing is based on the antipathy between grease and water. An image is drawn on a surface – usually a stone or metal plate – with a greasy medium, such as tusche (lihographic ink). The greasy drawing is fixed on to the plate by applying an acidic solution, such as gum arabic. The surface is then dampened and rolled with ink. The ink adheres only to the greasy areas and is repelled by the water. Paper is laid on the plate and pressure is applied by means of a press. In relief printing, the non-printing areas of a wood or linoleum block are cut away using gouges, knives, and other tools. The printing areas are left raised in relief and are rolled with ink. Paper is laid on the inked block and pressure is applied by means of a press or by burnishing (rubbing) the back of the paper. The most common forms of relief printing are woodcut, wood engraving, and linocut. In screen printing, the printing surface is a mesh stretched across a wooden frame. A stencil is applied to the mesh to seal the nonprinting areas and ink is scraped through the mesh to produce an image.

Paper · Printed image · Engraved or etched image · Metal plate · Inked area

INTAGLIO

Printed image · Damp surface rejects ink · Ink adheres to greasy image · Paper · Image drawn on stone with greasy medium

LITHOGRAPHIC

Paper · Raised figure · Wood block · Printed image · Inked surface

RELIEF

Ink forced through mesh · Paper · Wooden frame · Stencil · Printed image

SCREEN

LEATHER
INK DABBER

EQUIPMENT USED IN INTAGLIO PRINTING

ROCKER   SCRIBER   ROULETTE   SCRAPER   BURNISHER   CLAMP

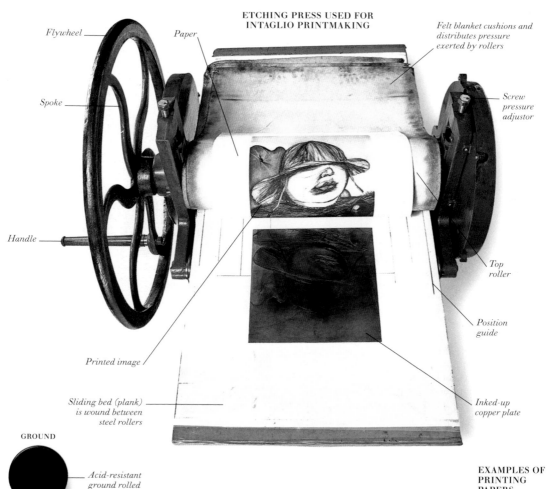

ETCHING PRESS USED FOR INTAGLIO PRINTMAKING

Flywheel

Paper

Felt blanket cushions and distributes pressure exerted by rollers

Spoke

Screw pressure adjustor

Handle

Top roller

Position guide

Printed image

Sliding bed (plank) is wound between steel rollers

Inked-up copper plate

GROUND

Acid-resistant ground rolled on to metal plate before etching

EXAMPLES OF PRINTING PAPERS

GROUND ROLLER

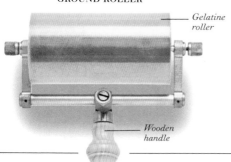

Gelatine roller

Wooden handle

EXAMPLE OF AN INTAGLIO PRINT
Annie with a Sun Hat, Jock McFadyen, 1993
Etched copper plate, 41 × 40 cm (16 × 15¾ in)

Printmaking 2

EXAMPLE OF A LITHOGRAPHIC STONE AND PRINT
Crown Gateway 2, Mandy Bonnell, 1987
Lithograph, 50 × 40 cm (19½ × 15¾ in)

IMAGE DRAWN ON STONE

LITHOGRAPIC PRINT

EXAMPLE OF A SCREEN PRINT
Sea Change, Patrick Hughes, 1992
Screen print, 77 × 94.5 cm (30 × 37 in)

SCREEN AND SQUEEGEE

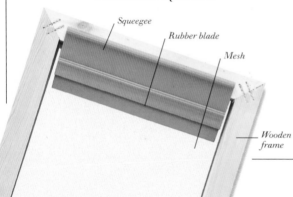

Squeegee

Rubber blade

Mesh

Wooden frame

EQUIPMENT USED IN LITHOGRAPHIC PRINTING

CRAYON AND HOLDER

LITHOGRAPHIC PENCIL

TUSCHE (LITHOGRAPHIC INK) PEN

ERASING STICK

EXPANDABLE SPONGE

TUSCHE (LITHOGRAPHIC INK) STICK

RUBBING INK

INK ROLLER

MILD ACIDIC SOLUTION

GUM ARABIC SOLUTION

WATER-BASED SCREEN PRINTING INKS

BLUE ACRYLIC INK

RED ACRYLIC INK

BROWN TEXTILE INK

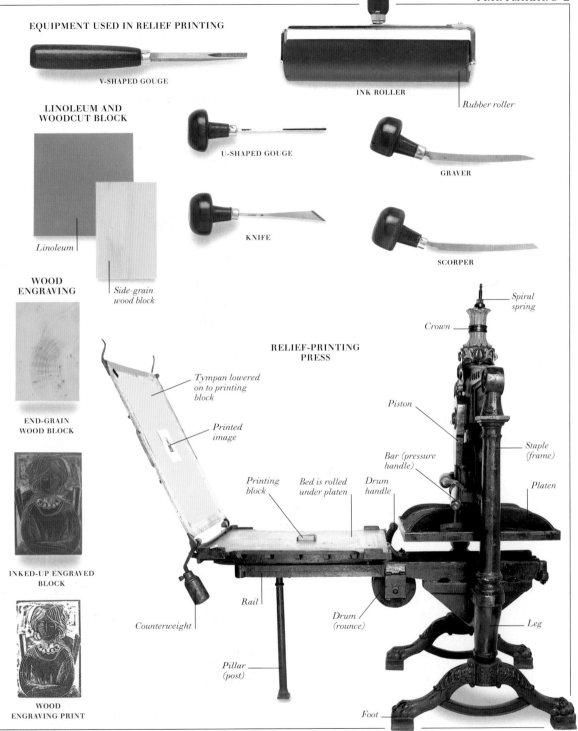

EQUIPMENT USED IN RELIEF PRINTING

V-SHAPED GOUGE

INK ROLLER

Rubber roller

LINOLEUM AND WOODCUT BLOCK

U-SHAPED GOUGE

GRAVER

Linoleum

KNIFE

Side-grain wood block

SCORPER

WOOD ENGRAVING

END-GRAIN WOOD BLOCK

INKED-UP ENGRAVED BLOCK

WOOD ENGRAVING PRINT

RELIEF-PRINTING PRESS

Spiral spring

Crown

Tympan lowered on to printing block

Piston

Printed image

Bar (pressure handle)

Staple (frame)

Printing block

Bed is rolled under platen

Drum handle

Platen

Counterweight

Rail

Drum (rounce)

Leg

Pillar (post)

Foot

Mosaic

MOSAIC IS THE ART OF MAKING patterns and pictures from tesserae (small, coloured pieces of glass, marble, and other materials). Different materials are cut into tesserae using different tools. Smalti (glass enamel) and marble are cut into pieces using a hammer and a hardy (a pointed blade) embedded in a log. Vitreous glass is cut into pieces using a pair of nippers. Mosaics can be made using a direct or indirect method. In the direct method, the tesserae are laid directly into a bed of cement–based adhesive. In the indirect method, the design is drawn in reverse on paper or cloth. The tesserae are then stuck face-down on the paper or cloth using water-soluble glue. Adhesive is spread with a trowel on to a solid surface – such as a wall – and the back of the mosaic is laid into the adhesive. Finally, the paper or cloth is soaked off to reveal the mosaic. Gaps between tesserae can be filled with grout. Grout is forced into gaps by dragging a grouting squeegee across the face of the mosaic. Mosaics are usually used to decorate walls and floors, but they can also be applied to smaller objects.

EQUIPMENT FOR BREAKING MARBLE

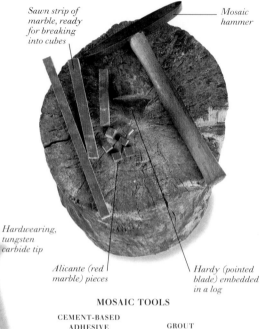

Sawn strip of marble, ready for breaking into cubes

Mosaic hammer

Alicante (red marble) pieces

Hardy (pointed blade) embedded in a log

NIPPERS

Hardwearing, tungsten carbide tip

Handle with rubber grip

MOSAIC TOOLS

CEMENT-BASED ADHESIVE

GROUT

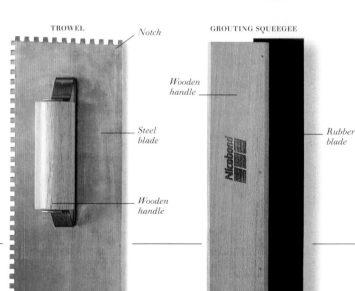

EXAMPLE OF A MOSAIC (DIRECT METHOD)
Seascape, Tessa Hunkin, 1993
Smalti mosaic on board
80 cm (31½ in) diameter

Gold-leaf smalti

SMALTI (GLASS ENAMEL)

RED SMALTI

YELLOW SMALTI

BLUE SMALTI

TROWEL

Notch

Steel blade

Wooden handle

GROUTING SQUEEGEE

Wooden handle

Rubber blade

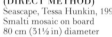

STAGES IN THE CREATION OF A MOSAIC (INDIRECT METHOD)

MOSAIC POT

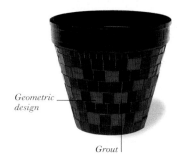

Geometric design

Grout

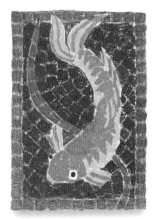

COLOUR SKETCH
A colour sketch is drawn
in oil pastel to give a clear
impression of how the finished
mosaic will look.

REVERSE IMAGE
Tesserae are glued face-down
on reverse image on paper.
Mosaic is then attached to solid
surface and paper is removed.

MOSAIC MOSQUE DESIGN

Floral design

Geometric border

*Andamenti
(line along
which tesserae
are laid)*

*Grout fills
the gaps
between the
tesserae*

*Mosaic
mounted
on board*

*Vitreous
glass cut into
triangular
shape with
nippers*

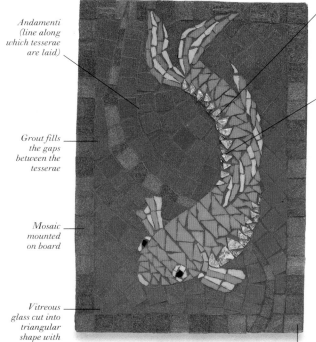

*Gold tessera
with ripple
finish*

*Gold tessera
placed upside-
down*

VITREOUS GLASS

**GREEN VITREOUS
GLASS WITH GOLD LEAF**

*Plain
finish*

*Ripple
finish*

**RED VITREOUS
GLASS**

SHEETS OF VITREOUS GLASS

**BLUE VITREOUS
GLASS**

FINISHED MOSAIC
Goldfish, Tessa Hunkin, 1993
Vitreous glass mosaic on board
35.5 × 25.5 cm (14 × 10 in)

*Border of square
vitreous glass*

Sculpture 1

THE TWO TRADITIONAL METHODS OF MAKING SCULPTURE are carving and modelling. A carved sculpture is made by cutting away the surplus from a block of hard material such as stone, marble, or wood. The tools used for carving vary according to the material being carved. Heavy steel points, claws, and chisels that are struck with a lump hammer are generally used for stone and marble. Sharp gouges and chisels that are struck with a wooden mallet are used for wood. Sculptures formed from hard materials are generally finished by filing with rasps, rifflers, and other abrasive implements. Modelling is a process by which shapes are built up, using malleable materials such as clay, plaster, and wax. The material is cut with wire-ended tools and modelled with the fingers or a variety of hardwood and metal implements. For large or intricate modelled sculptures an armature (frame), made from metal or wood, is used to provide internal support. Sculptures formed in soft materials may harden naturally or can be made more durable by firing in a kiln. Modelled sculptures are often first designed in wax or another material to be cast later in a metal (see pp. 454-455) such as bronze. The development of many new materials in the 20th century has enabled sculptors to experiment with new techniques such as construction (joining preformed pieces of material such as machine components, mirrors, and furniture) and kinetic (mobile) sculpture.

EXAMPLES OF MARBLE CARVING TOOLS

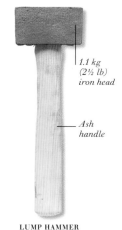

1.1 kg (2½ lb) iron head

Ash handle

LUMP HAMMER

EXAMPLES OF WOODCARVING TOOLS

CABINET RASP

STRAIGHT GOUGE

SALMON BEND GOUGE

CHISEL

Stone for sharpening woodcarving tools

Cedar box

ARKANSAS HONE-STONE

CARVING MALLET

CALLIPERS

Curved leg

Gap measures distance between two points on a sculpture

Wing nut

EXAMPLES OF RIFFLERS (FOR STONE, MARBLE, AND WOOD)

30 CM (12 IN) RIFFLER

15 CM (6 IN) RIFFLER

WIDE MARBLE CLAW

NARROW MARBLE CLAW

POINT

FLAT CHISEL

BULLNOSE CHISEL

Surface for sharpening stonecarving tools

DIAMOND WHETSTONE

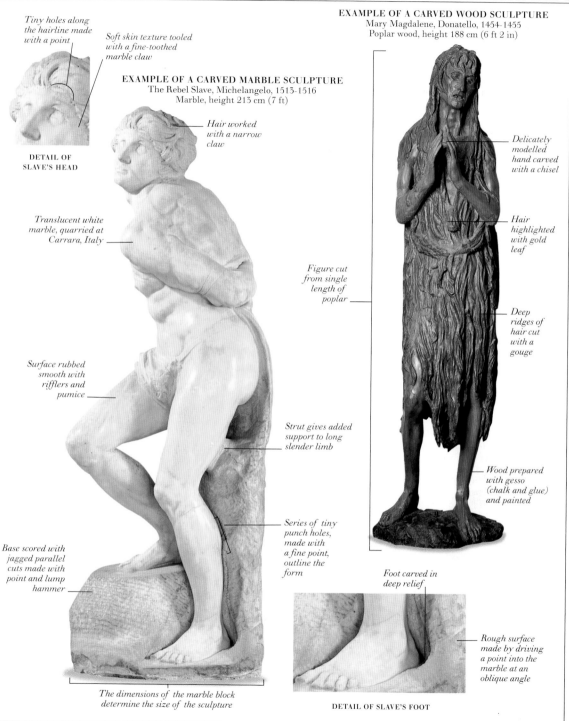

Tiny holes along the hairline made with a point

Soft skin texture tooled with a fine-toothed marble claw

EXAMPLE OF A CARVED WOOD SCULPTURE
Mary Magdalene, Donatello, 1454-1455
Poplar wood, height 188 cm (6 ft 2 in)

EXAMPLE OF A CARVED MARBLE SCULPTURE
The Rebel Slave, Michelangelo, 1513-1516
Marble, height 213 cm (7 ft)

Hair worked with a narrow claw

DETAIL OF SLAVE'S HEAD

Delicately modelled hand carved with a chisel

Translucent white marble, quarried at Carrara, Italy

Hair highlighted with gold leaf

Figure cut from single length of poplar

Deep ridges of hair cut with a gouge

Surface rubbed smooth with rifflers and pumice

Strut gives added support to long slender limb

Wood prepared with gesso (chalk and glue) and painted

Base scored with jagged parallel cuts made with point and lump hammer

Series of tiny punch holes, made with a fine point, outline the form

Foot carved in deep relief

The dimensions of the marble block determine the size of the sculpture

Rough surface made by driving a point into the marble at an oblique angle

DETAIL OF SLAVE'S FOOT

Sculpture 2

EXAMPLES OF MODELLING TOOLS

WIRE-ENDED CUTTING TOOL

CURVED MOULDING TOOL

SPATULA-ENDED WAX MODELLING TOOL

ROUNDED WAX MODELLING TOOL

EXAMPLES OF BRONZE FINISHING TOOLS

HOOKED RIFFLER

POINTED RIFFLER

SPIRIT LAMP (FOR HEATING WAX MODELLING TOOLS)

Wick

Brass holder

Glass bowl

Methylated spirit

STAGES IN THE LOST-WAX METHOD OF CASTING
Based on Mars, Giambologna, c.1546

Wax-covered wire armature

Wax riser (vertical, hollow rod)

Chaplet (iron nail)

Wax runner (horizontal, hollow rod)

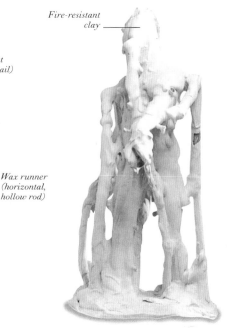

Fire-resistant clay

ORIGINAL MODEL
An original, solid wax model is made and preserved so that numerous replicas can be cast.

HOLLOW WAX FIGURE IS CAST
A new, hollow wax model is cast from the original model. It is filled with a plaster core that is held in place with nails. Wax runners and risers are attached.

FIGURE IS BAKED IN CASTING MOULD
The model is encased in clay and baked. The wax melts away (through the channels made by the wax rods) and is replaced by molten bronze.

MODELLING STAND AND ARMATURE

Aluminium wire figure

Fixed iron armature support

Screw-hole for fastening the iron to modelling board

Marine ply modelling board

Incision made with serrated tool

Rotating table top

Aluminium table stand

Height adjustor

Tripod

Clay smoothed to create the effect of soft skin

Strips of clay, added to the model, give the effect of folded drapery

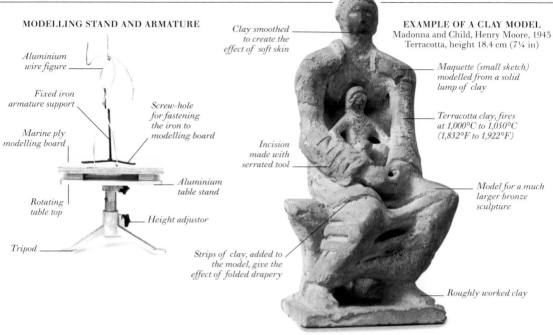

EXAMPLE OF A CLAY MODEL
Madonna and Child, Henry Moore, 1943
Terracotta, height 18.4 cm (7¼ in)

Maquette (small sketch) modelled from a solid lump of clay

Terracotta clay, fires at 1,000°C to 1,050°C (1,832°F to 1,922°F)

Model for a much larger bronze sculpture

Roughly worked clay

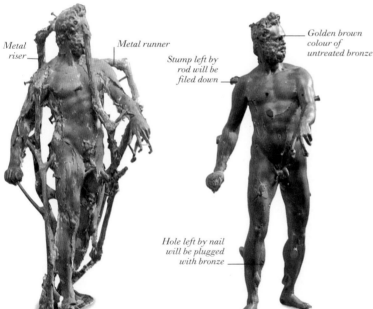

Metal riser

Metal runner

Stump left by rod will be filed down

Golden brown colour of untreated bronze

Hole left by nail will be plugged with bronze

Dark brown patina

STATUE IS STRIPPED OF CLAY
When the bronze has cooled, the clay mould is broken open to reveal the bronze statue with solid metal runners and risers.

STATUE IS FINISHED
The nails are pulled out and a large hole is made to remove the plaster core. When the metal rods have been sawn off, the sculpture is filed to refine the surface.

STATUE IS CLEANED
Finally the work is cleaned and polished. An artificial patina (colouring) is achieved by treating the surface with chemicals.

455

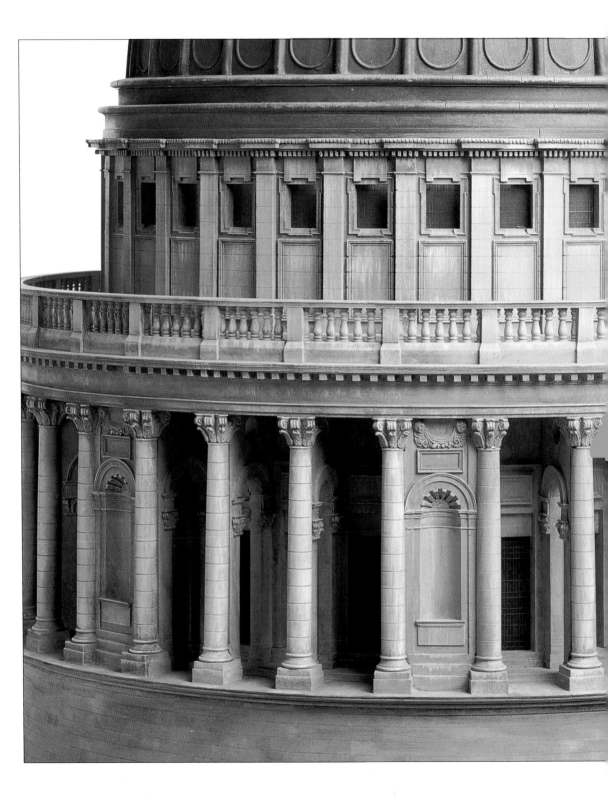

ARCHITECTURE

Ancient Egypt

THE CIVILIZATION OF THE ANCIENT EGYPTIANS (which lasted from about 3100 BC until it was finally absorbed into the Roman empire in 30 BC) is famous for its temples and tombs. Egyptian temples were often huge and geometric, like the Temple of Amon-Re (below and right). They were usually decorated with hieroglyphs (sacred characters used for picture-writing) and painted reliefs depicting gods, Pharaohs (kings), and queens. Tombs were particularly important to the Egyptians, who believed that the dead were resurrected in the after-life. The tombs were often decorated – as, for example, the surround of the false door opposite – in order to give comfort to the dead. The best-known ancient Egyptian tombs are the pyramids, which were designed to symbolize the rays of the sun. Many of the architectural forms used by the ancient Egyptians were later adopted by other civilizations; for example, columns and capitals were later used by the ancient Greeks (see pp. 460-461) and ancient Romans (see pp. 462-465).

FRONT VIEW OF HYPOSTYLE HALL, TEMPLE OF AMON-RE

Cornice decorated with cavetto moulding

Campaniform (open papyrus) capital

Architrave

Papyrus-bud capital

Socle

Side aisle

Central nave

Side aisle

SIDE VIEW OF HYPOSTYLE HALL, TEMPLE OF AMON-RE, KARNAK, EGYPT, c.1290 BC

Horus, the sun-god

Architrave

Stone slab forming flat roof of side aisle

Kepresh crown with disc

Chons, the moon-god

Amon-Re, king of the gods

Hathor, the sky-goddess

Papyrus motif

Cartouche (oval border) containing the titles of the Pharaoh (king)

Socle

Aisle running north-south

458

LIMESTONE FALSE DOOR WITH HIEROGLYPHS, TOMB OF KING TJETJI, GIZA, EGYPT, c.2400 BC

Lintel

Hieroglyph representing a house

Disc representing sun or light

Eroded image of Tjetji

Limestone stela (slab)

Hoe-shaped hieroglyph representing "mr" sound

Head of false door

Image of Tjetji's wife

Image of Tjetji's daughter

PLANT CAPITAL OF THE PTOLEMAIC-ROMAN PERIOD, EGYPT, 332-30 BC

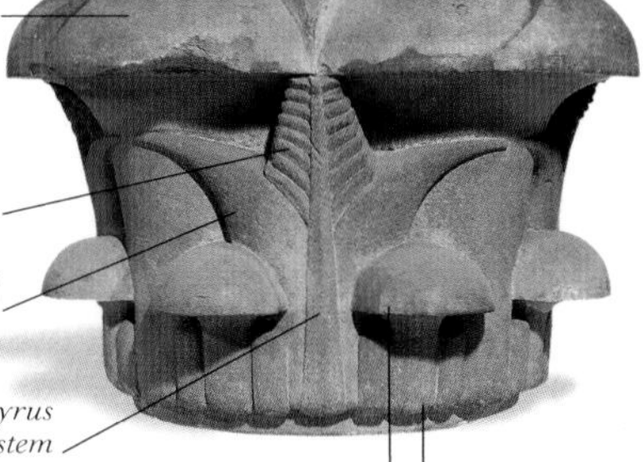

Palm leaf

Papyrus flower

Papyrus leaf

Papyrus stem

Lotus bud

Lotus stem

Cornice decorated with cavetto moulding

Bead moulding

Trellis window

Rectangular pier decorated with hieroglyphs

Elevated roof of central nave

Clerestory

Disc representing sun or light

Architrave

Square abacus

Papyrus-bud capital

Papyriform column

Shaft

Scene depicting a Pharaoh (king) paying homage to the god Amon-Re

Central nave

ANCIENT EGYPTIAN BUILDING DECORATION

DECORATED WINDOW, MEDINET HABU, EGYPT, C.1198BC

ROPE AND PATERAE DECORATION

CAPITAL WITH THE HEAD OF THE SKY-GODDESS HATHOR, TEMPLE OF ISIS, PHILAE, EGYPT, 283-47 BC

LOTUS AND PAPYRUS FRIEZE DECORATION

459

Ancient Greece

THE CLASSICAL TEMPLES OF ANCIENT GREECE were built according to the belief that certain forms and proportions were pleasing to the gods. There were three main ancient Greek architectural orders (styles), which can be distinguished by the decoration and proportions of their columns, capitals (column tops), and entablatures (structures resting on the capitals). The oldest is the Doric order, which dates from the seventh century BC and was used mainly on the Greek mainland and in the western colonies, such as Sicily and southern Italy. The Temple of Neptune, shown here, is a classic example of this order. It is hypaethral (roofless) and peripteral (surrounded by a single row of columns). About a century later, the more decorative Ionic order developed on the Aegean Islands. Features of this order include volutes (spiral scrolls) on capitals and acroteria (pediment ornaments). The Corinthian order was invented in Athens in the fifth century BC and is typically identified by an acanthus leaf on the capitals. This order was later widely used in ancient Roman architecture.

CAPITALS OF THE THREE ORDERS OF ANCIENT GREEK ARCHITECTURE

Abacus
Echinus
Annulet
Trachelion (neck)

DORIC CAPITAL, THE PROPYLAEUM (GATEWAY), THE ACROPOLIS, ATHENS, GREECE, 449 BC

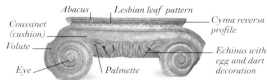

Abacus   Lesbian leaf pattern
Coussinet (cushion)
Cyma reversa profile
Volute
Echinus with egg and dart decoration
Eye
Palmette

IONIC CAPITAL, THE PROPYLAEUM (GATEWAY), TEMPLE OF ATHENA POLIAS, PRIENE, GREECE, c.334 BC

Mask
Abacus
Volute
Cauliculus
Acanthus leaf
Bell-shaped core

CORINTHIAN CAPITAL FROM A STOA (PORTICO), PROBABLY FROM ASIA MINOR

TEMPLE OF NEPTUNE, PAESTUM, ITALY, c.460 BC

Raking cornice
Pediment
Trachelion (neck)   Taenia   Triglyph   Metope   Glyph (channel)
Doric entablature
Pteron (external colonnade)
Euthynteria   Drum   Stylobate   Column of the Doric order

PLAN OF THE TEMPLE OF NEPTUNE, PAESTUM

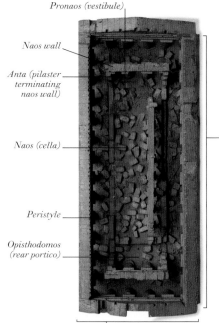

Pronaos (vestibule)

Naos wall

Anta (pilaster terminating naos wall)

Naos (cella)

Peristyle

Opisthodomos (rear portico)

Pteron (external colonnade)

Hexastyle pteron (colonnade of six columns)

ANCIENT GREEK BUILDING DECORATION

Volute

FACADE, TREASURY OF ATREUS, MYCENAE, GREECE, 1350-1250 BC

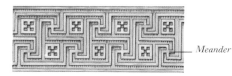

Meander

FRETWORK, PARTHENON, ATHENS, GREECE, 447-436 BC

ACROTERION, TEMPLE OF APHAIA, AEGINA, GREECE, 490 BC

Griffon (gryphon)

Raking cornice

ANTEFIXA, TEMPLE OF APHAIA, AEGINA, GREECE, 490 BC

Palmette

Volute

Regula (short fillet beneath taenia)

Eaves

Cornice

Frieze

Architrave

Capital

Shaft

Crepidoma (stepped base)

Entasis (slight curve of a column)

Intercolumniation

Fluting

Ancient Rome 1

IN THE EARLY PERIOD OF THE ROMAN EMPIRE extensive use was made of ancient Greek architectural ideas, particularly those of the Corinthian order (see pp. 460-461). As a result, many early Roman buildings – such as the Temple of Vesta (opposite) – closely resemble ancient Greek buildings. A distinctive Roman style began to evolve in the first century AD. This style developed the interiors of buildings (the Greeks had concentrated on the exterior) by using arches, vaults, and domes inside the buildings, and by ornamenting internal walls. Many of these features can be seen in the Pantheon. Exterior columns were often used for decorative, rather than structural, purposes, as in the Colosseum and the Porta Nigra (see pp. 464-465). Smaller buildings had timber frames with wattle-and-daub walls, as in the mill (see pp. 464-465). Roman architecture remained influential for many centuries, with some of its principles being used in the 11th century in Romanesque buildings (see pp. 468-469) and also in the 15th and 16th centuries in Renaissance buildings (see pp. 474-477).

ANCIENT ROMAN BUILDING DECORATION

FESTOON, TEMPLE OF VESTA, TIVOLI, ITALY, C.80 BC

RICHLY DECORATED ROMAN OVUM

INTERIOR OF THE PANTHEON, ROME, ITALY, 118-c.128

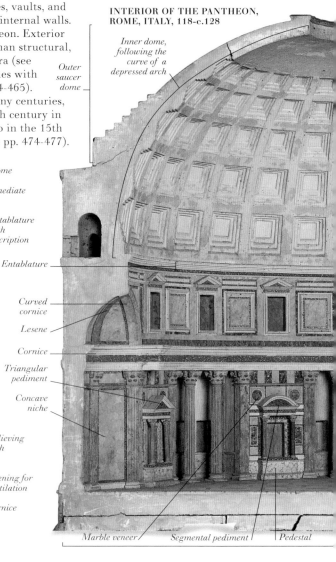

Inner dome, following the curve of a depressed arch

Outer saucer dome

Entablature

Curved cornice

Lesene

Cornice

Triangular pediment

Concave niche

Marble veneer   *Segmental pediment*   *Pedestal*

Series of concentric, step-like rings

Oculus

Outer saucer dome

Intermediate block

Dentil ornament

Engaged pediment

Entablature with inscription

Raking cornice

Pediment

Rotunda

Octastyle portico (eight-column portico)

FRONT VIEW OF THE PANTHEON

SIDE VIEW OF THE PANTHEON

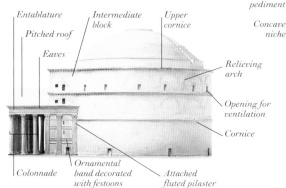

Entablature

Intermediate block

Upper cornice

Pitched roof

Eaves

Relieving arch

Opening for ventilation

Cornice

Colonnade

Ornamental band decorated with festoons

Attached fluted pilaster

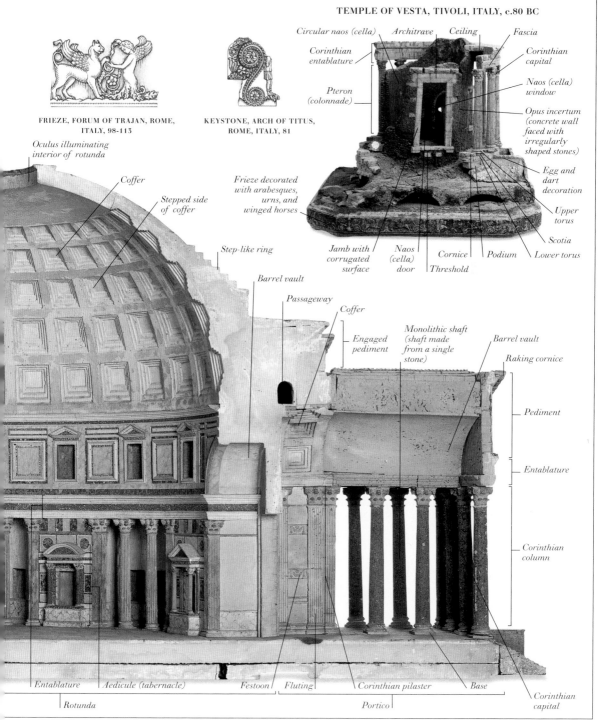

FRIEZE, FORUM OF TRAJAN, ROME,
ITALY, 98-113

KEYSTONE, ARCH OF TITUS,
ROME, ITALY, 81

TEMPLE OF VESTA, TIVOLI, ITALY, c.80 BC

Circular naos (cella)

Architrave

Ceiling

Fascia

Corinthian
entablature

Corinthian
capital

Pteron
(colonnade)

Naos (cella)
window

Opus incertum
(concrete wall
faced with
irregularly
shaped stones)

Egg and
dart
decoration

Upper
torus

Scotia

Lower torus

Jamb with
corrugated
surface

Naos
(cella)
door

Cornice

Podium

Threshold

Oculus illuminating
interior of rotunda

Coffer

Stepped side
of coffer

Frieze decorated
with arabesques,
urns, and
winged horses

Step-like ring

Barrel vault

Passageway

Coffer

Engaged
pediment

Monolithic shaft
(shaft made
from a single
stone)

Barrel vault

Raking cornice

Pediment

Entablature

Corinthian
column

Entablature

Aedicule (tabernacle)

Festoon

Fluting

Corinthian pilaster

Base

Corinthian
capital

Rotunda

Portico

463

Ancient Rome 2

SIDE VIEW OF A ROMAN MILL

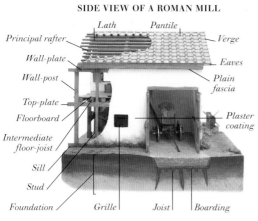

Lath
Pantile
Principal rafter
Verge
Wall-plate
Eaves
Wall-post
Plain fascia
Top-plate
Floorboard
Plaster coating
Intermediate floor-joist
Sill
Stud
Foundation
Grille
Joist
Boarding

FRONT VIEW OF A ROMAN MILL, 1ST CENTURY BC

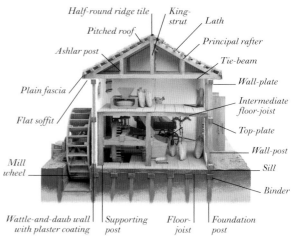

Half-round ridge tile
King-strut
Lath
Pitched roof
Principal rafter
Ashlar post
Tie-beam
Plain fascia
Wall-plate
Flat soffit
Intermediate floor-joist
Top-plate
Wall-post
Mill wheel
Sill
Binder
Wattle-and-daub wall with plaster coating
Supporting post
Floor-joist
Foundation post

THE COLOSSEUM (FLAVIAN AMPHITHEATRE), ROME, ITALY, 70-82

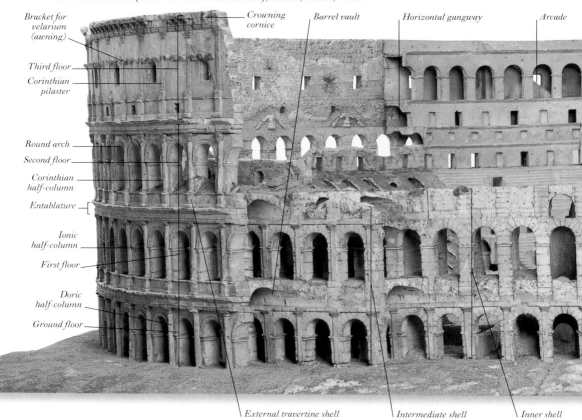

Bracket for velarium (awning)
Crowning cornice
Barrel vault
Horizontal gangway
Arcade
Third floor
Corinthian pilaster
Round arch
Second floor
Corinthian half-column
Entablature
Ionic half-column
First floor
Doric half-column
Ground floor
External travertine shell
Intermediate shell
Inner shell

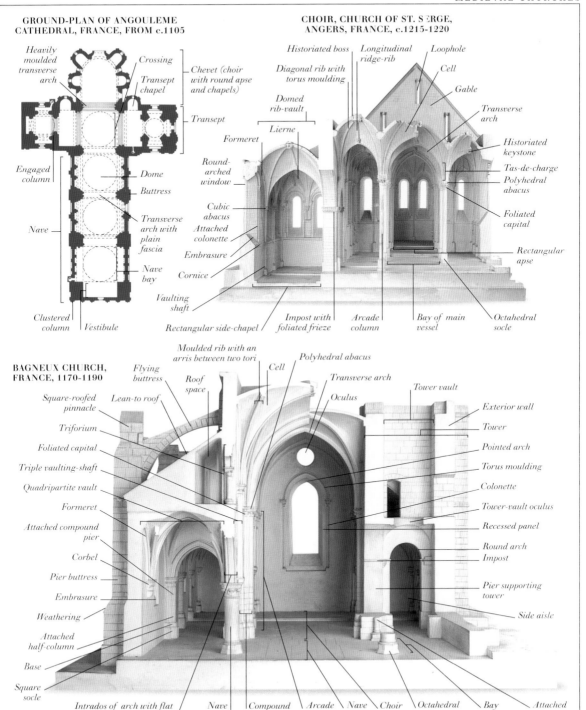

GROUND-PLAN OF ANGOULEME CATHEDRAL, FRANCE, FROM c.1105

Heavily moulded transverse arch

Crossing

Transept chapel

Chevet (choir with round apse and chapels)

Transept

Engaged column

Dome

Buttress

Transverse arch with plain fascia

Nave

Nave bay

Clustered column

Vestibule

CHOIR, CHURCH OF ST. SERGE, ANGERS, FRANCE, c.1215-1220

Historiated boss

Longitudinal ridge-rib

Loophole

Cell

Diagonal rib with torus moulding

Gable

Domed rib-vault

Transverse arch

Lierne

Historiated keystone

Formeret

Tas-de-charge

Round-arched window

Polyhedral abacus

Cubic abacus

Foliated capital

Attached colonette

Embrasure

Rectangular apse

Cornice

Vaulting shaft

Impost with foliated frieze

Arcade column

Bay of main vessel

Octahedral socle

Rectangular side-chapel

BAGNEUX CHURCH, FRANCE, 1170-1190

Moulded rib with an arris between two tori

Cell

Polyhedral abacus

Flying buttress

Roof space

Transverse arch

Tower vault

Square-roofed pinnacle

Lean-to roof

Oculus

Exterior wall

Triforium

Tower

Foliated capital

Pointed arch

Triple vaulting-shaft

Torus moulding

Quadripartite vault

Colonette

Formeret

Tower-vault oculus

Attached compound pier

Recessed panel

Corbel

Round arch

Pier buttress

Impost

Embrasure

Pier supporting tower

Weathering

Attached half-column

Side aisle

Base

Square socle

Intrados of arch with flat band between two tori

Nave column

Compound pier

Arcade

Nave

Choir

Octahedral socle

Bay

Attached colonette

469

Gothic 1

GOTHIC BUILDINGS are characterized by rib vaults, pointed or lancet arches, flying buttresses, decorative tracery and gables, and stained-glass windows. Typical Gothic buildings include the Cathedrals of Salisbury and old St. Paul's in England, and Notre Dame de Paris in France (see pp. 472-473). The Gothic style developed out of Romanesque architecture in France (see pp. 468-469) in the mid-12th century, and then spread throughout Europe. The decorative elements of Gothic architecture became highly developed in buildings of the English Decorated style (late 13th-14th century) and the French Flamboyant style (15th-16th century). These styles are exemplified by the tower of Salisbury Cathedral and the staircase in the Church of St. Maclou (see pp. 472-473), respectively. In both of these styles, embellishments such as ballflowers and curvilinear (flowing) tracery were used liberally. The English Perpendicular style (late 14th-15th century), which followed the Decorated style, emphasized the vertical and horizontal elements of a building. A notable feature of this style is the hammer-beam roof.

GOTHIC STAINED GLASS WITH FOLIATED SCROLL MOTIF, ON WOODEN FORM

GROUND-PLAN OF SALISBURY CATHEDRAL

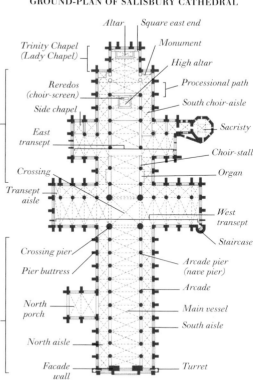

Altar
Square east end
Trinity Chapel (Lady Chapel)
Monument
High altar
Reredos (choir-screen)
Processional path
Side chapel
South choir-aisle
Choir
East transept
Sacristy
Choir-stall
Crossing
Organ
Transept aisle
West transept
Staircase
Crossing pier
Arcade pier (nave pier)
Pier buttress
Arcade
North porch
Main vessel
Nave
South aisle
North aisle
Facade wall
Turret

GOTHIC TORUS WITH BALLFLOWERS

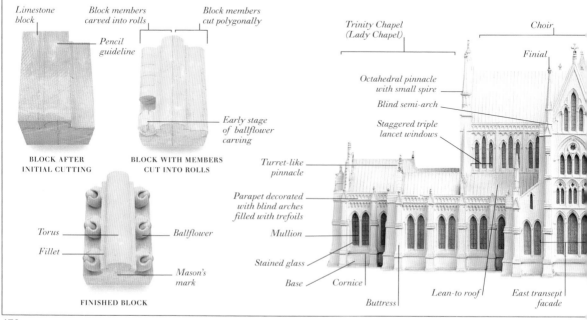

Limestone block
Block members carved into rolls
Block members cut polygonally
Pencil guideline
Early stage of ballflower carving

BLOCK AFTER INITIAL CUTTING

BLOCK WITH MEMBERS CUT INTO ROLLS

Torus
Ballflower
Fillet
Mason's mark

FINISHED BLOCK

Trinity Chapel (Lady Chapel)
Choir
Finial
Octahedral pinnacle with small spire
Blind semi-arch
Staggered triple lancet windows
Turret-like pinnacle
Parapet decorated with blind arches filled with trefoils
Mullion
Stained glass
Base
Cornice
Lean-to roof
East transept facade
Buttress

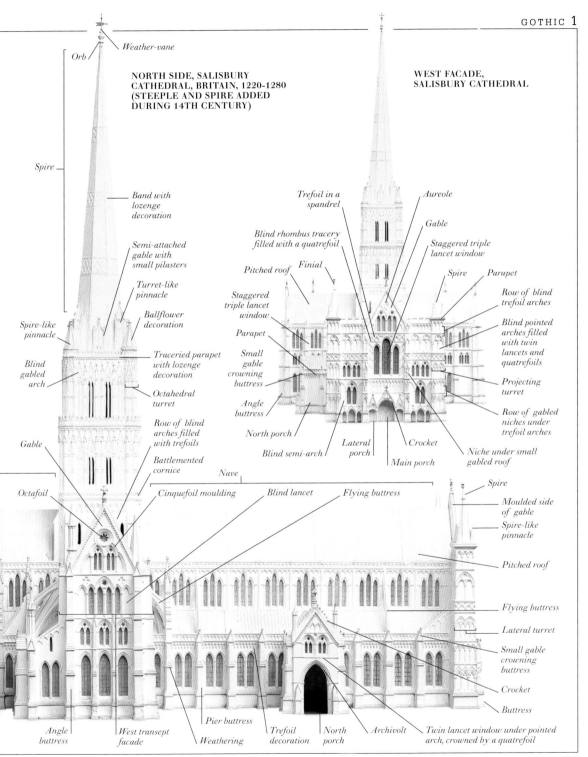

NORTH SIDE, SALISBURY CATHEDRAL, BRITAIN, 1220-1280 (STEEPLE AND SPIRE ADDED DURING 14TH CENTURY)

Orb

Weather-vane

Spire

Band with lozenge decoration

Semi-attached gable with small pilasters

Turret-like pinnacle

Ballflower decoration

Spire-like pinnacle

Traceried parapet with lozenge decoration

Blind gabled arch

Octahedral turret

Row of blind arches filled with trefoils

Gable

Battlemented cornice

Octafoil

Cinquefoil moulding

Blind lancet

Flying buttress

Nave

Angle buttress

West transept facade

Pier buttress

Weathering

Trefoil decoration

North porch

Archivolt

WEST FACADE, SALISBURY CATHEDRAL

Trefoil in a spandrel

Aureole

Gable

Blind rhombus tracery filled with a quatrefoil

Staggered triple lancet window

Pitched roof

Finial

Spire

Parapet

Staggered triple lancet window

Row of blind trefoil arches

Parapet

Blind pointed arches filled with twin lancets and quatrefoils

Small gable crowning buttress

Projecting turret

Angle buttress

Row of gabled niches under trefoil arches

North porch

Lateral porch

Crocket

Niche under small gabled roof

Blind semi-arch

Main porch

Spire

Moulded side of gable

Spire-like pinnacle

Pitched roof

Flying buttress

Lateral turret

Small gable crowning buttress

Crocket

Buttress

Twin lancet window under pointed arch, crowned by a quatrefoil

Gothic 2

CURVILINEAR (FLOWING) TRACERY FROM A
BALUSTRADE, 14TH OR 15TH CENTURY

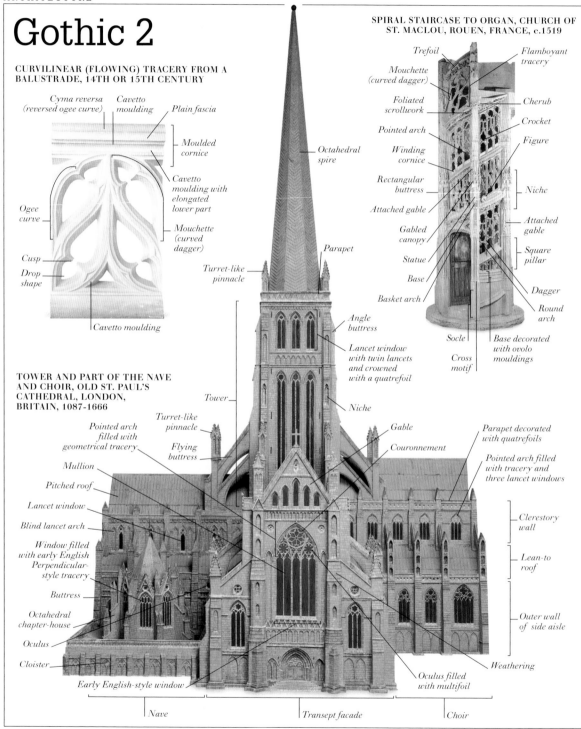

*Cyma reversa
(reversed ogee curve)*

*Cavetto
moulding*

Plain fascia

*Moulded
cornice*

*Cavetto
moulding with
elongated
lower part*

*Ogee
curve*

*Mouchette
(curved
dagger)*

Cusp

*Drop
shape*

Cavetto moulding

*Octahedral
spire*

Trefoil

*Mouchette
(curved dagger)*

*Foliated
scrollwork*

Pointed arch

*Winding
cornice*

*Rectangular
buttress*

Attached gable

*Gabled
canopy*

Statue

Base

Basket arch

*Flamboyant
tracery*

Cherub

Crocket

Figure

Niche

*Attached
gable*

*Square
pillar*

Dagger

*Round
arch*

Socle

*Cross
motif*

*Base decorated
with ovolo
mouldings*

Parapet

*Turret-like
pinnacle*

*Angle
buttress*

*Lancet window
with twin lancets
and crowned
with a quatrefoil*

TOWER AND PART OF THE NAVE
AND CHOIR, OLD ST. PAUL'S
CATHEDRAL, LONDON,
BRITAIN, 1087-1666

Tower

Niche

Gable

Couronnement

*Parapet decorated
with quatrefoils*

*Pointed arch filled
with tracery and
three lancet windows*

*Pointed arch
filled with
geometrical tracery*

*Turret-like
pinnacle*

*Flying
buttress*

Mullion

Pitched roof

Lancet window

Blind lancet arch

*Window filled
with early English
Perpendicular-
style tracery*

Buttress

*Octahedral
chapter-house*

Oculus

Cloister

*Clerestory
wall*

*Lean-to
roof*

*Outer wall
of side aisle*

Weathering

*Oculus filled
with multifoil*

Early English-style window

Nave

Transept facade

Choir

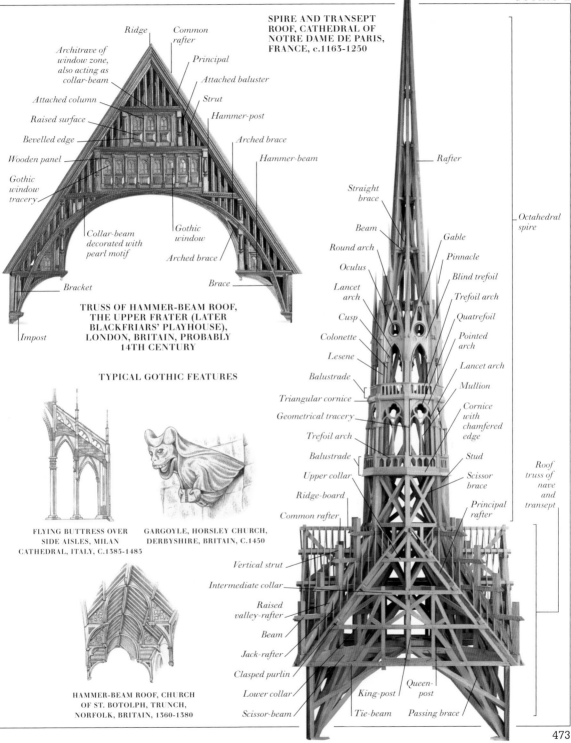

Ridge

Common rafter

Architrave of window zone, also acting as collar-beam

Principal

Attached baluster

Attached column

Strut

Raised surface

Hammer-post

Bevelled edge

Arched brace

Wooden panel

Hammer-beam

Gothic window tracery

Collar-beam decorated with pearl motif

Gothic window

Arched brace

Bracket

Brace

Impost

SPIRE AND TRANSEPT ROOF, CATHEDRAL OF NOTRE DAME DE PARIS, FRANCE, c.1163-1250

Rafter

Straight brace

Beam

Gable

Round arch

Pinnacle

Oculus

Blind trefoil

Lancet arch

Trefoil arch

Cusp

Quatrefoil

Colonette

Pointed arch

Lesene

Lancet arch

Balustrade

Mullion

Triangular cornice

Geometrical tracery

Cornice with chamfered edge

Trefoil arch

Balustrade

Stud

Upper collar

Scissor brace

Ridge-board

Principal rafter

Common rafter

Vertical strut

Intermediate collar

Raised valley-rafter

Beam

Jack-rafter

Clasped purlin

Queen-post

Lower collar

King-post

Scissor-beam

Tie-beam

Passing brace

Octahedral spire

Roof truss of nave and transept

TRUSS OF HAMMER-BEAM ROOF, THE UPPER FRATER (LATER BLACKFRIARS' PLAYHOUSE), LONDON, BRITAIN, PROBABLY 14TH CENTURY

TYPICAL GOTHIC FEATURES

FLYING BUTTRESS OVER SIDE AISLES, MILAN CATHEDRAL, ITALY, C.1385-1485

GARGOYLE, HORSLEY CHURCH, DERBYSHIRE, BRITAIN, C.1450

HAMMER-BEAM ROOF, CHURCH OF ST. BOTOLPH, TRUNCH, NORFOLK, BRITAIN, 1360-1380

473

Renaissance 1

THE RENAISSANCE was a European movement – lasting roughly from the 14th century to the mid-17th century – in which the arts and sciences underwent great changes. In architecture, these changes were marked by a return to the classical forms and proportions of ancient Roman buildings. The Renaissance originated in Italy, and the buildings most characteristic of its style can be found there, such as the Palazzo Strozzi shown here. Mannerism is a branch of the Renaissance style that distorts the classical forms; an example is the Laurentian Library staircase. As the Renaissance style spread to other European countries, many of its features were incorporated into the local architecture; for example, the Château de Montal in France (see pp. 476-477) incorporates aedicules (tabernacles).

FACADE ON TO PIAZZA, PALAZZO STROZZI

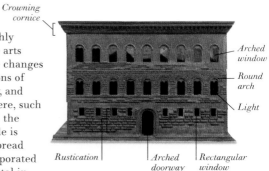

Crowning cornice

Arched window

Round arch

Light

Rustication

Arched doorway

Rectangular window

SIDE VIEW OF PALAZZO STROZZI, FLORENCE, ITALY, 1489 (BY G. DA SANGALLO, B. DA MAIANO, AND CRONACA)

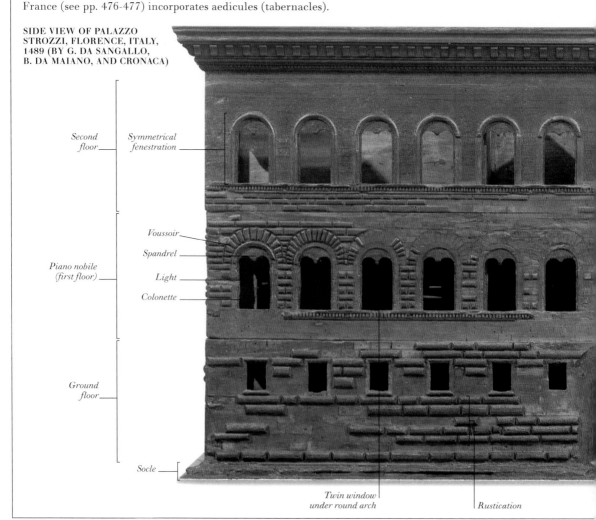

Second floor

Symmetrical fenestration

Voussoir

Spandrel

Piano nobile (first floor)

Light

Colonette

Ground floor

Socle

Twin window under round arch

Rustication

DETAILS FROM ITALIAN RENAISSANCE BUILDINGS

PANEL FROM DRUM OF DOME,
FLORENCE CATHEDRAL, 1420-1436

COFFERING IN DOME,
PAZZI CHAPEL,
FLORENCE, 1429-1461

STAIRCASE,
LAURENTIAN LIBRARY,
FLORENCE, 1559

PORTICO, VILLA ROTUNDA,
VICENZA, 1567-1569

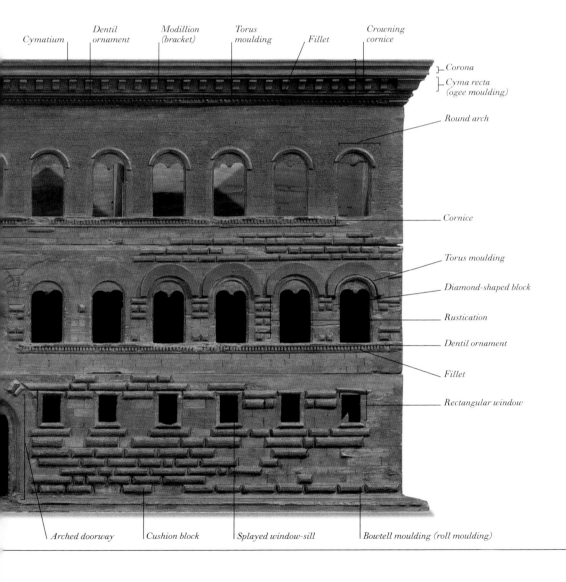

Cymatium

Dentil ornament

Modillion (bracket)

Torus moulding

Fillet

Crowning cornice

Corona

Cyma recta (ogee moulding)

Round arch

Cornice

Torus moulding

Diamond-shaped block

Rustication

Dentil ornament

Fillet

Rectangular window

Arched doorway

Cushion block

Splayed window-sill

Bowtell moulding (roll moulding)

Renaissance 2

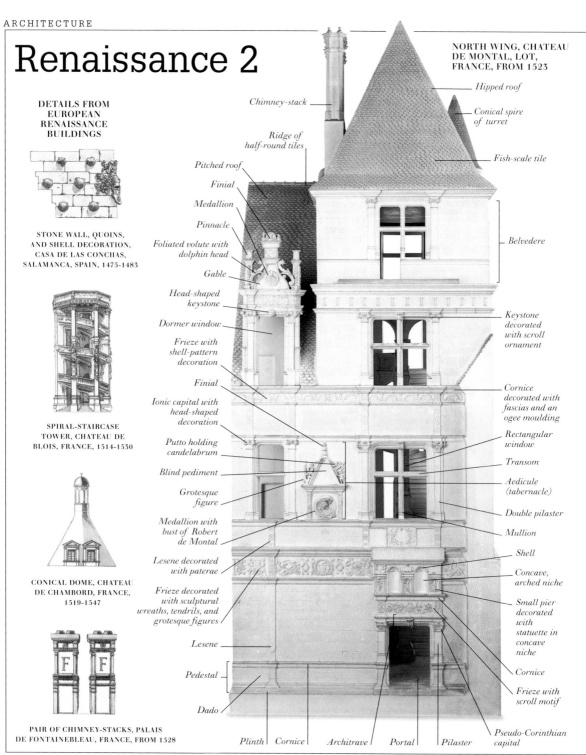

**DETAILS FROM
EUROPEAN
RENAISSANCE
BUILDINGS**

STONE WALL, QUOINS,
AND SHELL DECORATION,
CASA DE LAS CONCHAS,
SALAMANCA, SPAIN, 1475-1483

SPIRAL-STAIRCASE
TOWER, CHATEAU DE
BLOIS, FRANCE, 1514-1530

CONICAL DOME, CHATEAU
DE CHAMBORD, FRANCE,
1519-1547

PAIR OF CHIMNEY-STACKS, PALAIS
DE FONTAINEBLEAU, FRANCE, FROM 1528

Chimney-stack

Ridge of
half-round tiles

Pitched roof

Finial

Medallion

Pinnacle

Foliated volute with
dolphin head

Gable

Head-shaped
keystone

Dormer window

Frieze with
shell-pattern
decoration

Finial

Ionic capital with
head-shaped
decoration

Putto holding
candelabrum

Blind pediment

Grotesque
figure

Medallion with
bust of Robert
de Montal

Lesene decorated
with paterae

Frieze decorated
with sculptural
wreaths, tendrils, and
grotesque figures

Lesene

Pedestal

Dado

Hipped roof

Conical spire
of turret

Fish-scale tile

Belvedere

Keystone
decorated
with scroll
ornament

Cornice
decorated with
fascias and an
ogee moulding

Rectangular
window

Transom

Aedicule
(tabernacle)

Double pilaster

Mullion

Shell

Concave,
arched niche

Small pier
decorated
with
statuette in
concave
niche

Cornice

Frieze with
scroll motif

Pseudo-Corinthian
capital

Plinth   Cornice   Architrave   Portal   Pilaster

476

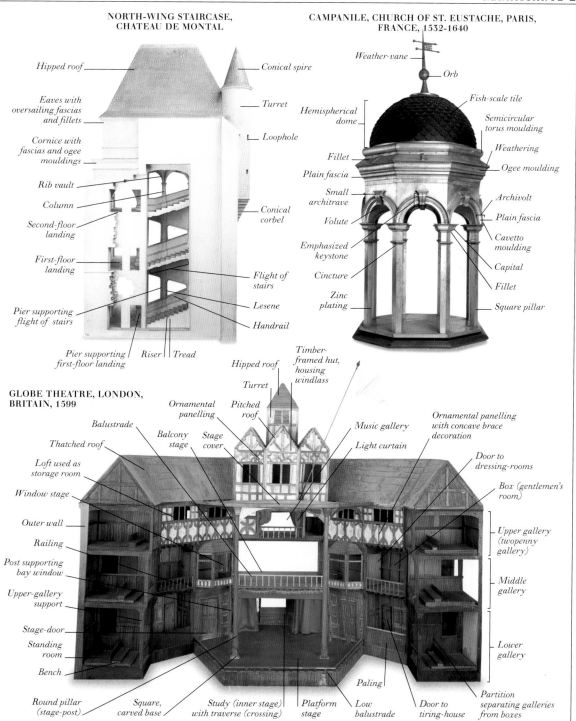

NORTH-WING STAIRCASE, CHATEAU DE MONTAL

Hipped roof

Eaves with oversailing fascias and fillets

Cornice with fascias and ogee mouldings

Rib vault

Column

Second-floor landing

First-floor landing

Pier supporting flight of stairs

Pier supporting first-floor landing

Riser

Tread

Conical spire

Turret

Loophole

Conical corbel

Flight of stairs

Lesene

Handrail

CAMPANILE, CHURCH OF ST. EUSTACHE, PARIS, FRANCE, 1532-1640

Weather-vane

Orb

Hemispherical dome

Fillet

Plain fascia

Small architrave

Volute

Emphasized keystone

Cincture

Zinc plating

Fish-scale tile

Semicircular torus moulding

Weathering

Ogee moulding

Archivolt

Plain fascia

Cavetto moulding

Capital

Fillet

Square pillar

GLOBE THEATRE, LONDON, BRITAIN, 1599

Balustrade

Thatched roof

Loft used as storage room

Window stage

Outer wall

Railing

Post supporting bay window

Upper-gallery support

Stage-door

Standing room

Bench

Round pillar (stage-post)

Square, carved base

Study (inner stage) with traverse (crossing)

Platform stage

Low balustrade

Paling

Door to tiring-house

Ornamental panelling

Balcony stage

Stage cover

Timber-framed hut, housing windlass

Hipped roof

Turret

Pitched roof

Music gallery

Light curtain

Ornamental panelling with concave brace decoration

Door to dressing-rooms

Box (gentlemen's room)

Upper gallery (twopenny gallery)

Middle gallery

Lower gallery

Partition separating galleries from boxes

477

Baroque and neoclassical 1

THE BAROQUE STYLE EVOLVED IN THE EARLY 17TH CENTURY in Rome. It is characterized by curved outlines and ostentatious decoration, as can be seen in the Italian church details (right). The baroque style was particularly widely favoured in Italy, Spain, and Germany. It was also adopted in Britain and France, but with adaptations. The British architects Sir Christopher Wren and Nicholas Hawksmoor, for example, used baroque features – such as the concave walls of St. Paul's Cathedral and the curved buttresses of the Church of St. George in the East (see pp. 480-481) – but they did so with restraint. Similarly, the curved buttresses and volutes of the Parisian Church of St. Paul-St. Louis are relatively plain. In the second half of the 17th century, a distinct classical style (known as neoclassicism) developed in northern Europe as a reaction to the excesses of baroque. Typical of this new style were churches such as the Madeleine (a proposed facade is shown below), as well as secular buildings such as the Cirque Napoleon (opposite) and the buildings of the British architect Sir John Soane (see pp. 482-483). In early 18th-century France, an extremely lavish form of baroque developed, known as rococo. The balcony from Nantes (see pp. 482-483) with its twisted ironwork and head-shaped corbels is typical of this style.

DETAILS FROM ITALIAN BAROQUE CHURCHES

SCROLLED BUTTRESS, CHURCH OF ST. MARIA DELLA SALUTE, VENICE, 1631-1682

STATUE OF THE ECSTASY OF ST. THERESA, CHURCH OF ST. MARIA DELLA VITTORIA, ROME, 1645-1652

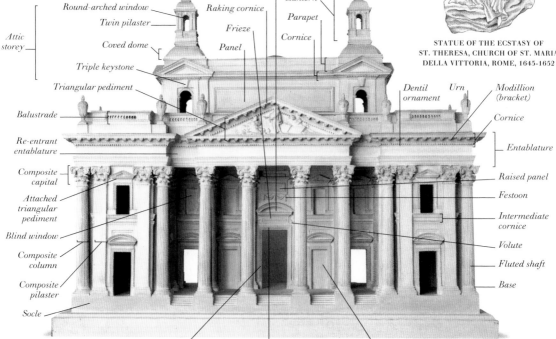

Attached segmental pediment
Lantern
Finial
Raking cornice
Parapet
Round-arched window
Frieze
Cornice
Twin pilaster
Attic storey
Coved dome
Panel
Triple keystone
Triangular pediment
Dentil ornament
Urn
Modillion (bracket)
Cornice
Balustrade
Entablature
Re-entrant entablature
Composite capital
Raised panel
Attached triangular pediment
Festoon
Blind window
Intermediate cornice
Composite column
Volute
Fluted shaft
Composite pilaster
Base
Socle
Door jamb
Architrave
Blind door

PROPOSED FACADE, THE MADELEINE (NEOCLASSICAL), PARIS, FRANCE, 1764 (BY P. CONTANT D'IVRY)

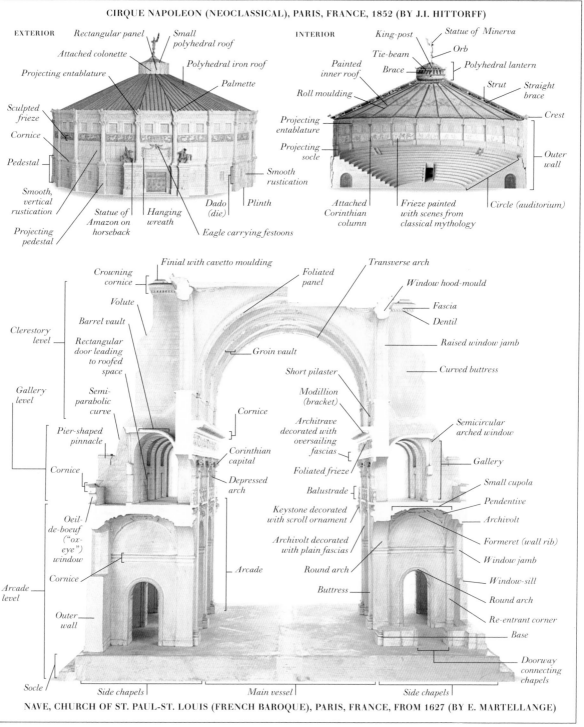

CIRQUE NAPOLEON (NEOCLASSICAL), PARIS, FRANCE, 1852 (BY J.I. HITTORFF)

EXTERIOR

Rectangular panel

Small polyhedral roof

Attached colonette

Polyhedral iron roof

Projecting entablature

Palmette

Sculpted frieze

Cornice

Pedestal

Smooth, vertical rustication

Smooth rustication

Statue of Amazon on horseback

Hanging wreath

Dado (die)

Plinth

Projecting pedestal

Eagle carrying festoons

INTERIOR

King-post

Statue of Minerva

Tie-beam

Orb

Painted inner roof

Brace

Polyhedral lantern

Roll moulding

Strut

Straight brace

Projecting entablature

Crest

Projecting socle

Outer wall

Attached Corinthian column

Frieze painted with scenes from classical mythology

Circle (auditorium)

Finial with cavetto moulding

Foliated panel

Transverse arch

Window hood-mould

Crowning cornice

Fascia

Volute

Dentil

Barrel vault

Raised window jamb

Clerestory level

Rectangular door leading to roofed space

Groin vault

Curved buttress

Short pilaster

Gallery level

Semi-parabolic curve

Modillion (bracket)

Semicircular arched window

Cornice

Architrave decorated with oversailing fascias

Pier-shaped pinnacle

Gallery

Corinthian capital

Foliated frieze

Small cupola

Cornice

Depressed arch

Balustrade

Pendentive

Oeil-de-boeuf ("ox-eye") window

Keystone decorated with scroll ornament

Archivolt

Archivolt decorated with plain fascias

Formeret (wall rib)

Cornice

Window jamb

Arcade

Round arch

Window-sill

Arcade level

Buttress

Round arch

Outer wall

Re-entrant corner

Base

Socle

Doorway connecting chapels

Side chapels

Main vessel

Side chapels

NAVE, CHURCH OF ST. PAUL-ST. LOUIS (FRENCH BAROQUE), PARIS, FRANCE, FROM 1627 (BY E. MARTELLANGE)

Baroque and neoclassical 2

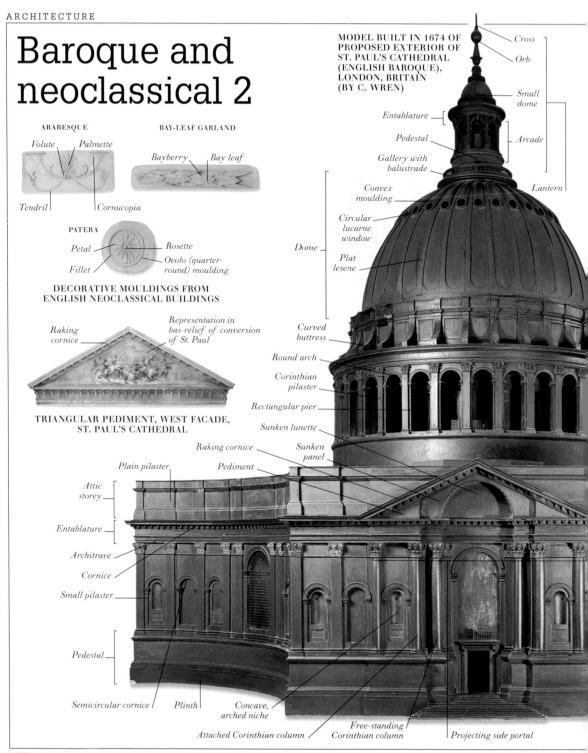

ARABESQUE

Volute
Palmette
Tendril
Cornucopia

BAY-LEAF GARLAND

Bayberry
Bay leaf

PATERA

Petal
Fillet
Rosette
Ovolo (quarter-round) moulding

DECORATIVE MOULDINGS FROM ENGLISH NEOCLASSICAL BUILDINGS

Raking cornice
Representation in bas-relief of conversion of St. Paul

TRIANGULAR PEDIMENT, WEST FACADE, ST. PAUL'S CATHEDRAL

Plain pilaster
Attic storey
Entablature
Architrave
Cornice
Small pilaster
Pedestal
Semicircular cornice
Plinth
Concave, arched niche
Attached Corinthian column
Free-standing Corinthian column
Projecting side portal
Pediment
Raking cornice
Sunken panel
Sunken lunette
Rectangular pier
Corinthian pilaster
Round arch
Curved buttress
Dome
Plat lesene
Circular lucarne window
Convex moulding
Gallery with balustrade
Pedestal
Entablature
Arcade
Lantern
Small dome
Cross
Orb

MODEL BUILT IN 1674 OF PROPOSED EXTERIOR OF ST. PAUL'S CATHEDRAL (ENGLISH BAROQUE), LONDON, BRITAIN (BY C. WREN)

CHURCH OF ST. GEORGE IN THE EAST (ENGLISH BAROQUE), LONDON, BRITAIN, 1714-1734 (BY N. HAWKSMOOR)

SOUTH SIDE   WEST FACADE

Fluted, circular pinnacle

Fluted capital

Pierced parapet

Plain buttress

Semicircular window

Urn

Platband

Sunken panel

Octahedral dome

Round-arched window

Triple keystone

Oeil-de-boeuf ("ox-eye") window

Cornice

Lateral pilaster-strip

Semicircular crypt-window

Plain pedestal

Square post

Octahedral turret

Plain frieze

East pediment

Semicircular apse

Emphasized keystone

Emphasized quoin

Label mould

Side entrance

Cornice

Steeple

Octahedral lantern

Stepped archivolt

Square stone block

Parapet

Three-tier belfry

Set-back buttress

Pepper-pot lantern

Cornice decorated with ogee moulding and fascias

Finial

Volute

Broken pediment

Raking cornice

Ionic capital

Continuous hood-mould

Triple band

Platband

Dog-leg staircase set in oval stone walls

Curved buttress

Ionic twin columns

Attic of drum

Stepped tetrahedral roof

Statuette

Urn

Drum

Entablature

Twin columns

Lantern

Rectangular window

Cruciform pedestal

Arcade

Circular lucarne window

Dome

Pedestal

Stepped cornice

Triangular lesene

Cornice

Raking cornice of facade pediment

Dentil ornament

Frieze

Corinthian capital

Corinthian twin pilasters

Dado

Re-entrant

Doorway

Architrave

Round-arched window

Concave wall

Emphasized keystone

Crepidoma (stepped base)

Corinthian capital

Rectangular vestibule

Baroque and neoclassical 3

DETAILS FROM BAROQUE, NEOCLASSICAL, AND ROCOCO BUILDINGS

PORTICO, THE VYNE, HAMPSHIRE, BRITAIN, 1654 (NEOCLASSICAL)

GILT IRONWORK FROM SCREEN, PALAIS DE VERSAILLES, FRANCE, 1669-1674 (FRENCH BAROQUE)

WINDOW, PALAZZO STANGA, CREMONA, ITALY, EARLY 18TH CENTURY (ROCOCO)

ATLAS (MALE CARYATID), UPPER BELVEDERE, VIENNA, AUSTRIA, 1721 (GERMAN-STYLE BAROQUE)

BALCONY, NANTES, FRANCE, 1730-1740 (ROCOCO)

CORNER OF THE NEW STATE PAPER OFFICE (NEOCLASSICAL), LONDON, BRITAIN, 1830-1831 (BY J. SOANE)

Classical-style entablature

Cornice

Frieze

Architrave

Pantile (S-shaped roofing tile)

Fascia

Eaves

Scroll-shaped corbel

Curved corbel

Second-floor window

Smooth rustication

Cornice

Drip-cap

Cornice

Frieze

Window architrave

Window jamb

First-floor window

Window-sill in the form of a frieze

Ground-floor window

Splayed window-sill

Vermiculated rustication

MASONRY OF A NICHE IN THE ROTUNDA (NEOCLASSICAL), BANK OF ENGLAND, LONDON, BRITAIN, 1794 (BY J. SOANE)

Scoop-pattern concave moulding

Keystone

Frieze

Spandrel

Semi-dome

Voussoir

Rotunda wall

Flat, rectangular niche

Rounded niche

Flat, square niche

TYRINGHAM HOUSE (NEOCLASSICAL), BUCKINGHAMSHIRE, BRITAIN, 1793-1797 (BY J. SOANE)

**ROOF LEVEL
(ATTIC LEVEL)**

Space for illumination above unroofed central hall

Chimney-stack

Space above unroofed main staircase

Flat roof

Oculus illuminating secondary staircase

Parapet rail

Balustrade

Baluster

Cornice

Attic storey of convex portico

Cornice

**FIRST-FLOOR LEVEL
(CHAMBER FLOOR)**

Upper level of central hall, open to floor below

Main staircase

Secondary staircase

Abacus

Triangular pilaster

Pilaster capital

First-floor storey of convex portico

Attached Tuscan twin pilasters

Window-sill

Bow front

**GROUND-FLOOR LEVEL
(PRINCIPAL FLOOR)**

Withdrawing-room

Central hall

Library and breakfast-room

Main staircase

Water-closet (toilet)

Eating-room

Secondary staircase

Segmented lintel course

Window-sill

Band incised with Greek-style fret ornament

Window architrave

Window jamb

Base

Basement

Plinth

Horizontal rustication

Vestibule (entrance hall)

Ground-floor storey of convex portico

**FACADE OF
TYRINGHAM HOUSE**

Chimney-stack

Rail

Baluster

Parapet

Balustrade

Cornice

Entablature

Voussoir

Capital

Basement window

Shaft

Ionic column

Entrance door

Circular entrance steps

Base

PROSTYLE COLONNADE

483

Arches and vaults

ARCHES ARE CURVED STRUCTURES used to bridge spans and to support the weight of upper parts of buildings, such as domes, as in St. Paul's Cathedral (below) and the antique temple (opposite). The voussoirs (wedge-shaped blocks) that form an arch (right) support each other and convert the downward force of the weight of the building into an outward force. This outward force is in turn transferred to buttresses, piers, or abutments. A vault is an arched roof or ceiling. There are four main types of vault (opposite). A barrel vault is a single vault, semicircular in cross-section; a groin vault consists of two barrel vaults intersecting at right-angles; a rib vault is a groin vault reinforced by ribs; and a fan vault is a rib vault in which the ribs radiate from the springing point (where the arch begins) like a fan.

PARTS OF AN ARCH

Voussoir · Keystone · Crown · Abutment

Abutment · Impost · Abutment · Intrados (soffit) · Springing point · Span

FRONT

Keystone · Extrados · Haunch · Intrados (soffit) · Abutment

SIDE

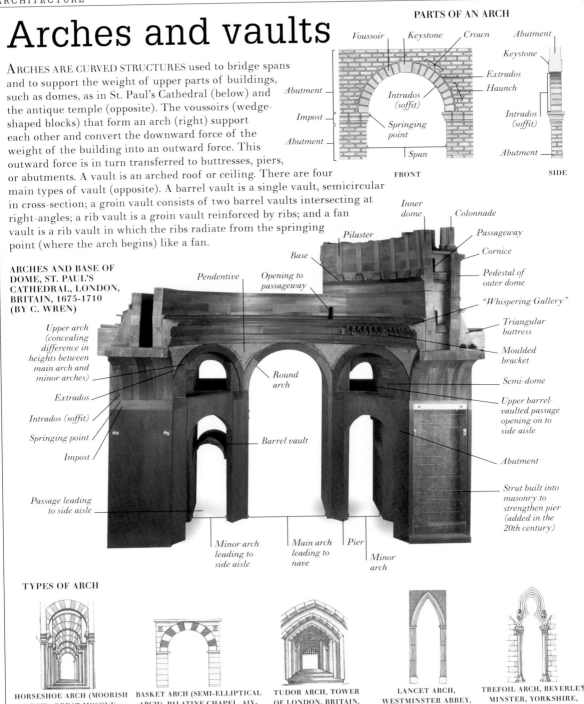

ARCHES AND BASE OF DOME, ST. PAUL'S CATHEDRAL, LONDON, BRITAIN, 1675-1710 (BY C. WREN)

Inner dome · Colonnade
Pilaster · Passageway
Base · Cornice
Pendentive · Opening to passageway · Pedestal of outer dome
"Whispering Gallery"
Upper arch (concealing difference in heights between main arch and minor arches) · Triangular buttress · Moulded bracket
Round arch · Semi-dome
Extrados · Upper barrel-vaulted passage opening on to side aisle
Intrados (soffit)
Springing point · Barrel vault
Impost · Abutment
Passage leading to side aisle · Strut built into masonry to strengthen pier (added in the 20th century)
Minor arch leading to side aisle · Main arch leading to nave · Pier · Minor arch

TYPES OF ARCH

HORSESHOE ARCH (MOORISH ARCH), GREAT MOSQUE, CORDORA, SPAIN, 785

BASKET ARCH (SEMI-ELLIPTICAL ARCH), PALATINE CHAPEL, AIX-LA-CHAPELLE, FRANCE, 790-798

TUDOR ARCH, TOWER OF LONDON, BRITAIN, C.1086-1097

LANCET ARCH, WESTMINSTER ABBEY, LONDON, BRITAIN, 1503-1519

TREFOIL ARCH, BEVERLEY MINSTER, YORKSHIRE, BRITAIN, C.1300

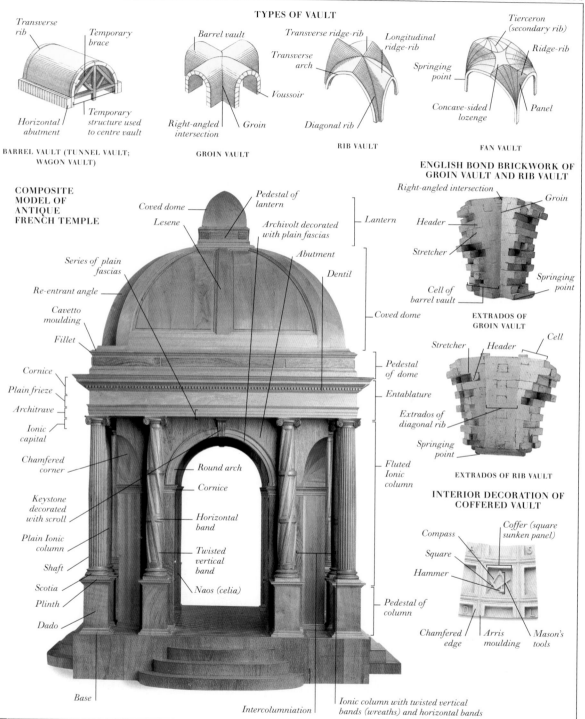

TYPES OF VAULT

BARREL VAULT (TUNNEL VAULT; WAGON VAULT)

Transverse rib
Temporary brace
Horizontal abutment
Temporary structure used to centre vault

GROIN VAULT

Barrel vault
Transverse arch
Voussoir
Right-angled intersection
Groin

RIB VAULT

Transverse ridge-rib
Longitudinal ridge-rib
Diagonal rib

FAN VAULT

Tierceron (secondary rib)
Ridge-rib
Springing point
Concave-sided lozenge
Panel

COMPOSITE MODEL OF ANTIQUE FRENCH TEMPLE

Coved dome
Lesene
Pedestal of lantern
Archivolt decorated with plain fascias
Lantern
Abutment
Dentil
Coved dome
Series of plain fascias
Re-entrant angle
Cavetto moulding
Fillet
Cornice
Plain frieze
Architrave
Ionic capital
Chamfered corner
Keystone decorated with scroll
Plain Ionic column
Shaft
Scotia
Plinth
Dado
Base
Round arch
Cornice
Horizontal band
Twisted vertical band
Naos (celia)
Intercolumniation
Pedestal of dome
Entablature
Fluted Ionic column
Pedestal of column
Ionic column with twisted vertical bands (wreaths) and horizontal bands

ENGLISH BOND BRICKWORK OF GROIN VAULT AND RIB VAULT

Right-angled intersection
Groin
Header
Stretcher
Cell of barrel vault
Springing point

EXTRADOS OF GROIN VAULT

Stretcher
Header
Cell
Extrados of diagonal rib
Springing point

EXTRADOS OF RIB VAULT

INTERIOR DECORATION OF COFFERED VAULT

Compass
Square
Hammer
Coffer (square sunken panel)
Chamfered edge
Arris moulding
Mason's tools

485

Domes

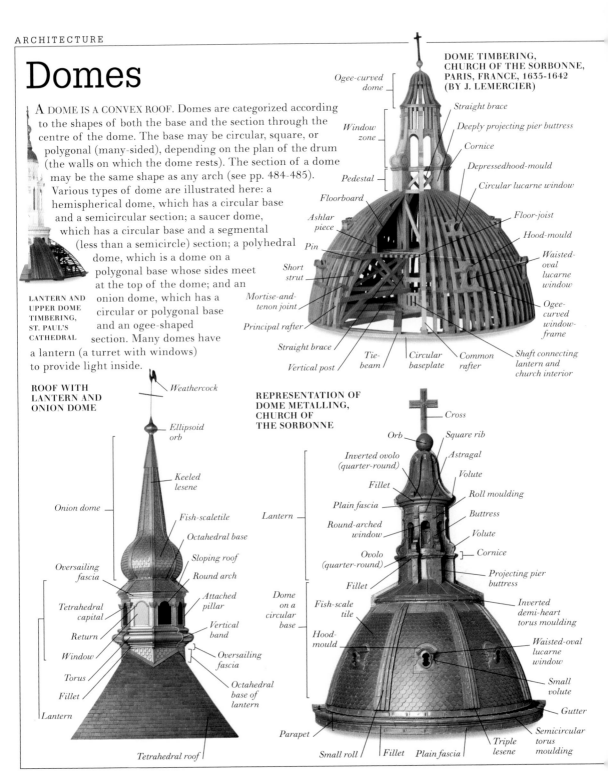

A DOME IS A CONVEX ROOF. Domes are categorized according to the shapes of both the base and the section through the centre of the dome. The base may be circular, square, or polygonal (many-sided), depending on the plan of the drum (the walls on which the dome rests). The section of a dome may be the same shape as any arch (see pp. 484-485). Various types of dome are illustrated here: a hemispherical dome, which has a circular base and a semicircular section; a saucer dome, which has a circular base and a segmental (less than a semicircle) section; a polyhedral dome, which is a dome on a polygonal base whose sides meet at the top of the dome; and an onion dome, which has a circular or polygonal base and an ogee-shaped section. Many domes have a lantern (a turret with windows) to provide light inside.

LANTERN AND UPPER DOME TIMBERING, ST. PAUL'S CATHEDRAL

DOME TIMBERING, CHURCH OF THE SORBONNE, PARIS, FRANCE, 1635-1642 (BY J. LEMERCIER)

Ogee-curved dome
Straight brace
Window zone
Deeply projecting pier buttress
Cornice
Pedestal
Depressedhood-mould
Circular lucarne window
Floorboard
Ashlar piece
Floor-joist
Hood-mould
Pin
Waisted-oval lucarne window
Short strut
Mortise-and-tenon joint
Ogee-curved window-frame
Principal rafter
Straight brace
Shaft connecting lantern and church interior
Vertical post
Tie-beam
Circular baseplate
Common rafter

ROOF WITH LANTERN AND ONION DOME

Weathercock
Ellipsoid orb
Keeled lesene
Onion dome
Fish-scaletile
Octahedral base
Sloping roof
Oversailing fascia
Round arch
Tetrahedral capital
Attached pillar
Return
Vertical band
Window
Torus
Oversailing fascia
Fillet
Octahedral base of lantern
Lantern
Tetrahedral roof

REPRESENTATION OF DOME METALLING, CHURCH OF THE SORBONNE

Cross
Orb
Square rib
Inverted ovolo (quarter-round)
Astragal
Volute
Fillet
Roll moulding
Plain fascia
Buttress
Lantern
Round-arched window
Volute
Ovolo (quarter-round)
Cornice
Fillet
Projecting pier buttress
Dome on a circular base
Fish-scale tile
Inverted demi-heart torus moulding
Hood-mould
Waisted-oval lucarne window
Small volute
Gutter
Parapet
Semicircular torus moulding
Small roll
Fillet
Plain fascia
Triple lesene

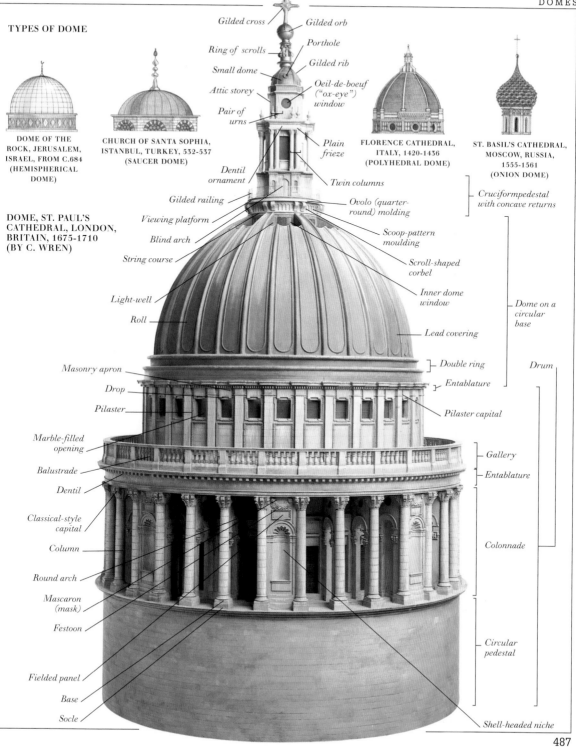

TYPES OF DOME

DOME OF THE ROCK, JERUSALEM, ISRAEL, FROM C.684 (HEMISPHERICAL DOME)

CHURCH OF SANTA SOPHIA, ISTANBUL, TURKEY, 532-537 (SAUCER DOME)

FLORENCE CATHEDRAL, ITALY, 1420-1436 (POLYHEDRAL DOME)

ST. BASIL'S CATHEDRAL, MOSCOW, RUSSIA, 1555-1561 (ONION DOME)

DOME, ST. PAUL'S CATHEDRAL, LONDON, BRITAIN, 1675-1710 (BY C. WREN)

Gilded cross

Gilded orb

Ring of scrolls

Porthole

Small dome

Gilded rib

Attic storey

Oeil-de-boeuf ("ox-eye") window

Pair of urns

Plain frieze

Dentil ornament

Twin columns

Gilded railing

Ovolo (quarter-round) molding

Viewing platform

Scoop-pattern moulding

Blind arch

Scroll-shaped corbel

String course

Inner dome window

Light-well

Roll

Lead covering

Cruciform pedestal with concave returns

Dome on a circular base

Masonry apron

Double ring

Drum

Drop

Entablature

Pilaster

Pilaster capital

Marble-filled opening

Gallery

Balustrade

Entablature

Dentil

Classical-style capital

Colonnade

Column

Round arch

Mascaron (mask)

Festoon

Circular pedestal

Fielded panel

Base

Socle

Shell-headed niche

487

Islamic buildings

OPUS SECTILE MOSAIC DESIGN

THE ISLAMIC RELIGION was founded by the prophet Mohammed, who was born in Mecca (in present-day Saudi Arabia) about 570 AD. In the following three centuries, Islam spread from Arabia to North Africa and Spain, as well as to India and much of the rest of Asia. The worldwide influence of Islam remains strong today. Common characteristics of Islamic buildings include ogee arches and roofs, onion domes, and walls decorated with carved stone, paintings, inlays, or mosaics. The most important type of Islamic building is the mosque – the place of worship – which generally has a minaret (tower) from which the muezzin (official crier) calls Muslims to prayer. Most mosques have a mihrab (decorative niche) that indicates the direction of Mecca. As figurative art is not allowed in Islam, buildings are ornamented with geometric and arabesque motifs, and inscriptions (frequently Koranic verses).

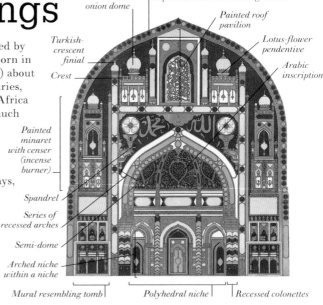

Bud-like onion dome

Depressed arch surrounding mihrab

Painted roof pavilion

Turkish-crescent finial

Lotus-flower pendentive

Crest

Arabic inscription

Painted minaret with censer (incense burner)

Spandrel

Series of recessed arches

Semi-dome

Arched niche within a niche

Mural resembling tomb

Polyhedral niche

Recessed colonettes

MIHRAB, JAMI MASJID (PRINCIPAL OR CONGREGATIONAL MOSQUE), BIJAPUR, INDIA, c.1636

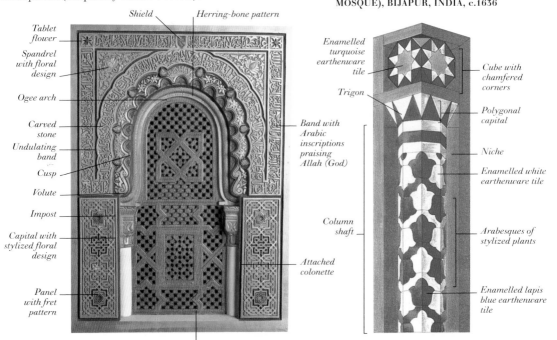

Shield

Herring-bone pattern

Tablet flower

Spandrel with floral design

Ogee arch

Carved stone

Undulating band

Cusp

Volute

Impost

Capital with stylized floral design

Panel with fret pattern

Jali (latticed screen) with geometrical patterns

ARCH, THE ALHAMBRA, GRANADA, SPAIN, 1333-1354

Enamelled turquoise earthenware tile

Trigon

Cube with chamfered corners

Polygonal capital

Band with Arabic inscriptions praising Allah (God)

Niche

Enamelled white earthenware tile

Column shaft

Arabesques of stylized plants

Attached colonette

Enamelled lapis blue earthenware tile

MIHRAB WITH COLUMN, EL-AINYI MOSQUE, CAIRO, EGYPT, 15TH CENTURY

EXAMPLES OF ISLAMIC MOSAICS, EGYPT AND SYRIA

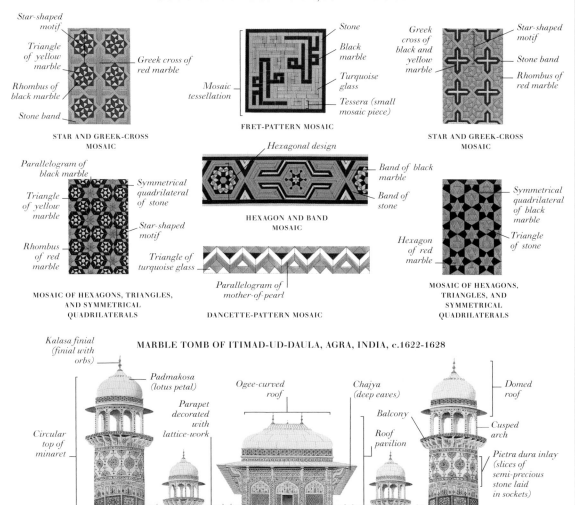

Star-shaped motif

Triangle of yellow marble

Greek cross of red marble

Rhombus of black marble

Stone band

STAR AND GREEK-CROSS MOSAIC

Stone

Black marble

Turquoise glass

Mosaic tessellation

Tessera (small mosaic piece)

FRET-PATTERN MOSAIC

Greek cross of black and yellow marble

Star-shaped motif

Stone band

Rhombus of red marble

STAR AND GREEK-CROSS MOSAIC

Parallelogram of black marble

Triangle of yellow marble

Symmetrical quadrilateral of stone

Star-shaped motif

Rhombus of red marble

MOSAIC OF HEXAGONS, TRIANGLES, AND SYMMETRICAL QUADRILATERALS

Hexagonal design

Band of black marble

Band of stone

HEXAGON AND BAND MOSAIC

Triangle of turquoise glass

Parallelogram of mother-of-pearl

DANCETTE-PATTERN MOSAIC

Symmetrical quadrilateral of black marble

Triangle of stone

Hexagon of red marble

MOSAIC OF HEXAGONS, TRIANGLES, AND SYMMETRICAL QUADRILATERALS

MARBLE TOMB OF ITIMAD-UD-DAULA, AGRA, INDIA, c.1622-1628

Kalasa finial (finial with orbs)

Padmakosa (lotus petal)

Ogee-curved roof

Chajya (deep eaves)

Domed roof

Parapet decorated with lattice-work

Balcony

Cusped arch

Circular top of minaret

Roof pavilion

Pietra dura inlay (slices of semi-precious stone laid in sockets)

Cornice

Bracket

Octahedral base of minaret

Spandrel decorated with arabesque

Star-pattern inlay

Sandstone plinth

Sandstone parapet decorated with lattice-work

Jali (latticed screen) with geometrical patterns

Depressed entrance arch

Sandstone stairway

Opus sectile mosaic (geometric mosaic) of stone, tile, glass, and enamel

South and east Asia

THE TRADITIONAL ARCHITECTURE of south and east Asia has been profoundly influenced by the spread from India of Buddhism and Hinduism. This influence is shown both by the abundance and by the architectural styles of temples and shrines in the region. Many early Hindu temples consist of rooms carved from solid rock-faces. However, free-standing structures began to be built in southern India from about the eighth century AD. Many were built in the Dravidian style, like the Temple of Virupaksha (opposite) with its characteristic antarala (terraced tower), perforated windows, and numerous arches, pilasters, and carvings. The earliest Buddhist religious monuments were Indian stupas, which consisted of a single hemispherical dome surmounted by a chattravali (shaft) and surrounded by railings with ornate gates. Later Indian stupas and those built elsewhere were sometimes modified; for example, in Sri Lanka, the dome became bell-shaped, and was called a dagoba. Buddhist pagodas, such as the Burmese example (right), are multistoreyed temples, each storey having a projecting roof. The form of these buildings probably derived from the yasti (pointed spire) of the stupa. Another feature of many traditional Asian buildings is their imaginative roof-forms, such as gambrel (mansard) roofs, and roofs with angle-rafters (below).

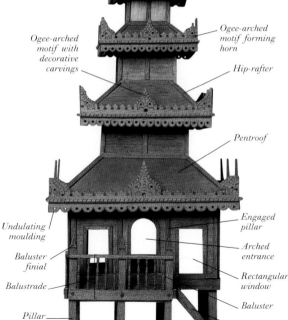

Gilded
band

Gilded iron
hti (crown)

Dubika (mast)

Arrow
motif

Torus moulding
with spiral
carving

Decorative
eaves board

Ogee-arched
motif with
decorative
carvings

Ogee-arched
motif forming
horn

Hip-rafter

Pentroof

DETAILS FROM EAST ASIAN BUILDINGS

**KASUGA-STYLE ROOF WITH
SUMIGI (ANGLE-RAFTERS),
KASUGADO SHRINE OF
ENJOJI, NARA, JAPAN,
12TH-14TH CENTURY**

**TERRACES, TEMPLE OF
HEAVEN, BEIJING, CHINA,
15TH CENTURY**

**GAMBREL (MANSARD) ROOF
WITH UPSWEPT EAVES AND
UNDULATING GABLES,
HIMEJI CASTLE, HIMEJI,
JAPAN, 1608-1609**

**CORNER CAPITAL WITH
ROOF BEAMS, POPCHU-SA
TEMPLE, POPCHU-SA, SOUTH
KOREA, 17TH CENTURY**

Undulating
moulding

Baluster
finial

Balustrade

Pillar

Engaged
pillar

Arched
entrance

Rectangular
window

Baluster

Straight
brace

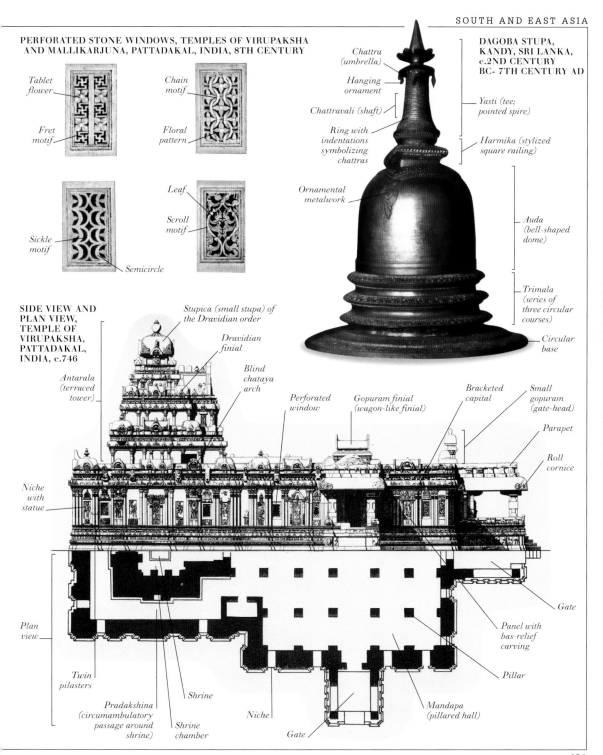

PERFORATED STONE WINDOWS, TEMPLES OF VIRUPAKSHA AND MALLIKARJUNA, PATTADAKAL, INDIA, 8TH CENTURY

Tablet flower

Fret motif

Chain motif

Floral pattern

Leaf

Scroll motif

Sickle motif

Semicircle

DAGOBA STUPA, KANDY, SRI LANKA, c.2ND CENTURY BC- 7TH CENTURY AD

Chattra (umbrella)

Hanging ornament

Chattravali (shaft)

Ring with indentations symbolizing chattras

Ornamental metalwork

Yasti (tee; pointed spire)

Harmika (stylized square railing)

Auda (bell-shaped dome)

Trimala (series of three circular courses)

Circular base

SIDE VIEW AND PLAN VIEW, TEMPLE OF VIRUPAKSHA, PATTADAKAL, INDIA, c.746

Stupica (small stupa) of the Dravidian order

Dravidian finial

Blind chataya arch

Antarala (terraced tower)

Perforated window

Gopuram finial (wagon-like finial)

Bracketed capital

Small gopuram (gate-head)

Parapet

Roll cornice

Niche with statue

Plan view

Gate

Panel with bas-relief carving

Pillar

Twin pilasters

Pradakshina (circumambulatory passage around shrine)

Shrine

Shrine chamber

Niche

Gate

Mandapa (pillared hall)

491

The 19th century

BUILDINGS OF THE 19TH CENTURY are characterized by the use of new materials and by a great diversity of architectural styles. From the end of the 18th century, iron and steel became widely used as alternatives to wood for the framework of buildings, as in the flax-spinning mill shown here. Built in Britain in 1796, this mill exemplifies an architectural style that became common throughout the industrialized world for more than a century. The Industrial Revolution also brought mass-production of building parts – a development that enabled the British architect Sir Joseph Paxton to erect London's Crystal Palace (a building made entirely of iron and glass) in only nine months, ready for the Great Exhibition of 1851. The 19th century saw a widespread revival of older architectural styles. For example, in the USA and Germany, Neo-Greek architecture was fashionable; in Britain and France, Neo-Baroque, Neo-Byzantine, and Neo-Gothic styles (as seen in the Palace of Westminster and Tower Bridge) were dominant.

Cast-iron wall-plate
Machinery space
Cast-iron mortise-and-tenon joint
Inverted T-section cast-iron beam
Segmentally arched brick vault
Paved ground floor

Pitched roof
Ridge
Verge
Gutter
Anchor-joint
Drain-pipe
End flange
Concrete floor
Tapering part of column
Strengthened central column

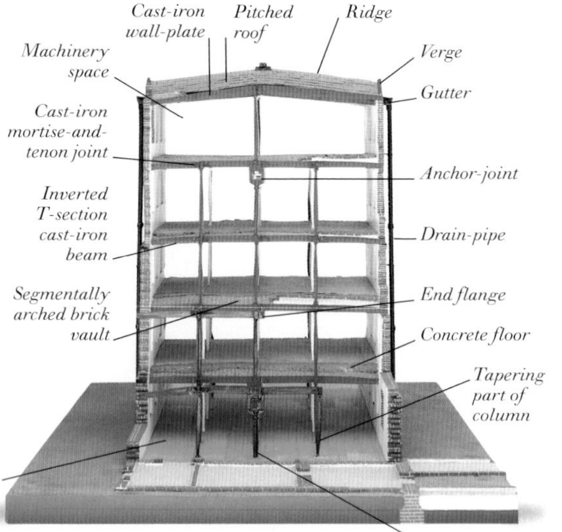

FLAX-SPINNING MILL, SHREWSBURY, BRITAIN, 1796 (BY C. BAGE)

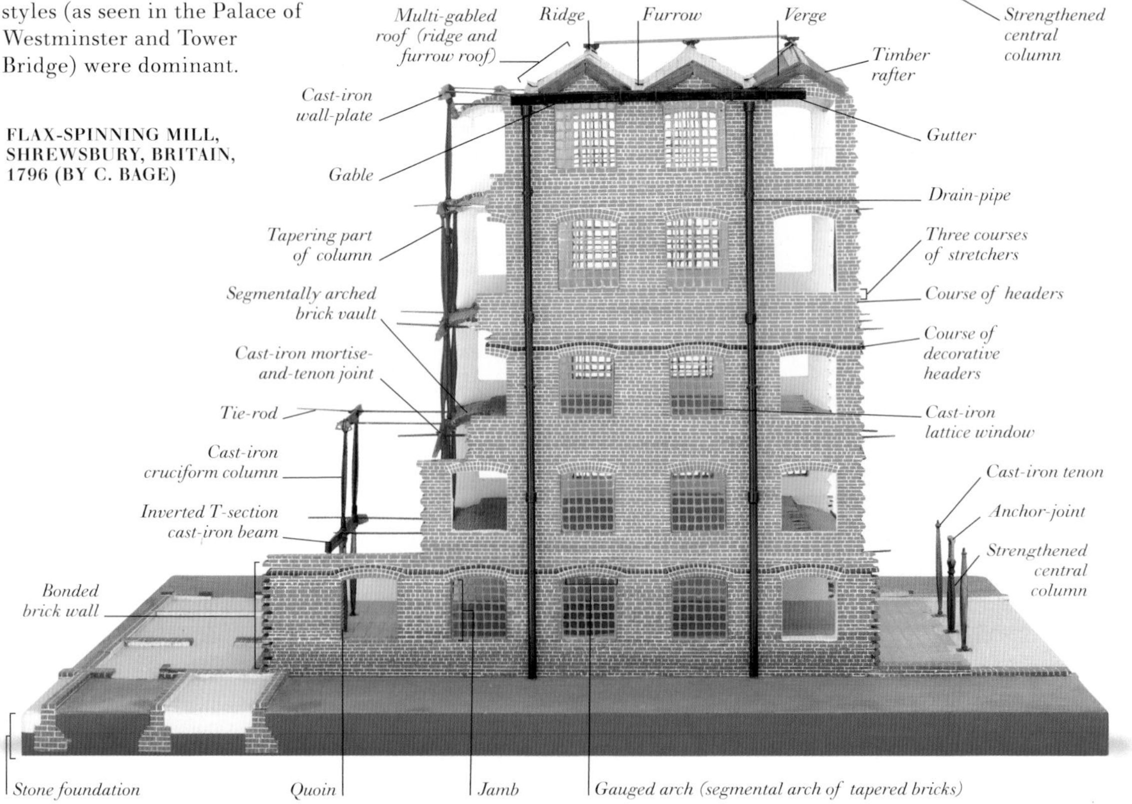

Multi-gabled roof (ridge and furrow roof)
Ridge
Furrow
Verge
Timber rafter
Cast-iron wall-plate
Gutter
Gable
Drain-pipe
Tapering part of column
Three courses of stretchers
Segmentally arched brick vault
Course of headers
Cast-iron mortise-and-tenon joint
Course of decorative headers
Tie-rod
Cast-iron lattice window
Cast-iron cruciform column
Cast-iron tenon
Inverted T-section cast-iron beam
Anchor-joint
Strengthened central column
Bonded brick wall

Stone foundation
Quoin
Jamb
Gauged arch (segmental arch of tapered bricks)

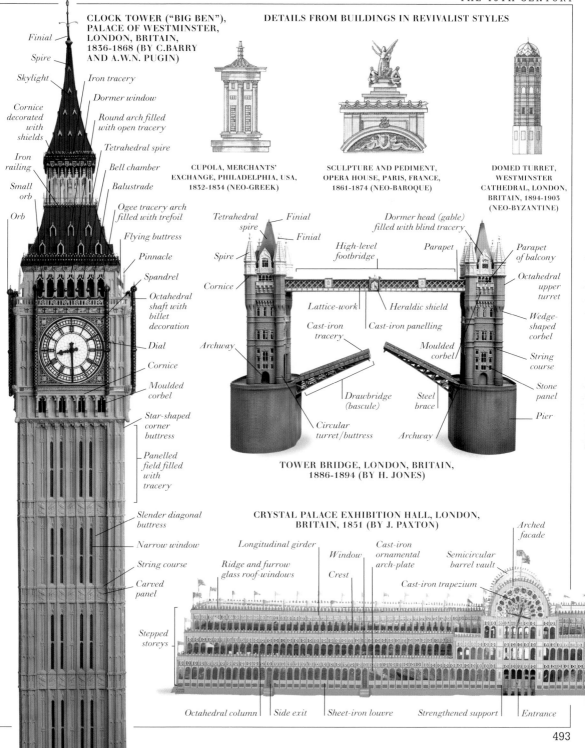

CLOCK TOWER ("BIG BEN"), PALACE OF WESTMINSTER, LONDON, BRITAIN, 1836-1868 (BY C.BARRY AND A.W.N. PUGIN)

Finial

Spire

Skylight

Iron tracery

Dormer window

Cornice decorated with shields

Round arch filled with open tracery

Tetrahedral spire

Iron railing

Bell chamber

Small orb

Balustrade

Orb

Ogee tracery arch filled with trefoil

Flying buttress

Pinnacle

Spandrel

Octahedral shaft with billet decoration

Dial

Cornice

Moulded corbel

Star-shaped corner buttress

Panelled field filled with tracery

Slender diagonal buttress

Narrow window

String course

Carved panel

Stepped storeys

DETAILS FROM BUILDINGS IN REVIVALIST STYLES

CUPOLA, MERCHANTS' EXCHANGE, PHILADELPHIA, USA, 1832-1834 (NEO-GREEK)

SCULPTURE AND PEDIMENT, OPERA HOUSE, PARIS, FRANCE, 1861-1874 (NEO-BAROQUE)

DOMED TURRET, WESTMINSTER CATHEDRAL, LONDON, BRITAIN, 1894-1903 (NEO-BYZANTINE)

Tetrahedral spire

Finial

Finial

Spire

Cornice

High-level footbridge

Dormer head (gable) filled with blind tracery

Parapet

Parapet of balcony

Octahedral upper turret

Lattice-work

Heraldic shield

Cast-iron tracery

Cast-iron panelling

Archway

Moulded corbel

Wedge-shaped corbel

String course

Drawbridge (bascule)

Steel brace

Stone panel

Circular turret/buttress

Archway

Pier

TOWER BRIDGE, LONDON, BRITAIN, 1886-1894 (BY H. JONES)

CRYSTAL PALACE EXHIBITION HALL, LONDON, BRITAIN, 1851 (BY J. PAXTON)

Longitudinal girder

Window

Cast-iron ornamental arch-plate

Arched facade

Ridge and furrow glass roof-windows

Crest

Semicircular barrel vault

Cast-iron trapezium

Octahedral column

Side exit

Sheet-iron louvre

Strengthened support

Entrance

The early 20th century

ARCHITECTURE OF THE EARLY 20TH CENTURY is notable for radical new types of steel-and-glass buildings – particularly skyscrapers – and the widespread use of steel-reinforced concrete. The steel-framed skyscraper was pioneered in Chicago in the 1880s, but did not become widespread until the first decades of the 20th century. As construction techniques were refined, skyscrapers became higher and higher; for example, the Empire State Building (right) of 1929-1931 has 102 storeys. Many buildings of this period were constructed from lightweight concrete slabs, which could be supported by cantilever beams or by pilotis (stilts), as in the Villa Savoye (below). The early 20th century also produced a great variety of architectural styles, some of which are illustrated opposite. Despite their diversity, the styles of this period generally had one thing in common: they were completely new, with few links to past architectural styles. This originality is in marked contrast to 19th-century architecture (see pp. 492-493), much of which was revivalist.

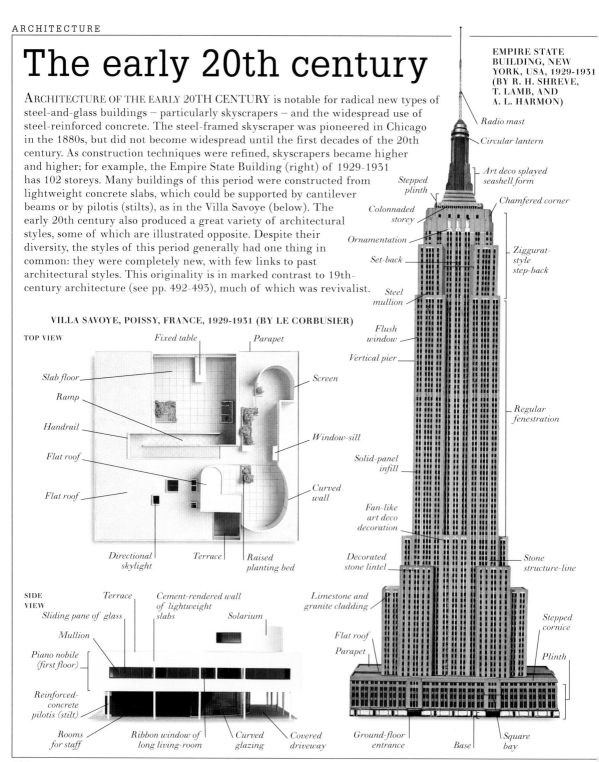

EMPIRE STATE BUILDING, NEW YORK, USA, 1929-1931 (BY R. H. SHREVE, T. LAMB, AND A. L. HARMON)

Radio mast

Circular lantern

Art deco splayed seashell form

Stepped plinth

Colonnaded storey

Ornamentation

Set-back

Chamfered corner

Ziggurat-style step-back

Steel mullion

Flush window

Vertical pier

Regular fenestration

Solid-panel infill

Fan-like art deco decoration

Decorated stone lintel

Stone structure-line

Limestone and granite cladding

Flat roof

Parapet

Stepped cornice

Plinth

Ground-floor entrance

Base

Square bay

VILLA SAVOYE, POISSY, FRANCE, 1929-1931 (BY LE CORBUSIER)

TOP VIEW

Fixed table

Parapet

Slab floor

Ramp

Handrail

Flat roof

Flat roof

Screen

Window-sill

Curved wall

Directional skylight

Terrace

Raised planting bed

SIDE VIEW

Terrace

Cement-rendered wall of lightweight slabs

Solarium

Sliding pane of glass

Mullion

Piano nobile (first floor)

Reinforced-concrete pilotis (stilt)

Rooms for staff

Ribbon window of long living-room

Curved glazing

Covered driveway

MIDWAY GARDENS, CHICAGO, USA, 1914 (BY F. L. WRIGHT)

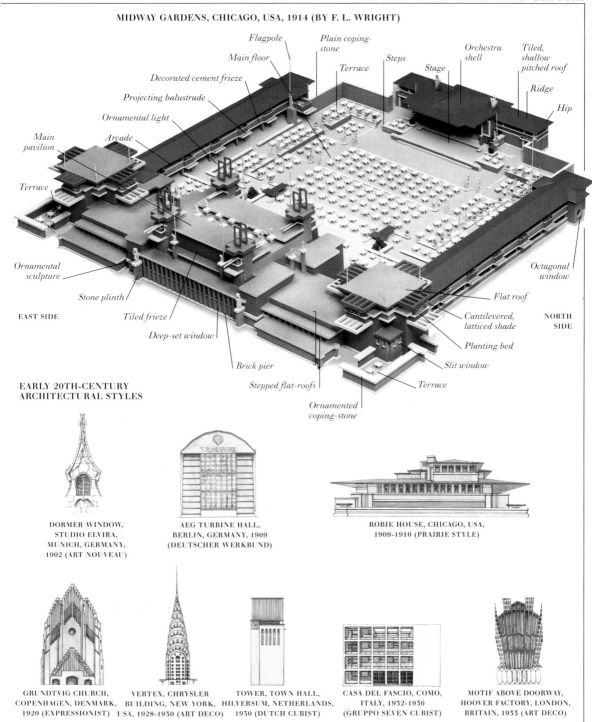

Flagpole

Plain coping-stone

Main floor

Terrace

Steps

Stage

Orchestra shell

Tiled, shallow pitched roof

Decorated cement frieze

Ridge

Projecting balustrade

Hip

Ornamental light

Main pavilion

Arcade

Terrace

Ornamental sculpture

Octagonal window

Stone plinth

EAST SIDE

Tiled frieze

Flat roof

Cantilevered, latticed shade

NORTH SIDE

Deep-set window

Planting bed

Brick pier

Slit window

Stepped flat-roofs

Terrace

Ornamented coping-stone

EARLY 20TH-CENTURY ARCHITECTURAL STYLES

DORMER WINDOW,
STUDIO ELVIRA,
MUNICH, GERMANY,
1902 (ART NOUVEAU)

AEG TURBINE HALL,
BERLIN, GERMANY, 1909
(DEUTSCHER WERKBUND)

ROBIE HOUSE, CHICAGO, USA,
1909-1910 (PRAIRIE STYLE)

GRUNDTVIG CHURCH,
COPENHAGEN, DENMARK,
1920 (EXPRESSIONIST)

VERTEX, CHRYSLER
BUILDING, NEW YORK,
USA, 1928-1930 (ART DECO)

TOWER, TOWN HALL,
HILVERSUM, NETHERLANDS,
1930 (DUTCH CUBIST)

CASA DEL FASCIO, COMO,
ITALY, 1932-1936
(GRUPPO SEVEN CUBIST)

MOTIF ABOVE DOORWAY,
HOOVER FACTORY, LONDON,
BRITAIN, 1933 (ART DECO)

Modern buildings 1

ARCHITECTURE SINCE ABOUT THE 1950s is generally known as modern architecture. One of its main influences has been functionalism – a belief that a building's function should be apparent in its design. Both the Centre Georges Pompidou (below and opposite) and the Hong Kong and Shanghai Bank (see pp. 498-499) are functionalist buildings: on each, elements of engineering and the building's services are clearly visible on the outside. In the 1980s, some architects rejected functionalism in favour of post-modernism, in which historical styles – particularly neoclassicism – were revived, using modern building materials and techniques. In many modern buildings, walls are made of glass or concrete hung from a frame, as in the Kawana House (right); this type of wall construction is known as curtain walling. Other modern construction techniques include the intricate interlocking of concrete vaults – as in the Sydney Opera House (see pp. 498-499) – and the use of high-tension beams to create complex roof shapes, such as the paraboloid roof of the Church of St. Pierre de Libreville (see pp. 498-499).

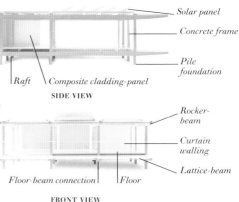

Solar panel
Concrete frame
Pile foundation
Raft
Composite cladding-panel
SIDE VIEW

Rocker-beam
Curtain walling
Lattice-beam
Floor-beam connection
Floor
FRONT VIEW

SERVICES FACADE, CENTRE GEORGES POMPIDOU, PARIS, FRANCE, 1977 (BY R. PIANO AND R. ROGERS)

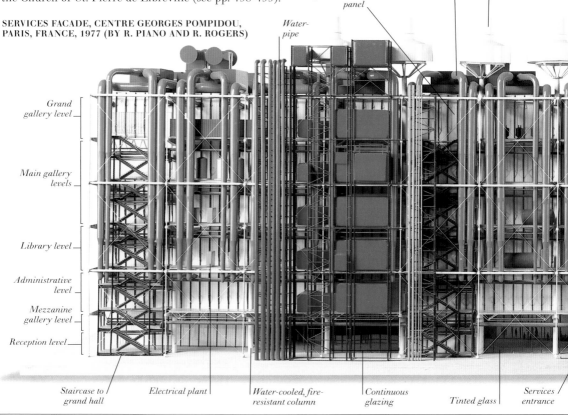

Metal-faced, fire-resistant panel
Air-conditioning duct
Cooling tower
Water-pipe

Grand gallery level
Main gallery levels
Library level
Administrative level
Mezzanine gallery level
Reception level

Staircase to grand hall
Electrical plant
Water-cooled, fire-resistant column
Continuous glazing
Tinted glass
Services entrance

PRINCIPAL FACADE, CENTRE GEORGES POMPIDOU

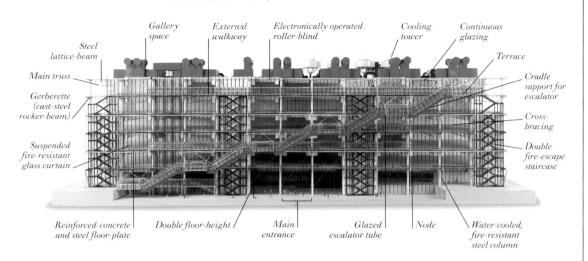

Gallery space
External walkway
Electronically operated roller-blind
Cooling tower
Continuous glazing
Steel lattice-beam
Terrace
Main truss
Cradle support for escalator
Gerberette (cast-steel rocker-beam)
Cross-bracing
Suspended fire-resistant glass curtain
Double fire-escape staircase
Reinforced-concrete and steel floor-plate
Double floor-height
Main entrance
Glazed escalator tube
Node
Water-cooled, fire-resistant steel column

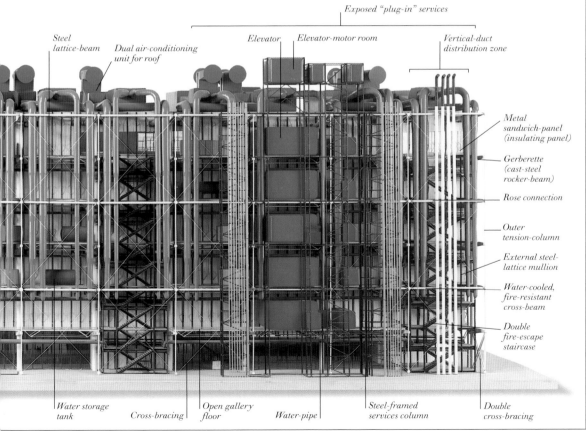

Exposed "plug-in" services
Steel lattice-beam
Dual air-conditioning unit for roof
Elevator
Elevator-motor room
Vertical-duct distribution zone
Metal sandwich-panel (insulating panel)
Gerberette (cast-steel rocker-beam)
Rose connection
Outer tension-column
External steel-lattice mullion
Water-cooled, fire-resistant cross-beam
Double fire-escape staircase
Water storage tank
Cross-bracing
Open gallery floor
Water-pipe
Steel-framed services column
Double cross-bracing

Modern buildings 2

HONG KONG AND SHANGHAI BANK, HONG KONG, 1981-1985 (BY N. FOSTER)

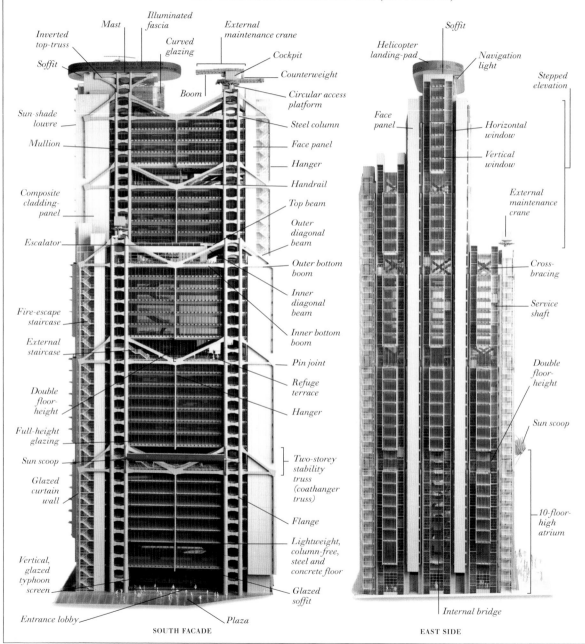

Inverted top-truss

Soffit

Mast

Illuminated fascia

Curved glazing

External maintenance crane

Cockpit

Counterweight

Boom

Circular access platform

Steel column

Sun-shade louvre

Face panel

Mullion

Hanger

Handrail

Composite cladding-panel

Top beam

Outer diagonal beam

Escalator

Outer bottom boom

Inner diagonal beam

Fire-escape staircase

Inner bottom boom

External staircase

Pin joint

Refuge terrace

Double floor-height

Hanger

Full-height glazing

Sun scoop

Two-storey stability truss (coathanger truss)

Glazed curtain wall

Flange

Lightweight, column-free, steel and concrete floor

Vertical, glazed typhoon screen

Glazed soffit

Entrance lobby

Plaza

SOUTH FACADE

Helicopter landing-pad

Soffit

Navigation light

Stepped elevation

Face panel

Horizontal window

Vertical window

External maintenance crane

Cross-bracing

Service shaft

Double floor-height

Sun scoop

10-floor-high atrium

Internal bridge

EAST SIDE

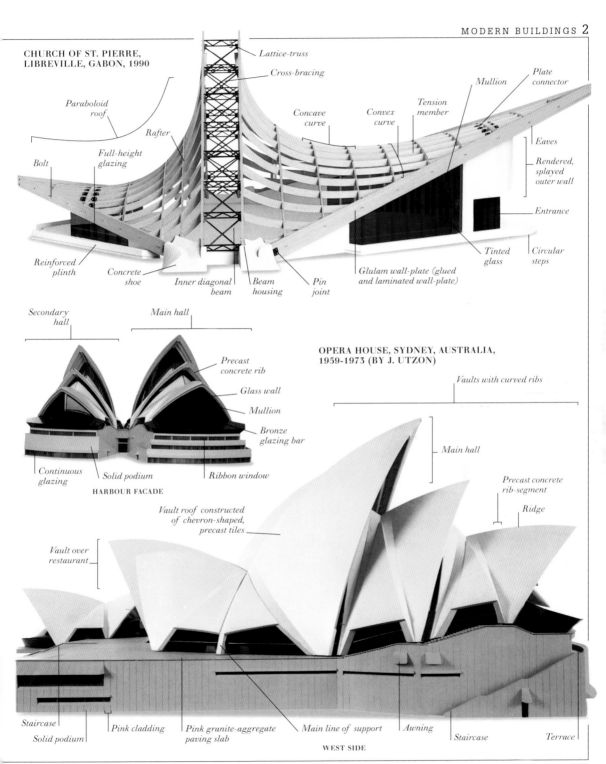

CHURCH OF ST. PIERRE, LIBREVILLE, GABON, 1990

Paraboloid roof

Lattice-truss

Cross-bracing

Rafter

Full-height glazing

Bolt

Concave curve

Convex curve

Tension member

Mullion

Plate connector

Eaves

Rendered, splayed outer wall

Entrance

Tinted glass

Circular steps

Reinforced plinth

Concrete shoe

Inner diagonal beam

Beam housing

Pin joint

Glulam wall-plate (glued and laminated wall-plate)

Secondary hall

Main hall

Precast concrete rib

Glass wall

Mullion

Bronze glazing bar

OPERA HOUSE, SYDNEY, AUSTRALIA, 1959-1973 (BY J. UTZON)

Vaults with curved ribs

Main hall

Precast concrete rib-segment

Ridge

Continuous glazing

Solid podium

Ribbon window

HARBOUR FACADE

Vault roof constructed of chevron-shaped, precast tiles

Vault over restaurant

Staircase

Solid podium

Pink cladding

Pink granite-aggregate paving slab

Main line of support

Awning

Staircase

Terrace

WEST SIDE

499

MUSIC

Musical notation

MUSICAL NOTATION IS ANY METHOD by which sounds are written down so that they can be read and performed by others. The present-day conventional system of notation uses a five-line stave (staff) – divided by vertical lines into sections known as bars – on which notes, rests, clefs, key signatures, time signatures, accidentals, and other symbols are written. A note indicates the duration of a sound and, according to its position on the stave, its pitch. Notes can be arranged on the stave in order of pitch to form a scale. A silence in the music is indicated by a rest. The clef, which is placed at the begininng of a stave, fixes the pitch. The key signature, which is placed after the clef, indicates the key. The time signature, placed after the key signature, shows the number of beats in a bar. Accidentals are used to indicate the raising or lowering of the pitch of a note.

EXAMPLE OF AN ORIGINAL MANUSCRIPT: THE PRODIGAL SON, ARTHUR SULLIVAN, 1869

ELEMENTS OF MUSICAL NOTATION

CLEFS

Treble (or G) clef

Alto (or C) clef

Bass (or F) clef

TIME SIGNATURES

Six-eight time

Three-four time

NOTES

Breve — Minim — Quaver

Semibreve | Crotchet | Semiquaver

RESTS

Breve rest — Minim rest — Quaver rest

Semibreve rest | Crotchet rest | Semiquaver rest

SCALE

C D E F G A B C

ACCIDENTALS

Sharp — Natural — Double sharp

Flat | Double flat | Key signature

Moderately fast and quiet — Tie (bind) — Repeat the previous bar

Treble clef

Bass clef

Four-four time (common time)

Key signature

Stave (staff)

Alto clef

Treble voice

Alto voice

Tenor voice

Bass voice

Organ part for right hand

Organ part for left hand

Organ pedal line

Instruments of the orchestra written in Italian

Bar line

Bar

Bass clef

Crotchet

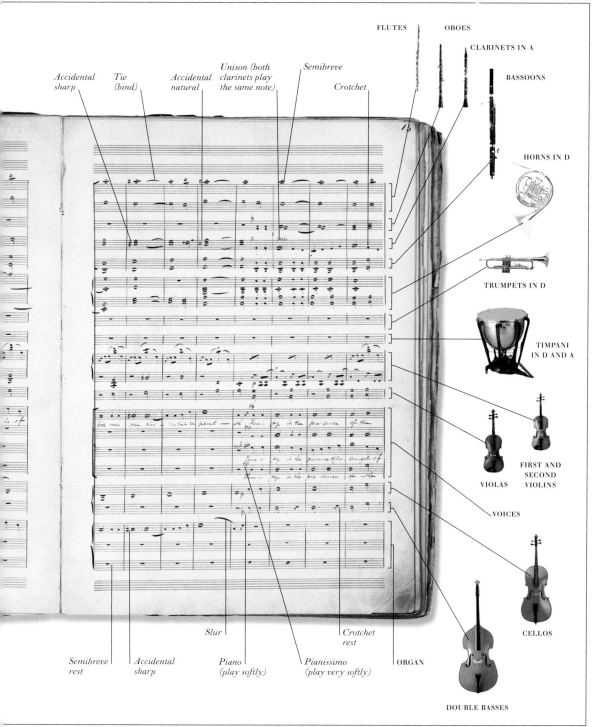

FLUTES

OBOES

CLARINETS IN A

BASSOONS

HORNS IN D

TRUMPETS IN D

TIMPANI IN D AND A

FIRST AND SECOND VIOLINS

VIOLAS

VOICES

CELLOS

DOUBLE BASSES

ORGAN

Accidental sharp

Tie (bind)

Accidental natural

Unison (both clarinets play the same note)

Semibreve

Crotchet

Semibreve rest

Accidental sharp

Slur

Piano (play softly)

Pianissimo (play very softly)

Crotchet rest

Orchestras

AN ORCHESTRA IS A GROUP of musicians that plays music written for a specific combination of instruments. The number and type of instruments included in the orchestra depends on the style of music being played. The modern orchestra (also known as a symphony orchestra) is made up of four sections of instruments – stringed, woodwind, brass, and percussion. The stringed section consists of violins, violas, cellos (violoncellos), double basses, and sometimes a harp (see pp. 510-511). The main instruments of the woodwind section are flutes, oboes, clarinets, and bassoons – the piccolo, cor anglais, bass clarinet, saxophone, and double bassoon (contrabassoon) can also be included if the music requires them (see pp. 508-509). The brass section usually consists of horns, trumpets, trombones, and the tuba (see pp. 506-507). The main instruments of the percussion section are the timpani (see pp. 518-519). The side drum, bass drum, cymbals, tambourine, triangle, tubular bells, xylophone, vibraphone, tam-tam (gong), castanets, and maracas can also be included in the percussion section (see pp. 516-517). The musicians are usually arranged in a semi-circle – strings spread along the front, woodwind and brass in the centre, and percussion at the back. A conductor stands in front of the musicians and controls the tempo (speed) of the music and the overall balance of the sound, ensuring that no instruments are too loud or too soft in relation to the others.

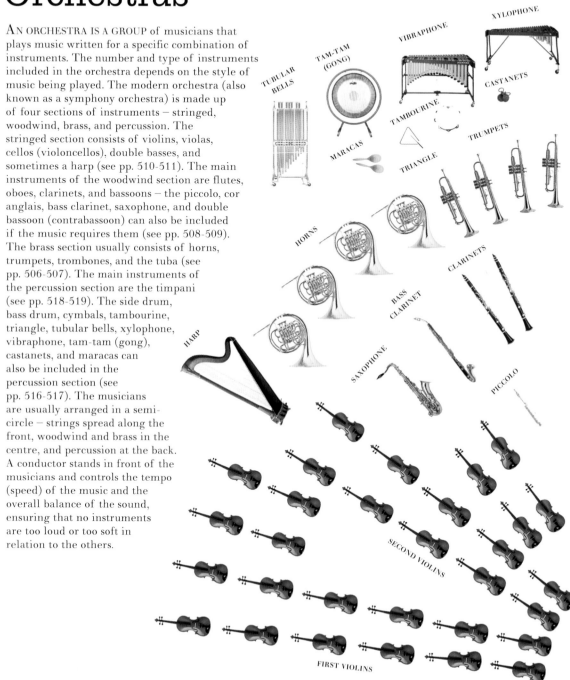

TUBULAR BELLS

TAM-TAM (GONG)

VIBRAPHONE

XYLOPHONE

CASTANETS

TAMBOURINE

MARACAS

TRIANGLE

TRUMPETS

HORNS

CLARINETS

BASS CLARINET

HARP

SAXOPHONE

PICCOLO

SECOND VIOLINS

FIRST VIOLINS

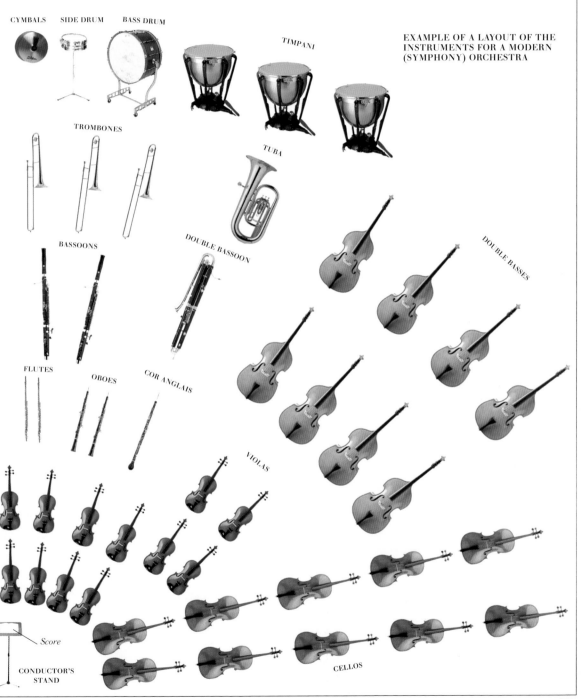

CYMBALS   SIDE DRUM   BASS DRUM

TIMPANI

EXAMPLE OF A LAYOUT OF THE
INSTRUMENTS FOR A MODERN
(SYMPHONY) ORCHESTRA

TROMBONES

TUBA

BASSOONS

DOUBLE BASSOON

DOUBLE BASSES

FLUTES

OBOES

COR ANGLAIS

VIOLAS

Score

CONDUCTOR'S
STAND

CELLOS

505

Brass instruments

BRASS INSTRUMENTS ARE WIND INSTRUMENTS that are made
of metal, usually brass. Although they appear in many
different shapes and sizes, all brass instruments have a
mouthpiece, a length of hollow tube, and a flared bell.
The mouthpiece of a brass instrument may be cup-
shaped, as in the cornet, or cone-shaped, as in the
horn. The tube may be wide or narrow, mainly
conical, as in the horn and tuba, or mainly cylindrical, as in
the trumpet and trombone. The sound of a brass instrument
is made by the player's lips vibrating against the mouthpiece,
so that the air vibrates in the tube. By changing lip tension,
the player can vary the vibrations and produce notes of
different pitches. The range of notes produced by a brass
instrument can be extended by means of a valve system.
Most brass instruments, such as the trumpet, have piston
valves that divert the air in the instrument along an extra
piece of tubing (known as a valve slide) when pressed down.
The total length of the tube is increased and the pitch of the
note produced is lowered. Instead of valves, the trombone
has a movable slide that can be pushed away from or drawn
toward the player. The sound of a brass instrument can also
be changed by inserting a mute into the bell of the instrument.

BUGLE

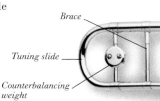

Brace
Tuning slide
Counterbalancing weight

SIMPLIFIED DIAGRAM SHOWING HOW A PISTON VALVE SYSTEM WORKS

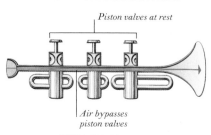

Piston valves at rest
Air bypasses piston valves

PISTON VALVES AT REST

First piston valve pressed down
Second and third piston valves at rest
Air diverted through first valve slide

PISTON VALVE PRESSED DOWN

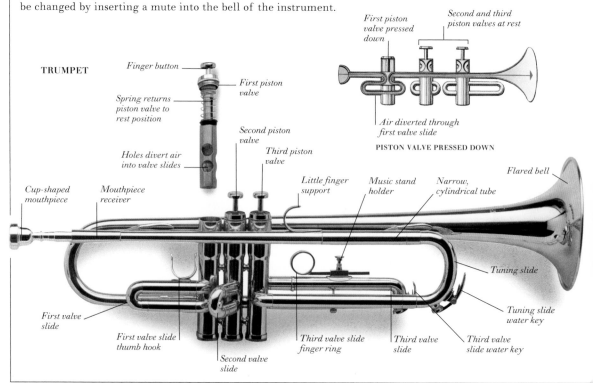

TRUMPET

Finger button
First piston valve
Spring returns piston valve to rest position
Second piston valve
Third piston valve
Holes divert air into valve slides
Little finger support
Music stand holder
Narrow, cylindrical tube
Flared bell
Cup-shaped mouthpiece
Mouthpiece receiver
Tuning slide
First valve slide
First valve slide thumb hook
Second valve slide
Third valve slide finger ring
Third valve slide
Tuning slide water key
Third valve slide water key

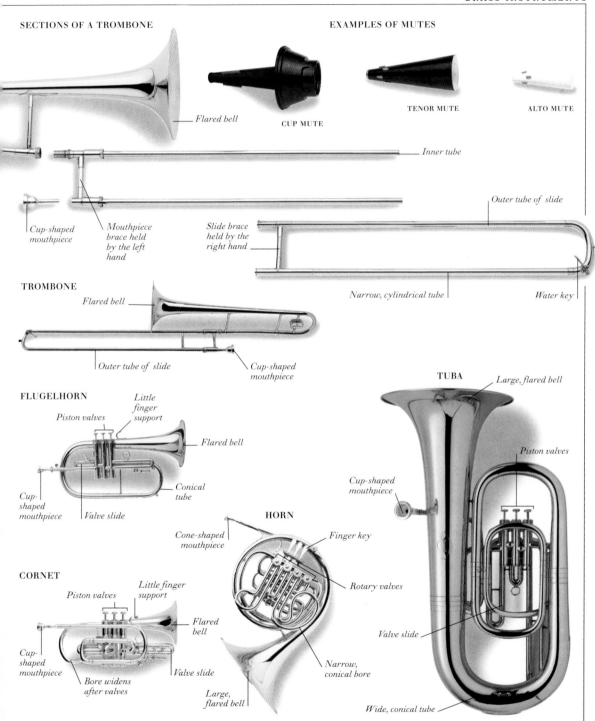

SECTIONS OF A TROMBONE

EXAMPLES OF MUTES

Flared bell

CUP MUTE

TENOR MUTE

ALTO MUTE

Inner tube

Outer tube of slide

Cup-shaped mouthpiece

Mouthpiece brace held by the left hand

Slide brace held by the right hand

Narrow, cylindrical tube

Water key

TROMBONE

Flared bell

Outer tube of slide

Cup-shaped mouthpiece

FLUGELHORN

Little finger support

Piston valves

Flared bell

Cup-shaped mouthpiece

Valve slide

Conical tube

HORN

Cone-shaped mouthpiece

Finger key

Rotary valves

CORNET

Little finger support

Piston valves

Flared bell

Cup-shaped mouthpiece

Bore widens after valves

Valve slide

Narrow, conical bore

Large, flared bell

TUBA

Large, flared bell

Piston valves

Cup-shaped mouthpiece

Valve slide

Wide, conical tube

507

Woodwind instruments

WOODWIND INSTRUMENTS ARE wind instruments that are generally made of wood, although some are made of metal or plastic. The sound of a woodwind instrument is produced by the vibration of air in a hollow tube. The air is made to vibrate by blowing across a blow hole – as in the flute and piccolo – or by blowing through a single reed – as in the clarinet and saxophone – or a double reed – as in the bassoon, cor anglais, and oboe. The pitch of a woodwind instrument can be changed by opening or closing holes cut into the tube of the instrument.

Bell

Double reed

Bell joint

Cylindrical, metal tube

Double reed

Curved crook

Key

Body joint

Conical, wooden tube

Tenor joint

Crook

Blow hole

Head joint

Conical, wooden tube

Upper joint

Lip plate

PICCOLO

Bass joint

Key

Double reed

Finger hole

Foot joint

Right-hand rest

Cork

Key

Key

Upper joint

Mouthpiece with single reed

Butt

Key

Key

Ligature

Middle joint

Middle joint

Cylindrical, metal tube

Body joint

Barrel joint

BASSOON

Finger hole

Cylindrical, wooden tube

Bell joint

Conical, wooden tube

Lip plate

Head joint

Key

Upper joint

Bulb-shaped bell

COR ANGLAIS

Blow hole

Bell joint

Middle joint

Flared bell

OBOE

FLUTE

Bell joint

Flared bell

CLARINET

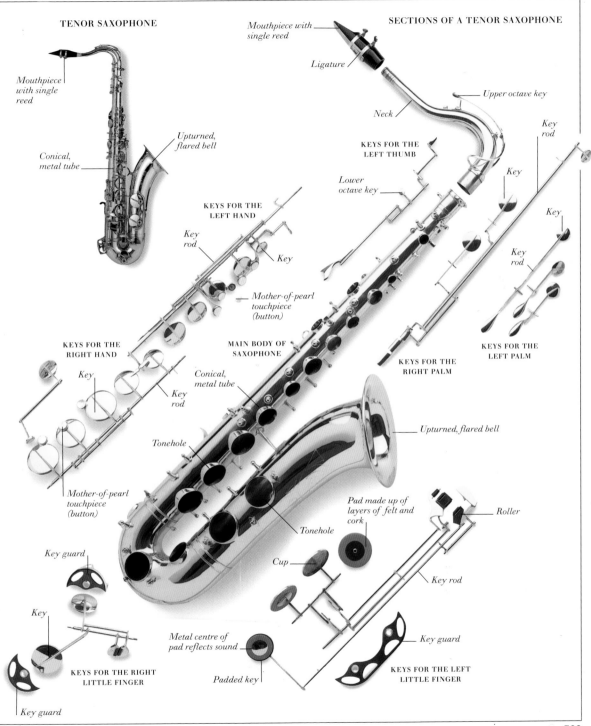

TENOR SAXOPHONE

SECTIONS OF A TENOR SAXOPHONE

Mouthpiece with single reed

Ligature

Upper octave key

Neck

Key rod

Mouthpiece with single reed

Upturned, flared bell

KEYS FOR THE LEFT THUMB

Lower octave key

Key

Conical, metal tube

KEYS FOR THE LEFT HAND

Key rod

Key

Key

Key rod

Key

Mother-of-pearl touchpiece (button)

KEYS FOR THE RIGHT HAND

MAIN BODY OF SAXOPHONE

KEYS FOR THE LEFT PALM

Key

Conical, metal tube

KEYS FOR THE RIGHT PALM

Key rod

Upturned, flared bell

Tonehole

Pad made up of layers of felt and cork

Roller

Mother-of-pearl touchpiece (button)

Tonehole

Key guard

Cup

Key rod

Key

Metal centre of pad reflects sound

Key guard

KEYS FOR THE RIGHT LITTLE FINGER

Padded key

KEYS FOR THE LEFT LITTLE FINGER

Key guard

509

Stringed instruments

STRINGED INSTRUMENTS PRODUCE SOUND by the vibration of stretched strings. This may be done by drawing a bow across the strings, as in the violin; or by plucking the strings, as in the harp and guitar (see pp. 512-513). The four modern members of the bowed string family are the violin, viola, cello (violoncello), and double bass. Each consists of a hollow, wooden body, a long neck, and four strings. The bow is a wooden stick with horsehair stretched across its length. The vibrations made by drawing the bow across the strings are transmitted to the hollow body, and this itself vibrates, amplifying and enriching the sound produced. The harp consists of a set of strings of different lengths stretched across a wooden frame. The strings are plucked by the player's thumbs and fingers – except the little finger of each hand – which produces vibrations that are amplified by the harp's soundboard. The pitch of the note produced by any stringed instrument depends on the length, weight, and tension of the string. A shorter, lighter, or tighter string gives a higher note.

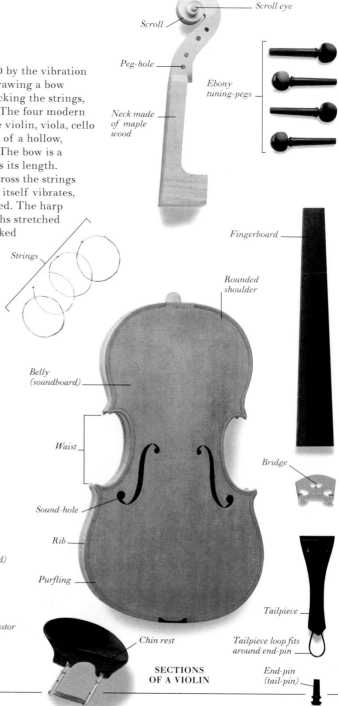

Scroll eye

Scroll

Peg-hole

Ebony tuning-pegs

Neck made of maple wood

Strings

Fingerboard

Rounded shoulder

Belly (soundboard)

Waist

Bridge

Sound-hole

Rib

Purfling

Chin rest

Tailpiece

Tailpiece loop fits around end-pin

End-pin (tail-pin)

SECTIONS OF A VIOLIN

Head

Point

Stick

Scroll

Peg-box

Scroll eye

Tuning-peg

Nut

Horsehair

String

Fingerboard

Rounded shoulder

Belly (soundboard)

Purfling

Waist

Sound-hole

Bridge

Tuning adjustor

Frog

Tailpiece

Screw

Chin rest

VIOLIN BOW

VIOLIN

HARP

- Crown
- Tuning-peg
- Neck (string arm)
- Shoulder
- String
- Soundboard
- Pillar
- Pedestal
- Foot
- Pedal

DOUBLE BASS BOW

- Head
- Point
- Inward-curving stick
- Horsehair
- Frog
- Screw

VIOLA

- Scroll
- Tuning-peg
- Scroll eye
- Peg-box
- Nut
- Fingerboard
- Belly (soundboard)
- String
- Rounded shoulder
- Purfling
- Waist
- Bridge
- Sound-hole
- Tuning adjustor
- Tailpiece
- Chin rest

CELLO (VIOLONCELLO)

- Scroll
- Scroll eye
- Peg-box
- Tuning-peg
- Nut
- Fingerboard
- String
- Belly (soundboard)
- Rounded shoulder
- Waist
- Sound-hole
- Bridge
- Tuning adjustor
- Tailpiece
- Spike

DOUBLE BASS

- Scroll
- Scroll eye
- Tuning-pegs at back of peg-box
- Nut
- Fingerboard
- String
- Sloping shoulder
- Belly (soundboard)
- Purfling
- Waist
- Bridge
- Rib
- Sound-hole
- Tailpiece
- Spike

511

Guitars

THE GUITAR IS A PLUCKED stringed instrument
(see pp. 510-511). There are two types of guitar –
acoustic and electric. Acoustic guitars have hollow
bodies and six or twelve strings. Plucking the strings
produces vibrations that are amplified by their hollow
bodies. Electric guitars usually have solid bodies and
six strings. Pick-ups placed under the strings convert
their vibrations into electronic signals that are magnified
by an amplifier, and sent to a loudspeaker where they are
converted into sounds (see pp. 520-521). Electric bass
guitars are very similar in structure to electric guitars,
and produce sound in the same way, but have four
strings and play bass notes.

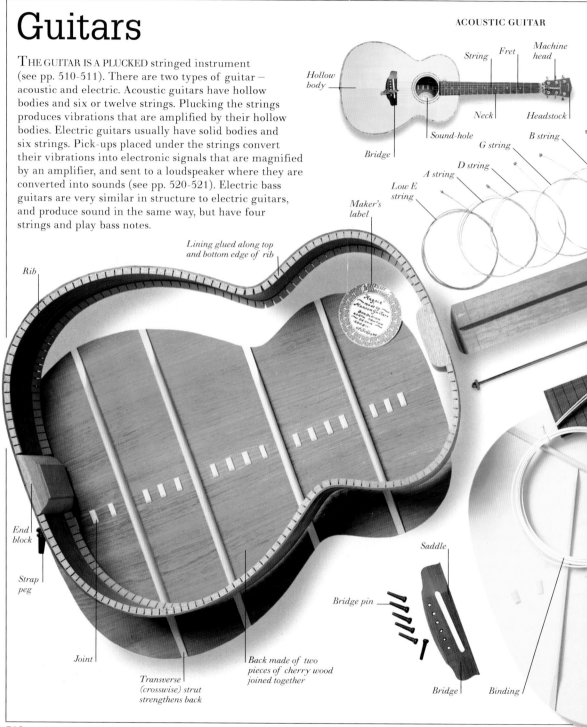

ACOUSTIC GUITAR

String

Fret

Machine head

Hollow body

Neck

Headstock

Sound-hole

B string

Bridge

G string

D string

A string

Low E string

Maker's label

Lining glued along top
and bottom edge of rib

Rib

End block

Strap peg

Joint

Transverse
(crosswise) strut
strengthens back

Back made of two
pieces of cherry wood
joined together

Saddle

Bridge pin

Bridge

Binding

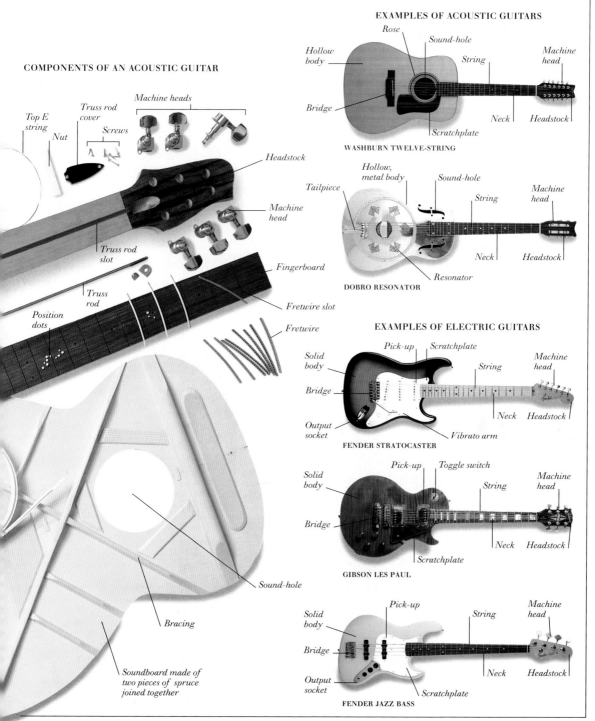

EXAMPLES OF ACOUSTIC GUITARS

COMPONENTS OF AN ACOUSTIC GUITAR

Rose

Hollow body

Sound-hole

String

Machine head

Bridge

Neck

Headstock

Scratchplate

WASHBURN TWELVE-STRING

Top E string

Truss rod cover

Machine heads

Screws

Nut

Headstock

Machine head

Truss rod slot

Truss rod

Fingerboard

Fretwire slot

Position dots

Fretwire

Hollow, metal body

Tailpiece

Sound-hole

String

Machine head

Neck

Headstock

Resonator

DOBRO RESONATOR

EXAMPLES OF ELECTRIC GUITARS

Solid body

Pick-up

Scratchplate

String

Machine head

Bridge

Neck

Headstock

Output socket

Vibrato arm

FENDER STRATOCASTER

Solid body

Pick-up

Toggle switch

String

Machine head

Bridge

Neck

Headstock

Scratchplate

GIBSON LES PAUL

Sound-hole

Bracing

Soundboard made of two pieces of spruce joined together

Solid body

Pick-up

String

Machine head

Bridge

Neck

Headstock

Output socket

Scratchplate

FENDER JAZZ BASS

513

Keyboard instruments

KEYBOARD INSTRUMENTS are instruments that are sounded by means of a keyboard. The organ and piano are two of the principal members of the keyboard family. The organ consists of pipes which are operated by one or more manuals (keyboards) and a pedal board. The pipes are lined up in rows (known as ranks or registers) on top of a wind chest. The sound of the organ is made when air is admitted into a pipe by pressing a key or pedal. The piano consists of wire strings stretched over a metal frame, and a keyboard and pedals that operate hammers and dampers. The piano frame is either vertical – as in the upright piano – or horizontal – as in the grand piano. When a key is at rest, a damper lies against the string to stop it vibrating. When a key is pressed down, the damper moves away from the string as the hammer strikes it, causing the string to vibrate and sound a note.

ORGAN PIPE

UPRIGHT PIANO

Muffler felt
Pressure bar
Tuning pin
Pin block
Hammer rail
Hammer
88–note keyboard
Wooden case
Keybed
Soundboard
Metal frame
String
Hitch pin
Treble bridge
Bass bridge

Una corda (soft) pedal
Sostenuto pedal
Damper (sustaining) pedal

ORGAN CONSOLE

Pipe
Pedal stop
Music stand
Swell stop
Choir stop
Swell manual (keyboard)
Great stop
Great manual (keyboard)
Choir manual (keyboard)
Thumb piston
Toe piston
Pedal board
Foot pedal
Swell pedal

UPRIGHT PIANO ACTION

KEY AT REST

String
Hammer
Damper lies against string, and stops it vibrating
Hammer rest
Back check
Damper lever
Action lever
Jack
Capstan screw
Key released

KEY PRESSED DOWN

String
Hammer strikes string
Damper moves away from string, allowing it to vibrate
Hammer rest
Back check
Damper lever
Action lever
Jack
Capstan screw
Key pressed down

CONCERT GRAND PIANO (VIEWED FROM ABOVE)

CONCERT GRAND PIANO (FRONT VIEW)

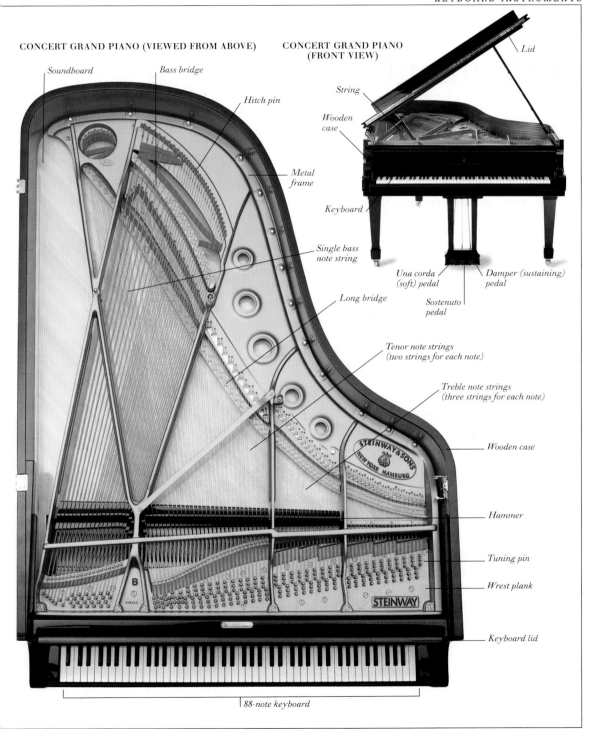

Soundboard

Bass bridge

Hitch pin

Metal frame

Single bass note string

Long bridge

Tenor note strings
(two strings for each note)

Treble note strings
(three strings for each note)

Wooden case

Hammer

Tuning pin

Wrest plank

Keyboard lid

88-note keyboard

Lid

String

Wooden case

Keyboard

Una corda
(soft) pedal

Sostenuto
pedal

Damper (sustaining)
pedal

STEINWAY & SONS
NEW YORK · HAMBURG

STEINWAY

B

Percussion instruments

TEMPLE BLOCKS

PERCUSSION INSTRUMENTS are a large group of instruments that produce sound by being struck, shaken, scraped, or clashed together. Most percussion instruments – such as the tam-tam (gong), cymbals, and maracas – do not have a definite pitch and are used for rhythm and impact, and the distinctive timbre (colour) of their sound. Other percussion instruments – such as the xylophone, vibraphone, and tubular bells – are tuned to a definite pitch and can play melody, harmony, and rhythms. The xylophone and vibraphone each have two rows of bars that are arranged in a similar way to the black and white keys of a piano. Metal tubes are suspended below the bars to amplify the sound. The vibraphone has electrically operated fans that rotate in the tubes and produce a vibrato (wavering pitch) effect.

TUBULAR BELLS

Tube struck with mallet

Hollow, metal tube

Damper bar

Metal frame

Mechanism linking pedal and damper bar

Row of tubes graduated in length and pitch

Damper pedal

EXAMPLES OF BEATERS

SOFT-HEADED BEATER

Fell-covered head

HARD-HEADED BEATER

Rosewood head

Leather-covered head

MALLET

Row of bars graduated in length and pitch

XYLOPHONE

Wooden bar struck with hard-headed beater

Hollow, metal tube

Metal stand

TAM-TAM (GONG)

Tam-tam struck in centre with soft-headed beater

Cord

Metal frame

PAISTE

Rim

Large, metal disc

CYMBALS

Leather strap fits around player's hand

Pad protects hands from vibrations

Thin, convex disc of copper and tin alloy

SECTIONS OF A MARACA

Wooden handle

Hollow, wooden head

Lead shot

CLAVES

Hardwood sticks clashed together to give a sharp crack

TRIANGLE

Steel rod bent into triangular shape

Steel beater

CASTANETS

Cord

Hollowed wood

VIBRAPHONE

Row of bars graduated in length and pitch

Metal bar struck with soft-headed beater

MUSSER

Metal frame

Damper pedal

Metal tube containing electrically operated fan that produces vibrato (wavering pitch) effect

Electric cable

Drums

A DRUM IS A percussion instrument that consists of a drumhead, made of skin or plastic, stretched over one or both ends of a hollow vessel (the body-shell). Drums are played in most parts of the world and are made in a number of different shapes and sizes. They can be divided into three groups according to the shape of the body-shell: frame drums (e.g., tambourines), bowl-shaped drums (e.g., timpani), and tubular drums (e.g., congas). Drums are usually sounded by striking the drumhead with the hands or with beaters, such as a hard-headed stick. The drumhead vibrates, and its vibrations are amplified by the hollow body-shell. The snare drum has wires − known as snares − stretched across the lower drumhead; the snares vibrate against the lower drumhead when the drum is played. Most drums, such as congas, do not have a definite pitch and can play only rhythms (see pp. 516-517). Other drums, such as timpani, have a definite pitch and can play melody, harmony, and rhythms. They can be tuned by adjusting the tension of the drumhead. Different types of drum can be combined together with other percussion instruments to form a drum kit. The basic components of the drum kit are bass drum, tom-toms, floor tom (tenor drum), snare drum, and cymbals.

TAMBOURINE

Crash cymbal

Tension key

DRUM KIT

Tension rod

Tom-tom

Lug

Hi-hat cymbal

Snare drum

Tripod stand

Chain

Tension screw

Felt-covered beater

Pedal

Pedal

SNARE DRUM (VIEWED FROM BELOW)

Snare mounting

Adjustable damper

Lug

Transparent lower drumhead

Upper drumhead

Snare

Stick

Snare release lever

EXAMPLES OF BEATERS

Acorn

HARD-HEADED STICK

Taper

SOFT-HEADED STICK

Felt-covered head

WIRE BRUSH

Wire bristles

Ride cymbal

Tension key

Tom-tom

Height adjustment key

Tension rod

Lug

Floor tom (tenor drum)

Tension rod

Lug

Wooden body-shell

Bass drum

Height adjustment key

Leg

Rubber foot

CONGAS

Metal hoop

Drumhead

Tension rod

Wooden body-shell

Tripod stand

Leg

TIMPANUM (KETTLE DRUM)

Drumhead

Tension rod

Metal hoop

Tuning gauge

Copper body-shell

Strut

Crown

Tension rod

Tuning pedal

Castor

Electronic instruments

ELECTRONIC INSTRUMENTS generate electronic signals that are magnified by an amplifier, and sent to a loudspeaker where they are converted into sounds. Synthesizers, and other electronic instruments, simulate the characteristic sounds of conventional instruments, and also create entirely new sounds. Most electronic instruments are keyboard instruments, but electronic wind and percussion instruments are also popular. A digital sampler records and stores sounds from musical instruments or other sources. When the sound is played back, the pitch of the original sound can be altered. A keyboard can be connected to the sampler so that a tune can be played using the sampled sounds. With a MIDI (Musical Instrument Digital Interface) system, a computer can be linked with other electronic instruments, such as keyboards and electronic drums, to make sounds together or in sequence. It is also possible, using music software, to compose and play music on a home computer.

ELECTRONIC DRUMS

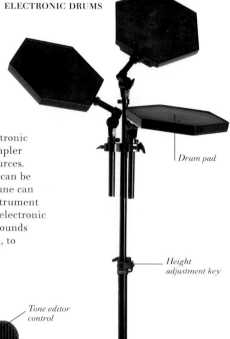

Drum pad

Height adjustment key

Tripod

HOME KEYBOARD

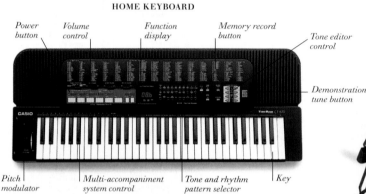

Power button

Volume control

Function display

Memory record button

Tone editor control

Demonstration tune button

Pitch modulator

Multi-accompaniment system control

Tone and rhythm pattern selector

Key

SYNTHESIZER

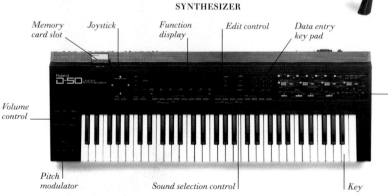

Memory card slot

Joystick

Function display

Edit control

Data entry key pad

Sound structure guide

Volume control

Pitch modulator

Sound selection control

Key

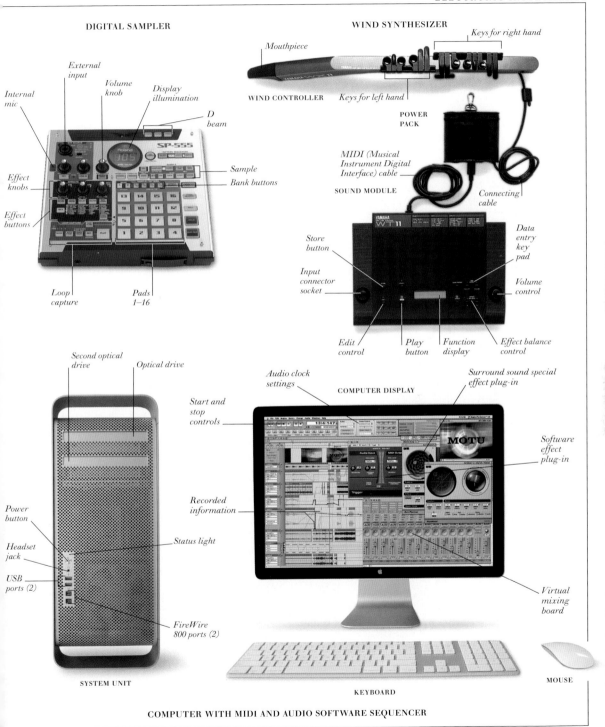

DIGITAL SAMPLER

Internal mic

External input

Volume knob

Display illumination

D beam

Effect knobs

Sample

Bank buttons

Effect buttons

Loop capture

Pads 1–16

WIND SYNTHESIZER

Mouthpiece

Keys for right hand

WIND CONTROLLER

Keys for left hand

POWER PACK

MIDI (Musical Instrument Digital Interface) cable

SOUND MODULE

Connecting cable

Store button

Data entry key pad

Input connector socket

Volume control

Edit control

Play button

Function display

Effect balance control

Second optical drive

Optical drive

Audio clock settings

Surround sound special effect plug-in

COMPUTER DISPLAY

Start and stop controls

Software effect plug-in

Power button

Recorded information

Headset jack

Status light

USB ports (2)

FireWire 800 ports (2)

Virtual mixing board

SYSTEM UNIT

MOUSE

KEYBOARD

COMPUTER WITH MIDI AND AUDIO SOFTWARE SEQUENCER

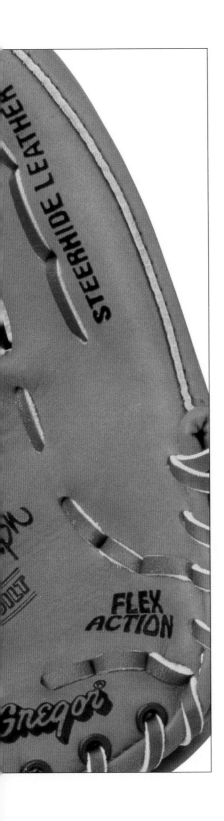

Sports

Soccer

GAMES INVOLVING KICKING A BALL have a long history and were recorded in China as early as 300 BC; in medieval Europe, street football was banned as a menace to the public; only in 1863 were the rules established, specifically banning carrying the ball for all players except the goalkeeper, and separating rugby from soccer. Soccer, officially termed association football, is a team sport in which players attempt to score goals by passing and dribbling the ball down the field past opposing defenders, and kicking or heading the ball into the goal net, outwitting the defending goalkeeper. Each team consists of ten outfield players (defenders, midfielders, and strikers) and a goalkeeper. Players from the opposing team may challenge the player in possession of the ball, but an illegal or foul tackle results in a penalty if a foul occurs inside the penalty area or a free kick if outside the penalty area. The round ball used in soccer is more easily controlled than the oval balls used in American, Canadian, and Australian rules football and in rugby. The result is a more "open" or flowing game which is played and watched by millions of people worldwide.

ASSISTANT REFEREE'S FLAG

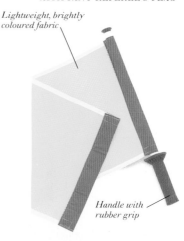

Lightweight, brightly coloured fabric

Handle with rubber grip

REFEREE'S EQUIPMENT

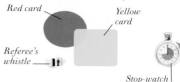

Red card

Yellow card

Referee's whistle

Stop-watch

PITCH MARKINGS

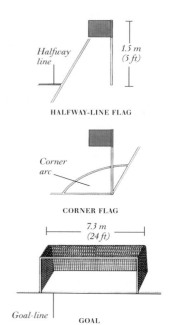

Halfway line

1.5 m (5 ft)

HALFWAY-LINE FLAG

Corner arc

CORNER FLAG

7.3 m (24 ft)

Goal-line

GOAL

SOCCER PITCH

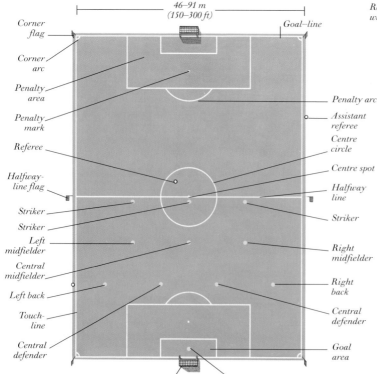

46–91 m (150–300 ft)

Corner flag

Corner arc

Penalty area

Penalty mark

Referee

Halfway-line flag

Striker

Striker

Left midfielder

Central midfielder

Left back

Touch-line

Central defender

Goal-line

Penalty arc

Assistant referee

Centre circle

Centre spot

Halfway line

Striker

Right midfielder

Right back

Central defender

Goal area

Goal

Goalkeeper

GOALKEEPER

Goalkeeper's shirt

Glove

Shorts

Shin guard

Sock

Soccer boot

SOCCER STRIP

Open-neck collar

Lightweight, man-made fabric team shirt

Team logo

Manufacturer's logo

Ribbed welt

Sponsor's logo

Manufacturer's name

Edge cut to fit perfectly

MAKING A SOCCER BALL

Hole punched in panel for stitching

Ball size number

Waxed thread

Needle

Bladder valve

Bladder made from latex rubber

Panels sewn together with ball inside out

Laminated panel

22–23 cm (8½–9 in)

Mitre

F.I.F.A. APPROVED

MULTIPLEX

Long cotton sock

Club crest

Team shorts

Synthetic bootlace

Interchangeable nylon stud

SOCCER BOOT

525

American football

In AMERICAN AND CANADIAN FOOTBALL, the object of the game is to get the ball across the opponent's goal line, either by passing or carrying it across (a touch-down), or by kicking it between their goalposts (a field goal). An American football team has 11 players on the field at a time, although up to 40 players can appear for each side in a single game. The agile "offence" tries to score points, and the heavy hitting "defence" holds back the opposition. When in possession of the ball, a team has four chances ("downs"), to move it at least ten yards (nine metres) up the field to make a "first down". The opposition gains possession if they fail, or by tackling and intercepting the ball. Canadian football is played on a larger field, with 12 men on each side. A team has only three chances to achieve a first down. Otherwise, the game is very similar to American football. Helmets, face masks, and layers of body padding are worn by the players for protection.

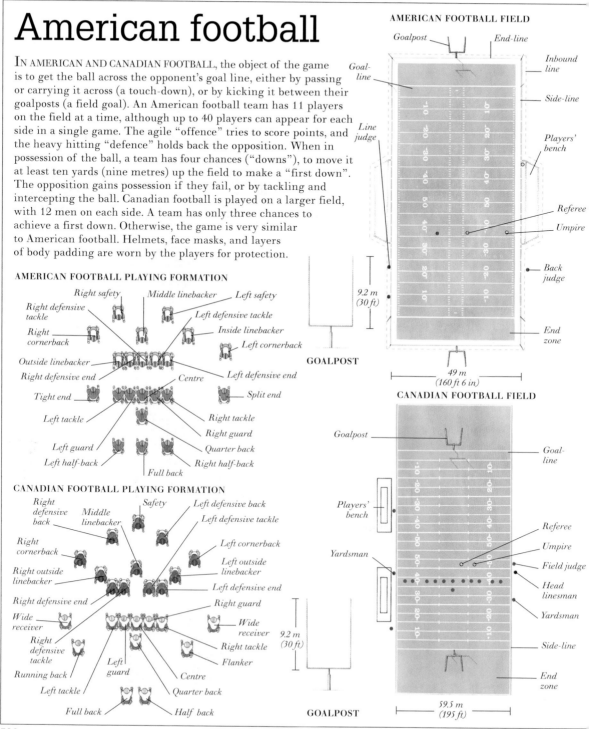

AMERICAN FOOTBALL FIELD

Goalpost
End-line
Inbound line
Goal-line
Side-line
Line judge
Players' bench
Referee
Umpire
Back judge
9.2 m (30 ft)
End zone
GOALPOST
49 m (160 ft 6 in)

AMERICAN FOOTBALL PLAYING FORMATION

Right safety
Middle linebacker
Left safety
Right defensive tackle
Left defensive tackle
Right cornerback
Inside linebacker
Left cornerback
Outside linebacker
Right defensive end
Centre
Left defensive end
Tight end
Split end
Left tackle
Right tackle
Right guard
Left guard
Quarter back
Left half-back
Right half-back
Full back

CANADIAN FOOTBALL PLAYING FORMATION

Right defensive back
Middle linebacker
Safety
Left defensive back
Left defensive tackle
Right cornerback
Left cornerback
Left outside linebacker
Right outside linebacker
Left defensive end
Right defensive end
Right guard
Wide receiver
Wide receiver
Right defensive tackle
Right tackle
Flanker
Running back
Left guard
Centre
Left tackle
Quarter back
Full back
Half back

CANADIAN FOOTBALL FIELD

Goalpost
Goal-line
Players' bench
Referee
Umpire
Yardsman
Field judge
Head linesman
Yardsman
Side-line
End zone
9.2 m (30 ft)
GOALPOST
59.5 m (195 ft)

PLAYER

Team logo

Helmet

Wrist pad

Player's number

Tie to shoulder pads

Thigh pad

Pants

Studded shoe

PROTECTIVE EQUIPMENT

28 cm (11 in)

Painted white ring

Lace

Brown pebbled leather

FOOTBALL

HELMET

Non-breakable plastic

Rubber-coated plastic

Shock absorber

SHOULDER PAD

BIKE

AIR·LITE

BLUE LASER 40-42

BIKE

Chest protector weight up to 2.5 kg (5 lb 8 oz)

RIB PADS

Strap ties on to shoulder pad

Tail bone pad

HIP PAD

Foam-sponge filling

UPPER ARM PAD

BIKE

ELBOW PAD

FINGERLESS GLOVE

Screw-in stud

BOOT

Fold-over leather tongue

Rigid plastic covering

PANTS

THIGH PAD

KNEE PAD

REFEREE'S SIGNALS

TIME OUT

TOUCH-DOWN OR FIELD GOAL

PERSONAL FOUL

OFFSIDE OR ENCROACHMENT

HOLDING

ILLEGAL MOTION

FIRST DOWN

PASS INTERFERENCE

Australian rules and Gaelic football

VARIETIES OF FOOTBALL have developed all over the world and Australian rules football is considered to be one of the roughest versions, allowing full body tackles although participants wear no protective padding. The game is played on a large, oval pitch by two sides, each of 18 players. Players can kick or punch the ball, which is shaped like a rugby ball, but cannot throw it. Running with the ball is permitted, as long as the ball touches the ground at least once every ten metres. The full backs defend two sets of posts. Teams try to score "goals" (six points) between the inner posts or "behinds" (one point) inside the outer posts. Each game has four quarters of 25 minutes, and the team with the most points at the end of the allotted time is the winner. In Gaelic football, an Irish version of soccer (see pp. 524–525), a size 5 soccer ball is used. Each team can have 15 players on the field at a time. Players are allowed to catch, fist, and kick the ball, or dribble it using their hands or feet, but cannot throw it. Teams are awarded three points for getting the ball into the net, and one point for getting it through the posts above the crossbar. Gaelic football is rarely played outside of Ireland.

START OF PLAY

Field umpire
Centre circle

SCORING

GOAL (6 POINTS)

BEHIND (1 POINT)

AUSTRALIAN RULES FOOTBALL FIELD

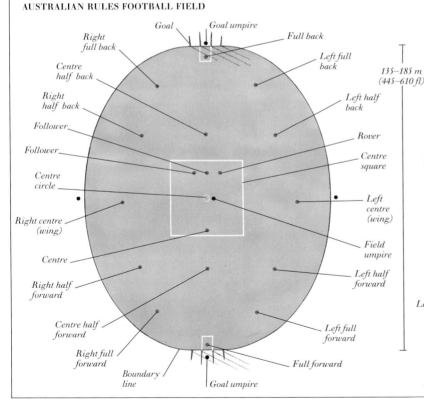

Goal *Goal umpire* *Full back*
Right full back
Centre half back
Left full back
Right half back
Left half back
Follower
Follower
Rover
Centre square
Centre circle
Left centre (wing)
Right centre (wing)
Centre
Field umpire
Right half forward
Left half forward
Centre half forward
Left full forward
Right full forward
Full forward
Boundary line
Goal umpire

135–185 m (445–610 ft)

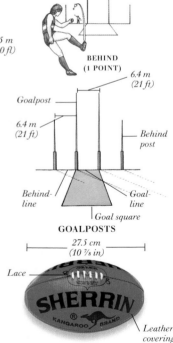

Goalpost
6.4 m (21 ft)
6.4 m (21 ft)
Behind post
Behind-line
Goal-line
Goal square
GOALPOSTS
27.5 cm (10 ⅞ in)
Lace
Leather covering
AUSTRALIAN RULES FOOTBALL

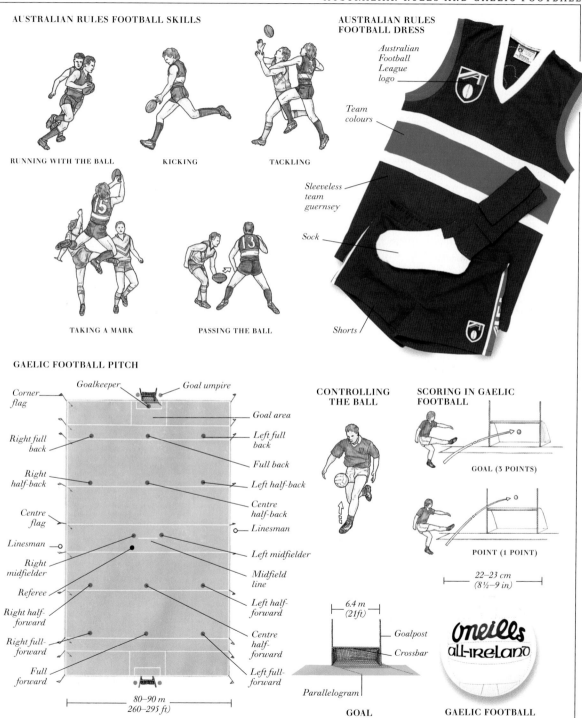

AUSTRALIAN RULES FOOTBALL SKILLS

RUNNING WITH THE BALL

KICKING

TACKLING

TAKING A MARK

PASSING THE BALL

AUSTRALIAN RULES FOOTBALL DRESS

Australian Football League logo

Team colours

Sleeveless team guernsey

Sock

Shorts

GAELIC FOOTBALL PITCH

Corner flag

Goalkeeper

Goal umpire

Goal area

Right full back

Left full back

Full back

Right half-back

Left half-back

Centre half-back

Centre flag

Linesman

Linesman

Left midfielder

Right midfielder

Midfield line

Referee

Left half-forward

Right half-forward

Centre half-forward

Right full-forward

Full forward

Left full-forward

80–90 m
260–295 ft)

CONTROLLING THE BALL

SCORING IN GAELIC FOOTBALL

GOAL (3 POINTS)

POINT (1 POINT)

22–23 cm
(8½–9 in)

6.4 m
(21ft)

Goalpost

Crossbar

Parallelogram

GOAL

oneills
all-ireland

GAELIC FOOTBALL

529

Rugby

RUGBY IS PLAYED WITH AN OVAL BALL, which may be carried, thrown, or kicked. There are two codes of rugby, both played at amateur and professional levels. Rugby Union is played by two teams of 15 players. They can score points in two ways: by placing the ball by hand over the opponents' goal-line (a try, scoring four points) or by kicking it over the crossbar of the opponent's goal (a conversion of a try, scoring two points; a penalty kick, scoring three points; or a drop-kick, scoring three points). Rugby League developed from the Union game but is played by 13 players. In League games, a try scores four points; a conversion scores two points; a drop goal scores one point, and a penalty kick scores two points. Scrummages occur in both codes when play stops following an infringement.

RUGBY UNION PITCH

- Touch in-goal line
- Goal-line
- 5 m line
- Scrum-half
- 10 m line
- Loose-head prop
- Flanker
- Lock forward
- Centre
- Left wing
- Centre
- Full back
- Goal
- Dead-ball line
- Touch-line
- Referee
- Hooker
- Tight-head prop
- Touch judge
- Flanker
- Lock forward
- Right wing
- Number 8
- Fly-half
- In-goal area
- 68 m (225 ft) maximum

RUGBY UNION SCRUMMAGE

- Loose-head prop
- Hooker
- Tight-head prop
- Scrum-half
- Flanker
- Flanker
- Lock forward
- Lock forward
- Number 8

RUGBY UNION GOALPOST

- 5.5 m (18 ft)
- Upright
- Crossbar
- Protective padding
- 3 m (9 ft 10 in)

RUGBY LEAGUE PITCH

- Touch in-goal
- Goal-line
- 10 m line
- Referee
- Touch judge
- Blind-side prop
- Second-row forward
- Loose forward
- Left wing
- Full back
- Goal
- Dead-ball line
- Touch in-goal line
- Touch-line
- Hooker
- Open-side prop
- Touch judge
- Second-row forward
- Scrum-half
- Stand-off half
- Centre
- Centre
- Right wing
- 68m (225 ft) maximum

RUGBY LEAGUE SCRUMMAGE

- Blind-side prop
- Hooker
- Open-side prop
- Scrum-half
- Second-row forward
- Second-row forward
- Loose forward

RUGBY LEAGUE GOALPOST

- 5.5 m (18 ft)
- Upright
- Crossbar
- Protective padding

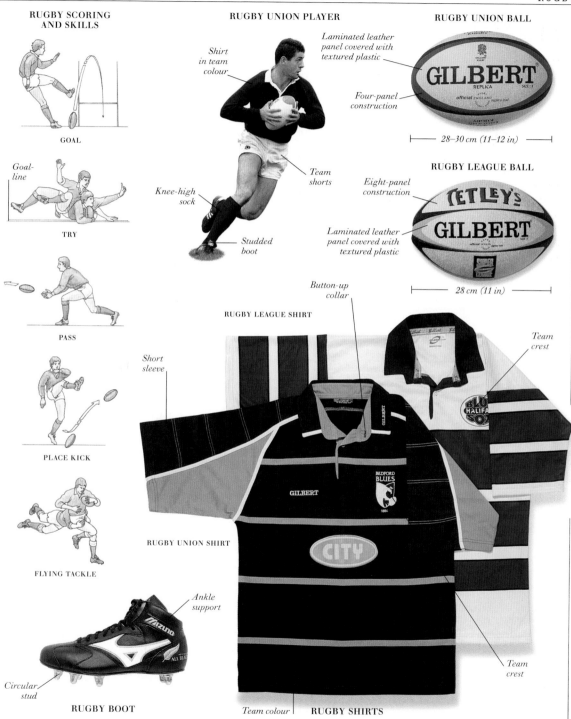

RUGBY SCORING AND SKILLS

GOAL

Goal-line

TRY

PASS

PLACE KICK

FLYING TACKLE

RUGBY UNION PLAYER

Shirt in team colour

Knee-high sock

Team shorts

Studded boot

RUGBY UNION BALL

Laminated leather panel covered with textured plastic

Four-panel construction

GILBERT
REPLICA   SIZE:1
official ENGLAND Replica ball

28–30 cm (11–12 in)

RUGBY LEAGUE BALL

Eight-panel construction

Laminated leather panel covered with textured plastic

TETLEY'S
GILBERT
SIZE:1

28 cm (11 in)

Button-up collar

RUGBY LEAGUE SHIRT

Team crest

Short sleeve

BLUE HALIFA

RUGBY UNION SHIRT

GILBERT

BEDFORD BLUES

CITY

Ankle support

Team crest

Circular stud

RUGBY BOOT

MIZUNO
ALL BLA

Team colour   **RUGBY SHIRTS**

Basketball

BASKETBALL IS A BALL GAME for two teams of five players, originally devised in 1890 by James Naismath for the Y.M.C.A. in Springfield, Massachusetts, U.S.A. The object of the game is to take possession of the ball and score points by throwing the ball into the opposing team's basket. A player moves the ball up and down the court by bouncing it along the ground or "dribbling"; the ball may be passed between players by throwing, bouncing, or rolling. Players may not run with or kick the ball, although pivoting on one foot is allowed. The game begins with the referee throwing the ball into the air and a player from each team jumping up to try and "tip" the ball to a team-mate. The length of the game and the number of periods played varies at different levels. There are amateur, professional, and international rules. No game ends in a draw. An extra period of five minutes is played, plus as many extra periods as are necessary to break the tie. In addition to the five players on court, each team has up to seven substitutes, but players may only leave the court with the permission of the referee. Basketball is a non-contact sport and fouls on other players are penalized by a throw-in awarded against the offending team; a free throw at the basket is awarded when a player is fouled in the act of shooting. Basketball is a fast-moving game, requiring both physical and mental coordination. Skilful tactical play matters more than simple physical strength and the agility of the players makes the game an excellent spectator sport.

BASKETBALL SKILLS

CHEST PASS

DRIBBLE

OVERHEAD PASS

LAY-UP SHOT

JUMP SHOT

LONG PASS

INTERNATIONAL BASKETBALL COUBT

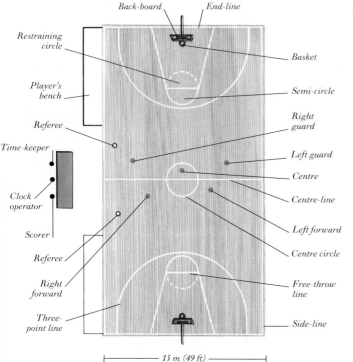

Back-board

End-line

Restraining circle

Player's bench

Referee

Time-keeper

Clock operator

Scorer

Referee

Right forward

Three-point line

Basket

Semi-circle

Right guard

Left guard

Centre

Centre-line

Left forward

Centre circle

Free-throw line

Side-line

15 m (49 ft)

BASKET AND BACK-BOARD

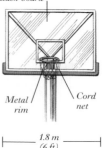

Back-board

Metal rim

Cord net

1.8 m (6 ft)

BASKET AND BACK-BOARD STRUCTURE

3.05 m (10 ft)

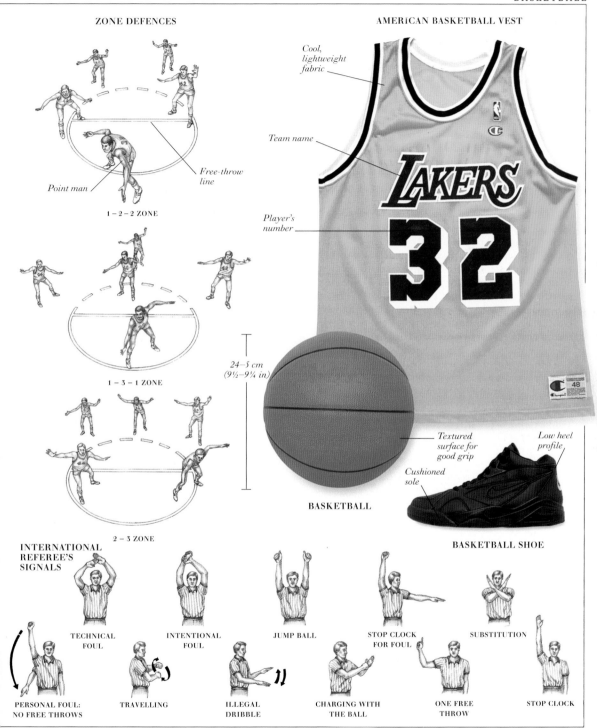

ZONE DEFENCES

Point man

Free-throw line

1 – 2 – 2 ZONE

1 – 3 – 1 ZONE

2 – 3 ZONE

AMERICAN BASKETBALL VEST

Cool, lightweight fabric

Team name

Player's number

LAKERS

32

24–5 cm
(9½–9¼ in)

BASKETBALL

Textured surface for good grip

Cushioned sole

Low heel profile

BASKETBALL SHOE

INTERNATIONAL REFEREE'S SIGNALS

TECHNICAL FOUL

INTENTIONAL FOUL

JUMP BALL

STOP CLOCK FOR FOUL

SUBSTITUTION

PERSONAL FOUL: NO FREE THROWS

TRAVELLING

ILLEGAL DRIBBLE

CHARGING WITH THE BALL

ONE FREE THROW

STOP CLOCK

Volleyball, netball, and handball

VOLLEYBALL, NETBALL, AND HANDBALL are fast-moving team sports played with balls on courts with a hard surface. In volleyball, the object of the game is to hit the ball over a net strung across the centre of the court so that it touches the ground on the opponent's side. The team of six players can take three hits to direct the ball over the net, although the same player cannot hit the ball twice in a row. Players can hit the ball with their arms, hands or any other part of their upper body. Teams score points only while serving. The first team to score 15 points, with a two-point margin over their opponent, wins the game. Netball is one of the few sports played exclusively by women. Similar to basketball (see pp.532–533), it is played on a slightly larger court with seven players instead of five. A team moves the ball towards the goal by throwing, passing, and catching it with the aim of throwing the ball through the opponents' goal net. Players are confined by their playing position to specific areas of the court. Team handball is one of the world's fastest games. Each side has seven players. A team moves the ball by dribbling, passing, or bouncing it as they run. Players may stop, catch, throw, bounce, or strike the ball with any part of the body above the knees. Each team tries to score goals by directing the ball past the opposition's goalkeeper into the net, which is similar to a soccer net.

VOLLEYBALL SHOTS

OVERHAND SERVE   SPIKE (SMASH)

UNDERHAND SERVE   FOREARM PASS (DIG)

VOLLEYBALL KIT

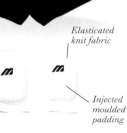

Team colours

Ribbed cuff

Cotton-knit jersey

Elasticated waist

Leather covering

Shorts

Elasticated knit fabric

Injected moulded padding

VOLLEYBALL COURT

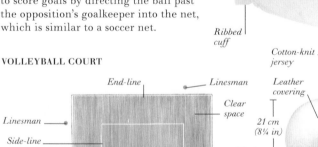

End-line
Linesman
Linesman
Side-line
Players' bench
Referee
Scorer
Net
Left forward
Back zone
Left back
Linesman

Clear space
Attack zone
Attack line
Umpire
Centre forward
Right forward
Centre back
Linesman
Service area
Server

9 m (29 ft 6 in)

Leather covering

21 cm (8¼ in)

VOLLEYBALL

VOLLEYBALL NET

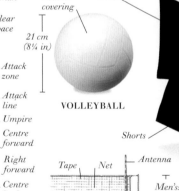

Tape   Net   Antenna

Post

Men's: 2.4 m (8 ft)
Women's: 2.2 m (7 ft 4 in)

KNEE PADS

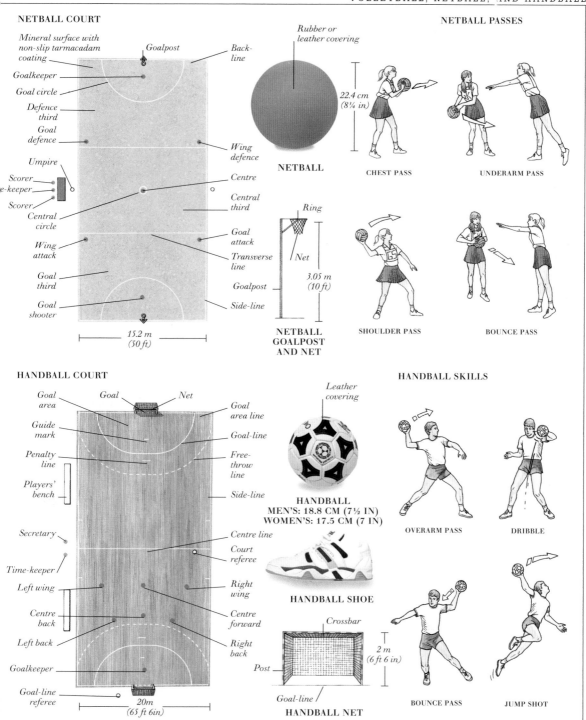

NETBALL COURT

Mineral surface with non-slip tarmacadam coating

Goalpost

Back-line

Goalkeeper

Goal circle

Defence third

Goal defence

Umpire

Scorer

e-keeper

Scorer

Central circle

Wing attack

Goal third

Goal shooter

Wing defence

Centre

Central third

Goal attack

Transverse line

Goalpost

Side-line

15.2 m
(50 ft)

NETBALL

Rubber or leather covering

22.4 cm
(8¼ in)

NETBALL

Ring

Net

3.05 m
(10 ft)

Goalpost

NETBALL GOALPOST AND NET

NETBALL PASSES

CHEST PASS

UNDERARM PASS

SHOULDER PASS

BOUNCE PASS

HANDBALL COURT

Goal area

Goal

Net

Goal area line

Guide mark

Goal-line

Penalty line

Free-throw line

Players' bench

Side-line

Secretary

Centre line

Court referee

Time-keeper

Left wing

Right wing

Centre back

Centre forward

Left back

Right back

Goalkeeper

Goal-line referee

20m
(65 ft 6in)

HANDBALL

Leather covering

**HANDBALL
MEN'S: 18.8 CM (7½ IN)
WOMEN'S: 17.5 CM (7 IN)**

HANDBALL SHOE

Crossbar

2 m
(6 ft 6 in)

Post

Goal-line

HANDBALL NET

HANDBALL SKILLS

OVERARM PASS

DRIBBLE

BOUNCE PASS

JUMP SHOT

535

Baseball

BASEBALL IS A BALL GAME for two teams of nine players. The batter hits the ball thrown by the opposing team's pitcher, into the area between the foul lines. He then runs round all four fixed bases in order to score a run, touching or "tagging" each base in turn. The pitcher must throw the ball at a height between the batter's armpits and knees, a height which is called the "strike zone". A ball pitched in this area that crosses over the "home plate" is called a "strike" and the batter has three strikes in which to try and hit the ball (otherwise he is "struck out"). The fielding team tries to get the batting team out by catching the ball before it bounces, tagging a player of the batting team with the ball who is running between bases, or by tagging a base before the player has reached it. Members of the batting team may stop safely at a base as long as it is not occupied by another member of their team. When the batter runs to first base, his team-mate at first base must run on to second – this is called "force play". A game consists of nine innings and each team will bat once during an inning. When three members of the batting team are out, the teams swap roles. The team with the greatest number of runs wins the game.

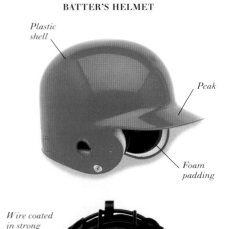

BATTER'S HELMET

Plastic shell

Peak

Foam padding

Wire coated in strong nylon

Plastic-coated foam padding

CATCHER'S MASK

BASEBALL PITCH

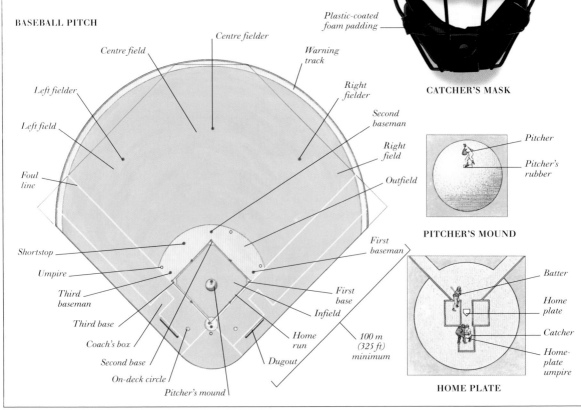

Centre field

Left fielder

Left field

Foul line

Shortstop

Umpire

Third baseman

Third base

Coach's box

Second base

On-deck circle

Pitcher's mound

Centre fielder

Warning track

Right fielder

Second baseman

Right field

Outfield

First baseman

First base

Infield

Home run

Dugout

100 m (325 ft) minimum

Pitcher

Pitcher's rubber

PITCHER'S MOUND

Batter

Home plate

Catcher

Home-plate umpire

HOME PLATE

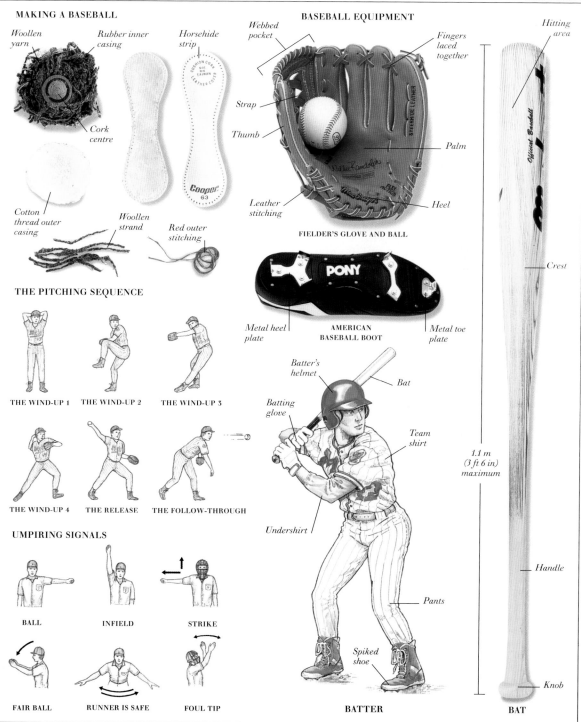

MAKING A BASEBALL

Woollen yarn

Rubber inner casing

Horsehide strip

Cork centre

Cotton thread outer casing

Woollen strand

Red outer stitching

BASEBALL EQUIPMENT

Webbed pocket

Fingers laced together

Strap

Thumb

STEERHIDE LEATHER

Palm

Leather stitching

Heel

FIELDER'S GLOVE AND BALL

PONY

Metal heel plate

AMERICAN BASEBALL BOOT

Metal toe plate

THE PITCHING SEQUENCE

THE WIND-UP 1

THE WIND-UP 2

THE WIND-UP 3

THE WIND-UP 4

THE RELEASE

THE FOLLOW-THROUGH

UMPIRING SIGNALS

BALL

INFIELD

STRIKE

FAIR BALL

RUNNER IS SAFE

FOUL TIP

Batter's helmet

Bat

Batting glove

Team shirt

Undershirt

Pants

Spiked shoe

BATTER

Hitting area

Official Baseball

Crest

1.1 m (3 ft 6 in) maximum

Handle

Knob

BAT

537

Cricket

CRICKET IS A BALL GAME PLAYED by two teams of eleven players on a pitch with two sets of three stumps (wickets). The bowler bowls the ball down the pitch to the batsman of the opposing team, who must defend the wicket in front of which he stands. The object of the game is to score as many runs as possible. Runs can be scored individually by running the length of the playing strip, or by hitting a ball which lands outside the boundary ("six"), or which lands inside the boundary but bounces or rolls outside ("four"); the opposing team will bowl and field, attempting to dismiss the batsmen. A batsman can be dismissed in one of several ways: by the bowler hitting the wicket with the ball ("bowled"); by a fielder catching the ball hit by the batsman before it touches the ground ("caught"); by the wicket-keeper or another fielder breaking the wicket while the batsman is attempting a run and is therefore out of his ground ("stumped" or "run out"); by the batsman breaking the wicket with his own bat or body ("hit wicket"); by a part of the batsman's body being hit by a ball that would otherwise have hit the wicket ("leg before wicket" ["lbw"]). A match consists of one or two innings and each innings ends when the tenth batsman of the batting team is out, when a certain number of overs (a series of six balls bowled) have been played, or when the captain of the batting team "declares" ending the innings voluntarily.

FORWARD DEFENSIVE STROKE

BACKWARD DEFENSIVE STROKE

ON-DRIVE

OFF-DRIVE

PULL

HOOK

SQUARE CUT

LEG GLANCE

POSSIBLE FIELD POSITIONS FOR AN AWAY SWING BOWLER TO A RIGHT-HANDED BATSMAN (IN RED) AND OTHER FIELD POSITIONS

Long on
Long off
Umpire
Bowler
Boundary line
Non-striking batsman
Deep mid-wicket
Extra cover
Mid-on
Mid-off
Silly mid-on
Silly mid-off
Forward short leg
Cover
Square leg
Point
Deep square leg
Gulley
Square-leg umpire
Third man
Batsman
Second slip
Long leg
Bowler
Leg slip
Return crease
Wicket-keeper
First slip
Fine leg
Sight screen

Wicket-keeper
Batsman
Wicket
Bowling crease
CRICKET PITCH
20 m (66 ft)
Bowler
Umpire
Non-striking batsman

CRICKET BALL AND WICKET

Leather skin
Seam
BALL
Bail
WICKET
Stump

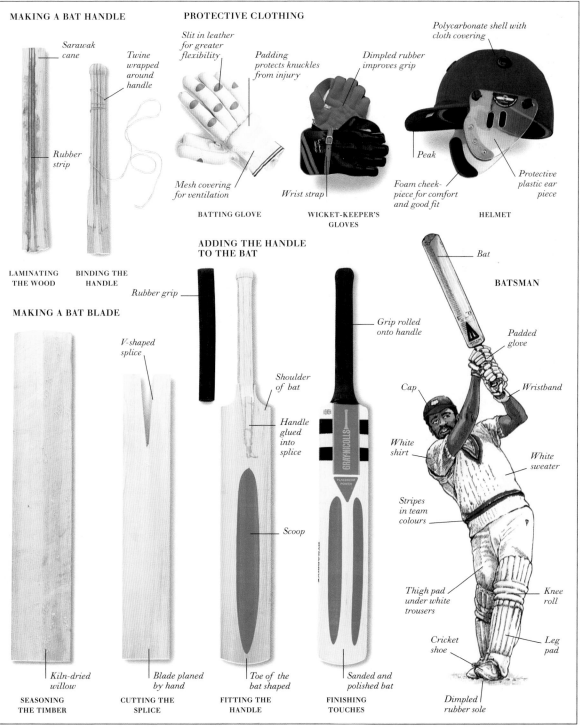

MAKING A BAT HANDLE

Sarawak cane

Twine wrapped around handle

Rubber strip

LAMINATING THE WOOD

BINDING THE HANDLE

PROTECTIVE CLOTHING

Slit in leather for greater flexibility

Padding protects knuckles from injury

Dimpled rubber improves grip

Polycarbonate shell with cloth covering

Peak

Mesh covering for ventilation

Wrist strap

Foam cheek-piece for comfort and good fit

Protective plastic ear piece

BATTING GLOVE

WICKET-KEEPER'S GLOVES

HELMET

ADDING THE HANDLE TO THE BAT

Rubber grip

Grip rolled onto handle

Bat

BATSMAN

MAKING A BAT BLADE

V-shaped splice

Shoulder of bat

Handle glued into splice

Scoop

Padded glove

Cap

Wristband

White shirt

White sweater

Stripes in team colours

Thigh pad under white trousers

Knee roll

Cricket shoe

Leg pad

Dimpled rubber sole

Kiln-dried willow

Blade planed by hand

Toe of the bat shaped

Sanded and polished bat

SEASONING THE TIMBER

CUTTING THE SPLICE

FITTING THE HANDLE

FINISHING TOUCHES

Hockey, lacrosse, and hurling

ALL OVER THE WORLD, TEAM GAMES have evolved which require that a ball be struck or carried, and tossed at the end of a stick. Early forms of these games include hurling, shinty, bandy, and pelota. Hockey is played by men and women: two teams of eleven players try to gain and keep possession of the ball and score goals by using the hockey stick to propel the ball into their opponents' goal net. Skills such as passing, pushing, or hitting the ball by slapping or lifting it in a flicking movement, and shooting at goal are crucial. Hockey is played indoors and outdoors on grass or synthetic pitches. Lacrosse is played internationally as a 12-a-side game for women and as 10-a-side game for men. The women's pitch has no absolute boundaries but the men's pitch has clearly defined side-lines and end-lines. The ball is kept in play by being carried, thrown or batted with the crosse, and rolled or kicked in any direction. In men's and women's lacrosse, play can continue behind the marked goal areas. Similar skills are required in hurling – a Gaelic field game played on the same pitch as Gaelic football (see pp. 528–529), using the same goalposts and net. In hurling, the ball may be struck with or carried on the hurley and, when off the ground, may be struck with the hand or kicked. Goals (three points) are scored when the ball passes between the posts and under the crossbar; one point is scored when it passes between the posts and over the crossbar.

GOALKEEPER'S EQUIPMENT

Air vent

Hard shell

Face mask

HELMET

Strap

Rigid palm

Padded wrist

GAUNTLET

HOCKEY STICK AND BALL

STICK

Handle

Tape

Steam-bent ash head

Blade

Stitched seam

7–7.5 cm
(2¼–3 in)

— 91 cm (3 ft) —

BALL

HOCKEY FIELD

Side-line

Centre forward

Inside right

Right wing

Right half

Right back

Corner flag

Shooting circle

Goal

Penalty spot

Five yard mark

Goal-line

Inside left

Left wing

Umpire

Centre half

Left half

Left back

Goalkeeper

55 m
(180 ft)

Protective overshoe

Padding protects toes against the hard ball

GOALKEEPER'S KICKER

Strap

2.1 m
(7 ft)

HOCKEY GOAL

540

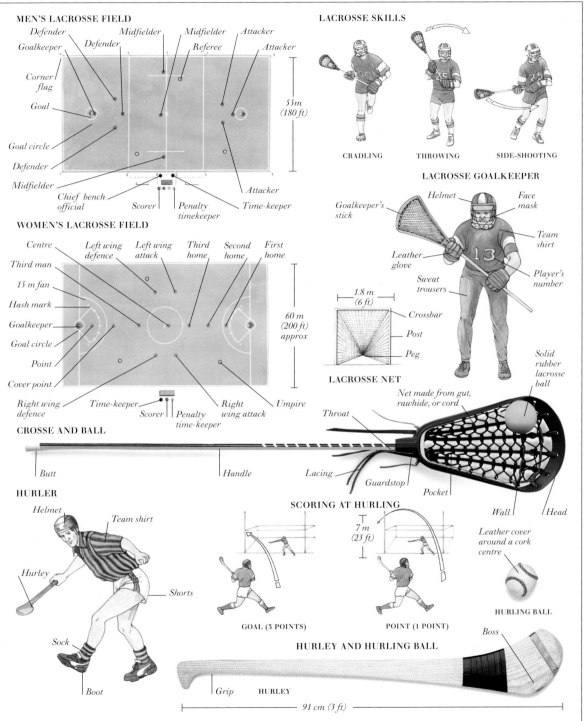

MEN'S LACROSSE FIELD

Defender
Goalkeeper
Midfielder
Midfielder
Referee
Attacker
Attacker
Defender
Corner flag
Goal
Goal circle
Defender
Midfielder
Chief bench official
Scorer
Penalty timekeeper
Attacker
Time-keeper

55 m (180 ft)

WOMEN'S LACROSSE FIELD

Centre
Left wing defence
Left wing attack
Third home
Second home
First home
Third man
15 m fan
Hash mark
Goalkeeper
Goal circle
Point
Cover point
Right wing defence
Time-keeper
Scorer
Penalty time-keeper
Right wing attack
Umpire

60 m (200 ft) approx

CROSSE AND BALL

Butt
Handle

HURLER

Helmet
Team shirt
Hurley
Shorts
Sock
Boot

LACROSSE SKILLS

CRADLING
THROWING
SIDE-SHOOTING

LACROSSE GOALKEEPER

Helmet
Face mask
Goalkeeper's stick
Team shirt
Leather glove
Player's number
Sweat trousers

1.8 m (6 ft)

Crossbar
Post
Peg

LACROSSE NET

Net made from gut, rawhide, or cord
Throat
Lacing
Guardstop
Pocket
Solid rubber lacrosse ball
Wall
Head

SCORING AT HURLING

7 m (23 ft)

GOAL (3 POINTS)
POINT (1 POINT)

Leather cover around a cork centre

HURLING BALL

Boss

HURLEY AND HURLING BALL

Grip
HURLEY
91 cm (3 ft)

Athletics

THE SPORTS that make up athletics are divided into two main groups: track events – which include sprinting, middle, and long distance running, relay running, hurdling, and walking – and field events which require jumping and throwing skills. Contests designed to test the speed, strength, agility, and stamina of athletes were held by the ancient Greeks over 4,000 years ago. However, the abolition of the Olympic Games in 393 AD meant that athletics were neglected until the revival of large-scale competitions in the mid-nineteenth century. Modern stadia offer areas reserved for the long jump, triple jump, and pole vault usually situated outside the running track. The javelin, shot, hammer, and discus are thrown within the track area. Most athletes specialize in one or two events but, in the heptathlon, women compete in seven events, held over two days: 200 m and 800 m races, 100 m hurdles, javelin, shot put, high jump, and long jump. In the decathlon, men compete in ten events over two days: 100 m, 400 m, and 1,500 m races, 110 m hurdles, javelin, discus, shot put, pole vault, high jump, and long jump.

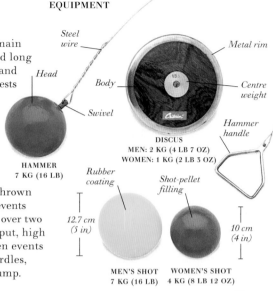

FIELD EVENT EQUIPMENT

Steel wire

Head

Swivel

Body

Metal rim

Centre weight

Hammer handle

DISCUS
MEN: 2 KG (4 LB 7 OZ)
WOMEN: 1 KG (2 LB 3 OZ)

HAMMER
7 KG (16 LB)

Rubber coating

Shot-pellet filling

12.7 cm (5 in)

10 cm (4 in)

MEN'S SHOT
7 KG (16 LB)

WOMEN'S SHOT
4 KG (8 LB 12 OZ)

JAVELIN　　Cord grip　　　Shaft　　　　　　　　　　　　　　　　　　Tip

Men: 2.6 m (8 ft 6 in)
Women: 2.3 m (7 ft 6 in)

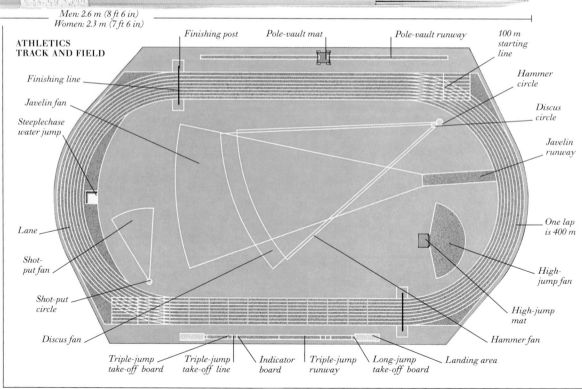

ATHLETICS TRACK AND FIELD

Finishing post
Pole-vault mat
Pole-vault runway
100 m starting line
Finishing line
Hammer circle
Javelin fan
Discus circle
Steeplechase water jump
Javelin runway
Lane
One lap is 400 m
Shot-put fan
High-jump fan
Shot-put circle
High-jump mat
Discus fan
Hammer fan
Triple-jump take-off board
Triple-jump take-off line
Indicator board
Triple-jump runway
Long-jump take-off board
Landing area

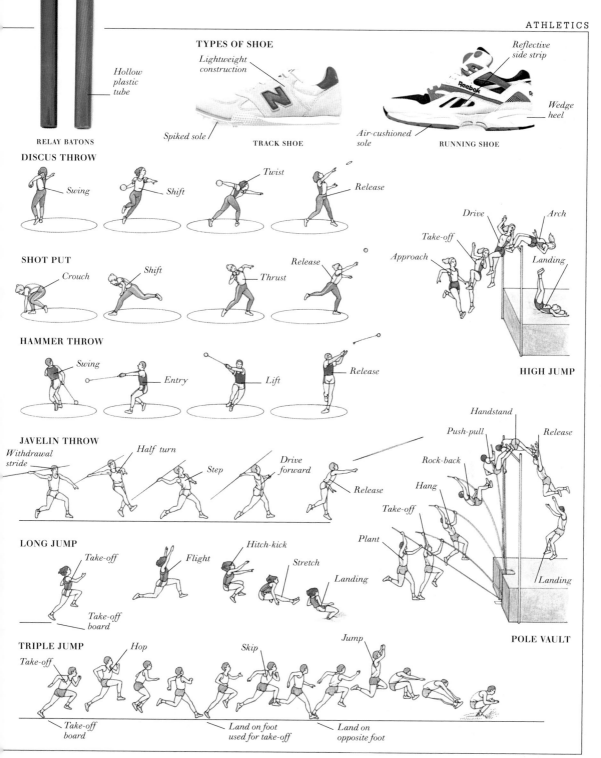

RELAY BATONS

Hollow plastic tube

TYPES OF SHOE

Lightweight construction

Spiked sole

TRACK SHOE

Reflective side strip

Reebok

Wedge heel

Air-cushioned sole

RUNNING SHOE

DISCUS THROW

Swing · Shift · Twist · Release

SHOT PUT

Crouch · Shift · Release · Thrust

HAMMER THROW

Swing · Entry · Lift · Release

JAVELIN THROW

Withdrawal stride · Half turn · Step · Drive forward · Release

LONG JUMP

Take-off · Flight · Hitch-kick · Stretch · Landing

Take-off board

TRIPLE JUMP

Take-off · Hop · Skip · Jump

Take-off board · Land on foot used for take-off · Land on opposite foot

HIGH JUMP

Drive · Arch · Take-off · Approach · Landing

POLE VAULT

Handstand · Push-pull · Release · Rock-back · Hang · Take-off · Plant · Landing

543

Racket sports

PROTECTIVE EYEWEAR

THE OBJECT OF ALL RACKET SPORTS is to make shots the opponent cannot return. Games are played by two players (singles) or four players (doubles). Racket shape and size is tailored to each sport, but all rackets are constructed of wood, plastic, aluminium, or high-performance materials such as fibreglass and carbon graphite. Racket strings are usually synthetic, although natural gut is still used. Tennis is played on a court divided by a low net. Opposing players serve alternate games. At least six games must be won to gain a set, and two or sometimes three sets are needed to win a match. Tennis courts may be concrete, grass, clay, or synthetic, each surface requiring a different style of play. Badminton is an indoor sport that is played with light, flexible rackets and a feather shuttlecock on a court with a high net. Players can score points only on their serve. The first to reach 15 points (11 points for women's singles) wins the game. Two games are needed to win a match. Squash and racketball are both played in enclosed courts. One player hits the ball against the front wall, and the other tries to return it before it bounces on the floor more than once. Squash rackets have smaller, rounder heads and stiffer frames than badminton rackets. In America, the game is played on a narrower court than an international court using a much harder ball. Squash games are played to nine points (international) or 15 points (American). In racketball, players use a ball that is larger and bouncier than a squash ball. The racket is thick and sturdy, with a large head, short handle, and a thong that loops around the wrist. Points can be won only when serving, and the first player to reach 21 points wins.

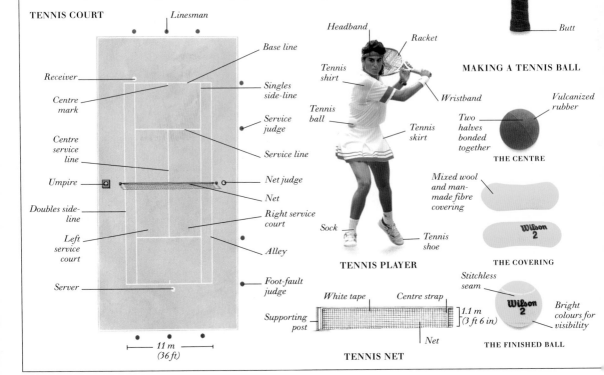

TENNIS RACKET

Synthetic string · *Frame* · *Head* · *Logo* · *Throat* · *Grip* · *Butt*

TENNIS COURT

Linesman · *Base line* · *Receiver* · *Singles side-line* · *Centre mark* · *Service judge* · *Centre service line* · *Service line* · *Umpire* · *Net judge* · *Net* · *Doubles side-line* · *Right service court* · *Left service court* · *Alley* · *Server* · *Foot-fault judge*

11 m (36 ft)

TENNIS PLAYER

Headband · *Racket* · *Tennis shirt* · *Wristband* · *Tennis ball* · *Tennis skirt* · *Sock* · *Tennis shoe*

TENNIS NET

White tape · *Centre strap* · *Supporting post* · *1.1 m (3 ft 6 in)* · *Net*

MAKING A TENNIS BALL

Vulcanized rubber · *Two halves bonded together*

THE CENTRE

Mixed wool and man-made fibre covering

THE COVERING

Wilson 2

Stitchless seam · *Bright colours for visibility*

THE FINISHED BALL

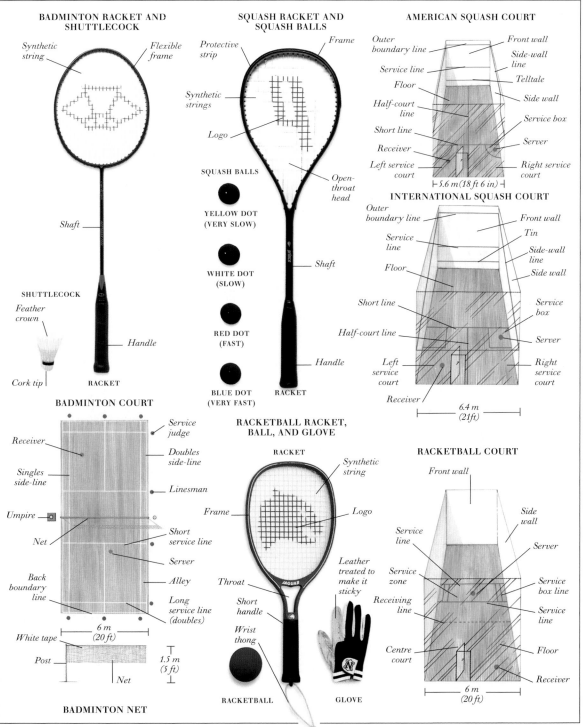

BADMINTON RACKET AND SHUTTLECOCK

Synthetic string

Flexible frame

Shaft

SHUTTLECOCK

Feather crown

Handle

Cork tip

RACKET

SQUASH RACKET AND SQUASH BALLS

Protective strip

Frame

Synthetic strings

Logo

SQUASH BALLS

YELLOW DOT (VERY SLOW)

WHITE DOT (SLOW)

RED DOT (FAST)

BLUE DOT (VERY FAST)

Open-throat head

Shaft

Handle

RACKET

AMERICAN SQUASH COURT

Outer boundary line

Front wall

Service line

Side-wall line

Floor

Telltale

Half-court line

Side wall

Short line

Service box

Receiver

Server

Left service court

Right service court

⊢ 5.6 m (18 ft 6 in) ⊣

INTERNATIONAL SQUASH COURT

Outer boundary line

Front wall

Service line

Tin

Side-wall line

Floor

Side wall

Short line

Service box

Half-court line

Server

Left service court

Right service court

Receiver

6.4 m (21ft)

BADMINTON COURT

Receiver

Service judge

Singles side-line

Doubles side-line

Umpire

Linesman

Net

Short service line

Back boundary line

Server

Alley

Long service line (doubles)

6 m (20 ft)

White tape

Post

1.5 m (5 ft)

Net

BADMINTON NET

RACKETBALL RACKET, BALL, AND GLOVE

RACKET

Synthetic string

Frame

Logo

Leather treated to make it sticky

Throat

Short handle

Wrist thong

JAGUAR

RACKETBALL

GLOVE

RACKETBALL COURT

Front wall

Side wall

Service line

Server

Service zone

Service box line

Receiving line

Service line

Centre court

Floor

Receiver

6 m (20 ft)

Golf

GOLF BALL
AND TEE

THE GAME OF GOLF was first played in Scotland some
400 years ago. Players are required to hit a ball, using
a wooden or iron club, from a smooth level point or "teeing
ground", down the "fairway", and on to a putting green where
the target hole is located. The fairway is a strip of clear land
along which there are natural hazards – such as ponds and streams,
man-made hazards – such as bunkers (sand-pits), and rough (areas
of uncut grass). Championship golf courses have 18 holes. The object
of the game is to hit the ball into each hole in turn, and to complete
the "round" using as few strokes as possible. Players compete
individually or in teams, playing the course together in
groups of two, three, or four. The two basic forms of
competition are match play and stroke play.
In match play, the side winning the majority
of holes over a certain number of rounds
wins the match. In stroke play,
the winner is the player who
finishes a certain number of
rounds having made
the fewest strokes.

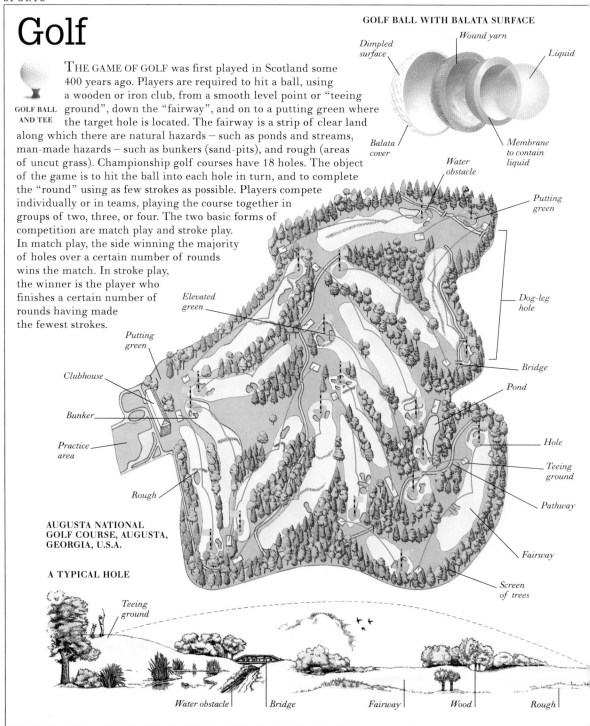

GOLF BALL WITH BALATA SURFACE

Dimpled surface

Wound yarn

Liquid

Balata cover

Membrane to contain liquid

Water obstacle

Putting green

Dog-leg hole

Bridge

Pond

Hole

Teeing ground

Pathway

Fairway

Screen of trees

Elevated green

Putting green

Clubhouse

Bunker

Practice area

Rough

**AUGUSTA NATIONAL
GOLF COURSE, AUGUSTA,
GEORGIA, U.S.A.**

A TYPICAL HOLE

Teeing ground

Water obstacle   *Bridge*   *Fairway*   *Wood*   *Rough*

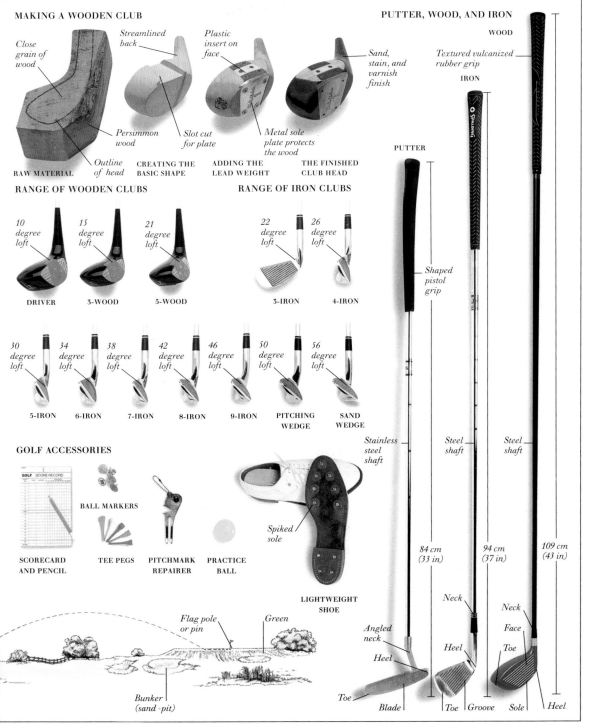

MAKING A WOODEN CLUB

Close grain of wood

Streamlined back

Plastic insert on face

Sand, stain, and varnish finish

Persimmon wood

Slot cut for plate

Metal sole plate protects the wood

Outline of head

RAW MATERIAL

CREATING THE BASIC SHAPE

ADDING THE LEAD WEIGHT

THE FINISHED CLUB HEAD

RANGE OF WOODEN CLUBS

10 degree loft — DRIVER

15 degree loft — 3-WOOD

21 degree loft — 5-WOOD

RANGE OF IRON CLUBS

22 degree loft — 3-IRON

26 degree loft — 4-IRON

30 degree loft — 5-IRON

34 degree loft — 6-IRON

38 degree loft — 7-IRON

42 degree loft — 8-IRON

46 degree loft — 9-IRON

50 degree loft — PITCHING WEDGE

56 degree loft — SAND WEDGE

GOLF ACCESSORIES

SCORECARD AND PENCIL

BALL MARKERS

TEE PEGS

PITCHMARK REPAIRER

PRACTICE BALL

Spiked sole

LIGHTWEIGHT SHOE

Flag pole or pin

Green

Bunker (sand-pit)

PUTTER, WOOD, AND IRON

WOOD

Textured vulcanized rubber grip

IRON

PUTTER

Shaped pistol grip

Stainless steel shaft

Steel shaft

Steel shaft

84 cm (33 in)

94 cm (37 in)

109 cm (43 in)

Neck

Neck

Angled neck

Heel

Heel

Face

Toe

Toe

Blade

Toe

Groove

Sole

Heel

Archery and shooting

TARGET SHOOTING AND ARCHERY EVOLVED as practice for hunting and battle skills. Modern bows, although designed according to the principles of early hunting bows, use laminates, fibreglass, dacron, and carbon, and are equipped with sights and stabilizers. Competitors in target archery shoot over distances of 30 m (100 ft), 50 m (165 ft), 70 m (230 ft), and 90 m (300 ft) for men, and 30 m (100 ft), 50 m (165 ft), 60 m (200 ft), and 70 m (230 ft) for women. The closer the shot is to the centre of the target, the higher the score. The individual scores are added up, and the archer with the highest total wins the competition. Crossbows are used in match competitions over 10 m (33 ft), and 30. m (100 ft). Rifle shooting is divided into three categories: smallbore, bigbore, and air rifle. Contests take place over a variety of distances and further subdivisions are based on the type of shooting position used: prone, kneeling, or standing. The Olympic biathlon combines cross-country skiing and rifle shooting over a course of approximately 20 km (12½ miles). Additional magazines of ammunition are carried in the butt of the rifles. Bigbore rifles fitted with a telescopic sight can be used for hunting and running game target shooting. Pistol shooting events, using rapid-fire pistols, target pistols, and air pistols, take place over 10 m (33 ft), 25 m (82 ft), and 50 m (165 ft) distances. In rapid-fire pistol shooting, a total of 60 shots are fired from a distance of 25 m (83 ft).

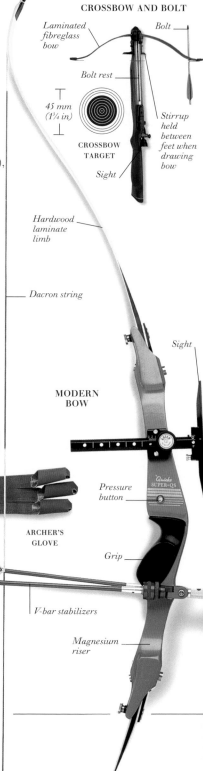

CROSSBOW AND BOLT

Laminated fibreglass bow

Bolt

Bolt rest

45 mm (1¼ in)

CROSSBOW TARGET

Stirrup held between feet when drawing bow

Sight

Hardwood laminate limb

Dacron string

Sight

MODERN BOW

Quicks SUPER-QS

Pressure button

Grip

V-bar stabilizers

Magnesium riser

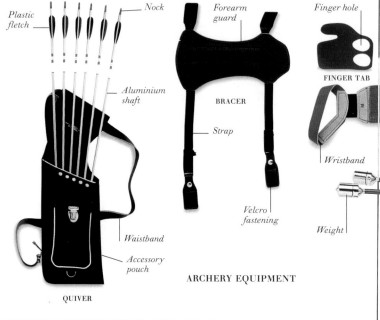

Plastic fletch

Nock

Aluminium shaft

Forearm guard

BRACER

Strap

Velcro fastening

Waistband

Accessory pouch

QUIVER

Finger hole

FINGER TAB

Wristband

ARCHER'S GLOVE

Weight

ARCHERY EQUIPMENT

**SMALLBORE
BIATHLON RIFLE**

Fore sight

*Rifle sight without
magnifying lens*

Barrel

Trigger

*Trigger
guard*

*Extra magazine
stored in rifle butt*

*5.6 mm (0.22 in)
calibre bullet*

Magazine

155 mm
(6 in)

**SMALLBORE
FREE RIFLE
TARGET FOR
50 M (165 FT)
RANGE**

**BIGBORE
HUNTING RIFLE**

Bolt

Telescopic sight

*Bolt
handle*

Open sight

Open sight

1 m
(39 in)

Sling fixing point

*7.62 mm
(0.3 in)
calibre
bullet*

AIR PISTOL

*Cocking
lever and
barrel*

**BIGBORE RIFLE
TARGET FOR
300 M (100° FT)
RANGE**

*Wooden grip
shaped to fit
the hand*

Piston

155 mm
(6 in)

TARGET PISTOL

197 mm
(7¼ in)

Back sight

Fore sight

Hammer

Sight pin

*Firing
pin*

**AIR-PISTOL
TARGET FOR
10 M (33 FT)
RANGE**

*Sight ring
attachment*

Magazine

*9 mm
(0.35 in)
calibre
bullet*

**PISTOL
TARGET FOR
18 M (60 FT)
RANGE**

Trigger

*Air-pistol
pellet*

Nock

FIELD ARROW

Metal tip

Feathering

Wooden shaft

Straw butt

*White inner
2 points*

*Aluminium
longrod stabilizer*

*Blue outer
5 points*

*Yellow inner 10
points (bull's-eye)*

ARCHERY TARGET

Ice hockey

ICE HOCKEY IS PLAYED by two teams of six players on an ice rink, with a goal net at each end. The object of this fast, and often dangerous, game is to hit a frozen rubber puck into the opposing team's net with a ice hockey stick. The game begins when the referee drops the puck between the sticks of two players from opposing teams, who "face off". The rink is divided into three areas: defending, neutral, and attacking zones. Players may move with the puck and pass the puck to one another along the ice, but may not pass it more than two zones across the rink markings. A goal is scored when the puck entirely crosses the goal-line between the posts and under the crossbar of the goal. A team may field up to 20 players although only six players are allowed on the ice at one time; substitutions occur frequently. Each game consists of three periods of 20 minutes, divided by breaks of 15 minutes.

GOALKEEPER

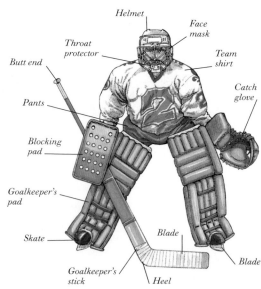

- Helmet
- Face mask
- Throat protector
- Team shirt
- Butt end
- Catch glove
- Pants
- Blocking pad
- Goalkeeper's pad
- Blade
- Skate
- Blade
- Goalkeeper's stick
- Heel

ICE HOCKEY RINK

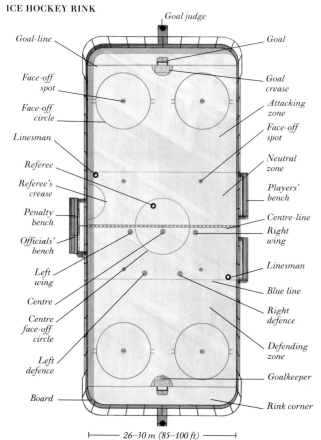

- Goal judge
- Goal-line
- Goal
- Face-off spot
- Goal crease
- Face-off circle
- Attacking zone
- Linesman
- Face-off spot
- Referee
- Neutral zone
- Referee's crease
- Players' bench
- Penalty bench
- Centre-line
- Officials' bench
- Right wing
- Left wing
- Linesman
- Centre
- Blue line
- Centre face-off circle
- Right defence
- Left defence
- Defending zone
- Board
- Goalkeeper
- Rink corner

26–30 m (85–100 ft)

THE FACE-OFF

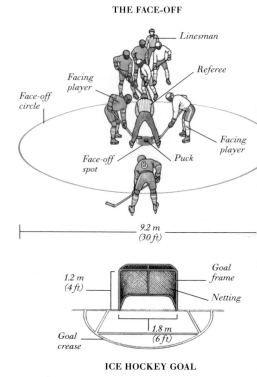

- Linesman
- Facing player
- Referee
- Face-off circle
- Face-off spot
- Facing player
- Puck

9.2 m (30 ft)

- 1.2 m (4 ft)
- Goal frame
- Netting
- Goal crease
- 1.8 m (6 ft)

ICE HOCKEY GOAL

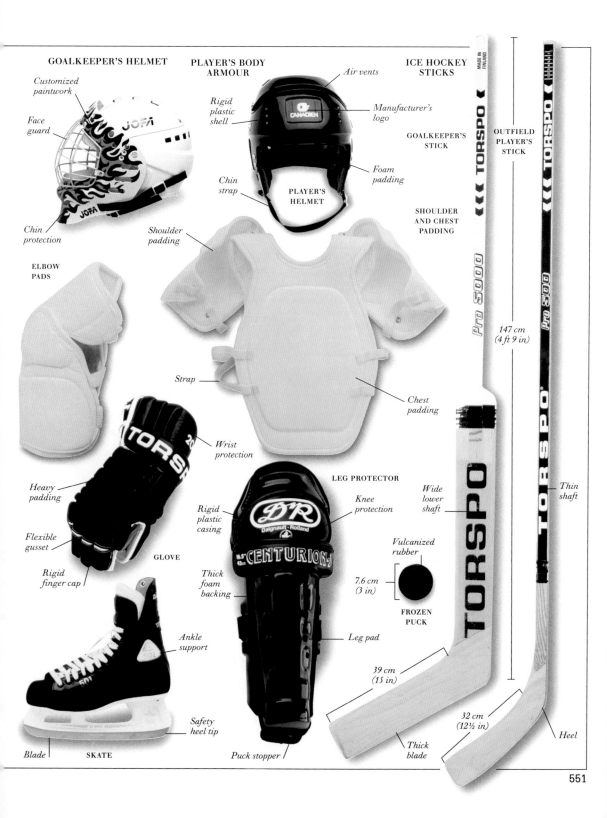

GOALKEEPER'S HELMET

Customized paintwork

Face guard

Chin protection

PLAYER'S BODY ARMOUR

Rigid plastic shell

Air vents

Manufacturer's logo

Chin strap

Foam padding

PLAYER'S HELMET

ICE HOCKEY STICKS

MADE IN FINLAND

GOALKEEPER'S STICK

OUTFIELD PLAYER'S STICK

SHOULDER AND CHEST PADDING

Shoulder padding

ELBOW PADS

Strap

Chest padding

Wrist protection

LEG PROTECTOR

Knee protection

Wide lower shaft

Thin shaft

Heavy padding

Flexible gusset

Rigid finger cap

GLOVE

Rigid plastic casing

CENTURION

Thick foam backing

Vulcanized rubber

7.6 cm (3 in)

FROZEN PUCK

Leg pad

Ankle support

Safety heel tip

Blade   **SKATE**

Puck stopper

39 cm (15 in)

Thick blade

32 cm (12½ in)

Heel

TORSPO Pro 5000

TORSPO Pro 500

TORSPO

147 cm (4 ft 9 in)

Alpine skiing

COMPETITIVE ALPINE SKIING is divided into four disciplines: downhill, slalom, giant slalom, and super-giant slalom (Super-G). Each one tests different skills. In downhill skiing, competitors race down a slope marked out by control flags, known as "gates", and are timed on a single run only. Competitors wear crash helmets, one-piece Lycra suits, and long skis with flattened tips to minimize air resistance. Slalom and giant slalom skiers negotiate a twisting course requiring balance, agility, and quick reactions. Courses are defined by pairs of gates. Racers must pass through each pair of gates to complete the course successfully. Competitors are timed on two runs over different courses, and the skier who completes the courses in the shortest time wins. The equipment and protective guards used by slalom skiers are shown opposite. In Super-G races, competitors ski a single run that combines the technical challenge of slalom with the speed of downhill. The course requires skiers to complete medium-to-long radius turns at high speed, and contain up to two jumps. Clothing is the same as for downhill, but slightly shorter skis are used.

DOWNHILL SKIER

Ski goggles

Helmet

One-piece lycra ski suit

Wrist strap

Ski pole

Basket

Ski boot

Safety binding

Tail

Ski glove

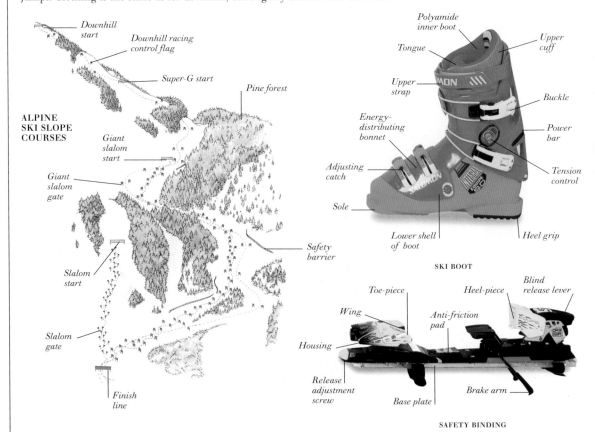

ALPINE SKI SLOPE COURSES

Downhill start

Downhill racing control flag

Super-G start

Pine forest

Giant slalom start

Giant slalom gate

Slalom start

Slalom gate

Safety barrier

Finish line

Polyamide inner boot

Tongue

Upper cuff

Upper strap

Buckle

Energy-distributing bonnet

Power bar

Adjusting catch

Tension control

Sole

Lower shell of boot

Heel grip

SKI BOOT

Toe-piece

Heel-piece

Blind release lever

Wing

Anti-friction pad

Housing

Release adjustment screw

Base plate

Brake arm

SAFETY BINDING

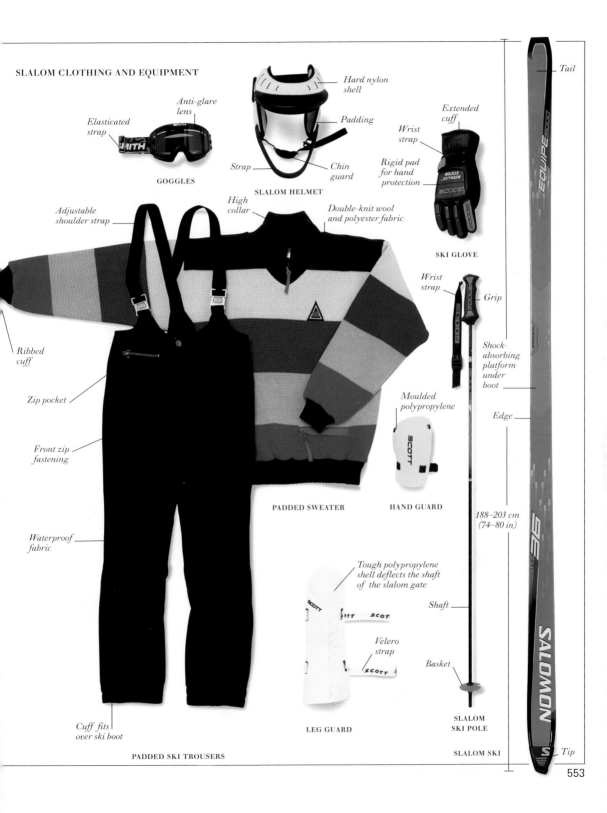

SLALOM CLOTHING AND EQUIPMENT

GOGGLES

Elasticated strap

Anti-glare lens

SLALOM HELMET

Hard nylon shell

Padding

Strap

Chin guard

SKI GLOVE

Extended cuff

Wrist strap

Rigid pad for hand protection

PADDED SWEATER

High collar

Double-knit wool and polyester fabric

Adjustable shoulder strap

Ribbed cuff

HAND GUARD

Moulded polypropylene

SLALOM SKI POLE

Wrist strap

Grip

SLALOM SKI

Tail

Shock-absorbing platform under boot

Edge

188–203 cm (74–80 in)

Shaft

Basket

Tip

PADDED SKI TROUSERS

Zip pocket

Front zip fastening

Waterproof fabric

Cuff fits over ski boot

LEG GUARD

Tough polypropylene shell deflects the shaft of the slalom gate

Velcro strap

553

Equestrian sports

EQUESTRIAN SPORTS HAVE TAKEN place throughout the world for centuries: events involving mounted horses were recorded in the Olympic Games of 642 BC. Showjumping, however, is a much more recent innovation, and the first competitions were held at the beginning of the 1900s. In this sport, horse and rider must negotiate a course of variable, unfixed obstacles, making as few mistakes as possible. Showjumping fences consist of wooden stands, known as standards or wings, that support planks or poles. Parts of the fence are designed to collapse on impact, preventing injury to the horse and rider. Judges penalise competitors for errors, such as knocking down obstacles, refusing jumps, or deviating from the course. Depending on the type of competition, the rider with the fewest faults, most points, or fastest time wins. There are two basic forms of horse racing – flat races and races with jumps, such as steeplechase or hurdle-races. Thoroughbred horses are used in this sport, as they have great strength and stamina and can achieve speeds of up to 65 kph (40 mph). Jockeys wear "silks" – caps and jackets designed in distinctive colours and patterns which help identify the horses. In harness racing, the horse is driven from a light, twowheeled carriage called a sulky. Horses are trained to trot and to pace, and different races are held for each of these types of gait. In pacing races, the horses wear hobbles to prevent them from breaking into a trot or gallop. Breeds such as the Standardbred and the French Trotter have been developed especially for this sport.

SHOWJUMPING SADDLE

High cantle

Deep seat

Pommel

Forward-cut flap

Knee roll

SHOWJUMPING FENCES

Standard

Foot

Plank

UPRIGHT PLANKS

Standard

Foot

Pole

UPRIGHT POLES

Back pole

Standard

Pole

Foot

TRIPLE BAR (STAIRCASE)

Standard

Pole

Foot

HOG'S-BACK

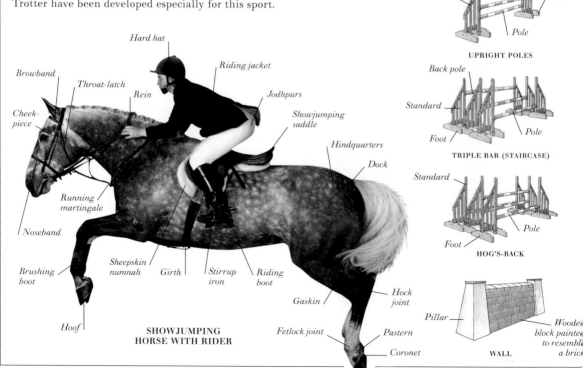

Hard hat

Riding jacket

Browband

Throat-latch

Rein

Jodhpurs

Cheek-piece

Showjumping saddle

Hindquarters

Dock

Running martingale

Noseband

Brushing boot

Sheepskin numnah

Girth

Stirrup iron

Riding boot

Hock joint

Gaskin

Hoof

SHOWJUMPING HORSE WITH RIDER

Fetlock joint

Pastern

Coronet

Pillar

Wooden block painted to resemble a brick

WALL

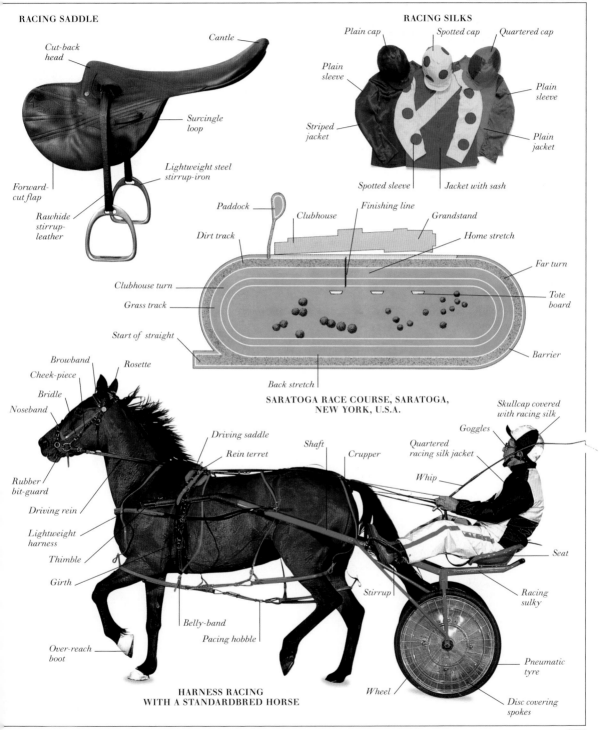

RACING SADDLE

Cantle

Cut-back head

Surcingle loop

Lightweight steel stirrup-iron

Forward-cut flap

Rawhide stirrup-leather

RACING SILKS

Plain cap

Spotted cap

Quartered cap

Plain sleeve

Striped jacket

Plain sleeve

Plain jacket

Spotted sleeve

Jacket with sash

Paddock

Clubhouse

Finishing line

Grandstand

Dirt track

Home stretch

Clubhouse turn

Far turn

Grass track

Tote board

Start of straight

Barrier

Back stretch

SARATOGA RACE COURSE, SARATOGA,
NEW YORK, U.S.A.

Browband

Rosette

Cheek-piece

Bridle

Noseband

Driving saddle

Rein terret

Shaft

Crupper

Skullcap covered with racing silk

Goggles

Quartered racing silk jacket

Whip

Rubber bit-guard

Seat

Driving rein

Lightweight harness

Thimble

Girth

Racing sulky

Stirrup

Belly-band

Pacing hobble

Over-reach boot

Pneumatic tyre

Wheel

HARNESS RACING
WITH A STANDARDBRED HORSE

Disc covering spokes

Judo and fencing

SIDE FOUR QUARTER HOLD

SINGLE WING

BODY DROP

ONE ARM SHOULDER THROW

SHOULDER WHEEL

SWEEPING LOW THROW

STOMACH THROW

KNEE WHEEL

COMBAT SPORTS ARE BASED ON THE SKILLS used in fighting. In these sports, the competitors may be unarmed – as in judo and boxing – or armed – as in fencing and kendo. Judo is a system of unarmed combat developed in the East. Translated from the Japanese the name means "the gentle way". Students learn how to turn an opponent's force to their own advantage. The usual costume is loose white trousers and a jacket, fastened with a cloth belt. The colour of belt indicates the student's level of expertise, from white-belted novices to the expert "black belts". Competitions take place on a mat or "shiaijo", 9 or 10 m (30 or 33 ft) square in size, bounded by "danger" and "safety" areas to prevent injury. Competitors try to throw, pin, or master their opponent by applying pressure to the arm joints or neck. Judo bouts are strictly monitored, and competitors receive points for superior technique, not for injuring their opponent. Fencing is a combat sport using swords, which takes place on a narrow "piste" 14 m (46 ft) long. Competitors try to touch specific target areas on their opponent with their sword or "foil" while avoiding being touched themselves. The winner is the one who scores the greatest number of hits. Fencers wear clothing made from strong white material, which affords maximum protection while allowing freedom of movement, steel mesh masks with padded bibs to protect the fencer's neck, and a long white glove on their sword hand. Fencing foils do not have sharpened blades, and their tips end in a blunt button to prevent injuries. Three types of swords are used – foils, épées, and sabres. Official foil and épée competitions always use an electric scoring system. The sword tips are connected to lights by a long wire that passes underneath each fencer's jacket. A bulb flashes when a hit is made.

JUDO KIT

JUDO MAT

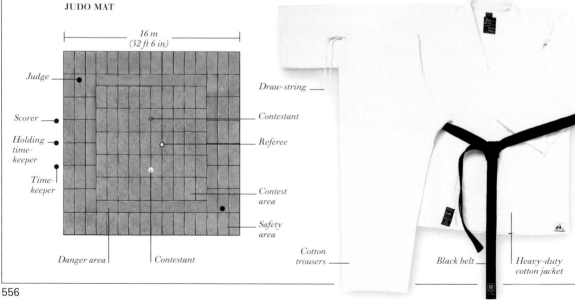

16 m
(52 ft 6 in)

Judge

Scorer

Holding time-keeper

Time-keeper

Danger area

Contestant

Contest area

Safety area

Draw-string

Contestant

Referee

Contest area

Safety area

Cotton trousers

Black belt

Heavy-duty cotton jacket

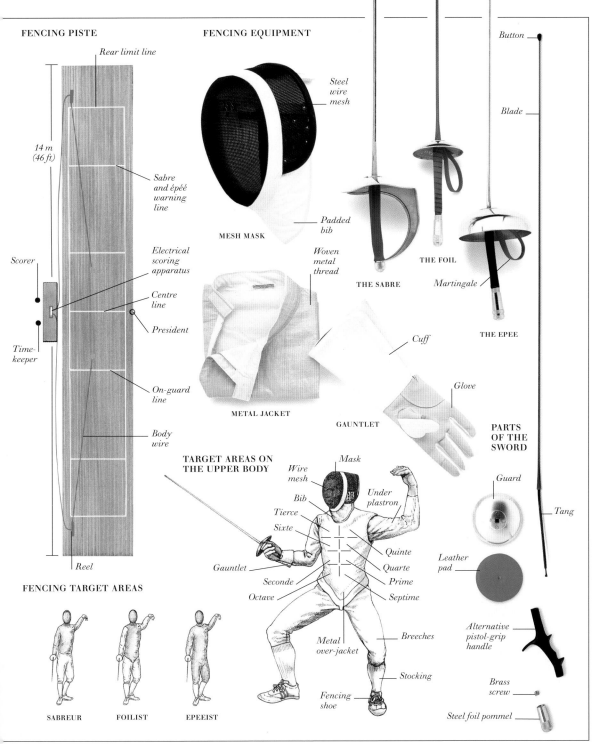

FENCING PISTE

Rear limit line

14 m (46 ft)

Sabre and épéé warning line

Scorer

Electrical scoring apparatus

Centre line

President

Time-keeper

On-guard line

Body wire

Reel

FENCING TARGET AREAS

SABREUR

FOILIST

EPEEIST

FENCING EQUIPMENT

Steel wire mesh

Padded bib

MESH MASK

Woven metal thread

METAL JACKET

Cuff

GAUNTLET

Glove

THE SABRE

THE FOIL

Martingale

THE EPEE

Button

Blade

PARTS OF THE SWORD

Guard

Tang

Leather pad

Alternative pistol-grip handle

Brass screw

Steel foil pommel

TARGET AREAS ON THE UPPER BODY

Mask

Wire mesh

Bib

Under plastron

Tierce

Sixte

Quinte

Gauntlet

Quarte

Seconde

Prime

Octave

Septime

Metal over-jacket

Breeches

Stocking

Fencing shoe

557

Swimming and diving

SWIMMING GOGGLES

SWIMMING WAS INCLUDED in the first modern Olympic Games in 1896 and diving events were added in 1904. Swimming is both an individual and a team sport and races take place over a predetermined distance in one of the four major categories of stroke – freestyle (usually front crawl), butterfly, breaststroke, and backstroke. Competition pools are clearly marked for racing and anti-turbulence lane lines are used to separate the swimmers and help keep the water calm. The first team or individual to finish the race is the winner. Competitive diving is divided into men's and women's springboard and platform (highboard) events. There are six official groups of dives: forward dives, backward dives, armstand dives, twist dives, reverse dives, and inward dives. Competitors perform a set number of dives and after each one a panel of judges awards marks according to the quality of execution and the degree of difficulty.

STYLES OF DIVES

Starting position

Hands above head

Legs fully stretched

Flight

Arched back

Toes pointed

Entry

Feet together

Hands close together

FORWARD DIVE

BACKWARD DIVE

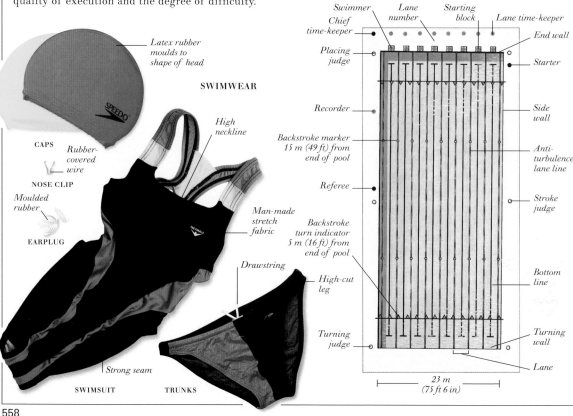

SWIMWEAR

Latex rubber moulds to shape of head

CAPS

Rubber-covered wire

NOSE CLIP

Moulded rubber

EARPLUG

High neckline

Man-made stretch fabric

Drawstring

High-cut leg

Strong seam

SWIMSUIT

TRUNKS

SWIMMING POOL

Swimmer

Lane number

Starting block

Lane time-keeper

Chief time-keeper

End wall

Placing judge

Starter

Recorder

Side wall

Backstroke marker 15 m (49 ft) from end of pool

Anti-turbulence lane line

Referee

Stroke judge

Backstroke turn indicator 5 m (16 ft) from end of pool

Bottom line

Turning judge

Turning wall

Lane

23 m (75 ft 6 in)

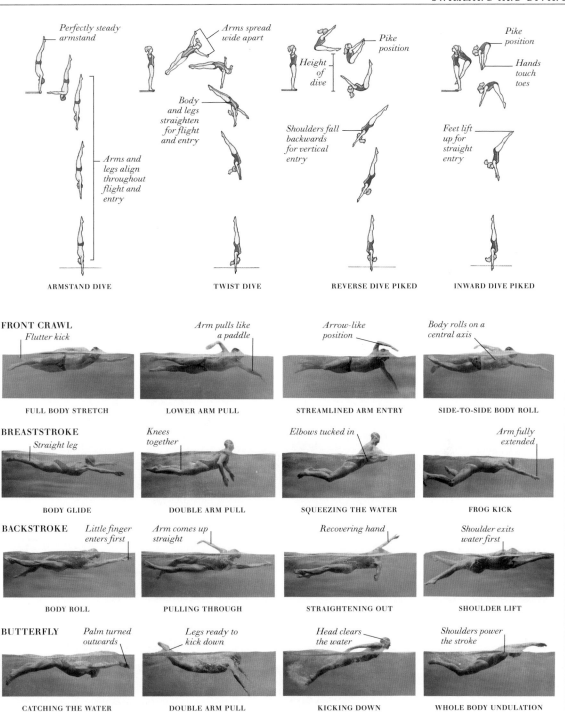

Perfectly steady armstand

Arms and legs align throughout flight and entry

ARMSTAND DIVE

Arms spread wide apart

Body and legs straighten for flight and entry

TWIST DIVE

Pike position

Height of dive

Shoulders fall backwards for vertical entry

REVERSE DIVE PIKED

Pike position

Hands touch toes

Feet lift up for straight entry

INWARD DIVE PIKED

FRONT CRAWL
Flutter kick

FULL BODY STRETCH

Arm pulls like a paddle

LOWER ARM PULL

Arrow-like position

STREAMLINED ARM ENTRY

Body rolls on a central axis

SIDE-TO-SIDE BODY ROLL

BREASTSTROKE
Straight leg

BODY GLIDE

Knees together

DOUBLE ARM PULL

Elbows tucked in

SQUEEZING THE WATER

Arm fully extended

FROG KICK

BACKSTROKE
Little finger enters first

BODY ROLL

Arm comes up straight

PULLING THROUGH

Recovering hand

STRAIGHTENING OUT

Shoulder exits water first

SHOULDER LIFT

BUTTERFLY
Palm turned outwards

CATCHING THE WATER

Legs ready to kick down

DOUBLE ARM PULL

Head clears the water

KICKING DOWN

Shoulders power the stroke

WHOLE BODY UNDULATION

Canoeing, rowing, and sailing

WATERBORNE SPORTS are as varied as the crafts used. There are two disciplines in rowing; sweep rowing, in which each rower has one oar and sculling, in which rowers use two oars. There are a number of different Olympic and competitive rowing events for both men and women. The number of rowers and weight classes vary. Some rowing events use a coxswain; a steersman who does not row but directs the crew. Kayaks and canoes are used in straight sprint and slalom races. Slalom races take place over a course consisting of 20 to 25 gates, including at least six upstream gates. In yacht racing, competitors must complete prescribed courses, organized by the race committees, in the shortest possible time, using sail power only. Olympic events include classes for keel boats, dinghies, and catamarans.

SAILING GEAR

Sleeveless long johns

Buoyancy aid

Long-sleeved jacket

Neoprene material

Belt

GLOVE

Bootlace

Ribbed top

Non-slip sole

BOOT

ONE-PERSON KAYAK AND PADDLE

Blade

Rim

Shaft

Nose cone

Right rail

Cockpit

Back strap

Stern

High density polythene

Toggle

Bow

Left rail

Seat

Cockpit rim

SINGLE SCULL AND OARS (WITH CLOTH DECKING REMOVED)

Adjusting screw

Gate clamp

Gate

Neck

Shaft

Stroke-side oar

Spoon

Blade

Colours

Rigger

Grip

Bow-side oar

Button

Loom

Sycamore beam

Stretcher

Water shoot

Aft shoulder

Shoe

Keel

Spruce beam

Diagonal frame

Aluminium beam

Bung

Sternpost

Kelson (keelson)

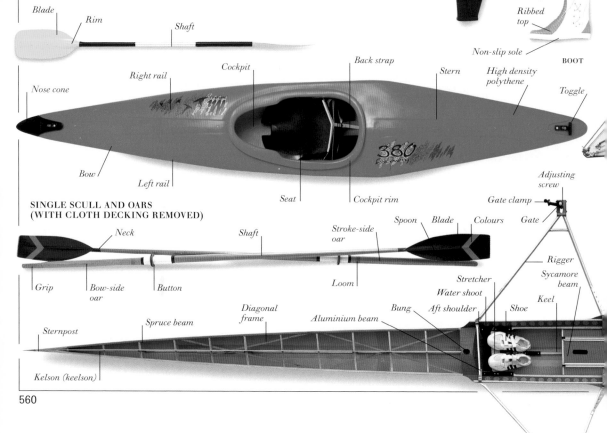

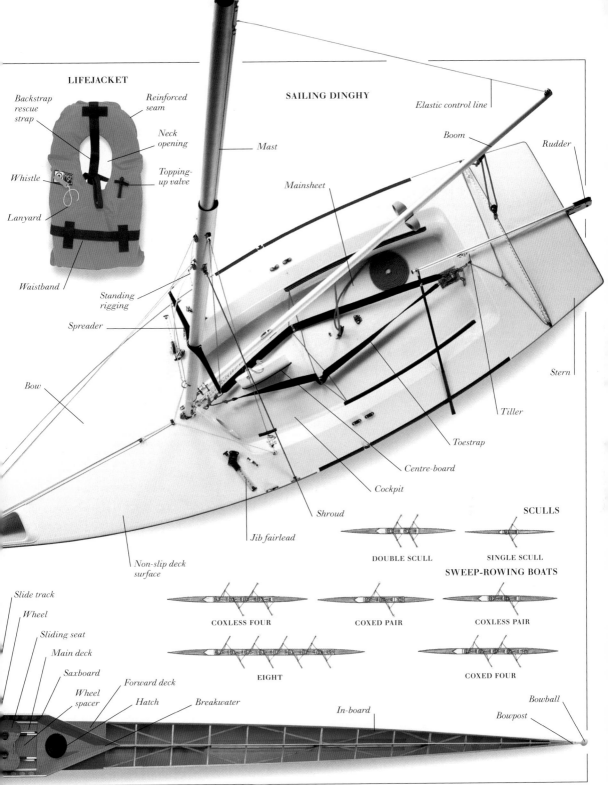

LIFEJACKET

Backstrap rescue strap

Reinforced seam

Neck opening

Whistle

Topping-up valve

Lanyard

Waistband

Standing rigging

Spreader

Bow

Non-slip deck surface

SAILING DINGHY

Elastic control line

Boom

Rudder

Mast

Mainsheet

Stern

Tiller

Toestrap

Centre-board

Cockpit

Shroud

Jib fairlead

SCULLS

DOUBLE SCULL

SINGLE SCULL

SWEEP-ROWING BOATS

COXLESS FOUR

COXED PAIR

COXLESS PAIR

EIGHT

COXED FOUR

Slide track

Wheel

Sliding seat

Main deck

Saxboard

Wheel spacer

Forward deck

Hatch

Breakwater

In-board

Bowball

Bowpost

Angling

ANGLING MEANS FISHING WITH A ROD, reel, line, and lure. There are several different types of angling: freshwater coarse angling, for members of the carp family and pike; freshwater game angling, for salmon and trout; and sea angling, for sea fish such as flatfish, bass, and mackerel. Anglers use a variety of methods of catching fish. These include bait fishing, in which bait (food to allure the fish) is placed on a hook and cast into the water; fly fishing, in which a natural or artificial fly is used to lure the fish; and spinning, in which a lure that looks like a small fish revolves as it is pulled through the water. The angler uses the rod, reel, and line to cast the lure over the water. The reel controls the line as it spills off the spool and as it is wound back. Weights may be fixed to the line so that it will sink. Swivels are attached to prevent the line from twisting. When a fish bites, the hook must become embedded in its mouth and remain there while the catch is reeled in.

Keeper ring

Drag spindle

Disk drag

Handgrip

Drag washer

Disk spring

Gear retainer

Dual click gear

Retaining screw

Check pawl cover

Check pawl

Check slide

Check spring

REELS

Spool-release button

Reel foot (reel scoop)

Plate-nut

Click mechanism

Mechanical brake

Side plate

Centrifugal brake

Spool

Handle

Star drag

Level-wind system

MULTIPLIER REEL

Reel foot (reel scoop)

Unskirted spool

Handle

Line

Tension nut (drag adjustment)

Ratchet (anti-reverse device)

Handgrip

Reel

Bail arm

FIXED-SPOOL REEL

HOOKS, SWIVELS, AND WEIGHTS

Eye

Shank

Gape

ANATOMY OF A HOOK

Bend

Throat

Point

Barb

TREBLE HOOK

ABERDEEN HOOK

REVERSED BEND HOOK

EXAMPLES OF BARREL SWIVELS

HILLMAN ANTI-KINK WEIGHT

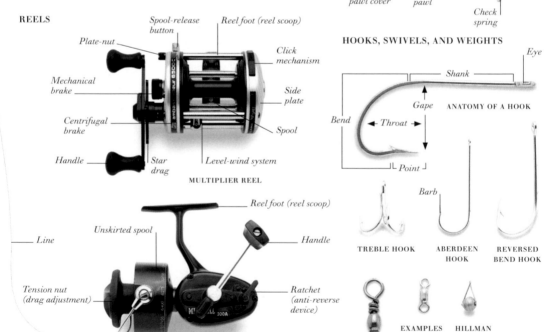

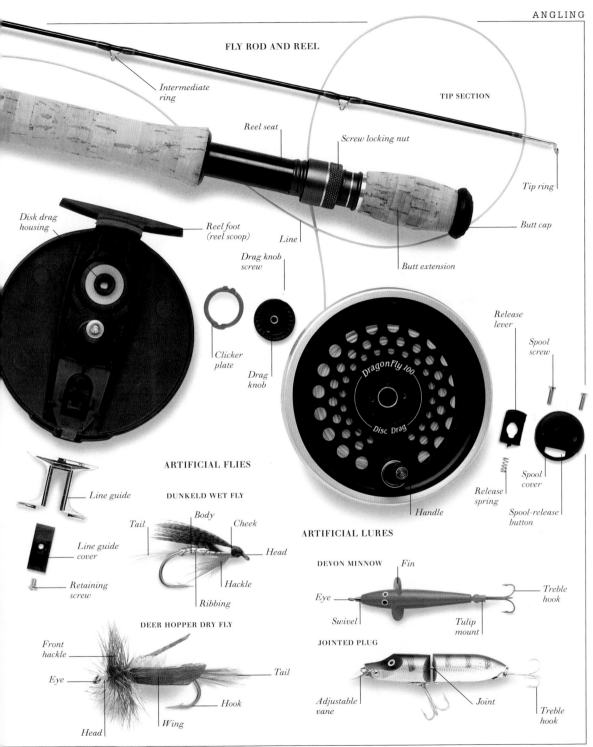

FLY ROD AND REEL

Intermediate ring

TIP SECTION

Reel seat

Screw locking nut

Tip ring

Disk drag housing

Reel foot (reel scoop)

Line

Butt cap

Drag knob screw

Butt extension

Release lever

Spool screw

DragonFly 100

Disc Drag

ARTIFICIAL FLIES

Clicker plate

Drag knob

Line guide

DUNKELD WET FLY

Release spring

Spool cover

Handle

Spool-release button

Line guide cover

Tail

Body

Cheek

Head

Hackle

Ribbing

ARTIFICIAL LURES

Retaining screw

DEER HOPPER DRY FLY

DEVON MINNOW   Fin

Eye

Swivel

Treble hook

Tulip mount

Front hackle

Eye

Tail

JOINTED PLUG

Hook

Adjustable vane

Joint

Head

Wing

Treble hook

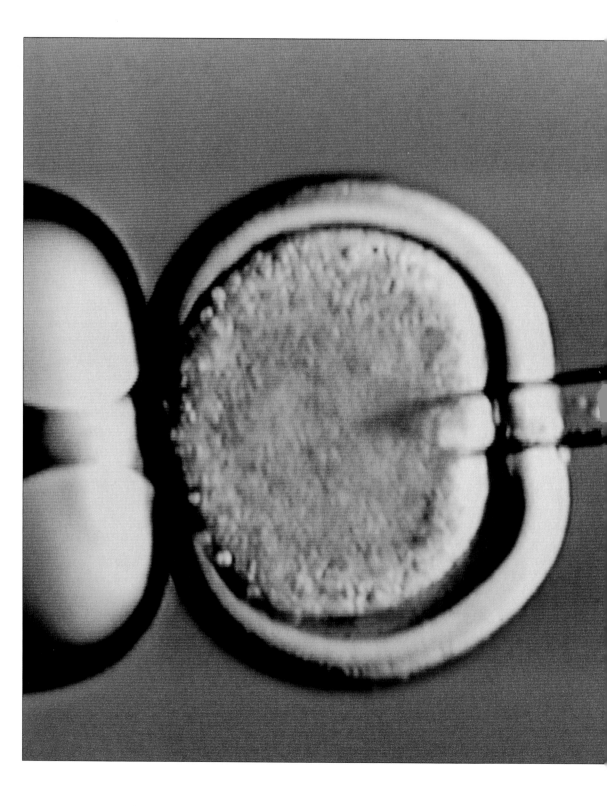

THE MODERN WORLD

Personal computer

PERSONAL COMPUTERS (PCs) fall into two main types: IBM-compatible PCs, known simply as PCs, and Apple Macintosh PCs, known as "Macs". They differ in the way files and programs, and the user's access to them, are organized, and programs must be tailored for each type. However, in most other respects PCs and Macs have much in common. Both contain microchips, or integrated circuits, that store and process data. The "brain" of any PC is a chip known as the central processing unit (CPU), which performs mathematical operations in order to run program instructions and receive, store, and output data. The most powerful personal computer CPUs today can perform more than a billion calculations a second. Data can be input via CDs, USB memory sticks, and other storage media. Highly portable laptop and network PCs are also in widespread use. Most PCs are able to communicate with many other devices, including digital cameras (see pp. 580-81) and smartphones (see pp. 588-89).

LED-backlit glossy wide-screen

Keyboard

Mouse

iMAC

USB ports (4)

Audio in jack

Headphone jack

Firewire 800 port

Ethernet port

Mini display port

Powercord connector

REAR OF iMAC

Webcam

LCD display

Keyboard

Touchpad

Fingerprint reader

Left touchpad button

Right touchpad button

Headphone jacks (2)

Audio in jack

HP PAVILION DV4 LAPTOP

Optical drive

Power connector

USB ports (2)

Expansion port

Remote control

Display

Digital media slot

Security cable slot

RG-45 (network) port

HDMI port

eSATA/ USB port

External monitor port

SIDE VIEW OF HP PAVILION DV4 LAPTOP

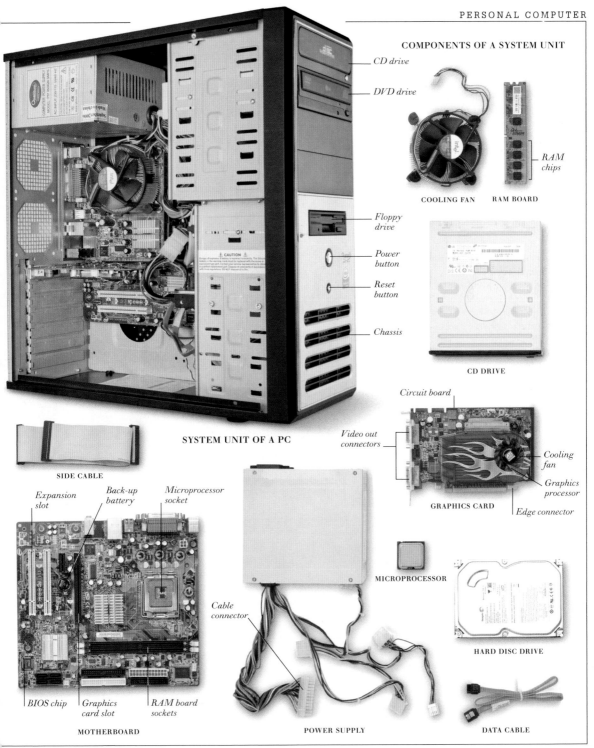

COMPONENTS OF A SYSTEM UNIT

CD drive

DVD drive

RAM chips

COOLING FAN   RAM BOARD

Floppy drive

Power button

Reset button

Chassis

CD DRIVE

SYSTEM UNIT OF A PC

Circuit board

Video out connectors

Cooling fan

Graphics processor

SIDE CABLE

GRAPHICS CARD

Edge connector

Expansion slot

Back-up battery

Microprocessor socket

MICROPROCESSOR

Cable connector

HARD DISC DRIVE

BIOS chip

Graphics card slot

RAM board sockets

MOTHERBOARD

POWER SUPPLY

DATA CABLE

567

Tablet computer

Sleep/wake button

BY THE EARLY 1990s electronic circuitry had been miniaturized to such an extent that it was possible to make small handheld computing devices. The first of these was the Personal Digital Assistant (PDA), which offered features including an address book, calendar, and notepad. In recent years, PDAs have been overtaken by smartphones with Internet and email access (see pp. 588–589). A related product is the e-book reader, which stores books in digital form and uses "electronic paper" to mimic the appearance of ink on real paper. An e-book reader no bigger than a thin paperback can store several thousand digital books in its memory. The most recent handheld computing device is the tablet computer. This looks like a thin flat display, but it is actually a complete computer. Tablet computers are typically controlled by a touch-sensitive screen and have a wireless link to other computers and the Internet. They run software applications, or apps, downloaded from the Internet. The most popular tablet computer currently is the Apple iPad. It has a multi-touch interface that enables its screen to detect the movements of fingertips. As well as selecting options and apps by touching the screen, images can be enlarged or shrunk by moving fingertips apart or together on the screen.

APPLE IPAD | *Home button* | *App icon*

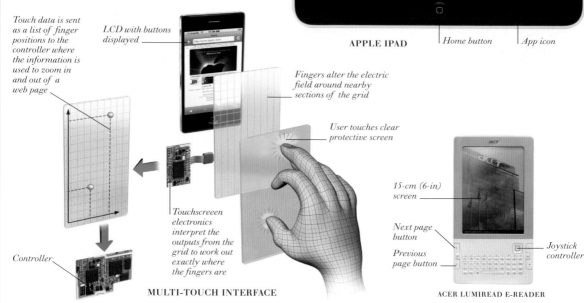

Touch data is sent as a list of finger positions to the controller where the information is used to zoom in and out of a web page

LCD with buttons displayed

Fingers alter the electric field around nearby sections of the grid

User touches clear protective screen

Controller

Touchscreeen electronics interpret the outputs from the grid to work out exactly where the fingers are

MULTI-TOUCH INTERFACE

15-cm (6-in) screen

Next page button

Previous page button

Joystick controller

ACER LUMIREAD E-READER

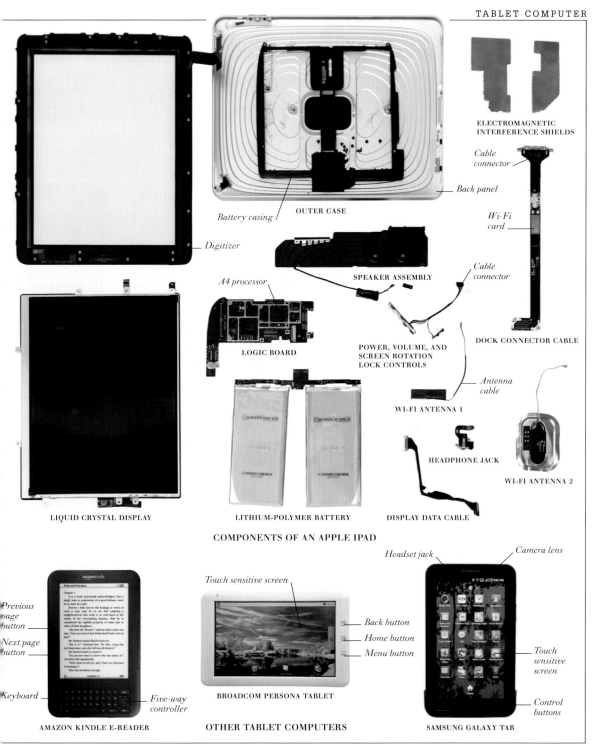

ELECTROMAGNETIC
INTERFERENCE SHIELDS

Cable connector

Back panel

Wi-Fi card

Battery casing

OUTER CASE

Digitizer

A4 processor

Cable connector

SPEAKER ASSEMBLY

DOCK CONNECTOR CABLE

LOGIC BOARD

POWER, VOLUME, AND
SCREEN ROTATION
LOCK CONTROLS

Antenna cable

WI-FI ANTENNA 1

HEADPHONE JACK

WI-FI ANTENNA 2

LIQUID CRYSTAL DISPLAY

LITHIUM-POLYMER BATTERY

DISPLAY DATA CABLE

COMPONENTS OF AN APPLE IPAD

Headset jack

Camera lens

Touch sensitive screen

Previous
page
button

Next page
button

Back button

Home button

Menu button

Touch
sensitive
screen

Keyboard

Five-way
controller

BROADCOM PERSONA TABLET

Control
buttons

AMAZON KINDLE E-READER

OTHER TABLET COMPUTERS

SAMSUNG GALAXY TAB

Flatbed scanner

SCANNERS CONVERT physical images into electronic form, allowing them to be sent over the Internet, displayed on a website, stored on a computer, and manipulated using specialized software. Scanners work by detecting and analysing light reflected from an opaque image, such as a photographic print. Some can also scan photographic transparencies by analysing light that has passed through the image. Flatbed scanners contain a unit, called the scan head, that contains a lamp, mirrors, a lens, and an array of CCDs (Charge-Coupled Devices). The carriage passes beneath the image; the lamp shines light on to or through the original; the mirrors reflect the light on to the lens, which focuses it on to the CCD array. Each CCD detects the brightness of light from a particular pixel (picture element) along a· horizontal strip and converts this data into an electric signal. For colour images, the light is usually passed through red, green, and blue filters and then directed to the CCD array so that it can be broken down into its component colours. This information is then converted to digital form. The quality of the image depends on its resolution, measured in dpi (Dots Per Inch).

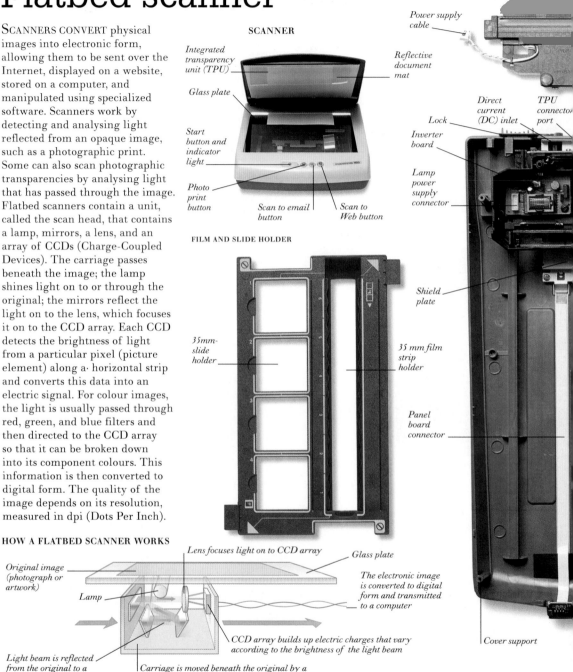

SCANNER

Integrated transparency unit (TPU)

Glass plate

Start button and indicator light

Photo print button

Scan to email button

Scan to Web button

Reflective document mat

Power supply cable

Direct current (DC) inlet

TPU connector port

Lock

Inverter board

Lamp power supply connector

Shield plate

Panel board connector

Cover support

FILM AND SLIDE HOLDER

35mm-slide holder

35 mm film strip holder

HOW A FLATBED SCANNER WORKS

Original image (photograph or artwork)

Lamp

Lens focuses light on to CCD array

Glass plate

The electronic image is converted to digital form and transmitted to a computer

CCD array builds up electric charges that vary according to the brightness of the light beam

Light beam is reflected from the original to a series of mirrors

Carriage is moved beneath the original by a stepper motor in a rapid series of tiny steps

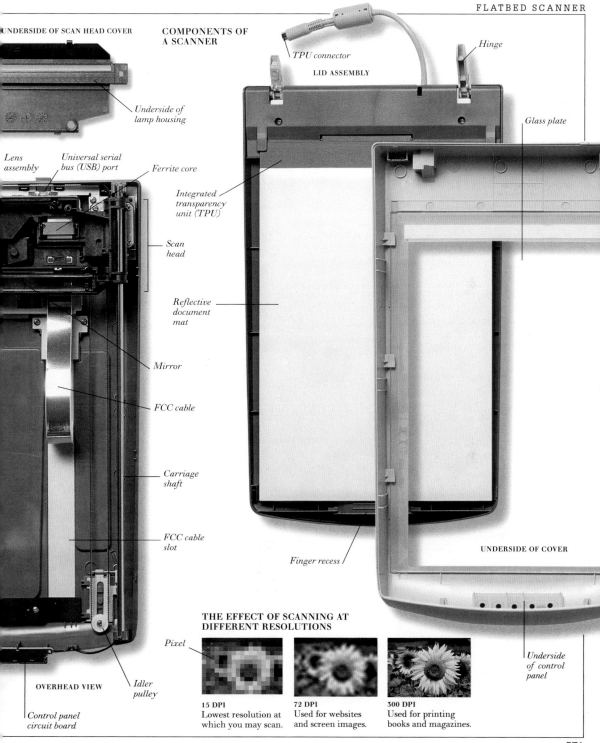

UNDERSIDE OF SCAN HEAD COVER

COMPONENTS OF
A SCANNER

*Underside of
lamp housing*

TPU connector

LID ASSEMBLY

Hinge

Glass plate

*Lens
assembly*

*Universal serial
bus (USB) port*

Ferrite core

*Integrated
transparency
unit (TPU)*

*Scan
head*

*Reflective
document
mat*

Mirror

FCC cable

*Carriage
shaft*

*FCC cable
slot*

UNDERSIDE OF COVER

Finger recess

*Underside
of control
panel*

OVERHEAD VIEW

*Idler
pulley*

*Control panel
circuit board*

**THE EFFECT OF SCANNING AT
DIFFERENT RESOLUTIONS**

Pixel

15 DPI
Lowest resolution at
which you may scan.

72 DPI
Used for websites
and screen images.

300 DPI
Used for printing
books and magazines.

Airbus 380

CROSS-SECTION OF FUSELAGE

THE AIRBUS A380 WAS CONCEIVED in the early 1990s to compete with, and if possible replace, the Boeing 747. Work began in earnest on what was then called the A3XX in 1994. Its maiden flight was in April 2005. The A380's shape is subtly moulded to minimize drag from its ovoid fuselage. The structure makes extensive use of composite materials, such as thermoplastics and GLARE (aluminium and glass fibre). Its engines are very powerful, but also very efficient. It is claimed that when carrying 550 passengers, the A380 uses only 2.9 litres (¾ gallon) of fuel per passenger per 100km (60 miles).

INTERIOR VIEW OF BUSINESS CLASS CABIN

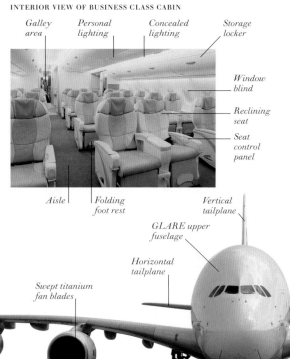

Galley area

Personal lighting

Concealed lighting

Storage locker

Window blind

Reclining seat

Seat control panel

Aisle

Folding foot rest

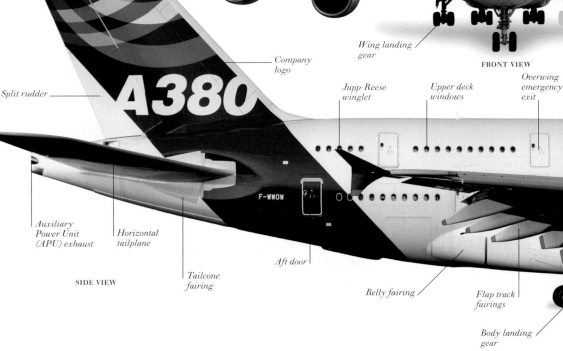

Vertical tailplane

GLARE upper fuselage

Horizontal tailplane

Obstruction light

Swept titanium fan blades

Wing landing gear

FRONT VIEW

Company logo

Jupp-Reese winglet

Upper deck windows

Overwing emergency exit

Split rudder

A380

F-WWOW

Auxiliary Power Unit (APU) exhaust

Horizontal tailplane

Aft door

Belly fairing

Flap track fairings

Body landing gear

SIDE VIEW

Tailcone fairing

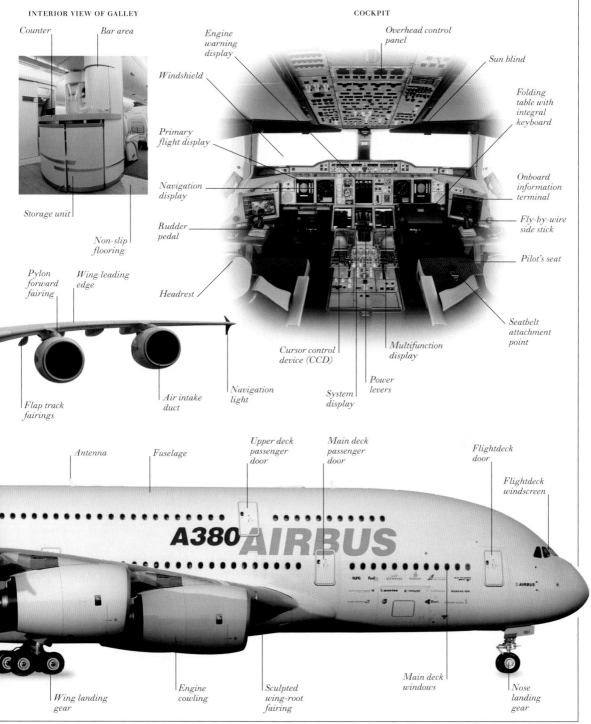

INTERIOR VIEW OF GALLEY

Counter

Bar area

Storage unit

Non-slip
flooring

COCKPIT

Engine
warning
display

Overhead control
panel

Sun blind

Windshield

Folding
table with
integral
keyboard

Primary
flight display

Navigation
display

Onboard
information
terminal

Fly-by-wire
side stick

Rudder
pedal

Pilot's seat

Headrest

Seatbelt
attachment
point

Cursor control
device (CCD)

Multifunction
display

Power
levers

System
display

Navigation
light

Pylon
forward
fairing

Wing leading
edge

Flap track
fairings

Air intake
duct

Antenna

Fuselage

Upper deck
passenger
door

Main deck
passenger
door

Flightdeck
door

Flightdeck
windscreen

A380 AIRBUS

Wing landing
gear

Engine
cowling

Sculpted
wing-root
fairing

Main deck
windows

Nose
landing
gear

Inkjet printer

INKJET PRINTERS EXPEL ink droplets from hundreds of tiny jets, or nozzles, on to a medium, such as paper, to print an image. Each droplet corresponds to a single pixel (picture element). Black-and-white printers use only black ink, while colour printers overprint combinations of the printing colours (cyan, yellow, magenta, and black) to create a full colour range. The printhead containing the nozzles moves sideways across the paper, creating a line of pixels, before the paper moves slightly forward so the next line can be printed. Two basic methods are used to eject ink: thermal, in which ink is heated to form an expanding bubble that expels a droplet from the nozzle, and piezoelectric, in which an electric current expands a crystal causing it to push out the ink droplet. The printer shown here can print digital photographs directly from a memory card.

EPSON STYLUS PHOTO 895 COLOUR INKJET PRINTER

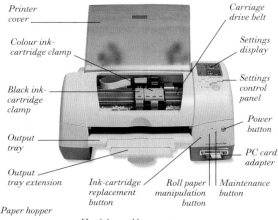

Printer cover

Colour ink-cartridge clamp

Black ink-cartridge clamp

Output tray

Output tray extension

Carriage drive belt

Settings display

Settings control panel

Power button

PC card adapter

Ink-cartridge replacement button

Roll paper manipulation button

Maintenance button

Paper hopper

OVERHEAD VIEW WITH OUTER CASING REMOVED

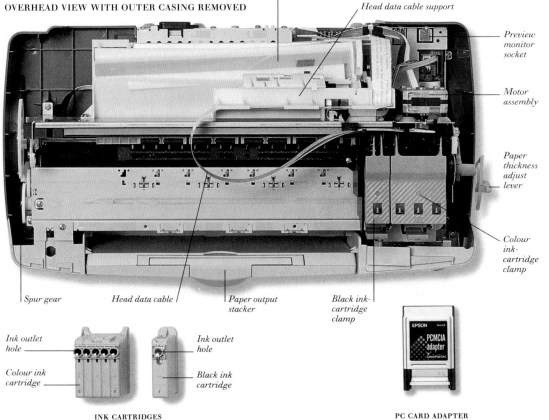

Head data cable support

Preview monitor socket

Motor assembly

Paper thickness adjust lever

Colour ink-cartridge clamp

Spur gear

Head data cable

Paper output stacker

Black ink-cartridge clamp

Ink outlet hole

Colour ink cartridge

Ink outlet hole

Black ink cartridge

INK CARTRIDGES

PC CARD ADAPTER

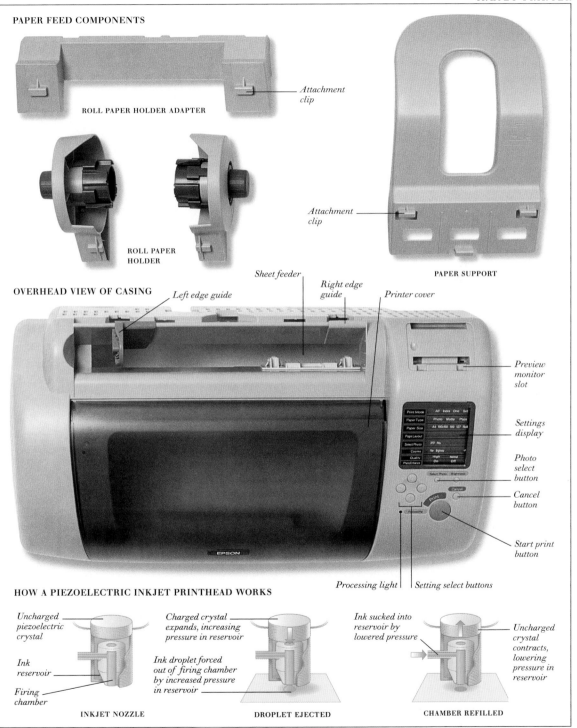

PAPER FEED COMPONENTS

Attachment clip

ROLL PAPER HOLDER ADAPTER

ROLL PAPER HOLDER

Attachment clip

PAPER SUPPORT

OVERHEAD VIEW OF CASING

Sheet feeder

Left edge guide

Right edge guide

Printer cover

Preview monitor slot

Settings display

Photo select button

Cancel button

Start print button

Processing light *Setting select buttons*

EPSON

HOW A PIEZOELECTRIC INKJET PRINTHEAD WORKS

Uncharged piezoelectric crystal

Ink reservoir

Firing chamber

INKJET NOZZLE

Charged crystal expands, increasing pressure in reservoir

Ink droplet forced out of firing chamber by increased pressure in reservoir

DROPLET EJECTED

Ink sucked into reservoir by lowered pressure

Uncharged crystal contracts, lowering pressure in reservoir

CHAMBER REFILLED

The Internet

THE INTERNET CONSISTS OF TENS of thousands of computer networks linked together to form one huge global network, allowing any computer on one network to communicate with any computer on another. The two main services used on the Internet are email and the World Wide Web. Email allows text messages to be sent – along with attached computer files, images, or video clips, for example – to other computers on the Internet. The Web consists of billions of pages made up of digital files that are stored on computers across the world and can be viewed using a Web browser. The Web also provides interactive access to various services, for example banking and shopping.

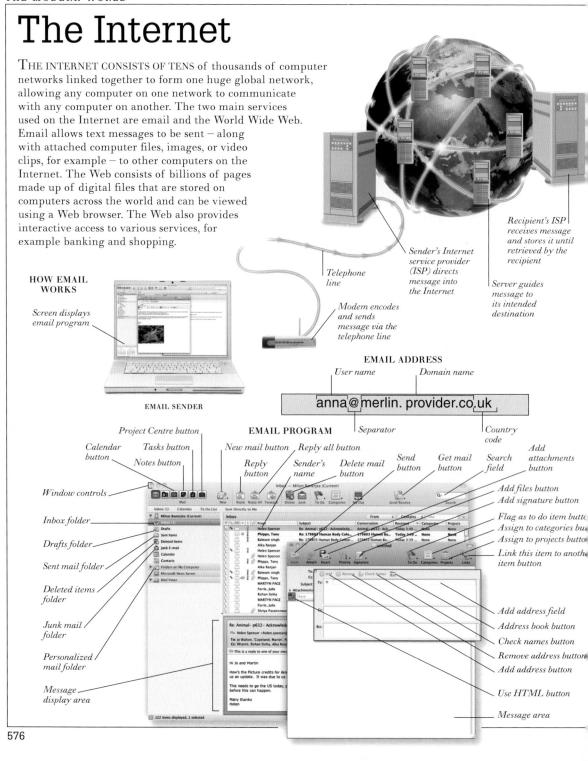

Recipient's ISP receives message and stores it until retrieved by the recipient

Server guides message to its intended destination

Sender's Internet service provider (ISP) directs message into the Internet

Telephone line

Modem encodes and sends message via the telephone line

HOW EMAIL WORKS

Screen displays email program

EMAIL SENDER

EMAIL ADDRESS

User name *Domain name*

anna@merlin. provider.co.uk

Separator *Country code*

EMAIL PROGRAM

Project Centre button

Calendar button *Tasks button* *New mail button* *Reply all button*

Notes button *Reply button* *Sender's name* *Delete mail button* *Send button* *Get mail button* *Search field* *Add attachments button*

Window controls

Add files button
Add signature button

Inbox folder

Flag as to do item butto
Assign to categories bu
Assign to projects butto

Drafts folder

Sent mail folder

Link this item to anoth item button

Deleted items folder

Junk mail folder

Add address field
Address book button
Check names button
Remove address button
Add address button

Personalized mail folder

Message display area

Use HTML button

Message area

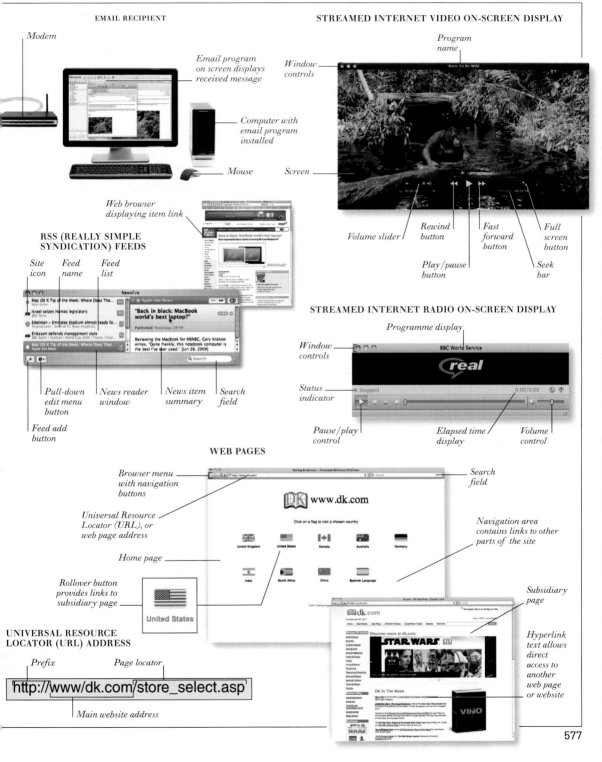

EMAIL RECIPIENT

Modem

Email program on screen displays received message

Computer with email program installed

Mouse

STREAMED INTERNET VIDEO ON-SCREEN DISPLAY

Program name

Window controls

Screen

Volume slider

Rewind button

Play/pause button

Fast forward button

Full screen button

Seek bar

Web browser displaying item link

RSS (REALLY SIMPLE SYNDICATION) FEEDS

Site icon

Feed name

Feed list

Pull-down edit menu button

News reader window

News item summary

Search field

Feed add button

STREAMED INTERNET RADIO ON-SCREEN DISPLAY

Programme display

Window controls

Status indicator

Pause/play control

Elapsed time display

Volume control

WEB PAGES

Browser menu with navigation buttons

Universal Resource Locator (URL), or web page address

Home page

Rollover button provides links to subsidiary page

United States

UNIVERSAL RESOURCE LOCATOR (URL) ADDRESS

Prefix

Page locator

http://www/dk.com/store_select.asp

Main website address

Search field

Navigation area contains links to other parts of the site

Subsidiary page

Hyperlink text allows direct access to another web page or website

Electronic games

MARIO SPORTS MIX WII

VIDEO GAMES HAVE BEEN around since the early 1970s. They are played on PCs, arcade machines, on a TV using a home console, and on portable hand-held consoles. Players use devices such as joysticks and control pads with buttons to control movement and action on screen. The latest generation of consoles uses motion sensor technology to allow players to manipulate objects on screen by simply moving the controller. The most advanced game systems respond to gestures and commands spoken by a player, without any need to use a hand controller. The game itself is stored in the form of digital information on CD, DVD, or microchip – which may be integral or stored in a removable cartridge – or on an internal hard disk. A central processing unit (CPU) (see pp. 566–567) is needed to process commands from the players, while specialized graphics chips are used to process the complex mapping and texturing functions that make modern games appear so realistic.

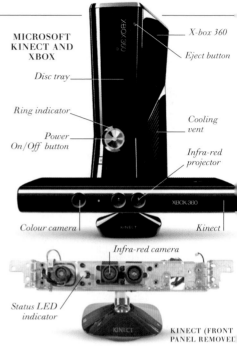

MICROSOFT KINECT AND XBOX

X-box 360
Eject button
Disc tray
Ring indicator
Cooling vent
Power On/Off button
Infra-red projector
Colour camera
Kinect
Infra-red camera
Status LED indicator
KINECT (FRONT PANEL REMOVED)

NINTENDO 3DS

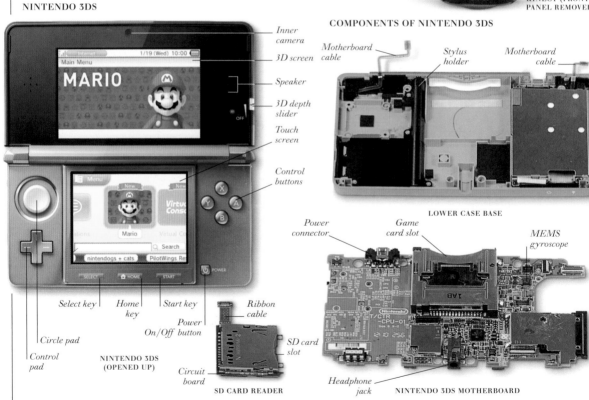

Inner camera
3D screen
Speaker
3D depth slider
Touch screen
Control buttons

Select key
Home key
Start key
Power On/Off button
Circle pad
Control pad

NINTENDO 3DS (OPENED UP)

Ribbon cable
SD card slot
Circuit board
SD CARD READER

COMPONENTS OF NINTENDO 3DS

Motherboard cable
Stylus holder
Motherboard cable

LOWER CASE BASE

Power connector
Game card slot
MEMS gyroscope

Headphone jack
NINTENDO 3DS MOTHERBOARD

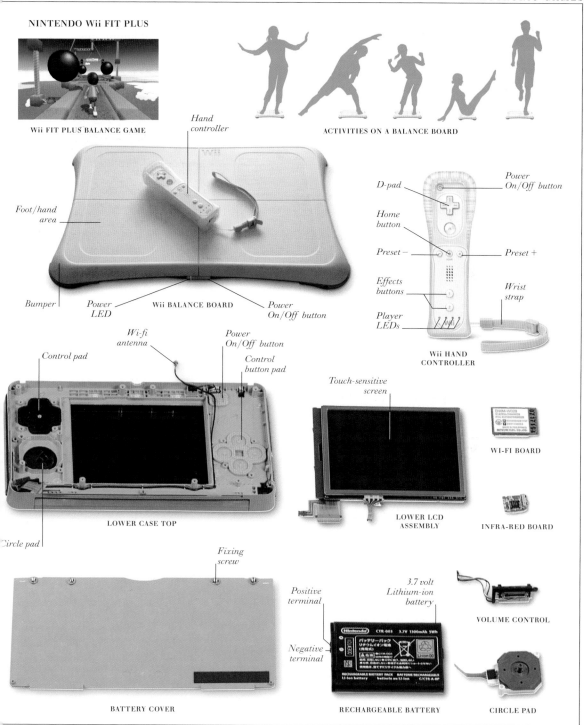

NINTENDO Wii FIT PLUS

Wii FIT PLUS BALANCE GAME

ACTIVITIES ON A BALANCE BOARD

Hand controller

Foot/hand area

Bumper

Power LED

Wii BALANCE BOARD

Power On/Off button

D-pad

Power On/Off button

Home button

Preset −

Preset +

Effects buttons

Wrist strap

Player LEDs

Wii HAND CONTROLLER

Wi-fi antenna

Power On/Off button

Control pad

Control button pad

Touch-sensitive screen

WI-FI BOARD

Circle pad

LOWER CASE TOP

LOWER LCD ASSEMBLY

INFRA-RED BOARD

Fixing screw

Positive terminal

3.7 volt Lithium-ion battery

Negative terminal

VOLUME CONTROL

BATTERY COVER

RECHARGEABLE BATTERY

CIRCLE PAD

Digital camera

FOR MORE THAN 200 YEARS, CAMERAS recorded
pictures as chemical changes in silver-containing
substances, on a strip of flexible, celluloid film.
The digital camera records pictures in electronic
form. At its heart is a specialized integrated
circuit known as a charge-coupled device (CCD).
This has millions of micro-units known as pixels.
It works in the opposite way to a miniature
computer or TV screen. Instead of electric signals
making pixels shine, when light hits a pixel it
generates a tiny electrical signal, according to
the light's colour and brightness. The signals
from the CCD's millions of pixels are analogue:
they vary continuously in a wave-like fashion.
They are converted by a microchip to digital
codes of numbers, represented as on-off electronic
pulses. The digital signals are processed and fed
to the camera's internal memory or a removable
memory device such as a data card or memory
stick. Photographs can be downloaded from a
digital camera to a computer via a cable or in
some cases a wireless link. Some digital cameras
automatically reduce blurring caused by camera
shake or fast movement, some can record video
clips as well as still pictures.

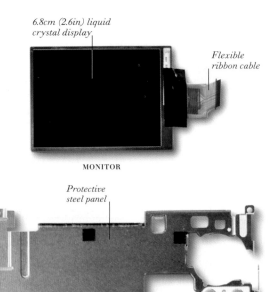

6.8cm (2.6in) liquid crystal display

Flexible ribbon cable

MONITOR

Protective steel panel

CHASSIS

Keypad

HOW A DIGITAL CAMERA WORKS

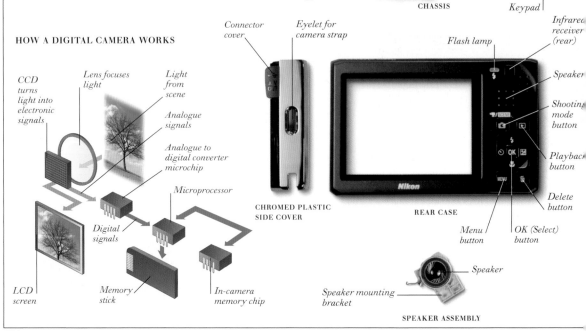

CCD turns light into electronic signals

Lens focuses light

Light from scene

Analogue signals

Analogue to digital converter microchip

Microprocessor

Digital signals

LCD screen

Memory stick

In-camera memory chip

Connector cover

Eyelet for camera strap

CHROMED PLASTIC
SIDE COVER

Flash lamp

Infrared receiver (rear)

Speaker

Shooting mode button

Playback button

Delete button

Nikon

REAR CASE

Menu button

OK (Select) button

Speaker

Speaker mounting bracket

SPEAKER ASSEMBLY

COMPONENTS OF NIKON COOLPIX S1000PJ

Shutter release button

Projector button

TOP PANEL

Focusing lens

Filters

Projector LED

Ribbon cable

PROJECTOR ASSEMBLY

Projector assembly cover

CODEC with speaker driver and video buffet

Display controller chip

LOGIC BOARD

Projector window

Flash window

Lens

Self-timer lamp

Infra-red receiver (front)

Nikon

COOLPIX

NIKKOR 5X WIDE OPTICAL ZOOM VR 5.0-25.0mm f3.9-5.8

FRONT CASE

Camera module connector

CCD image sensor

CAMERA MODULE

Nikon LITHIUM ION BATTERY PACK EN-EL12 3.7V 1050mAh 3.9Wh
JFBC
NIKON CORPORATION, JAPAN

Lithium-ion battery

EN-EL12 RECHARGEABLE BATTERY

Lens cover motor

LENS COVER

TYPES OF DIGITAL CAMERA

Mode selector

Shutter button

Nikon
5000

Lens release button

DIGITAL SLR

18–55mm zoom lens

On/off button

Shutter button

SONY

Lens release button

16mm interchangeable lens

DIGITAL CAMERA WITH INTERCHANGEABLE LENS

Water-resistant case

Strap mount

Shutter button

Electronic flash

Canon PowerShot D10

12.1

Lamp

Microphone

Lens

UNDERWATER DIGITAL CAMERA

Shutter button

Microphone

Left lens

Right lens

TWIN CCD
3D HD

Flash

3D FUJIFILM

Lens cover

3D DIGITAL CAMERA

Digital camcorder

A CAMCORDER records a scene as a sequence of 25 or 30 still images per second, along with sound. It comprises a video camera to capture light from the scene, a viewfinder through which the scene may be viewed, a screen on which the recorded scene may be viewed, a charge-coupled device (CCD) to convert the visual data into an electric signal, and a means of storing the signal. Digital video cameras convert the signal into digital form – a series of separate measurements of the initial analogue (continuously varying) signal. They record the digital signal, usually on a chip or hard disk. Camcorders often have a slot where a memory card can be inserted to expand the memory and store longer recordings or more still pictures.

COMPONENTS OF A JVC EVERIO CAMCORDER

JVC Everio

MONITOR SHELL

MONITOR MOUNT

MONITOR FRAME

Screen connector

6.8-cm (2.7-in) LCD screen

MONITOR SCREEN

OK button

Grip belt

Battery

Power/ Charge lamp

Access lamp

Zoom select lever

Speaker

Play button

Auto/Manual recording button

Info button

Menu button

AV terminal

LEFT SIDE

Power/charge lamp

Access lamp

LEFT OUTER SHELL

Lens cover

Microphone

LCD monitor

TOP VIEW

LENS COVER ASSEMBLY

Speaker

SPEAKER CIRCUIT BOARD

Monitor frame

USB
terminal

DC
terminal

Start/Stop
button

LCD
monitor

Battery

REAR VIEW

Grip belt

MOTHERBOARD

CHASSIS

Lens cover
switch

**RIGHT
OUTER SHELL**

Grip belt
release lever

CCD
mounting
peg

Lens

SAMSUNG 4GB

SDHC CARD

CCD chip

SENSOR BOARD

Start/Stop
button

3.6-volt lithium-
ion battery

LENS UNIT

LENS UNIT MOUNT

**GRIP BELT
FASTENER**

Zoom
select lever

OK
button

JVC

GRIP BELT

REAR PANEL

CONTROL UNIT

**RECHARGEABLE
BATTERY**

Home cinema

HOME CINEMA REPLICATES a real "movie theatre" using pictures displayed on a high-quality widescreen television set, such as a plasma TV, and surround sound from strategically sited loudspeakers. The source for sound and vision is a DVD (Digital Versatile Disc). Its player uses standard CD (Compact Disc) digital technology, but with a higher density of laser-read microscopic pits – more than 20 billion such pits in multi-level spiral tracks that, stretched out, would extend nearly 40km (25 miles). Blu-ray is a high-quality DVD system that fits much more data on its disc than standard DVDs, allowing High Definition video files to be stored. It is hard for the human ear to discern the direction of low-pitched sounds, so these emanate from a central bass speaker, often built into or below the screen unit. High-pitched sounds, the direction of which is easier to detect, emanate from mid- and high-frequency speakers positioned around the viewer. Plasma screens use fluorescent tube ("strip-light") technology. Tiny three-cell pixels, each about one millimetre across, contain red, green, and blue phosphor chemicals and a gas mix. Where electric pulses coincide for a split second in the criss-cross matrix of wire electrodes, the gas energizes and emits ultraviolet light, which in turn makes the phosphor glow.

BLU-RAY PLAYER

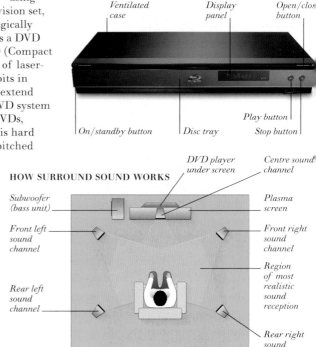

Ventilated case

Display panel

Open/close button

On/standby button

Disc tray

Play button

Stop button

HOW SURROUND SOUND WORKS

DVD player under screen

Centre sound channel

Subwoofer (bass unit)

Plasma screen

Front left sound channel

Front right sound channel

Rear left sound channel

Region of most realistic sound reception

Rear right sound channel

WIDE-SCREEN PLASMA DISPLAY

Mid-grey bezel

Damped anti-shock swivel base

16:9 (width:height) screen proportions fit human field of vision

HOW A PLASMA SCREEN WORKS

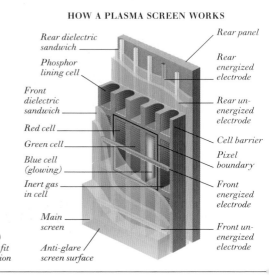

Rear dielectric sandwich

Rear panel

Phosphor lining cell

Rear energized electrode

Front dielectric sandwich

Rear un-energized electrode

Red cell

Green cell

Cell barrier

Blue cell (glowing)

Pixel boundary

Inert gas in cell

Front energized electrode

Main screen

Anti-glare screen surface

Front un-energized electrode

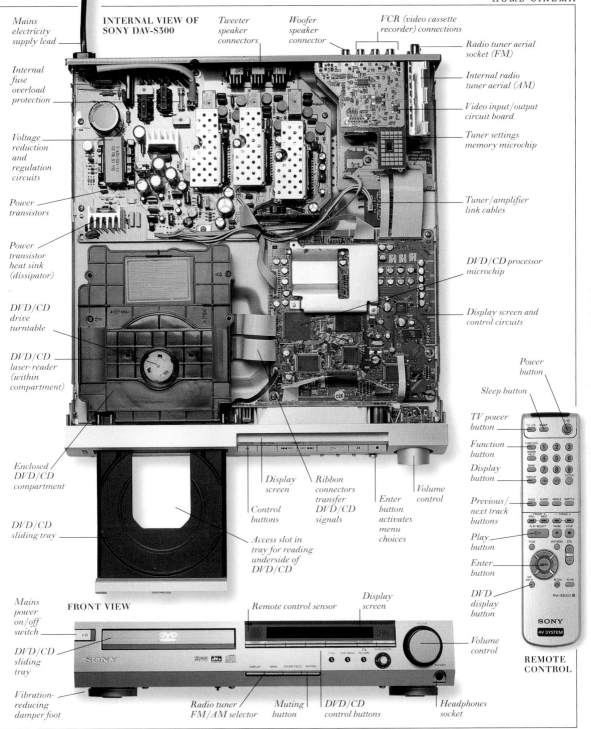

INTERNAL VIEW OF
SONY DAV-S300

Mains
electricity
supply lead

Internal
fuse
overload
protection

Voltage
reduction
and
regulation
circuits

Power
transistors

Power
transistor
heat sink
(dissipator)

DVD/CD
drive
turntable

DVD/CD
laser-reader
(within
compartment)

Enclosed
DVD/CD
compartment

DVD/CD
sliding tray

Tweeter
speaker
connectors

Woofer
speaker
connector

VCR (video cassette
recorder) connections

Radio tuner aerial
socket (FM)

Internal radio
tuner aerial (AM)

Video input/output
circuit board

Tuner settings
memory microchip

Tuner/amplifier
link cables

DVD/CD processor
microchip

Display screen and
control circuits

Display
screen

Ribbon
connectors
transfer
DVD/CD
signals

Control
buttons

Access slot in
tray for reading
underside of
DVD/CD

Enter
button
activates
menu
choices

Volume
control

Power
button

Sleep button

TV power
button

Function
button

Display
button

Previous/
next track
buttons

Play
button

Enter
button

DVD
display
button

SONY
AV SYSTEM

RM-SS300

REMOTE
CONTROL

FRONT VIEW

Mains
power
on/off
switch

DVD/CD
sliding
tray

Vibration-
reducing
damper foot

Remote control sensor

Radio tuner
FM/AM selector

Muting
button

DVD/CD
control buttons

Display
screen

Volume
control

Headphones
socket

SONY

DVD

585

Personal music and video

THE FIRST BATTERY-DRIVEN PORTABLE source of sound and music was the transistor radio of the 1950s. In the 1970s, the magnetic audio cassette tape allowed recordings to be played on portable tape players. Also, new metal alloys permitted the tiny but high-power magnets needed for lightweight earphones. In the 1980s, compact discs brought music into the digital era. Sony's MD, or minidisc, introduced re-recordable CDs that used magnetic and optical technology. From the mid 1990s, music could be stored in all-electronic digital form in a microchip, usually in the MP3 file format. These files can be transferred between devices and via the Internet. Today, a variety of portable media gadgets can record, play, and store video, photographs, and music in electronic form.

MP3 PLAYERS

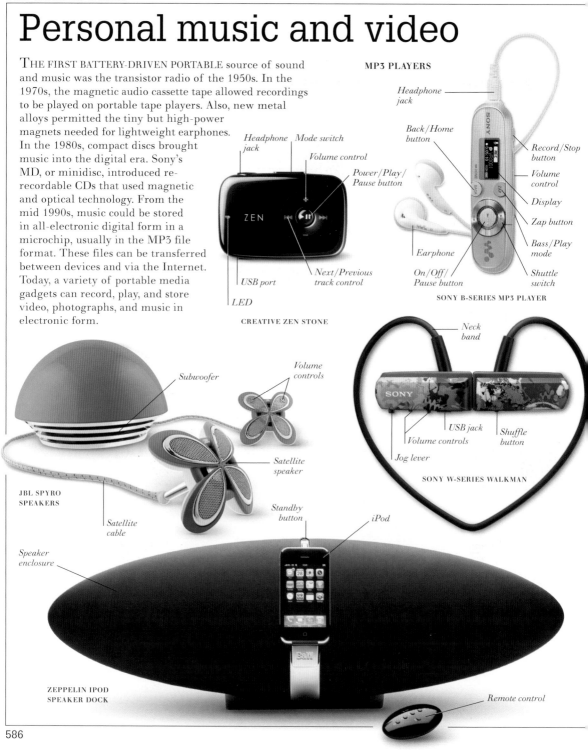

Headphone jack
Mode switch
Volume control
Power/Play/Pause button
Next/Previous track control
USB port
LED

CREATIVE ZEN STONE

Headphone jack
Back/Home button
Record/Stop button
Volume control
Display
Zap button
Bass/Play mode
Earphone
On/Off/Pause button
Shuttle switch

SONY B-SERIES MP3 PLAYER

Subwoofer
Volume controls
Satellite speaker
Satellite cable

JBL SPYRO SPEAKERS

Neck band
USB jack
Shuffle button
Volume controls
Jog lever

SONY W-SERIES WALKMAN

Standby button
iPod
Speaker enclosure
Remote control

ZEPPELIN IPOD SPEAKER DOCK

COMPONENTS OF MICROSOFT ZUNE HD

FRONT PANEL

Power button

Digitizer

Home button

Front panel

Base plate

CHASSIS

Power button cover

LOGIC BOARD

3.7-volt battery

Media button bezel

Audio codec chip

EEPROM memory chip

Headphone jack

Sync port

MICROSOFT ZUNE HD

DISPLAY

8.4 cm (3.3 in) OLED display

Ribbon cable

REAR VIEW

Back panel

Tri-wing screw

Bottom backplate

SIDE VIEW

Back panel

Media button

Power button

Touchscreen

Media button

music
videos
pictures
radio
marketplace
social
more

Headphone jack

Sync port

Home button

Mobile phones

IN THE EARLY 1990s, THE MOBILE PHONE (or cellphone) was a rare luxury, but in recent years it has outsold almost every other electrical gadget – as a professional tool, domestic convenience, and even a fashion accessory. Mobile phones have also generally shrunk in size, due to improvements in rechargeable batteries, which now store more electricity for longer in a smaller package, and to smaller, more efficient electronics that use less electricity. A "mobile" is basically a low-power radio receiver-transmitter, plus a tiny microphone to convert sounds into electrical signals, and a small speaker that does the reverse. When the mobile phone is activated, it sends out a radio signal that is answered by nearby mast transmitter-receivers. The phone locks onto the clearest signal and uses this while within range (the range of each transmitter is known as a cell). The phone continuously monitors signal strength and switches to an alternative transmitter when necessary. The phone's liquid crystal display (LCD) shows numbers, letters, symbols, and colour pictures. Newer models have a larger screen for more complex colour images, and commonly incorporate a camera, radio, and MP3 functionality. Smartphones, which are increasingly widespread, contain additional software and more may be downloaded. Smartphones typically offer Internet and email access, PDA-like functions (see pp. 568–569), and may even contain GPS navigation software.

Top microphone *Front camera* *Receiver* *Status bar* *Earpiece*

Bottom microphone *Home button* *Speaker*

I-PHONE 4

Menu key *Home key* *Back key* *Search key*

LG OPTIMUS 2X

HOW A MOBILE PHONE WORKS

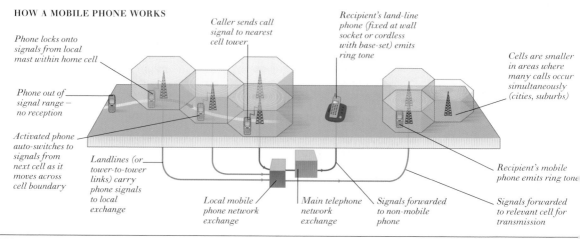

Phone locks onto signals from local mast within home cell

Caller sends call signal to nearest cell tower

Recipient's land-line phone (fixed at wall socket or cordless with base-set) emits ring tone

Cells are smaller in areas where many calls occur simultaneously (cities, suburbs)

Phone out of signal range – no reception

Activated phone auto-switches to signals from next cell as it moves across cell boundary

Landlines (or tower-to-tower links) carry phone signals to local exchange

Local mobile phone network exchange

Main telephone network exchange

Signals forwarded to non-mobile phone

Recipient's mobile phone emits ring tone

Signals forwarded to relevant cell for transmission

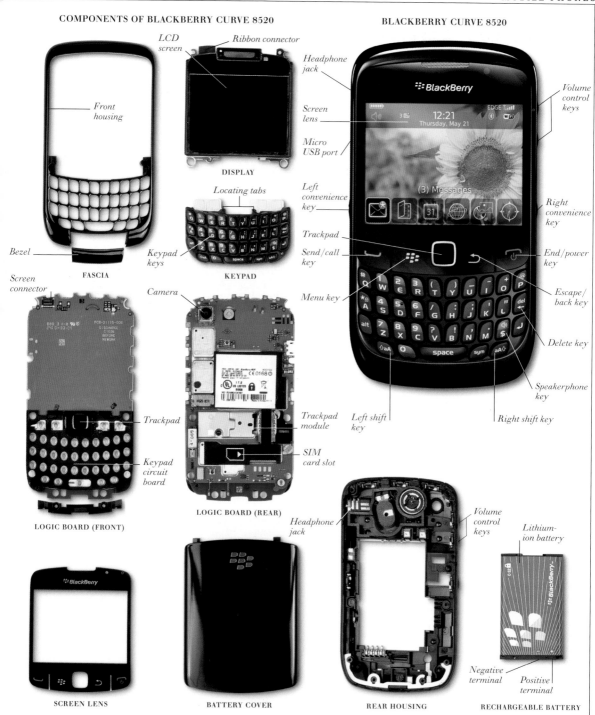

COMPONENTS OF BLACKBERRY CURVE 8520

BLACKBERRY CURVE 8520

LCD screen

Ribbon connector

Front housing

DISPLAY

Locating tabs

Bezel

Keypad keys

FASCIA

KEYPAD

Screen connector

Camera

Trackpad

Trackpad

Keypad circuit board

Trackpad module

SIM card slot

LOGIC BOARD (FRONT)

LOGIC BOARD (REAR)

SCREEN LENS

BATTERY COVER

REAR HOUSING

Headphone jack

Screen lens

Micro USB port

Left convenience key

Trackpad

Send/call key

Menu key

Left shift key

Headphone jack

Volume control keys

Right convenience key

End/power key

Escape/ back key

Delete key

Speakerphone key

Right shift key

Volume control keys

Lithium-ion battery

Negative terminal

Positive terminal

RECHARGEABLE BATTERY

589

Global positioning system

THE GLOBAL POSITIONING SYSTEM (GPS) is a network of 24 navigation satellites orbiting the Earth that people can use to pinpoint their position. The satellites orbit at a height of 20,000 kilometres (12,500 miles). A GPS receiver picks up signals from any of these satellites that are above the horizon. It uses information in each signal to work out how far away it is from the satellite. It can calculate its position on the Earth's surface when it has information from at least three satellites. A basic GPS receiver shows the latitude and longitude of its position on its screen. More advanced receivers, especially those designed for use in vehicles, show their position on a digital map. These receivers often show extra information, such as the vehicle's speed and the length of the journey. Some receivers warn drivers if they exceed the speed limit for a road and even tell drivers which traffic lane to use at the next junction. Directions are shown on the screen and also spoken by a synthesized voice.

IN-CAR GPS

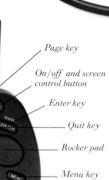

Ante,

Page key

On/off and screen control button

Enter key

Quit key

Rocker pad

Menu key

Speak key

Liquid crystal display (LCD) screen

Zoom keys

Find key

Route key

HOW GPS WORKS

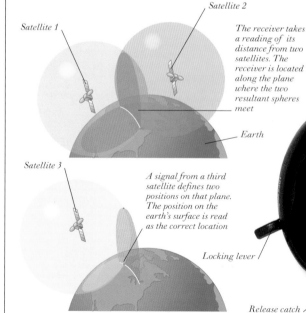

Satellite 1

Satellite 2

The receiver takes a reading of its distance from two satellites. The receiver is located along the plane where the two resultant spheres meet

Earth

Satellite 3

A signal from a third satellite defines two positions on that plane. The position on the earth's surface is read as the correct location

Locking lever

IN-CAR MOUNTING BRACKET ASSEMBLY

QUICK-RELEASE BASE

MOUNTING BRACKET

Release catch

Ratcheted base

Speaker
plug

Waterproof
case

Sling

Power plug

COMPONENTS OF AN IN-CAR GPS

High-contrast
liquid crystal
display (LCD)
screen

Data plug

Antenna

GARMIN ETREX HAND-HELD GPS

Memory
battery

Data plug
socket

Main printed
circuit board
(PCB)

Rear case

USB PROGRAMMER ASSEMBLY

Shielded
receiver

Data
cartridge

Universal serial
bus (USB)
programmer

SPARE FUSES

Front case

Liquid crystal
display (LCD)
assembly

Underside
of control
pad

Vacuum cleaner

IN A CONVENTIONAL VACUUM CLEANER, an electric motor
spins a fan that sucks in air carrying dust and debris. The air
is forced through tiny pores in a dust bag, trapping most
particles. In the 1990s, James Dyson's dual cyclone "bag-less"
design did away with the dust bag – and the reduced airflow
caused by clogging of its pores. An electrically driven fan
creates a partial vacuum within the machine. This sucks air
into the machine past a rotating brush that loosens dirt. The
air flows into a cylinder-shaped bin. As the air whirls around
the bin like a miniature storm, or cyclone, larger particle
are flung outwards and fall to the bottom of the bin. The
air then passes through perforations into a cone-shaped
inner bin and then into a series of smaller cones, spinning
faster all the time and flinging smaller and smaller particle
out. The nearly clean air exits the
machine through micro-filters that
trap the tiniest particles. Some
Dyson vacuum cleaners run on
a large ball instead of wheels.
The ball makes it easier to
steer the cleaner.

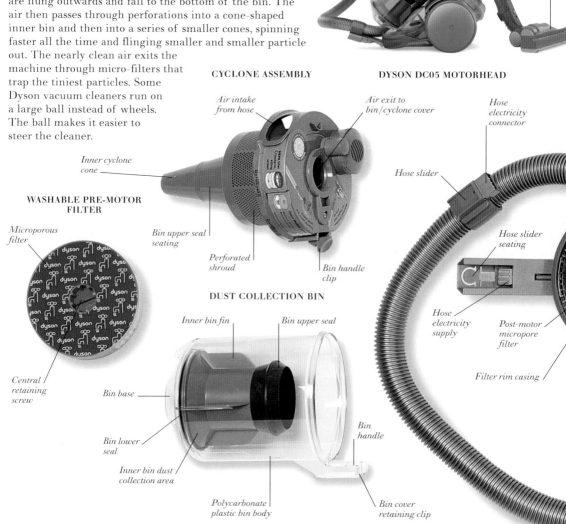

*Wand handle and
brushbar controls*

Upper wand

Lower wand

*Motorized
brushbar
floor tool*

CYCLONE ASSEMBLY

DYSON DC05 MOTORHEAD

*Air intake
from hose*

*Air exit to
bin/cyclone cover*

*Hose
electricity
connector*

*Inner cyclone
cone*

Hose slider

**WASHABLE PRE-MOTOR
FILTER**

*Microporous
filter*

*Bin upper seal
seating*

*Perforated
shroud*

*Bin handle
clip*

*Hose slider
seating*

*Central
retaining
screw*

*Hose
electricity
supply*

*Post-motor
micropore
filter*

DUST COLLECTION BIN

Inner bin fin

Bin upper seal

Filter rim casing

Bin base

*Bin
handle*

*Bin lower
seal*

*Inner bin dust
collection area*

*Polycarbonate
plastic bin body*

*Bin cover
retaining clip*

**OVERHEAD VIEW OF
DYSON DC05 MOTORHEAD**

ACCESSORIES

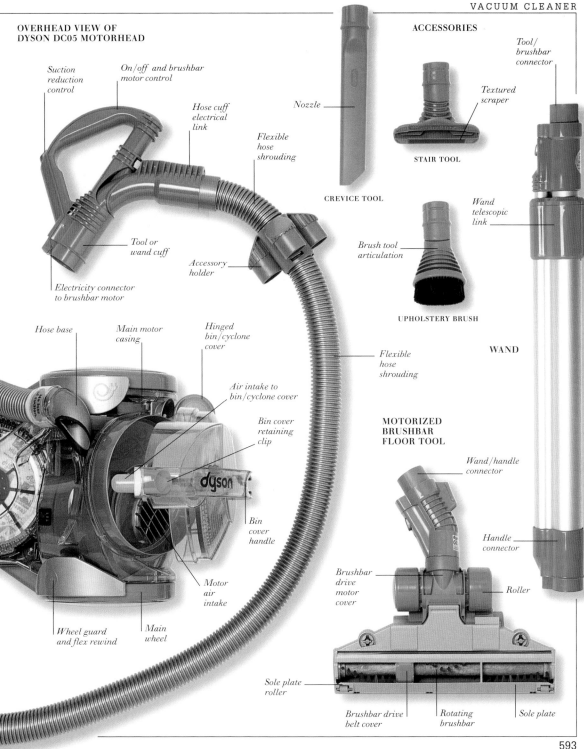

Suction
reduction
control

On/off and brushbar
motor control

Hose cuff
electrical
link

Flexible
hose
shrouding

Nozzle

Tool/
brushbar
connector

Textured
scraper

STAIR TOOL

CREVICE TOOL

Tool or
wand cuff

Accessory
holder

Electricity connector
to brushbar motor

Wand
telescopic
link

Brush tool
articulation

UPHOLSTERY BRUSH

Hose base

Main motor
casing

Hinged
bin/cyclone
cover

Air intake to
bin/cyclone cover

Bin cover
retaining
clip

Flexible
hose
shrouding

WAND

**MOTORIZED
BRUSHBAR
FLOOR TOOL**

Wand/handle
connector

Bin
cover
handle

Motor
air
intake

Handle
connector

Brushbar
drive
motor
cover

Roller

Wheel guard
and flex rewind

Main
wheel

Sole plate
roller

Brushbar drive
belt cover

Rotating
brushbar

Sole plate

593

Iron and washer-dryer

IN THE DAYS BEFORE WASHING MACHINES, laundry was done by hand – washed in a barrel, squeezed in a roller-mangle, hung on a line, and smoothed with an iron heated on the hob or stove. In the 1880s electrically heated irons were one of the first home electrical appliances. Today's iron still applies heat, sometimes moistened with steam, to dampen and flatten garment fibres. Machines with electric heaters and motors took the strain out of washing from the 1910s. Up to the 1960s, three machines were needed to wash, spin, and dry. Now clothes are swirled in a rotating ribbed tub of hot water, then spun fast to throw off most of the water, before slowly tumbling in electrically heated air to dry – all in one appliance.

FRONT VIEW OF A MIELE WASHER-DRYER

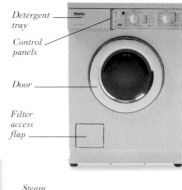

Detergent tray

Control panels

Door

Filter access flap

COMPONENTS OF A STEAM IRON

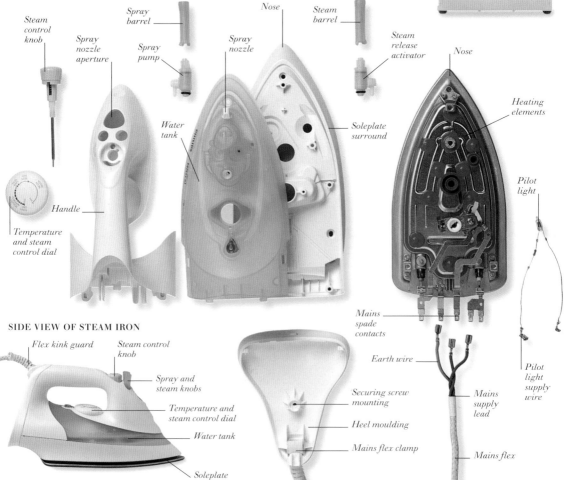

Steam control knob

Spray nozzle aperture

Spray barrel

Spray pump

Nose

Spray nozzle

Steam barrel

Steam release activator

Nose

Heating elements

Water tank

Soleplate surround

Pilot light

Handle

Temperature and steam control dial

Mains spade contacts

Earth wire

Pilot light supply wire

SIDE VIEW OF STEAM IRON

Flex kink guard

Steam control knob

Spray and steam knobs

Temperature and steam control dial

Water tank

Soleplate

Securing screw mounting

Heel moulding

Mains flex clamp

Mains supply lead

Mains flex

COMPONENTS OF A MIELE WASHER-DRYER

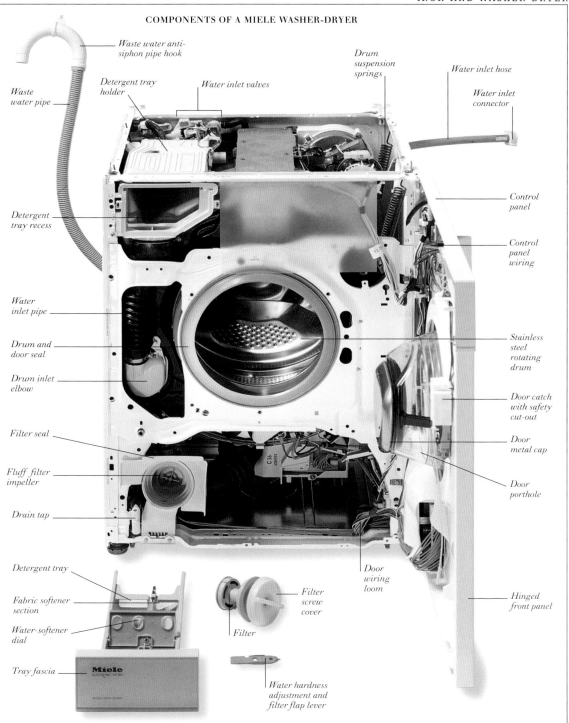

Waste water anti-siphon pipe hook

Detergent tray holder

Water inlet valves

Drum suspension springs

Water inlet hose

Water inlet connector

Waste water pipe

Detergent tray recess

Water inlet pipe

Drum and door seal

Drum inlet elbow

Filter seal

Fluff filter impeller

Drain tap

Control panel

Control panel wiring

Stainless steel rotating drum

Door catch with safety cut-out

Door metal cap

Door porthole

Door wiring loom

Hinged front panel

Detergent tray

Fabric softener section

Water-softener dial

Tray fascia

Filter screw cover

Filter

Water hardness adjustment and filter flap lever

Miele

Microwave combination oven

CONVENTIONAL OVENS use electrically warmed elements or a flame to heat food. In a microwave oven heat energy is created by electromagnetic waves produced by a magnetron and led by waveguides into the oven compartment. These microwaves cannot pass through the compartment's metal casing, being reflected within and spread evenly by a fan. But they do pass through most types of plastic, ceramics, and glass. Therefore platters or containers made from these materials are suitable for use in microwave ovens. A combination oven also has conventional heating elements, to grill and "brown" in the traditional fashion, either alone or in conjunction with microwaves.

MICROWAVE COMBINATION OVEN

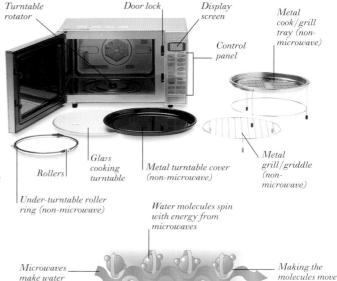

Turntable rotator
Door lock
Display screen
Control panel
Metal cook/grill tray (non-microwave)
Rollers
Glass cooking turntable
Metal turntable cover (non-microwave)
Metal grill/griddle (non-microwave)
Under-turntable roller ring (non-microwave)

HOW MICROWAVES HEAT FOOD

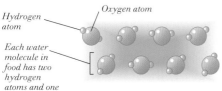

Oxygen atom
Hydrogen atom
Each water molecule in food has two hydrogen atoms and one oxygen atom

Water molecules spin with energy from microwaves

Microwaves make water molecules vibrate

Making the molecules move generates heat

SIDE VIEW OF MICROWAVE COMBINATION OVEN

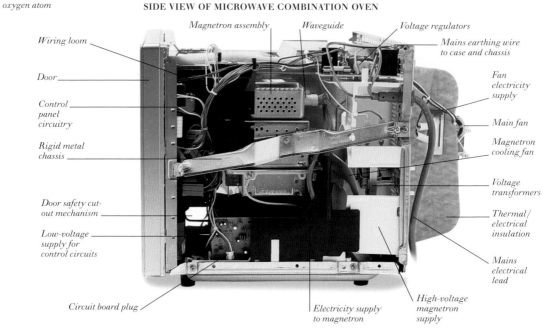

Magnetron assembly
Waveguide
Voltage regulators
Wiring loom
Mains earthing wire to case and chassis
Door
Fan electricity supply
Control panel circuitry
Main fan
Rigid metal chassis
Magnetron cooling fan
Voltage transformers
Door safety cut-out mechanism
Thermal/electrical insulation
Low-voltage supply for control circuits
Mains electrical lead
Circuit board plug
Electricity supply to magnetron
High-voltage magnetron supply

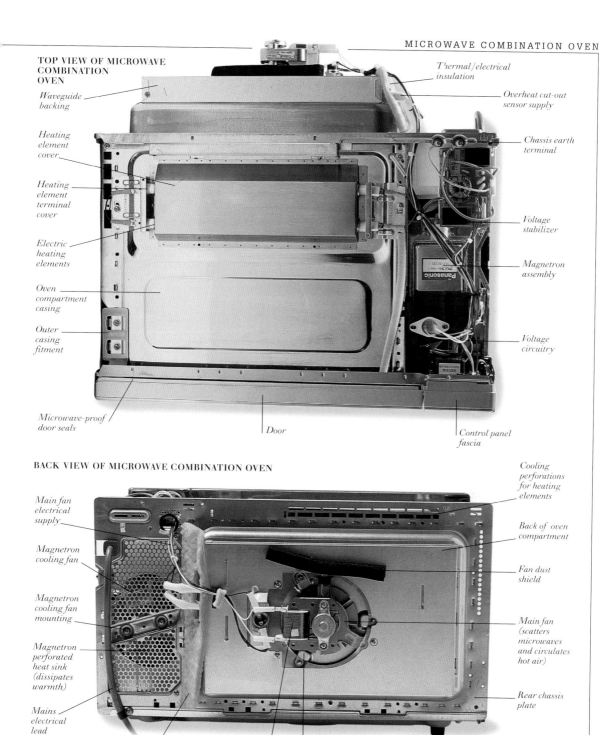

TOP VIEW OF MICROWAVE COMBINATION OVEN

Waveguide backing

Heating element cover

Heating element terminal cover

Electric heating elements

Oven compartment casing

Outer casing fitment

Microwave-proof door seals

Thermal/electrical insulation

Overheat cut-out sensor supply

Chassis earth terminal

Voltage stabilizer

Magnetron assembly

Voltage circuitry

Door

Control panel fascia

BACK VIEW OF MICROWAVE COMBINATION OVEN

Main fan electrical supply

Magnetron cooling fan

Magnetron cooling fan mounting

Magnetron perforated heat sink (dissipates warmth)

Mains electrical lead

Thermal/electrical insulation

Fan transformer

Vibration-reducing fan mounting

Cooling perforations for heating elements

Back of oven compartment

Fan dust shield

Main fan (scatters microwaves and circulates hot air)

Rear chassis plate

597

Toaster

MOST ELECTRIC TOASTERS not only grill slices of bread, they also pop them up when ready. While the slices rest on a spring-loaded rack, electric heating elements toast the bread. At the same time, a bimetallic strip heats and expands. One of the two metals in this strip expands more quickly than the other, causing the strip to curve. As it bends, it completes an electrical circuit and activates an electromagnet. The magnet attracts a catch, releasing the spring that holds the rack down in the toaster. The elements switch off, and the toasted slices pop up.

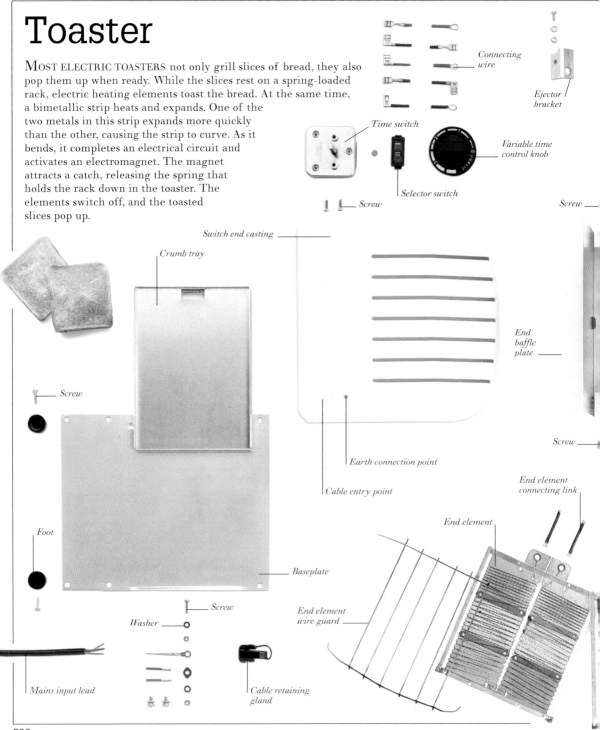

Connecting wire

Ejector bracket

Time switch

Variable time control knob

Selector switch

Screw

Screw

Switch end casting

Crumb tray

End baffle plate

Screw

Screw

Earth connection point

Cable entry point

End element connecting link

End element

Foot

Baseplate

End element wire guard

Screw

Washer

Mains input lead

Cable retaining gland

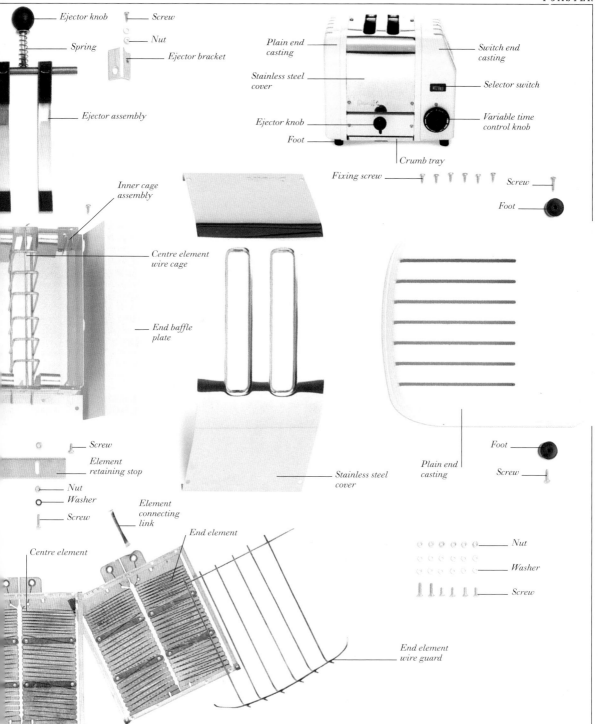

Ejector knob

Screw

Nut

Ejector bracket

Spring

Ejector assembly

Plain end casting

Stainless steel cover

Ejector knob

Foot

Switch end casting

Selector switch

Variable time control knob

Crumb tray

Fixing screw

Screw

Foot

Inner cage assembly

Centre element wire cage

End baffle plate

Screw

Element retaining stop

Nut

Washer

Screw

Element connecting link

Centre element

End element

Stainless steel cover

Plain end casting

Foot

Screw

Nut

Washer

Screw

End element wire guard

Drills

THE ELECTRICALLY POWERED MOTOR OF A POWER DRILL, cooled by a fan, turns a shaft at high speed. The shaft connects, in turn, to a system of gears that rotates a chuck even faster. Clamped by the chuck, a sharp bit cuts out the hole, and at the same time the bit's screw-shaped grooves channel the waste out of the hole. For drilling hard materials, many power drills have a hammer mechanism: when this is operated a ratchet in the gearcase causes the chuck and bit to pound in and out as they drill. A hand drill, although slower and less forceful than a power drill, is easier to control. For cutting wide holes, carpenters often prefer a brace-and-bit. This acts like a lever: the bowed handle of the brace moves a larger distance than the bit, turning the bit with extra force.

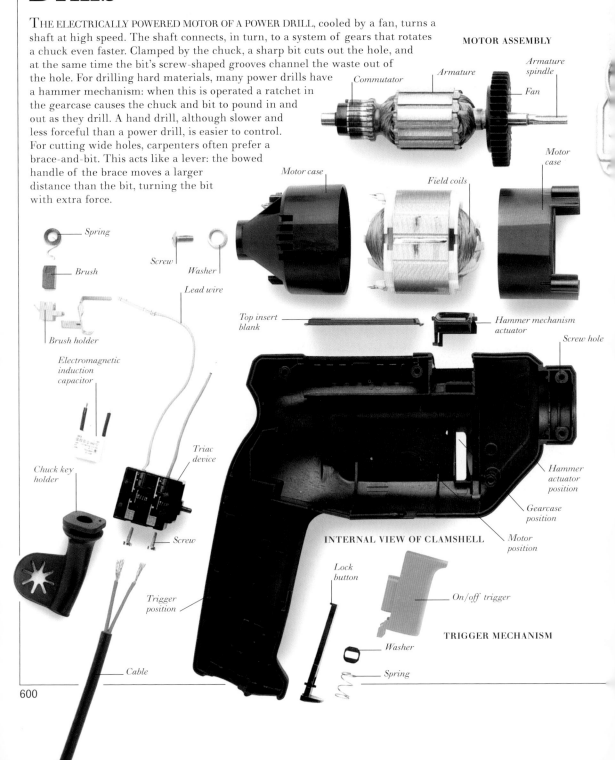

MOTOR ASSEMBLY

Commutator

Armature

Armature spindle

Fan

Motor case

Motor case

Field coils

Spring

Screw

Washer

Brush

Lead wire

Top insert blank

Hammer mechanism actuator

Screw hole

Brush holder

Electromagnetic induction capacitor

Triac device

Chuck key holder

Screw

INTERNAL VIEW OF CLAMSHELL

Hammer actuator position

Gearcase position

Motor position

Lock button

On/off trigger

Trigger position

TRIGGER MECHANISM

Washer

Cable

Spring

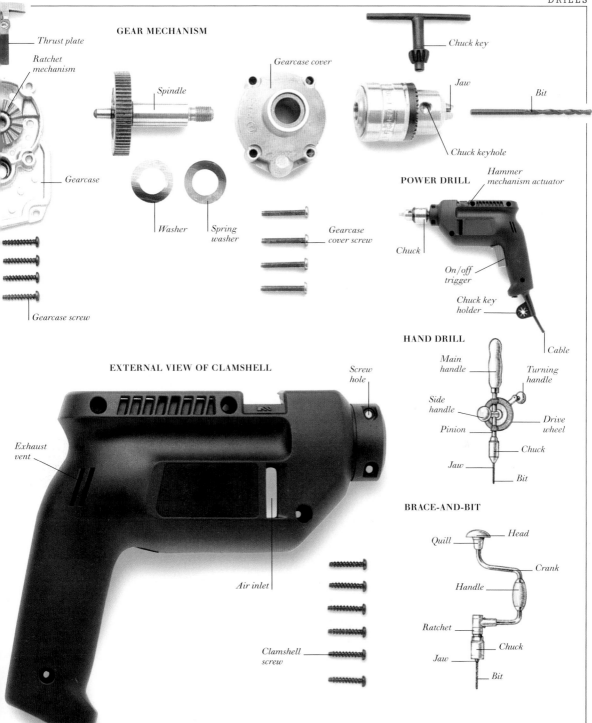

GEAR MECHANISM

Thrust plate

Ratchet mechanism

Spindle

Gearcase cover

Chuck key

Jaw

Bit

Gearcase

Washer

Spring washer

Gearcase cover screw

Chuck keyhole

Gearcase screw

POWER DRILL

Hammer mechanism actuator

Chuck

On/off trigger

Chuck key holder

Cable

HAND DRILL

Main handle

Turning handle

Side handle

Pinion

Drive wheel

Chuck

Jaw

Bit

EXTERNAL VIEW OF CLAMSHELL

Screw hole

Exhaust vent

Air inlet

Clamshell screw

BRACE-AND-BIT

Quill

Head

Crank

Handle

Ratchet

Chuck

Jaw

Bit

House of the future

HOUSES IN THE FUTURE are likely to be more environmentally friendly and energy-efficient than older dwellings, by making better use of materials and intelligent control systems. The Integer house was designed by Cole Thompson Associates, Bree Day Partnership, and Paul Hodgkins Associates, and built in conjunction with the Building Research Establishment in the UK. One of its key features is a large conservatory that warms one side of the house. Extensive use is made of recycled, natural, and renewable materials and energy. The walls are made from timber and insulated with fibre from recycled newspaper; waste water from the bathrooms is saved and used to flush the toilets; and a wind turbine and solar panels contribute some of the electricity requirements. Many elements were prefabricated off site for ease of construction. The Integer house uses only half the energy and a third less water than a traditionally built house.

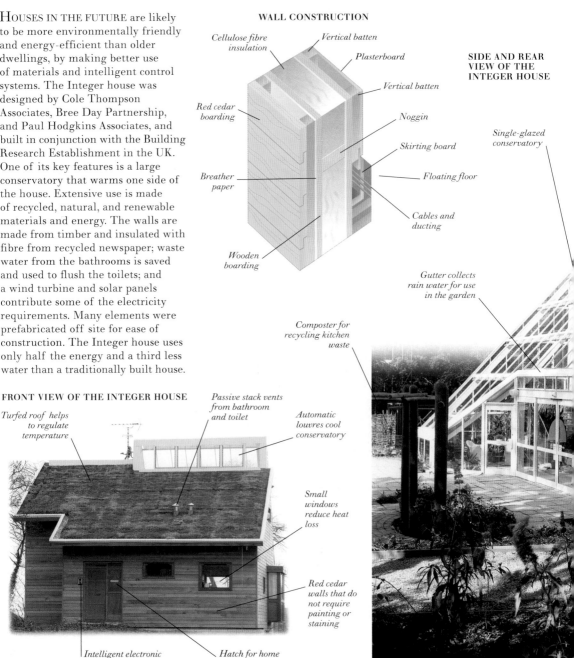

WALL CONSTRUCTION

Cellulose fibre insulation

Vertical batten

Plasterboard

Vertical batten

Red cedar boarding

Noggin

Skirting board

Breather paper

Floating floor

Cables and ducting

Wooden boarding

SIDE AND REAR VIEW OF THE INTEGER HOUSE

Single-glazed conservatory

Gutter collects rain water for use in the garden

Composter for recycling kitchen waste

FRONT VIEW OF THE INTEGER HOUSE

Passive stack vents from bathroom and toilet

Automatic louvres cool conservatory

Turfed roof helps to regulate temperature

Small windows reduce heat loss

Red cedar walls that do not require painting or staining

Intelligent electronic door-lock

Hatch for home deliveries

ROOF CONSTRUCTION

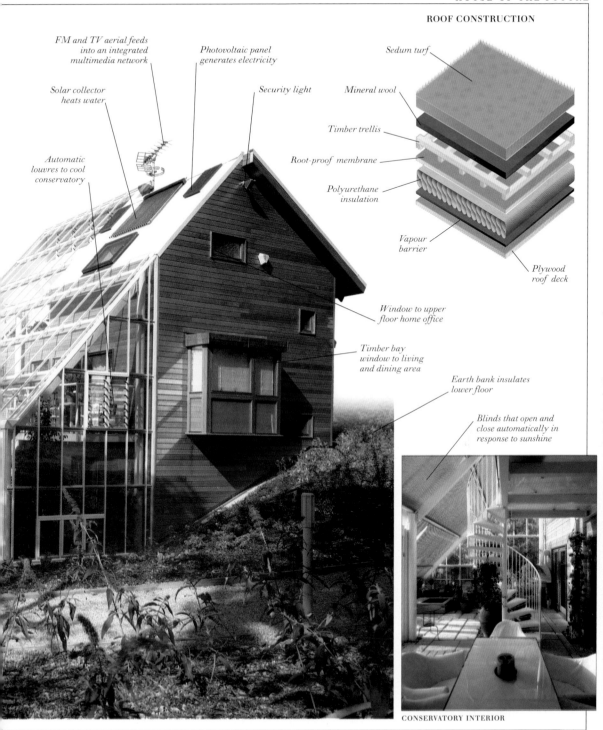

FM and TV aerial feeds
into an integrated
multimedia network

Photovoltaic panel
generates electricity

Solar collector
heats water

Security light

Automatic
louvres to cool
conservatory

Sedum turf

Mineral wool

Timber trellis

Root-proof membrane

Polyurethane
insulation

Vapour
barrier

Plywood
roof deck

Window to upper
floor home office

Timber bay
window to living
and dining area

Earth bank insulates
lower floor

Blinds that open and
close automatically in
response to sunshine

CONSERVATORY INTERIOR

Renewable energy

RENEWABLE ENERGY COMES from sources that do not become depleted as we use the energy. When a fossil fuel such as coal is burned, it is gone forever, but a renewable source remains available no matter how much is used. The tides, waves, flowing water, sunlight, and the wind are all renewable sources of energy. Wind and water energy are captured by a device called a turbine. The turbine spins and drives an electricity generator. Energy from sunlight, or solar energy, is changed into electricity in two main ways. One uses mirrors to concentrate solar energy and magnify its heating effect which is used to change water into steam to drive turbines. Photovoltaic cells change sunlight directly into electricity. A cell is made from two layers of silicon. One gives out electrons (negative particles) and the other receives them. Sunlight knocks electrons out of atoms where the two layers meet, separating them from the positive particles. The electrons are attracted to one layer of the cell, the positive particles to the other layer. Electrons are naturally attracted to the positive particles, but to come together again, the electrons must flow out of the cell, through an external electric circuit, or load, and back to the other side of the cell, creating a charge. The cell supplies electric current for as long as light keeps falling on it.

VESTAS V47 WIND TURBINE

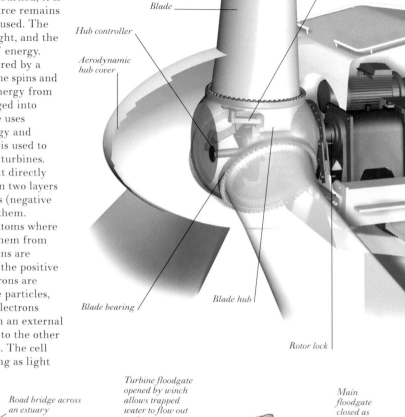

Blade pitch control

Blade

Hub controller

Aerodynamic hub cover

Blade bearing

Blade hub

Rotor lock

TIDAL POWER

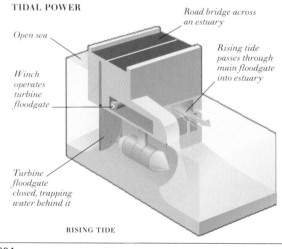

Road bridge across an estuary

Open sea

Rising tide passes through main floodgate into estuary

Winch operates turbine floodgate

Turbine floodgate closed, trapping water behind it

RISING TIDE

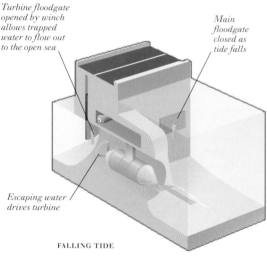

Turbine floodgate opened by winch allows trapped water to flow out to the open sea

Main floodgate closed as tide falls

Escaping water drives turbine

FALLING TIDE

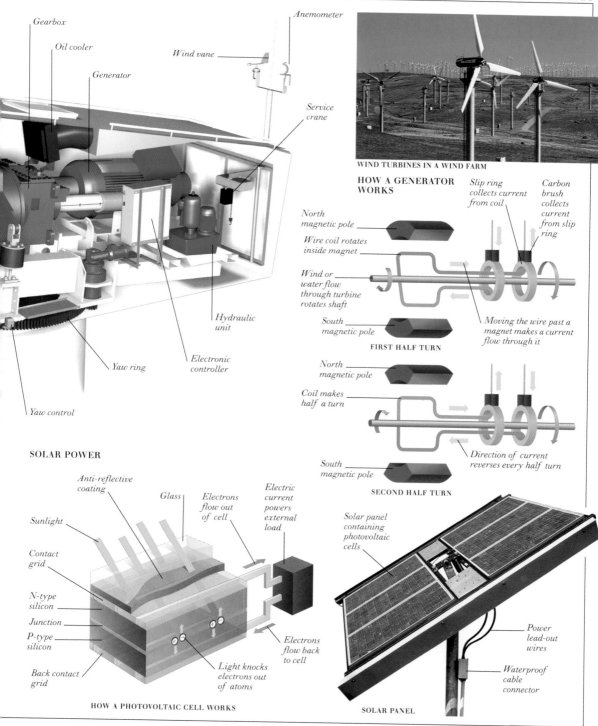

Gearbox

Oil cooler

Generator

Anemometer

Wind vane

Service
crane

WIND TURBINES IN A WIND FARM

**HOW A GENERATOR
WORKS**

Slip ring
collects current
from coil

Carbon
brush
collects
current
from slip
ring

North
magnetic pole

Wire coil rotates
inside magnet

Wind or
water flow
through turbine
rotates shaft

South
magnetic pole

Moving the wire past a
magnet makes a current
flow through it

FIRST HALF TURN

North
magnetic pole

Coil makes
half a turn

Hydraulic
unit

Electronic
controller

Yaw ring

Yaw control

South
magnetic pole

Direction of current
reverses every half turn

SECOND HALF TURN

SOLAR POWER

Anti-reflective
coating

Glass

Electrons
flow out
of cell

Electric
current
powers
external
load

Sunlight

Contact
grid

N-type
silicon

Junction

P-type
silicon

Back contact
grid

Light knocks
electrons out
of atoms

Electrons
flow back
to cell

Solar panel
containing
photovoltaic
cells

Power
lead-out
wires

Waterproof
cable
connector

HOW A PHOTOVOLTAIC CELL WORKS

SOLAR PANEL

Cloning technology

IN A LIVING CELL THE GENETIC MATERIAL DNA (deoxyribonucleic acid) contains thousands of units called genes that carry instructions for development, growth, and repair of the living creature. During normal reproduction, half the mother's genetic material contained in an egg cell joins with half the genetic material from the father carried in a sperm cell, to form a unique new genome (set of genes) for a new life. During the early stages of embryo development, the fertilized egg divides into stem cells, which have the potential to become specialized into the hundreds of cell types in a body. Through therapeutic cloning, stem cells can be produced in a laboratory. It is hoped that in the future this technology can be used to grow new tissue that can be transplanted back into the donor to treat illness, without fear of rejection — when the body recognizes a transplanted part as "foreign" because it has different genes, and tries to destroy it. In another form of cloning, performed experimentally using animals, genetic material from a donor animal has been inserted into an egg from another animal that has been emptied of its own genetic material, to produce an animal genetically identical to the donor.

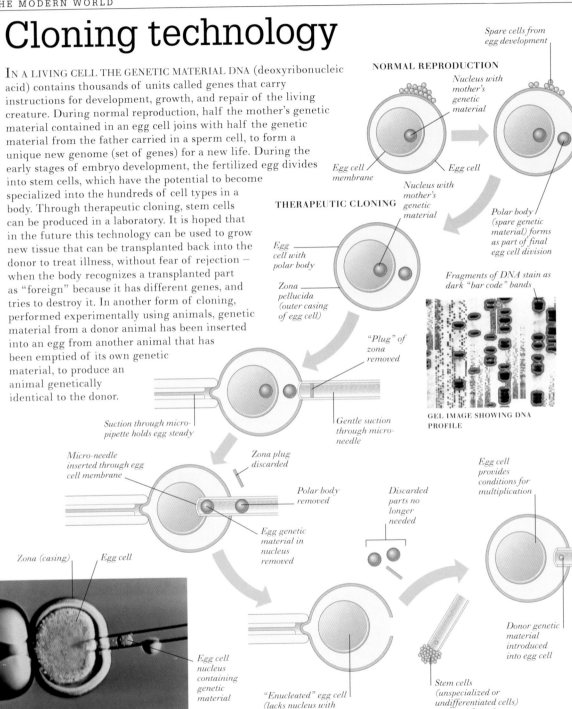

NORMAL REPRODUCTION

Spare cells from egg development

Nucleus with mother's genetic material

Egg cell membrane

Egg cell

Nucleus with mother's genetic material

Polar body (spare genetic material) forms as part of final egg cell division

THERAPEUTIC CLONING

Egg cell with polar body

Zona pellucida (outer casing of egg cell)

Fragments of DNA stain as dark "bar code" bands

"Plug" of zona removed

GEL IMAGE SHOWING DNA PROFILE

Suction through micro-pipette holds egg steady

Gentle suction through micro-needle

Micro-needle inserted through egg cell membrane

Zona plug discarded

Polar body removed

Discarded parts no longer needed

Egg cell provides conditions for multiplication

Egg genetic material in nucleus removed

Zona (casing)

Egg cell

Egg cell nucleus containing genetic material

"Enucleated" egg cell (lacks nucleus with genetic material)

Stem cells (unspecialized or undifferentiated cells) collected from donor

Donor genetic material introduced into egg cell

GENETIC MATERIAL REMOVED FROM EGG

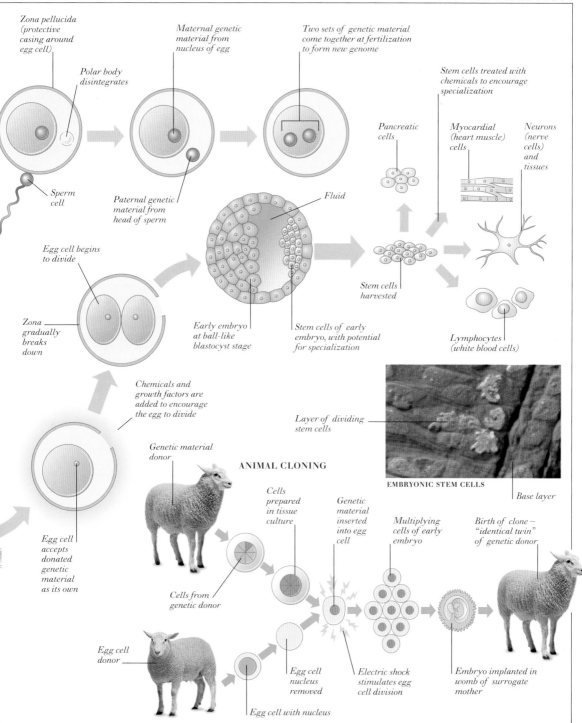

Zona pellucida (protective casing around egg cell)

Polar body disintegrates

Maternal genetic material from nucleus of egg

Two sets of genetic material come together at fertilization to form new genome

Stem cells treated with chemicals to encourage specialization

Pancreatic cells

Myocardial (heart muscle) cells

Neurons (nerve cells) and tissues

Sperm cell

Paternal genetic material from head of sperm

Fluid

Egg cell begins to divide

Zona gradually breaks down

Early embryo at ball-like blastocyst stage

Stem cells of early embryo, with potential for specialization

Stem cells harvested

Lymphocytes (white blood cells)

Chemicals and growth factors are added to encourage the egg to divide

Layer of dividing stem cells

Genetic material donor

ANIMAL CLONING

Cells prepared in tissue culture

Genetic material inserted into egg cell

Multiplying cells of early embryo

Birth of clone – "identical twin" of genetic donor

EMBRYONIC STEM CELLS

Base layer

Egg cell accepts donated genetic material as its own

Cells from genetic donor

Egg cell donor

Egg cell nucleus removed

Electric shock stimulates egg cell division

Embryo implanted in womb of surrogate mother

Egg cell with nucleus

Robots

ROBOTS ARE
MACHINES THAT CAN
carry out a variety of
tasks on their own,
with little or no human
control. Most robots are
mechanical arms used to build
things in factories. The end of the
robot's arm can be fitted with
different tools for gripping, drilling,
cutting, welding, and painting. Robot
toys have become popular, too. They
incorporate sensors that respond to
sounds and sometimes touch. Some of them
can even understand spoken words. Scientists are
also trying to create more advanced, human-like
robots that can see, hear, learn, and make their own
decisions. ASIMO, a robot developed by the Japanese
car manufacturer Honda, is one of these advanced
humanoid robots. ASIMO stands for Advanced Step
in Innovative MObility. It looks like a small astronaut
wearing a backpack. ASIMO can walk, talk, carry things,
recognize familiar faces, and respond to its name. It was
the first robot that could walk independently and climb
stairs. There are robot toys too, in the shape of animals
with simple artificial intelligence.

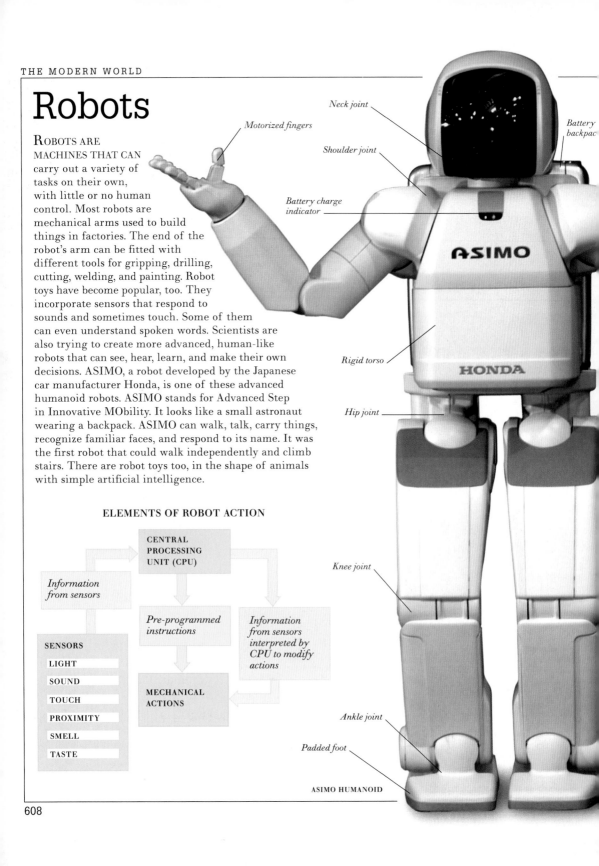

Neck joint

Motorized fingers

Shoulder joint

Battery
backpack

Battery charge
indicator

ASIMO

Rigid torso

HONDA

Hip joint

Knee joint

Ankle joint

Padded foot

ASIMO HUMANOID

ELEMENTS OF ROBOT ACTION

CENTRAL
PROCESSING
UNIT (CPU)

Information
from sensors

Pre-programmed
instructions

Information
from sensors
interpreted by
CPU to modify
actions

SENSORS

LIGHT

SOUND

TOUCH

PROXIMITY

SMELL

TASTE

MECHANICAL
ACTIONS

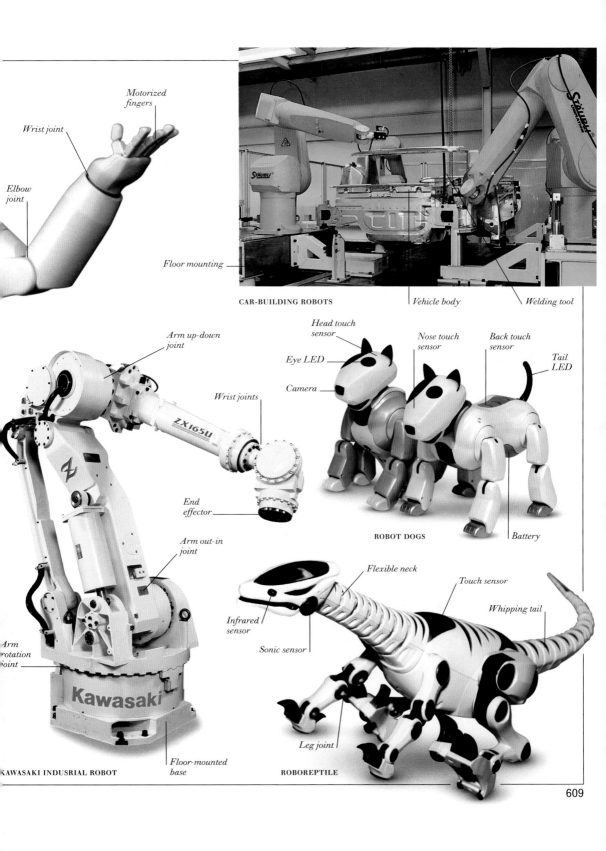

Wrist joint

Motorized fingers

Elbow joint

Floor mounting

CAR-BUILDING ROBOTS

Vehicle body

Welding tool

Arm up-down joint

Wrist joints

End effector

Arm out-in joint

Arm rotation joint

KAWASAKI INDUSRIAL ROBOT

Floor-mounted base

Head touch sensor

Nose touch sensor

Back touch sensor

Eye LED

Tail LED

Camera

ROBOT DOGS

Battery

Flexible neck

Touch sensor

Infrared sensor

Whipping tail

Sonic sensor

Leg joint

ROBOREPTILE

High-performance microscopes

OPTICAL MICROSCOPES FORM A MAGNIFIED image by using lenses to bend light. Some special-purpose optical microscopes used in industry and research are designed for observing particular materials, such as living cells. They produce magnifications of up to about 2,000. Electron microscopes produce magnifications of as much as 50 million, although 2 million is more typical. Their images are formed by means of electrons focused by magnetic lenses. There are two main types: scanning electron microscopes (SEMs) scan electrons back and forth across the surface of a specimen; transmission electron microscopes (TEMs) transmit electrons through a thin slice of the specimen.

FEI TECNAI G² TRANSMISSION ELECTRON MICROSCOPE

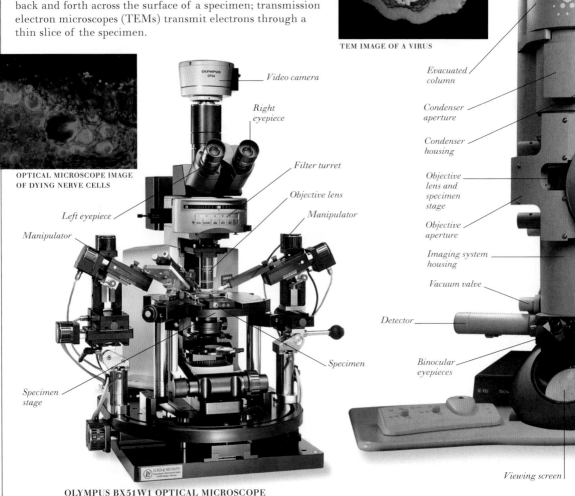

TEM IMAGE OF A VIRUS

OPTICAL MICROSCOPE IMAGE OF DYING NERVE CELLS

Video camera

Right eyepiece

Filter turret

Objective lens

Manipulator

Left eyepiece

Manipulator

Specimen

Specimen stage

OLYMPUS BX51W1 OPTICAL MICROSCOPE

Electron gun housing

Evacuated column

Condenser aperture

Condenser housing

Objective lens and specimen stage

Objective aperture

Imaging system housing

Vacuum valve

Detector

Binocular eyepieces

Viewing screen

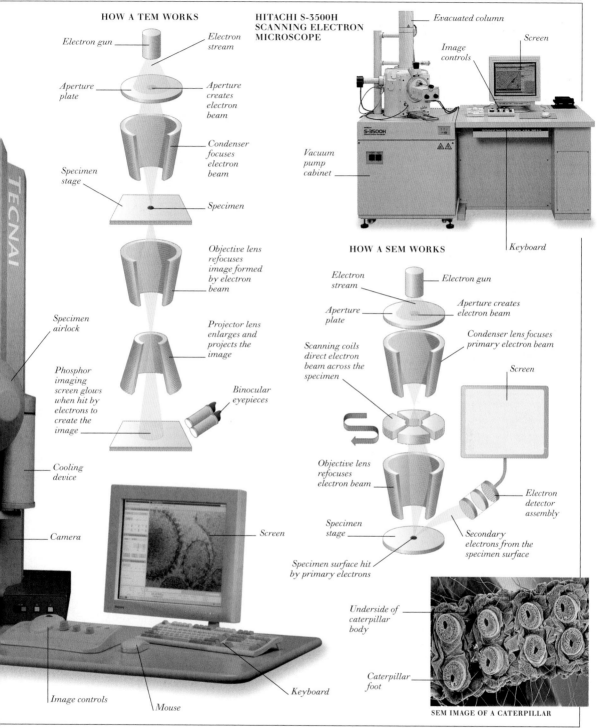

HOW A TEM WORKS

Electron gun

Electron stream

Aperture plate

Aperture creates electron beam

Condenser focuses electron beam

Specimen stage

Specimen

Objective lens refocuses image formed by electron beam

Projector lens enlarges and projects the image

Specimen airlock

Phosphor imaging screen glows when hit by electrons to create the image

Binocular eyepieces

Cooling device

Camera

Screen

Image controls

Mouse

Keyboard

HITACHI S-3500H SCANNING ELECTRON MICROSCOPE

Evacuated column

Image controls

Screen

Vacuum pump cabinet

Keyboard

HOW A SEM WORKS

Electron stream

Electron gun

Aperture plate

Aperture creates electron beam

Condenser lens focuses primary electron beam

Scanning coils direct electron beam across the specimen

Screen

Objective lens refocuses electron beam

Electron detector assembly

Specimen stage

Secondary electrons from the specimen surface

Specimen surface hit by primary electrons

Underside of caterpillar body

Caterpillar foot

SEM IMAGE OF A CATERPILLAR

Space telescope

SPACE TELESCOPES ORBIT THE EARTH hundreds of kilometres above the ground, their instruments collecting light from stars and galaxies. Telescopes in space have a clearer view than those on Earth, because they are unaffected by the Earth's atmosphere, which absorbs or distorts much of this radiation. There are a variety of types of space telescopes designed to observe different types of light. The Hubble Space Telescope observes infra-red, ultraviolet, and visible light. It can detect objects that are 100 times fainter than those any telescopes on Earth can see. When this 11,000-kilogram (12-ton), 13-metre (43-foot) long telescope was launched by the Space Shuttle in 1990, it was found that its primary mirror was faulty and its images were blurred. Astronauts fitted extra optics to correct the problem in 1993.

IMAGES TAKEN BY HUBBLE

Pillar of gas

CONE NEBULA

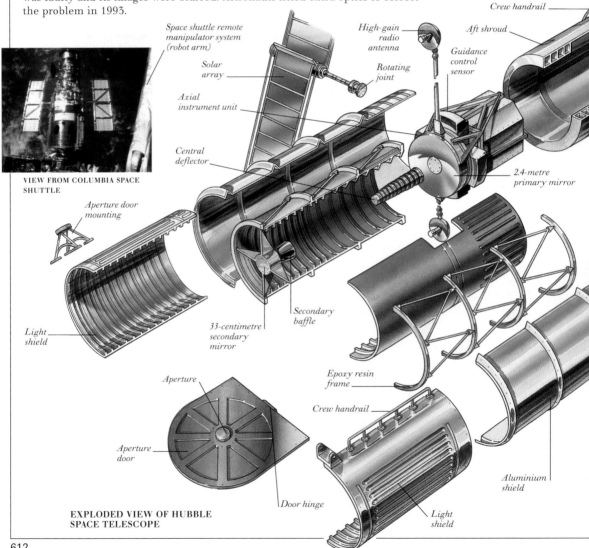

VIEW FROM COLUMBIA SPACE SHUTTLE

Space shuttle remote manipulator system (robot arm)

Solar array

Axial instrument unit

Central deflector

High-gain radio antenna

Rotating joint

Crew handrail

Aft shroud

Guidance control sensor

2.4-metre primary mirror

Aperture door mounting

Light shield

33-centimetre secondary mirror

Secondary baffle

Epoxy resin frame

Crew handrail

Aperture

Aperture door

Door hinge

Light shield

Aluminium shield

EXPLODED VIEW OF HUBBLE SPACE TELESCOPE

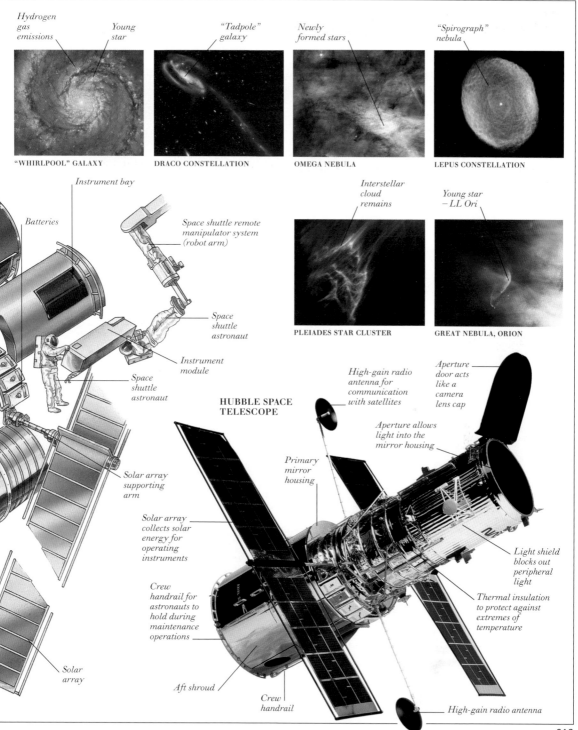

Hydrogen gas emissions

Young star

"WHIRLPOOL" GALAXY

"Tadpole" galaxy

DRACO CONSTELLATION

Newly formed stars

OMEGA NEBULA

"Spirograph" nebula

LEPUS CONSTELLATION

Interstellar cloud remains

PLEIADES STAR CLUSTER

Young star – LL Ori

GREAT NEBULA, ORION

Instrument bay

Batteries

Space shuttle remote manipulator system (robot arm)

Space shuttle astronaut

Instrument module

Space shuttle astronaut

Solar array supporting arm

Solar array collects solar energy for operating instruments

Crew handrail for astronauts to hold during maintenance operations

Solar array

Aft shroud

Crew handrail

High-gain radio antenna for communication with satellites

Aperture door acts like a camera lens cap

Aperture allows light into the mirror housing

Primary mirror housing

HUBBLE SPACE TELESCOPE

Light shield blocks out peripheral light

Thermal insulation to protect against extremes of temperature

High-gain radio antenna

613

Probing the Solar System

SPACE PROBES HAVE VISITED every planet in the Solar System. They take photographs and gather data that cannot be collected using Earth-based equipment. Some probes fly past or orbit around planets or moons, while others land. Two Voyager space probes flew past the outer planets in the 1970s and 1980s. Two Viking spacecraft landed on Mars in 1976. The Magellan spacecraft orbited Venus from 1989 and mapped its surface. The Pathfinder spacecraft landed on Mars in 1997 and released a rover vehicle to explore the surface. The Mars Exploration Rover (MER) Mission landed two rovers in 2003. The Cassini space probe reached Saturn in 2004, and in 2005 its mini-probe, Huygens, landed on one of its moons, Titan, and became the first probe to land on a moon of another planet.

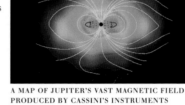

A MAP OF JUPITER'S VAST MAGNETIC FIELD PRODUCED BY CASSINI'S INSTRUMENTS

DIONE, ONE OF SATURN'S MOONS, ORBITING ABOVE THE "A" RING

PANORAMIC VIEW OF TITAN TAKEN AS HUYGENS DESCENDED

THE ROCK-STREWN SURFACE OF TITAN, PHOTOGRAPHED BY HUYGENS

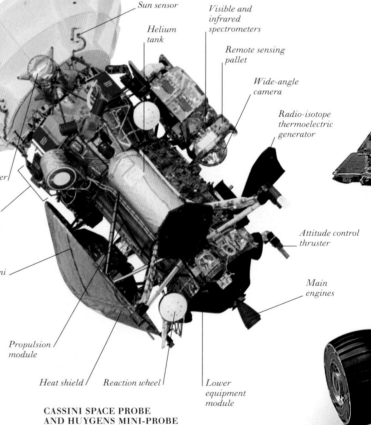

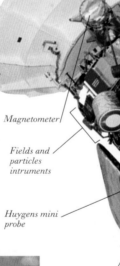

High-gain antenna

Sun sensor

Helium tank

Visible and infrared spectrometers

Remote sensing pallet

Wide-angle camera

Radio-isotope thermoelectric generator

Magnetometer

Fields and particles intruments

Huygens mini probe

Attitude control thruster

Main engines

Propulsion module

Heat shield

Reaction wheel

Lower equipment module

CASSINI SPACE PROBE AND HUYGENS MINI-PROBE

Panoramic camera (Pancam)

Navigation camera (Navcam)

COBBLESTONES LYING IN TROUGHS BETWEEN DUST RIPPLES ON THE MARTIAN SURFACE, PHOTOGRAPHED BY ROVER "OPPORTUNITY"

Heat shield

Thruster cluster

Star scanner

Propellant tank

Low dain antenna

Cruise stage

Cruise electronics module

Pancam mast assembly

Backshell contains lander craft and rover

MARS EXPLORATION ROVER SPACECRAFT

Ultra-high frequency (UHF) antenna

Third stage motor

Rover equipment deck

High gain antenna

Magnet array

Delta II launch vehicle second stage

Solar array

Aft bogie

Bogie wheel strut

Front hazard avoidance camera

Aft rocker

Warm electronics box

Forward rocker

Instrument deployment device

Rocker deployment actuator

MARS EXPLORATION ROVER (MER)

Aluminium wheel

Political map of the world

This map depicts the political boundaries of the world's nations. There are currently 196 independent countries in the world – a marked increase from the 82 that existed in 1950. With the trend towards greater fragmentation, most recently with the creation of Southern Sudan in July 2011, this figure is likely to increase. The largest country in the world is the Russian Federation, which covers 17,075,400 sq. km (6,592,800 sq. mi.), while the smallest is the Vatican City, covering 0.44 sq. km (0.17 sq. mi.). Under the Antarctic Treaty of 1959, no countries are permitted territorial claims in Antarctica.

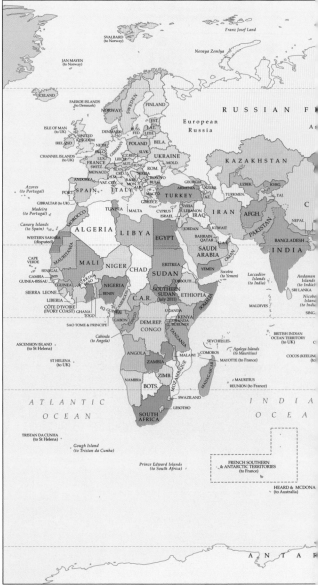

ABBREVIATIONS	
AFGH.	Afghanistan
ALB.	Albania
AUT.	Austria
AZ. OR AZERB.	Azerbaijan
B. & H.	Bosnia & Herzegovina
BELG.	Belgium
BELO.	Belorussia
BOTS.	Botswana
BULG.	Bulgaria
CAMB.	Cambodia
C.A.R.	Central African Republic
CRO.	Croatia
CZ. REP.	Czech Republic
DOM. REP.	Dominican Republic
EST.	Estonia
HUNG.	Hungary
KYRG.	Kyrgyzstan
LAT.	Latvia
LIECH.	Liechtenstein
LITH.	Lithuania
LUX.	Luxemburg
MACED.	Macedonia
MOLD.	Moldavia
MON.	Montenegro
NETH.	Netherlands
PORT.	Portugal
ROM.	Romania
RUSS. FED.	Russian Federation
SLVK.	Slovakia
SLVN.	Slovenia
S.M.	San Marino
SWITZ.	Switzerland
TAJ.	Tajikistan
THAI.	Thailand
TURKMEN.	Turkmenistan
U.A.E.	United Arab Emirates
UZBEK.	Uzbekistan
VAT. CITY	Vatican City
ZIMB.	Zimbabwe

Disclaimer:—The external boundaries of India as shown on this map are neither correct nor authentic.

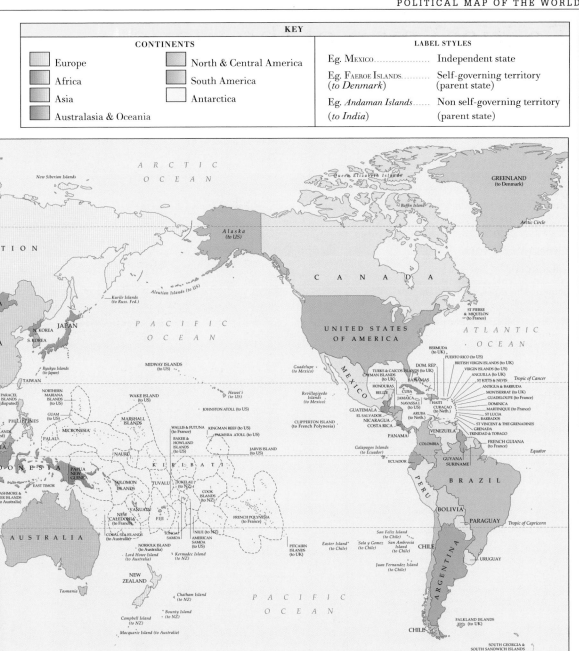

Time zones

The world is divided into 24 time zones, measured in relation to 12 noon Coordinated Universal Time (UTC), on the Greenwich Meridian (0°). Time advances by one hour for every 15° longitude east of Greenwich (and goes back one hour for every 15° west), but the system is adjusted in line with administrative boundaries. Numbers on the map indicate the number of hours that must be added to, or subtracted from UTC to calculate the time in each zone. Thus, eastern USA (−5) is 5 hours behind UTC.

TYPES OF CALENDAR

GREGORIAN

The 365-day Gregorian calendar was introduced by Pope Gregory XIII in 1582 and is now in use throughout most of the Western world. Every four years (leap year) an extra day is added. Below are the names of the months (and number of days).

January (31)	July (31)
February (28, 29 in	August (31)
leap years)	September (30)
March (31)	October (31)
April (30)	November
May (31)	December (31)
June (30)	

JEWISH

The Jewish calendar is a lunar calendar adapted to the solar year. It normally has 12 months but in leap years,which occur seven times in every cycle of 19 years, there are 13 months. The years are reckoned from the Creation (which is placed at 3761 BC); the months are Nisan, Iyyar, Sivan, Thammuz, Ab, Elul, Tishri, Hesvan, Kislev, Tebet, Sebat, and Adar, with an intercalary month (First Adar) being added in leap years.

MUSLIM

The Muslim calendar is based on a year of 12 months, each month beginning roughly at the time of the New Moon. The months are Muharram, Safar, Rabi'I, Rabi'II, Jumada I, Jumada II, Rajab, Sha'ban, Ramadan, Shawwal, Dhu l-Qa'dah, and Dhu l-Hijja.

CHINESE

The Chinese calendar is a lunar calendar, with a year consisting of 12 months. Intercalary months are added to keep the calendar in step with the solar year of 365 days. Months are referred to by a number within a year, but also by animal names that, from ancient times, have been attached to years and hours of the day.

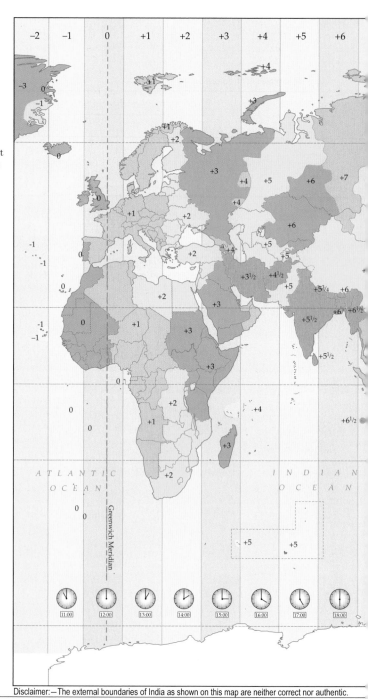

Disclaimer:—The external boundaries of India as shown on this map are neither correct nor authentic.

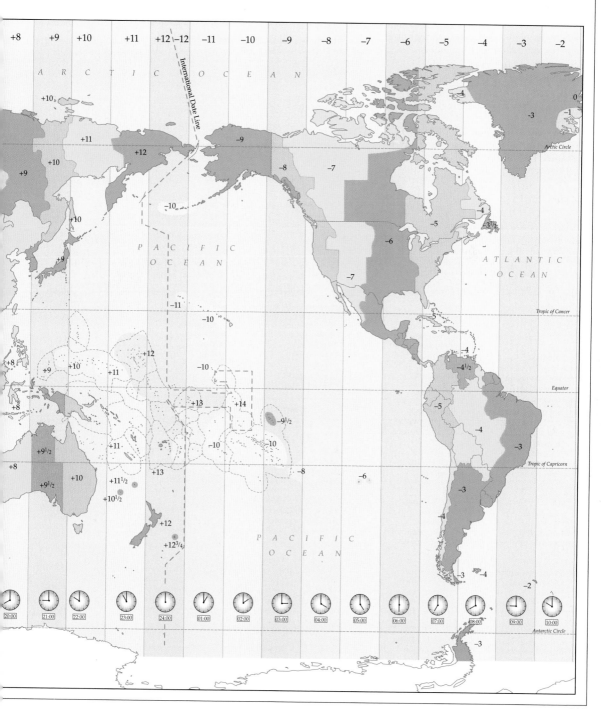

Useful data

UNITS OF MEASUREMENT

METRIC UNIT	EQUIVALENT
Length	
1 centimetre (cm)	10 millimetres (mm)
1 metre (m)	100 centimetres
1 kilometre (km)	1,000 metres
Mass	
1 kilogram (kg)	1,000 grams (g)
1 tonne (t)	1,000 kilograms
Area	
1 square centimetre (cm²)	100 square millimetres (mm²)
1 square metre (m²)	10,000 square centimetres
1 hectare	10,000 square metres
1 square kilometre (km²)	1,000,000 square metres
Volume	
1 cubic centimetre (cc)	1 millilitre (ml)
1 litre (l)	1,000 millilitres
1 cubic metre (m³)	1,000 litres
Capacity (liquid and dry measures)	
1 centilitre (cl)	10 millilitres (ml)
1 decilitre (dl)	10 centilitres
1 litre (l)	10 decilitres
1 decalitre (dal)	10 litres
1 hectolitre (hi)	10 decalitres
1 kilolitre (kl)	10 hectolitres

IMPERIAL UNIT	EQUIVALENT
Length	
1 foot (ft)	12 inches (in)
1 yard (yd)	3 feet
1 rod (rd)	5.5 yards
1 mile (mi)	1,760 yards
Mass	
1 dram (dr)	27.344 grains (gr)
1 ounce (oz)	16 drams
1 pound (lb)	16 ounces
1 hundredweight (cwt) (long)	112 pounds
1 hundredweight (cwt) (short)	100 pounds
1 ton (long)	2,240 pounds
1 ton (short)	2,000 pounds
Area	
1 square foot (ft²)	144 square inches (in²)
9 square feet	1 square yard (yd²)
1 acre	4,840 square yards
1 square mile	640 acres
Volume	
1 cubic foot	1,728 cubic inches
1 cubic yard	27 cubic feet
Capacity (liquid and dry measures)	
1 fluidram (fl dr)	60 minims (min)
1 fluid ounce (fl oz)	8 fluidrams
1 gill (gi)	5 fluid ounces
1 pint (pt)	4 gills
1 quart (qt)	2 pints
1 gallon (gal)	4 quarts
1 peck (pk)	2 gallons
1 bushel (bu)	4 pecks

NUMBER SYSTEMS

ROMAN	ARABIC
I	1
II	2
III	3
IV	4
V	5
VI	6
VII	7
VIII	8
IX	9
X	10
XI	11
XII	12
XIII	13
XIV	14
XV	15
XX	20
XXI	21
XXX	30
XL	40
L	50
LX	60
LXX	70
LXXX	80
XC	90
C	100
CI	101
CC	200
CCC	300
CD	400
D	500
DC	600
DCC	700
DCCC	800
CM	900
M	1,000
MM	2,000

METRIC - IMPERIAL CONVERSIONS

TO CONVERT	INTO	MULTIPLY BY
Length		
Centimetres	inches	0.3937
Metres	feet	3.2810
Kilometres	miles	0.6214
Metres	yards	1.0940
Mass		
Grams	ounces	0.0352
Kilograms	pounds	2.2050
Tonnes	long tons	0.9843
Tonnes	short tons	1.1025
Area		
Square centimetres	square inches	0.1550
Square metres	square feet	10.7600
Hectares	acres	2.4710
Square kilometres	square miles	0.3861
Square metres	square yards	1.1960
Volume		
Cubic centimetres	cubic inches	0.0610
Cubic metres	cubic feet	35.3100
Capacity		
Litres	pints	1.7600
Litres	gallons	0.2200

IMPERIAL - METRIC CONVERSIONS

TO CONVERT	INTO	MULTIPLY BY
Length		
Inches	centimetres	2.5400
Feet	metres	0.3048
Miles	kilometres	1.6090
Yards	metres	0.9144
Mass		
Ounces	grams	28.3500
Pounds	kilograms	0.4536
Long tons	tonnes	1.0160
Short tons	tonnes	0.9070
Area		
Square inches	square centimetres	6.4520
Square feet	square metres	0.0929
Acres	hectares	0.4047
Square miles	square kilometres	2.5900
Square yards	square metres	0.8361
Volume		
Cubic inches	cubic centimetres	16.3900
Cubic feet	cubic metres	0.0283
Capacity		
Pints	litres	0.5683
Gallons	litres	4.5460

628

631

632

634

638

640

641

642

646

649

656

665

666

668

Acknowledgments

Dorling Kindersley would like to thank
(in order of sections):

**The Universe
(consultant editors – Sue Becklake,
Gevorkyan Tatyana Alekseyevna):**

John Becklake; the Memorial Museum of
Cosmonautics, Moscow; The Cosmos Pavilion,
Moscow; The United States Space and Rocket Centre,
Alabama; Broadhurst, Clarkson and Fuller Ltd;
Susannah Massey

**Prehistoric Earth
(consultant editors – William Lindsay, Martyn
Bramwell, Dr Ralph E. Molnar, David
Lambert):**

Dr Monty Reid, Andrew Neuman, and the staff of the
Royal Tyrrell Museum of Palaeontology, Drumheller,
Alberta; Dr Angela Milner and the staff of the
Department of Palaeontology, the Natural History
Museum, London; Professor W. Ziegler and the
staff, in particular Michael Loderstaedt, of the
Naturmuseum Senckenburg, Frankfurt; Dr Alexander
Liebau, Axel Hunghrebüller, Reiner Schoch, and the
staff of the Institut und Museum für Geologie und
Paläontologie der Universität, Tübingen; Rupert Wild
of the Institut für Paläontologie, Staatliches Museum
für Naturkunde, Stuttgart; Dr Scheiber of the
Stadtmuseum, Nördlingen; Professor Dr Dietrich
Herm of Staatssammlung für Paläontologie und
Historische Geologie, München; Dr Michael Keith-
Lucas of the Department of Botany, University of
Reading; Richard Walker; American Museum of
Natural History, New York

**Plants
(consultant editor – Richard Walker):**

Diana Miller; Lawrie Springate; Karen Sidwell; Chris
Thody; Michelle End; Susan Barnes and Chris Jones
of the EMU Unit of the Natural History Museum,
London; Jenny Evans of Kew Gardens, London; Kate
Biggs of the Royal Horticultural Society Gardens,
Wisley, Surrey; Spike Walker of Microworld Services;
Neil Fletcher; John Bryant of Bedgebury Pinetum,
Kent; Dean Franklin

**Animals
(consultant editor – Richard Walker):**

David Manning's Animal Ark; Intellectual Animals;
Howletts Zoo, Canterbury; John Dunlop; Alexander
O'Donnell; Sue Evans of the Royal Veterinary
College, London; Dr Geoff Potts and Fred Frettsome
of the Marine Biological Association of the United
Kingdom, Plymouth; Jeremy Adams of the Booth
Museum of Natural History, Brighton; Derek Telling
of the Department of Anatomy, University of Bristol;
the Natural History Museum, London; Andy Highfield
of the Tortoise Trust; Brian Harris of the Aquarium,
London Zoo; the Invertebrate Department, London
Zoo; Dr Harold McClure of the Yerkes Regional
Primate Research Center, Emory University, Atlanta,
Georgia; Nielson Lausen of the Harvard Medical
School, New England Regional Primates Research

Centre, Southborough, Massachusetts; Dr Paul
Hopwood of the Department of Veterinary Anatomy,
University of Sydney; Dean Franklin

**The Human Body
(consultant editors – Dr Frances Williams,
Dr Fiona Payne, Richard Cummins FRCS):**

Derek Edwards and Dr Martin Collins, British School
of Osteopathy; Dr M.C.E. Hutchinson of the
Department of Anatomy, United Medical and Dental
Schools of Guy's and St Thomas' Hospitals, London.
Models – Barry O'Rorke (Bodyline Agency) and
Pauline Swaine (MOT Model Agency)

**Geology, Geography, and Meteorology
(consultant editor – Martyn Bramwell):**

Dr John Nudds of the Manchester Museum,
Manchester; Dr Alan Wooley and Dr Andrew Clark
of the Natural History Museum, London; Graham
Bartlett of the National Meteorological Library and
Archive, Bracknell; Tony Drake of BP Exploration,
Uxbridge; Jane Davies of the Royal Society of
Chemistry, Cambridge; Dr Tony Waltham of
Nottingham Trent University, Nottingham; staff of
the Smithsonian Institute, Washington; staff of the
United States Geological Survey, Washington; staff
of the National Geographic Society, Washington;
staff of Edward Lawrence Associates (Export Ltd),
Midhurst; John Farndon; David Lambert

**Rail and Road
Rail (consultant editor – John Coiley)**
Michael Ashworth of the London Transport Museum

**Road (consultant editors – David Burgess-Wise,
Hugo Wilson)**
The National Motor Museum, Beaulieu; Alf Newell of
Renault UK Ltd; David Suter of Cheltenham Cutaway
Exhibits Ltd; Francesca Riccini of the Science
Museum, London. Signore Amadelli of the Museo
dell' Automobile Carlo Biscaretti di Ruffia; Paul
Bolton of the Mazda MCL Group; Duncan Bradford
of Reg Mills Wire Wheels; John and Leslie Brewster
of Autocavan; David Burgess-Wise; Trevor Cass of
Garrett Turbo Service; John Corbett of The Patrick
Collection; Gary Crumpler of Williams Grand Prix
Engineering; Mollie Easterbrooke and Duncan
Gough of Overland Ltd; Arthur Fairley of the
Vauxhall Motor Company; Paul Foulkes-Halbard of
Filching Manor Motor Museum; Frank Gilbert of
I. Wilkinson and Son Ltd; Paolo Gratton of Gratton
Museum; Colvin Gunn of Gunn and Son; Judy Hogg
of Ecurie Bertelli; Milton Holman of Dream Cars;
Ian Matthews of IMAT Electronics; Eric Neal of
Jaguar Cars Ltd; Paul Niblett, Keith Davidson, Mark
Reumel, and David Woolf of Michelin Tyre plc; Doug
Nye; Kevin O'Keefe of O'Keefe Cars; Seat UK; Ian
Whitley; Raj Johal and Andy Faiers of the Honda
Institute; Roger Smith; Jim Stirling of Ironbridge
Gorge Museum, Staffordshire; Jon Taylor; Doug
Thompson; Martyn Watkins of Ford Motor Company
Ltd; John Cattermole, Customer Services Manager at
London Northern Buses; F. W. Evans Cycles Ltd;
Trek UK Ltd (Bicycle); Sam Grimmer; Colin Uttley

**Physics and Chemistry
(consultant editor – Jack Challoner)**

**Sea and Air
Sea (consultant editors – Geoff Hales and
Harvey B. Loomis):**
David Spence, Gillian Hutchinson, David Topliss,
Simon Stephens, Robert Baldwin, Jonathan Betts, all
of the National Maritime Museum, London; Ian Friel;
Simon Turnage of Captain O.M. Watts of London Ltd;
Davey and Company Ltd, Great Dunmow; Avon
Inflatables Ltd, Llanelli; Musto Ltd, Benfleet; Peter
Martin of Spencer Rigging Ltd, Southampton; Peter
Rowson of Ratseys Sailmakers, Southampton;
Swiftech Ltd, Wallingford; Colin Scattergood of the
Barrow Boat Company Ltd, Colchester; Professor J.S.
Morrison of the Trireme Trust, Cambridge; The Cutty
Sark Maritime Trust; Adrian Daniels of Kelvin
Hughes Marine Instruments, London; Arthur
Credland of Hull City Council Museums and Art
Galleries; The Hull Maritime Society; Gerald Clark;
Peter Fitzgerald of the Science Museum, London;
Alec Michael of HMB Subwork Ltd, Great Yarmouth,
and Ray Ward of the OSEL Group, Great Yarmouth;
Richard Bird of UWI, Weybridge; Walker Marine
Instruments, Birmingham; The International Sailing
Craft Association; The Exeter Maritime Museum;
Jane Wilson of the Trinity Lighthouse Company,
London; The Imperial War Museum Collections;
Thorn Security Ltd; Michael Bach

Air (consultant editor – Bill Gunston):
Aeromega Helicopters, Stapleford; Aero Shopping,
London; Avionics Mobile Services Ltd, Watford;
Roy Barber and John Chapman of the RAF Museum,
Hendon; Mitch Barnes Aviation, London; Mike Beach;
British Caledonian Flight Training Ltd; Fred Coates
of Helitech (Luton) Ltd; Michael Cuttell and CSE
Aviation Ltd, Oxford; Dowty Aerospace Landing Gear,
Gloucester; Guy Hartcup of the Airship Association;
Anthony Hooley, Chris Walsh, and David Cord of
British Aerospace Regional Aircraft Ltd; Ken Huntley
of Mid-West Aero Engines Ltd; Imperial War
Museum, Duxford; The London Gliding Club,
Dunstable; Musée des Ballons, Calvados; Noel Penny
Turbines Ltd; Andy Pavey of Aviation Scotland Ltd;
Tony Pavey of Thermal Aircraft Developments,
London; the Commanding Officer and personnel
of RAF St Athan; the Commanding Officer and
personnel of RAF Wittering; The Science Museum,
London; Ross Sharp of the Science Museum,
Wroughton; The Shuttleworth Collection; Skysport
Engineering; Mike Smith; Solar Wings Ltd,
Marlborough; Julian Temple of Brooklands Museum
Trust Ltd; Kelvin Wilson of Flying Start

**Architecture
(consultant editor – Alexandra Kennedy):**
Stephen Cutler for advice and text; Gavin Morgan of
the Museum of London, London; Chris Zeuner of the
Weald and Downland Museum, Singleton, Sussex;
Alan Hills and James Putnam of the British Museum,
London; Dr Simon Penn and Michael Thomas of the
Avoncroft Museum of Buildings, Bromsgrove,

Worcestershire; Christina Scull of Sir John Soane's Museum, London; Paul Kennedy and John Williamson of the London Door Company, London; Lou Davis of The Original Box Sash Window Company, Windsor; Goddard and Gibbs Studios Ltd, London, for access to stained glass windows; The Royal Courts of Justice, Strand, London; Charles Brooking and Peter Dalton for access to the doors and windows in the Charles Brooking Collection, University of Greenwich, Dartford, Kent; Clare O'Brien of the Shakespeare Globe Trust, Shakespeare's Globe Museum, Bear Gardens, Southwark, London; Ken Teague of the Horniman Museum, London; Canon Haliburton, Mike Payton, Ken Stones, and Anthony Webb of St Paul's Cathedral, London; Roy Spring of Salisbury Cathedral; Reverend Gillean Craig of the Church of St George in the East, London; the Science Museum, London; Dr Neil Bingham; Lin Kennedy of Historic Royal Palaces; Katy Harris of Sir Norman Foster and Partners; Production Design, Thames Television plc, London; Dominique Reynier of Le Centre Georges Pompidou, Paris; Denis Roche of Le Musée National des Monuments Français, Paris; Franck Gioria and students of Les Compagnons du Devoir, Paris, for access to construction models; Frank Folliot of Le Musée Carnavalet, Paris; Dr Martina Harms of Hessische Landesmuseums, Darmstadt; Jefferson Chapman of the University of Tennessee, Knoxville, for access to the model of the Hypostyle Hall, Temple of Amon-Re; staff of the Palazzo Strozzi, Florence; staff of the Sydney Opera House, Sydney; staff of the Empire State Building, New York; Nick Jackson; Ann Terrell

The Visual Arts
(consultant editor – Pip Seymour):
Rosemary Simmons; Michael Taylor of Paupers Press, London; Tessa Hunkin and Emma Biggs of Mosaic Workshop, London; John Tiranti, Jonathan Lyons of Alec Tiranti Ltd, London; Chris Hough; Dr Ashok Roy; Satwinder Sehmi of Alphabet Soup, London; Phillip Poole of Cornelissens, London; George Weil and Sons Ltd, London; The National Gallery, London; Chris Webster of the Tate Gallery, London; China Art Cultural Centre, London; London Graphic Centre, London; A.P. Fitzpatrick, London; Flowers Graphics, London; Intaglio Printmaker, London; Falkiner Papers, London; Edgar Udny and Co, London; John Green

Music
(consultant editor – Susan Sturrock):
Boosey and Hawkes Music Publishers Ltd, London, for permission to reproduce extract from The Prodigal Son by Arthur Sullivan; The Bass and Drum Cellar, London; Empire Drums and Percussion, London; Argents (part of World of Music), London; Bill Lewington Ltd, London; Frobenius organ at Kingston Parish Church, Surrey; Yamaha-Kemble Music (UK) Ltd, Tilbrook, Milton Keynes; Yamaha Atelier, London; Akai (UK) Ltd, Hounslow, Middlesex; Casio Electronics Co. Ltd, London; Roland (UK) Ltd, Fleet, Hampshire; Richard Schulman; Andy Brown of Musictrack

Sports
The Sports Council Information Centre, London; The British Olympic Games Committee; Brian Crennell of Black's Leisure Group (First Sport); Lillywhites of Piccadilly, London; Mitre Sports International Ltd, Huddersfield; David Bloomfield of the Football Association; Denver Athletics Ltd, Norfolk; Greg Everest and Keith Birley of the British League of Australian Rules Football; Peter McNally of the Gaelic Athletic Association; Jeremy Garman of James Gilbert Ltd.; Rex King of the Rugby Football Union, Twickenham; Neil Tunnicliffe and John Huxley of the Rugby Football League, Leeds; Wayne Patterson of the Basketball Hall of Fame, Springfield, Connecticut; Brian Coleman of the English Basketball Association; All American Imports, Northampton; George Bulman of the English Volleyball Association; Julie Longdon of Mizuno Mallory (UK) Ltd; Juliet Stanford of the All-England Netball Association; Jeff Rowland of the British Handball Association; Cally Melin of Adidas UK Ltd; Patrick Donnely of the Baseball Hall of Fame, Cooperstown, New York; Ian Lepage and Stephen Barlow of the Hockey Association, Milton Keynes; Alison Taylor and Anita Mason of the All England Women's Lacrosse Association, Birmingham; David Shuttleworth of the English Lacrosse Union; Les Barnett and Jock Bentley of the British Athletic Federation Ltd, Birmingham; Mike Gilks of the Badminton Association of England; Gurinder Purewall for advice on archery; Chris McCartney of the US Archery Association; Geoff Doe of the National Smallbore Rifle Association, Bisley, Surrey, for information and reference material on shooting; Fagan Sports Goods Distributors, Surrey; Konrad Bartelski for advice on skiing; The British Ski Federation, Edinburgh; Mike Barnett of Snow and Rock of London; Sally Spurway of Mast-Co. Ltd, Reading; Sarah Morgan for advice on equestrian sports; Steve Brown and the New York Racing Association Inc, New York; Danrho of London; Alan Skipp and James Chambers of the Amateur Fencing Association, London; Carla Richards of the US Fencing Association; Hamilton Bland and John Dryer of the Amateur Swimming Association, Loughborough; Cotswold Camping Ltd, London; Tim Spalton of Glyn Locke (Racing Shells) Ltd, Chalgrove; Terry Friel of the US Rowing Association; House of Hardy; Leeda Fishing Tackle

The Modern World
John Lewis, Brent Cross, for the loan of products for photography; Apple Computers UK; Palm Inc.; Epson UK; Naynesh Mistry of Brother UK; Nintendo; Sony UK; Nokia Mobile Phones Ltd; Sony Ericsson; Tony Broad of Garmin Europe; Dualit Ltd; Black and Decker Ltd; James Honour of the Buildings Research Establishment; Craig Anders of Cole Thompson Associates; Vestas Wind Systems; Bryan Adams of MIT; Dr Julian Heath of *Microscopy and Analysis*; Fei UK Ltd; Steve Parker; Ian Graham

PHOTOGRAPHY:
M. Alexander; Peter Anderson; Colin Bowling; Charles Brooks; Jane Burton; Peter Chadwick; Simon Clay; Gordon Clayton; John Coiley; Andy Crawford; Geoff Dann; Philip Dowell; John Downs; Mike Dunning; Torla Evans; David Exton; Paul Forrester; Robert and Anthony Fretwell of Fretwell Photography Ltd.; Philip Gatward; Steve Gorton; Anna Hodgson; Gary Kevin; J. Heseltine; Cyril Laubscher; John Lepine; Lynton Gardiner (American Museum of Natural History, New York); Steve Gorton; Michelangelo Gratton; Judith Harrington; Peter Hayman; Anna Hodgson; Colin Keates; Gary Kevin; Dave King; Bob Langrish; Brian D.Morgan; Nick Nicholls; Nick Parfitt; Tim Parmenter and Colin Keates (Natural History Museum, London); Tim Ridley; Dave Rudkin; Philippe Sebert; James Stevenson; Clive Streeter; Harry Taylor; Matthew Ward; Jerry Young

PHOTOGRAPHIC ASSISTANCE:
Kevin Zak; Gary Ombler; Govind Mittal

ILLUSTRATORS:
Julian Baum; Rick Blakeley; Kuo Rang Chen; Karen Cochrane; Simone End; Ian Fleming; Roy Flooks; Mark Franklin; David Gardner; Will Giles; Mick Gillah; David Hopkins; Selwyn Hutchinson; Mei Lim; Linden Artists; Nick Loates; Chris Lyon; Kathleen McDougall; Coral Mula; Sandra Pond; Dave Pugh; Colin Rose; Graham Rosewarne; John Temperton; Halli Verrinder; John Woodcock; Chris Woolmer

MODEL MAKERS:
Roby Braun; David Donkin; Morrison Frederick; Gordon Models; John Holmes; Graham High and Jeremy Hunt of Centaur Studios; Richard Kemp; Kelvin Thatcher; Paul Wilkinson

ADDITIONAL DESIGN ASSISTANCE:
Stefan Morris; Ulysses Santos; Suchada Smith; Niyati Gosain; Jomin Johny; Ridhi Khanna; Amit Malhotra; Payal Rosalind Malik; Anamica Roy; Ira Sharma; Balwant Singh

ADDITIONAL EDITORIAL ASSISTANCE:
Helen Castle; Colette Connolly; Camela Decaire; Nick Harris; Andrea Horth; Stewart McEwen; Damien Moore; Melanie Tham; Pragati Nagpal; Suparna Sengupta; Anita Kakar; Divya Chandhok

INDEX: Kay Wright; Lynn Bresler